Marine Cargo Operations

MATERIALS HANDLING AND PACKAGING SERIES

James R. Bright, Advisory Editor

MARINE CARGO OPERATIONS
   Charles L. Sauerbier

PACKAGE DESIGN ENGINEERING
   Kenneth Brown

INDUSTRIAL PACKAGING
   Walter F. Friedman and Jerome J. Kipnees

WAREHOUSE OPERATIONS PLANNING AND MANAGEMENT
   Andrew J. Briggs

Marine Cargo Operations

CAPTAIN CHARLES L. SAUERBIER, USNR

Master Mariner

Chief, Cargo Section
Department of Nautical Science
U.S. Merchant Marine Academy

JOHN WILEY & SONS

New York · London · Sydney

TO RACHEL EMMA

Foreword to the series

Undoubtedly, materials handling is the most universal physical activity of all mankind. From cradle to grave—throughout each day—man himself acts as a materials handling device. Perhaps the great common denominator in our economic life is the act of handling things. The steel mill and the dairy have little production art in common except handling. This is so throughout the great part of economic endeavor. We cannot turn our eyes on any of man's major activities without seeing movement. Yet, strangely enough, materials handling has been almost the last function to be systematically and aggressively mechanized. For thousands of years we have concentrated on techniques of making things, and have given relatively little attention to the techniques of moving them.

There are two noteworthy exceptions, of course: transportation and motion study. It is odd that we have developed a rational approach for moving things across vast distances as well as one for moving things within arm's reach, and yet we have neglected the gap between. Comparatively speaking, we have ignored this field of "short-range" transportation. As a result, thousands upon thousands of factories and distribution activities are paying for the ridiculous anachronism of sandwiching the finest of modern production technologies between materials handling methods of unknown and unconsidered efficiency.

This has not been the case in all fields. Mining, for instance, and the handling of bulk materials in volume have been well and efficiently mechanized for many years. However, the factory and the distribution system, which we consider to be the key to the fruitfulness of our modern world, have been relatively neglectful of mechanization of materials handling.

Since World War II the general appreciation of the importance of materials handling has changed radically. Materials handling has probably been the uppermost topic and objective of industrial engineers and other production experts during the past 10 years. Unfortunately, information to enable engineers to do a good job of materials handling has been scarce. There have been thousands of articles written about materials handling; yet there are scarcely half a dozen books on the subject. The need has been great for a systematic presentation of basic technology and analysis in the materials handling field.

It is the aim of this series to provide the practicing engineer and the advanced student with useful how-to-do-it books that will enable him to do an effective materials handling job. The series is a frank recognition that no one book on this subject can serve all the special areas of the field. It is our aim, therefore, to create for the industrialist a library of specialized information out of which he may choose those volumes that best serve his particular needs. We will not attempt to draw hard and fast lines as to where one topic starts and another stops—as to what kind of equipment is properly within one field and not within another. Rather, appropriate topics will be welded together so as to be useful to various categories of industry.

This series, then, marks the beginning of an effort to synthesize the knowledge of up-to-date materials handling practice in a number of functional areas. The publishers join me in inviting materials handling men to contribute their ideas, suggestions, criticism, professional information, and manuscripts. It is our hope that the volumes of this series will help to crystallize knowledge of this subject and expand our ability to handle materials efficiently in every industry.

JAMES R. BRIGHT
CONSULTING EDITOR

Lexington, Massachusetts
April 1956

Preface

The safe and economical movement of material and personnel, in peace and war, is the mission of the shipping industry. This book was written to help the shipping industry fulfill its mission by presenting, formally and systematically, the basic principles and techniques of cargo operations.

The plan of attack grew out of experience within the confines of a classroom, which I believe is a good testing ground for the methodology used in the presentation of any idea or group of ideas. As I wrote, I slanted the discussions toward the members of the shipowner's operations group, whose work is one of the most important factors in accomplishing the shipping industry's mission. The individuals who make up this group, working close to the heart of the problems related to the safe and economical movement of cargo, are a *team* in every sense of the word. They include the operations manager, terminal superintendent, marine superintendent, the stevedore, the ship's Master, and the staffs of these executives.

The more basic information each individual member of the operation team has about cargo operations, the greater will be the probability of a successful shipping venture. I have attempted to set forth and discuss as many of the tasks, concepts, and facts affecting cargo operations as I could encompass within a book of reasonable size. If the discussion has been directed to any particular segment of the operations group, it is toward the ship's Master and his deck officers, but the substance of the discussion is no less valuable to others. I believe that this part of the operations team is often underrated in many organizations. The ship's

Master and officers physically follow the shipping cycle more closely than any other group in the shipowner's organization. They are in an ideal position to observe and evaluate operating methods. They can do much to improve any given system. A deficiency of information among these men may prove very costly. Examples proving the truth of this statement are endless in number and increase daily.

One has to study the litigation resulting from cargo claims for only a short time to be convinced that in many cases damage to cargo and the legal action resulting were needless. The losses are actually greater than one would believe by merely reading the records of maritime cases, because many times one party clearly recognizes his liability and settles out of court.

It has been well established that the expense of the cargo operations represents, on the average, between 40 and 50 per cent of the total operating costs of the general cargo carrier. One terminal manager, whose ships were on a comparatively short run, told me that his company's cargo operation costs amounted to 70 per cent of the total operating costs. With the operating budget amounting to several millions yearly, it is obvious that any increase in the efficiency of the cargo operations will result in appreciable savings. It is felt that some of the discussions contained in this book, especially those concerning basic principles, may help clarify certain issues related to the efficiency of the cargo operation through the elimination, to some extent, of pure opinion, and the provision of a sound and factual basis upon which to proceed.

Much of the success of a shipping venture depends upon intelligent coordination of movement among all individuals and groups participating in the business of overseas commerce. This coordination should be present from the domestic shipper's terminal in the hinterland, through the marine terminal, to the foreign consignee, and then, with other commodities, back to the shores of the mother country. I hope that this book will contribute to this coordination of movement by giving a better understanding of the full shipping cycle to many who are involved in it only partially.

During World War II, a large percentage of the materiel sent overseas arrived in a damaged condition. The importance of safe movement of materiel is increased in time of war, yet we witnessed a considerable lack of safe movement and general coordination in the last war. When the quantities involved are considered, the potential savings in materiel and manpower should stimulate the interest of all thinking men. When a useless machine arrives overseas, all the labor that has gone into its creation, from the raw material to the finished product, is made equal to zero. The need for an adequate reference-text to guide and train a large influx of personnel in the event of a national emergency is obvious. I hope that this book will contribute to an increase in the *usable* materiel arriving overseas in case such a need should ever arise again.

Much of the text is based on scientific fact, but there are a number of recommendations regarding methods, procedures, and even philosophies that are set forth as "best" purely in my own opinion. Such opinion is based upon much study and nearly a quarter of a century's experience in the marine shipping industry. There is undoubtedly room for argument on some of these points, and there may be some omissions that will come to the mind of the careful reader. With respect to these items, the author invites written comment from all who care to discuss such points.

During the last decade there has been an increase in the amount of pure research leading toward factual answers to some of the questions that arise when considering marine cargo operations. Most of the progress that has been made in research has come about in the last five years. It appears that if this interest in the field continues at the same level for an extended period, there should be some truly remarkable developments during the next decade. A hint of these efforts and the direction which they may take is given in the last chapter.

I do not believe it is possible for me to acknowledge all of my intellectual indebtedness within the space allotted to the preface, hence I will not attempt it. I am sure the reader will not object. I hope that the many friends and associates who assisted me in gathering, evaluating, and editing the material will not feel that I am ungrateful for their assistance.

CHARLES L. SAUERBIER
CAPTAIN, USNR

U.S. Merchant Marine Academy
King's Point, New York
April 1956

Contents

CHAPTER 1

Shipowner's organization

for cargo procurement,

stowage, care, and delivery

This chapter is a brief account of the duties and responsibilities of the personnel of a steamship company who assist the shipowner in carrying out the functions related to the processes of procuring, receiving, loading, carrying, discharging, and delivering the cargo.

Figure 1-1 is an organization chart showing the titles and line of authority down to the principal department heads. There is no need to discuss the obvious responsibilities and duties of the *president*. He is the chief executive and policy maker for the entire organization, and as such he must have a profound understanding of all phases of steamship line operation. To itemize and discuss his duties further would necessitate a detailed recitation of the functions of all departments, which is beyond the scope of this book.

THE TRAFFIC DEPARTMENT

The traffic manager. The traffic department of a company that is engaged in carrying a large number of passengers as well as cargo will have two divisions: one division headed by a *passenger traffic manager* and another division headed by a *freight traffic manager*. If a very small number of passengers or none at all is carried, the passenger division may be dispensed with or the functions absorbed by other sections of the company. The freight traffic division is nearly always the larger of the two, and the freight traffic manager has the greater responsibility. The primary duties of this officer are soliciting cargo and managing an efficient system of processing the cargo to and from all ports served by the line.

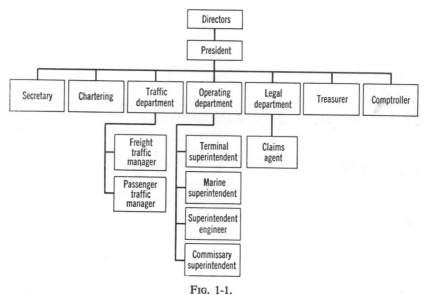

Fig. 1-1.

Although solicitation of cargoes and management of the groups doing the clerical processing of such cargo are the freight traffic manager's primary duty, he has other very important secondary duties. He participates in steamship company conferences as the company representative, conducts and analyzes surveys of routes and extensions, considers new ship construction and chartering needs insofar as the problems deal with cargo services, and he keeps abreast of the flow, progress, and general tendencies of traffic.

The rate conference. A brief explanation of the term "conference" seems in order. Steamship companies in an effort to control competition to some degree have developed organizations known as conferences. These conferences are in reality a form of trade association and seek to reach agreements between members relative to freight rates, sailing schedules, and trade routes. Such conferences may be quite informally conducted or they may be very formally organized. A strict and formal organization is necessary where there are a number of lines operating a cargo service over the same route. The competition is very intense under such conditions.

Figure 1-2 is a diagram showing the organization controlled by the freight traffic manager. A universal characteristic of the freight traffic division is its dichotomy into two sections. The largest of these two sections is the one handling outbound cargo; the other section handles the inbound cargo.

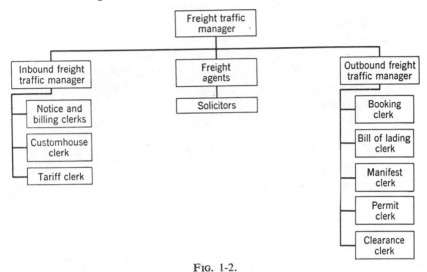

Fig. 1-2.

The outbound section. The *outbound freight traffic manager* has supervisory control over the staff as shown in the diagram. This staff is concerned with booking cargo, preparing the shipping documents necessary for the smooth flow of cargo, and payment of the charges connected with transportation of cargo. The practical operation of this part of the freight department is best covered by presenting a narrative description of the functions of the most important desks together with appropriate explanatory comments.

THE BOOKING DESK. We will start at the booking desk which is the logical beginning point. A shipper, wishing to use the services offered by a common carrier serving an overseas route, would first contact the booking desk and give the booking clerk all necessary information concerning his shipment. This is done over the phone in many instances. The booking clerk has before him a schedule of all ships on the service for which he is booking cargo. Companies operating ships over several routes may have a desk for each service. The schedule will list all discharging ports and loading ports, the dates the ship is to be ready for loading at these ports, and the sailing dates.

When booking for a given ship commences, the first step is to prepare data on the ship and enter it on the first page of what is to become the *engagement sheet*. The engagement sheet is the controlling document for booking a given ship. The data entered on this sheet will be such things as the cargo deadweight capacity available; the cubic capacity available; information concerning deep tanks, heavy lifts, length limits, refrigeration capacity, and similar information relative to the ship's ability to carry cargo.

BROKEN STOWAGE. The cubic capacity that the ship has available is based on an assumed value of 25% for the broken stowage. Broken stowage values will always vary because they are a function of several uncertain factors (see p. 131). If large amounts of uniform sized packages are included in a cargo under the conditions of the service, this assumed value may be lowered to 20% or even 10%. At best the assumed value is only a rough guess at what the actual broken stowage figure will be. Broken stowage is defined as that space in a loaded cargo hold that is not filled by cargo. It is the space occupied by dunnage, the space between packages such as drums, and the space that is left over the last tier placed in stowage. The percentage of broken stowage resulting from the stowage of a complete shipload would be equal to the difference between the ship's bale capacity and the volume of the cargo stowed in the ship, divided by the bale capacity and multiplied by 100. If the broken stowage percentage for a small section of a hatch is desired, you proceed in the same way except that instead of the bale capacity of the ship you would use the volume represented by the length, breadth, and height of the stowed cargo block. A general equation for broken stowage percentage is:

$$L = \frac{V - v}{V} \times 100$$

where L is the percentage of broken stowage.

V is the volume consumed in stowing the cargo.

v is the volume of the cargo stowed in V.

It is difficult to make an accurate estimate of the amount of broken stowage that will occur in connection with any given commodity on any given ship. A questionnaire sent to a number of stevedores on the Atlantic and Gulf Coasts by Taylor [1] produced widely separated esti-

[1] T. R. Taylor, Stowage of Ship Cargoes, *Miscellaneous Series* 92, U.S. Dept. of Commerce, pp. 53–54.

mates for the broken stowage values of various cargo items. If this survey proved nothing else, it at least pointed out that in the active field opinions as to what the broken stowage will be in any given case will vary greatly.

The accuracy of the estimate made by any individual can be increased with experience very rapidly if a few data are taken, such as that recommended on p. 234.

THE ENGAGEMENT SHEET. The booking clerk maintains the engagement sheet day by day until all booking is completed. On the pages following the data page, all information regarding each shipment booked for a particular ship is recorded. The engagement sheet is a running account of the status of the proposed cargo to be laden on the ship. As such, it is obvious that it must contain such basic information as:

1. The weight of each package and the weight of the entire shipment.
2. The maximum measurements of the containers and the total cubic of the shipment.
3. The total number of packages in each shipment.
4. The name of the shipper.
5. The name of the consignee.
6. The descriptive or shipping name of the cargo. The name used must be informative enough to explain the characteristics of the cargo so that a decision can be made regarding its care and custody.

After each day, the cargo booked is recapitulated, and the outbound freight traffic manager can tell at a glance how much of the total capacity of the ship is consumed. One page of the engagement sheet is devoted to the recapitulation of all bookings daily. The total booked at any moment can be determined easily. The total booked is compared to the total actually received on the piers from information phoned into the freight department daily by the receiving clerk's office on the pier. Some operations may find the cargo booked only a day or so before delivery to the pier. In other operations, booking may be several days to a few weeks before the ship is ready to receive the cargo.

The booking of a cargo is the first step in the total evolution of cargo operations. During this first step, the difference between success or failure of the venture may be decided.

FULL AND DOWN CONDITION. The carrier realizes a profit that will vary directly with the experience and knowledge of the freight traffic manager in arranging for and booking cargoes. In times of heavy competition when cargo is scarce and full loads are not available, some of the problems connected with the booking desk are solved by the circumstances. The objective, however, is always the same: to book a cargo that will use up all of the cargo deadweight of the ship and at the same time consume all of her available cubic capacity. When a ship is loaded so that these conditions are met, she is known as being loaded *full and down*. A ship is full and down when her volume is full and she is down to her legal draft marks. Theoretically, when loaded in this fashion, she is carrying her greatest paying load.

In times of cargo shortages, there is little probability of overbooking a ship. Many ships will sail neither full nor down. However, when there is plenty of cargo available, the ship may be overbooked as a regular policy of the company. Overbooking by about 10% of the ship's capacity, either deadweight or cubic, helps to protect the ship-owner from the nondelivery of cargo to the piers in time to be loaded on the ship in question. There may be cases where cargo is booked, de-livered to the pier, but still cannot be loaded, such as in the case of a failure to obtain an export license. If cargo is booked and the ship becomes loaded before that cargo has been placed on board, the cargo simply is rebooked and loaded on the next ship.

THE SHIPPING PERMIT. After the booking has been phoned into the booking desk, the shipper picks up a *shipping permit* from the permit clerk in the freight department. The shipping permit states the time and date that the shipper is to deliver the cargo to the pier. Shipping permits ordinarily will not be issued until the shipper is able to supply the freight department with an export license number and an export declaration number. This is because both of these must be obtained before the cargo can be loaded, and if the cargo is accepted on the shipowner's piers, it may lie there taking up valuable space while the shipper is attempting to obtain customs clearance. When competition is heavy, minor risks of this kind may be taken. Such decisions would be made by the traffic manager.

At the time of picking up the shipping permits, the shipper is pro-vided with blank copies of the *dock receipts* and *bills of lading*. The shipper must fill out these forms with all descriptive data concerning the cargo, such as the name of shipper and consignee; the cubic and weight dimensions of the packages; and a descriptive name of the commodity, type of container, export license, and export declaration numbers.

THE DOCK RECEIPT. The dock receipt is a shipping paper that fully describes a given shipment. When the shipment has been duly received by the carrier on its pier, the signature of an authorized agent on the dock receipt is the shipper's evidence that the cargo described thereon has been delivered to the custody of the carrier. Some notations may be made on the face of the dock receipt if the cargo received is not found to be precisely as described on it.

THE BILL OF LADING. The bill of lading is the most important of all the shipping papers used in negotiations between shipper and carrier. It contains a complete description of the shipment, and it also sets forth the provisions under which the cargo is shipped. It is the contract between the shipper and the shipowner for the transportation services involved. Its provisions are based on either the Harter Act of 1893 or the Carriage of Goods by Sea Act of 1936, depending upon whether the carrier is operating in domestic or foreign trade routes, respectively. Under certain conditions, the bill of lading is negotiable and the shipper can use it as the basis for a draft. There are two major types of bills of lading. The most common is the *order,* the type that is drawn up to the order of the shipper. Under this type of bill of lading, the shipper has not yet been paid for the cargo being shipped. Therefore, before the cargo can be obtained by the consignee at the port of discharge, the shipper must release the cargo by presenting the consignee with an endorsed bill of lading. The carrier is authorized to release the cargo to the consignee only if he presents the endorsed bill of lading. This arrangement is for the financial protection of the shipper. The other type of bill of lading is the *straight bill.* The straight bill of lading is drawn directly in the name of the consignee and needs no endorsement by the shipper before delivery is authorized at the port of discharge. A little more discussion with respect to the immunities and responsibilities of the shipper and shipowner will be found in Chap. 2, as these factors are controlled by the provisions of the bill of lading used on ocean carriers.

THE TERMINAL SUPERINTENDENT AND STAFF. We now shift to Fig. 1-3 which is a diagram of the organization under the *terminal superintendent.* The terminal superintendent supervises the operation of the various piers making up the terminal facilities. He is in charge of the cargoes that are received, delivered, loaded, and discharged over the piers. Each pier of the terminal is under a *pier superintendent;* these officers act as assistants to the terminal superintendent. The pier superintendents are supplied copies of the engagement sheets by the freight department. From these sheets the pier superintendents will prepare tentative stowage plans for the cargoes. These plans and the problems involved in *laying out* the ships will be discussed in greater detail later. The flow of cargo onto the piers will be in accordance with the shipping permits that are issued by the freight department following the booking procedure. Under certain conditions, the loading procedure can be considerably complicated by imprudent issuance of shipping permits. Congestion on the piers may be a result, or difficulties in following the tentative stowage plan may be introduced.   Cargo is brought to the piers by truck, railroad, or on lighters.

RECEIVING PROCEDURE ON THE PIER.   The *chief receiving clerk* supervises the staff in charge of receiving and checking the cargo onto the pier. The receiving office is equipped with windows that are manned by clerks prepared to process the papers of specific connecting carrier types.   If the amount of traffic warrants, there will be a window for each type of the three connecting carriers mentioned above.   If not, the number may be

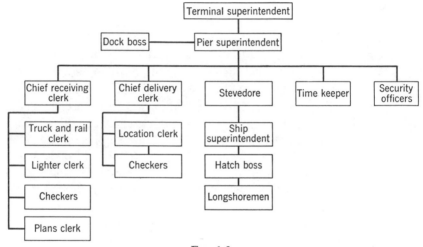

FIG. 1-3.

reduced so that one window may take care of two types and so on.   The clerk manning the window processes the dock receipt which should be filled out by the shipper before it is given to the trucker (assuming a truck is the connecting carrier).   The routine at each window is similar. On the date appearing on the shipping permit, the shipper's truck arrives at the pier entrance.   The trucker presents his copies of the dock receipt to the clerk manning the truck window.   The clerk checks the copies over to see that they are properly made out.   Besides noting that the data regarding the cargo are the same as those appearing on the shipping permit, the clerk also checks the export license number, export declaration number, and the shipping permit number.   The receiving clerk may also have a copy of the engagement sheet, and the shipment will be checked off on that.   If there are any discrepancies, the clerk may receive the shipment, but he will stamp all copies of the dock receipt with the words: "Hold on dock."   This hold on dock order will prevent the cargo from being loaded until it is properly cleared.

After checking all copies of the dock receipt, the receiving clerk enters the trucker's truck license number on the dock receipt, assigns a number to the dock receipt, makes out a gate pass, and finally assigns a checker to the truck. The checker accompanies the truck to the point on the pier where the cargo is to be unloaded. This may be a point on the pier where the cargo is to be temporarily stored, sometimes referred to as the *general assembly area.* A more efficient method is to plan so as to by-pass the general assembly area and place the cargo from the truck at a point where it will rest until it is picked up for movement to the pier apron. From this point it is placed on the ship's cargo hook and hoisted on board. The pier position prior to the pier apron is often referred to as the *pickup* point. On some piers, the truck will proceed to an un-loading platform where the cargo is unloaded directly onto a pallet. The pallet will be taken to the pickup point from the unloading plat-form. This last arrangement obviates the need for the trucks going into the actual warehouse area. Control over pilferage is much better if trucks can be kept out of the warehouse area. Use of a general as-sembly area is inefficient, for it requires another handling and every handling of the cargo package causes the expense of the total operation to increase. The cargo should go directly to the pickup point from the bed of the truck, preferably onto a pallet in that area. When the cargo is to be loaded, it is picked up and taken to a position under the cargo hook on the pier apron.

The *dock boss* will designate the point where the cargo will be un-loaded from the truck, and the truck will proceed there. As the truck is unloaded, the checker checks each package. He checks the dimen-sions, marks, and general characteristics of the cargo to see that they all are as stated on the dock receipt. If there are any damages, shortages, or discrepancies, the checker makes appropriate notations on the dock receipt. These notations are, in effect, corrections to the data listed on the dock receipt by the shipper. Later, these modifications, or as they are more accurately called "exceptions," are used to correct the bills of lading so that the carrier is not held responsible for shortages and dam-ages occurring before the cargo was received into his custody.

When the truck has discharged the cargo appearing on the dock re-ceipt and it has been checked, the checker will make out a *tally slip.* The tally slip contains information concerning the entire shipment, such as total number of packages, consignee marks, shipper's name, ship on which the shipment is to be loaded, the weight, and the measurements. One copy of this tally slip is secured to the shipment.

The trucker returns to the truck window of the receiving clerk's office with a copy of the tally slip and the dock receipt. The receiving clerk now signs the dock receipt and presents a copy to the trucker. This copy of the dock receipt is the shipper's receipt for cargo delivered into the custody of the shipowner. Later, this dock receipt is presented by the shipper to the bill of lading clerk in the freight department when picking up the bill of lading for the shipment.

There is little variation of the above routine at the lighter window. The principal difference is that the lighter captain will present, with his dock receipt, a manifest of the cargo on his lighter to the receiving clerk. The receiving clerk signs this manifest after the cargo has been properly received and checked onto the dock. The dock receipt and tally slip are processed in the same manner as described for the truck. A daily lighter report is made out which gives all the information regarding all the cargo received by lighter each day. After completion of receiving for any one ship, a complete lighter report is prepared covering all the cargo received by lighter for the given ship. Lighters may be kept at the pier only for a limited time. If kept beyond the specified time, demurrage will be charged. If released under the allowed time for discharging, the pier is given credit which can be accrued.

ADDITIONAL CLERICAL WORK IN FREIGHT DEPARTMENT. We will now leave the cargo on the pier and return to the freight department. We find the shipper appearing with his signed copy of the dock receipt and copies of the bill of lading. The bill of lading clerk checks all the data appearing on the dock receipt with those on the bill of lading. The bill of lading is then passed to a desk where the tariff is assigned, and the bill of lading is given a number. The assignment of the tariff rate is very important. If the carrier is a member of a conference, it must be done in accordance with the rules set down by that conference. The clerk doing this has several volumes listing all the commodities that might be carried as cargo on any of the various services. If no listing appears, there is a general cargo rate that will apply. The general cargo rate might be listed as follows: 0.80/1.50. This means that the cargo is shipped for $0.80 per cu ft or $1.50 per 100 lb. The choice of which rate the shipper is charged is at the shipowner's option. The choice is always made so that the greatest income is obtained. The freight charges are entered on the bill of lading, after which it goes to a front desk. Later the shipper or his agent calls for the bill of lading and pays the charges. One copy of the dock receipt would have been forwarded to the freight department from the receiving clerk's office, and the bill of lading data would be checked before the shipper or his agent appeared. The bill of lading would then be signed by the traffic manager, or an authorized clerk, to signify the shipowner's agreement to the terms of the contract represented by the bill of lading provisions.

Copies of the bill of lading go to the *manifest clerk*. The manifest clerk makes out the manifest from these bills of lading. The manifest is a complete list of the cargo loaded on the ship. The manifest gives the descriptive name of the cargo, marks, destination, shipper and consignee, weight, cubic, number of packages, and other data. Preparation of the manifest requires speed and accuracy. It must be used to clear the ship, yet it cannot be started until the loading of the ship starts. Mistakes on the manifest may leave the shipowner open to fines.

Inbound section. The above has been concerned with outbound cargo. Inbound cargo offers much less detail of work and hence a smaller staff is needed to handle it. The *inbound freight traffic manager* is concerned primarily with obtaining rapid and correct customs clearances for all cargo and sending out *arrival notices* to all consignees to insure prompt removal from the piers. The consignee is given a copy of the bill of lading which he presents at the customhouse. If all is in order, the customs office will issue the consignee a release which will authorize the customs office on the pier to release the goods. Following the issuance of the custom's release order, the consignee returns the bill of lading to the inward freight office where he receives a company release order for the shipment.

When the cargo is discharged from the ship, it enters the control area of the *chief delivery clerk,* who is under the supervision of the terminal superintendent or pier superintendent. The delivery clerk is charged with receiving the cargo from the ship and then releasing it to the consignee or his agents according to a set legal procedure. When a trucker arrives at a pier to pick up cargo, he will have in his possession a *release order*. There are several types of releases. The release may be from the consignee of the cargo; in this case it is called a *paid delivery* release. *In-transit releases* are issued when the cargo is to be delivered to another carrier for transportation to the hinterland, generally with the understanding that all customs and duty fees will be paid there. An entire shipment or only parts of a shipment may be taken to the U.S. Appraiser's Warehouse so that its value may be appraised to check on the duty required or for other reasons. When cargo is being picked up for delivery to the appraiser's warehouse, the customs will issue an *appraiser's release order*. This allows the cargo to be picked up and transported to the warehouse. *Re-export releases* are issued when the cargo is to be picked up for delivery to another pier where it will be loaded on another ship for re-export. If a free zone exists in the port, releases to the *free zone* will also be used.

Regardless of the type of release, the delivery routine is the same. The chief delivery clerk will have had a *delivery book* prepared from a copy of the ship's manifest some time before the consignees start calling for their cargo. In the delivery book, all the cargo is listed alphabetically by consignee. Each entry contains all the descriptive data concerning the cargo that would appear on the bill of lading. Another book that may be called a *location book* is kept by a clerk of the same office. The location book shows the location of each shipment on the pier after it has been discharged. The dock boss, under directions of the pier superintendent, designates the stowage location of all shipments discharged from the ship.

Upon arrival at the pier, the trucker proceeds to the delivery clerk's office and has his release papers checked. He then proceeds to the customs office on the dock and gets clearance permits from the customs. He returns to the delivery clerk where a checker is assigned to his truck. The clerk keeping the location book directs the checker and trucker to the point where the cargo is located. The checker checks the cargo onto the truck and makes out three copies of a tally slip. The trucker returns to the delivery office with one copy of the tally slip. A clerk checks the data on the tally slip with those appearing in the delivery book. If they are the same and all is in order, the delivery clerk will sign the tally slip and issue the trucker a gate pass, or the tally slip may be used as a gate pass. The trucker will also sign the delivery book indicating his approval of the checks made. When a given shipment has been completely delivered to the consignee or his agents, the word "completed" is stamped over the entry concerning the shipment in the delivery book.

Cargo left on the pier beyond the *free time* period may be removed by the customs office to a customs warehouse. The free time period is generally five days, beginning the day after the cargo has been discharged. Demurrage will be charged against the consignee for every day the cargo is left on the pier beyond the free time period.

The claims agent. The *cargo claims agent* may be under either the traffic manager, the terminal superintendent, or attached to the legal department. The routine in the claims office would be similar regardless of the office having supervisory control. Claims can be minimized by alert checking when the cargo is received on the dock and by alert deck officers when the cargo is being loaded onto the ship. All information regarding damaged and recoopered cargoes is routed to the claims office on standard company forms. Such information is filed by ship and shipper upon receipt. The information may never be referred to again unless the company is contacted by a claimant. If a request for a settlement is received, the data are checked and a quick settlement is attempted.

The majority of cases are settled without litigation. At times, however, the need for litigation arises, and the case goes to court. In such cases, the provisions of the bill of lading will be used by both parties concerned as a basis for settlement. These provisions will be discussed in Chap. 2; they have great significance in their modification of the duties of the ship's officers.

The most frequent type of claim is for shortages, such as when 500 cases are checked onto the ship and only 494 checked off. The missing packages may never have been loaded, or their contents might have been pilfered during the time that the packages were in the hands of the carrier. In such cases, the ship is liable and settlement is quick. The claims agent will review the facts of the case and make certain the claimant is not claiming more than the actual loss. In the case of cargo damage from any cause, an effort may be made to settle on a percentage basis if there is reason to believe that insufficiency of packaging or some cause beyond the responsibility of the carrier contributed to the damage of the shipment in question. When such cases reach the courts, the shipper generally maintains that the cause of the damage is attributable to either improper stowage or improper care and custody. The carrier will maintain that the damage was attributable to one of several other causes but frequently claims it was mismanagement on the part of the ship's complement.

Variation of systems. The foregoing has been an attempt to outline briefly the organization and the mechanics involved in procuring cargo for the common carrier and for getting it as far as the marine terminal over which it must pass in transit as it leaves the land carrier and comes under the jurisdiction of the water carrier. It must be pointed out that the description given of the process is not representative of any one company. The exact procedure varies from company to company depending upon the size of the organization and the trade routes served by it.

The stevedore. Before concluding this orientation discussion, it is necessary to cover the functions of the *stevedore* and the *ship's officers* as they apply to cargo operations. The *stevedore,* who may be a company employee or a contractor, is in charge of the actual loading or discharging procedure. He may assist the terminal or pier superintendent in *laying out* the ship. Laying out is a phrase used to describe the preparation of the tentative stowage plan. The stevedore's primary duty, however, is to execute the plan. The stevedore will generally work with more than one vessel at the terminal, hence he is in need of assistants. His immediate assistants are known as *ship superintendents* or *walking bosses*. The term "walking boss" is used primarily on the west coast of the United States. For every hold or cargo compartment working cargo, there will be a *gang* of longshoremen. The number of long-shoremen in each gang is controlled strictly by union regulations. One man in the gang will be known as the *gang boss* and he acts as the fore-man. The gang boss is the intermediary between the longshoremen and the walking boss. Generally eight men will be assigned to the hold and six men to the dock; there will be two winch drivers, a hatch tender, and some drivers of lift trucks or other equipment. The gang generally runs to about sixteen or twenty men, but there is no universal standard.

Some contract stevedores supply the steamship operator with more services than simply the working of the cargo into or out of the ship. The contract may provide for complete terminal operation which in-cludes, of course, the functions of receiving and delivering as described above. Such work would be done in close liaison with the steamship company freight and operations departments.

Ship's officers. Leaving the dock and going aboard the ship with the cargo, we come in contact with that part of the shipowner's organization which will be responsible for the cargo during its period on the ship. This group consists of the master and his deck officers, supervised by the *marine superintendent* (see Fig. 1-4). The master of the ship is the responsible ship's officer who acts as the shipowner's agent in many instances during normal operating procedure. In these days of shiploads of hundreds of general cargo items and rapid operating techniques, it is impos-sible for the master of the ship to carry out the duties and assume the responsibilities that many lay-men attribute to him. Large modern steamship companies have complete staffs to do the work of procuring cargoes, checking them on board, and processing the many legal shipping papers necessary to operate the vessel. However, the

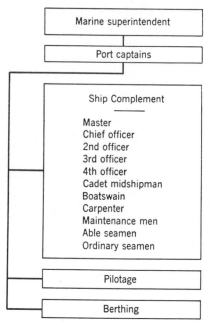

FIG. 1-4.

master still stands as the shipowner's expert representative with respect to the handling and stowing of the cargoes booked for carriage. As such, he should instruct and organize his officers so that they will understand precisely what is desired in the stowage of the cargo on hand and have the spirit and depth of knowledge to insist intelligently on what is best. Briefly stated, the master and deck officers have the responsibility of seeing that there never are grounds for a shipper of cargo to claim improper care and custody as a cause of cargo damage.

Briefing of officers concerning cargo operations. The first officer should be briefed by the master and the walking boss or the pier superintendent regarding the tentative plans for stowing the vessel's cargo. The second and third officers should be present during this meeting also. This briefing is frequently missing in practical operations in spite of the obvious need for responsible officers being informed of any operation over which they will be expected to hold some degree of control. Company operations managers should insist that such essential briefing steps always be taken.

Duties while loading. Once the loading of the cargo commences, all of the ship's officers must concern themselves with checking on the stowage of all items that come on board the ship. They must know what is and what is not correct stowage, then they must insist that all stowage is done correctly. Just what is correct stowage is a question that will be answered in detail in Chap. 4.

The ship's officers also make certain that the ship's cargo handling equipment is correctly rigged, and they keep a record of where all cargo is stowed on the ship. This record should be the primary duty of one of the ship's officers. From the data taken by observation, a final as-stowed cargo plan should be prepared. In most large steamship companies of today, a *plans clerk* will be attached to the office of the chief receiving clerk. The plans clerk is responsible for preparing a final stowage plan. In practice, however, the interest of the shipowner is served best by the officers of the ship keeping such a plan. Plans clerks are not as closely associated with the actual stowage as the ship's officers nor are they by nature as interested. Serious mistakes may appear on the plans prepared by clerks simply from the mechanics used in their preparation. The necessity for preparing a plan of the stowage will increase the ship's officers' knowledge of the stowage on the ship which they are going to take to sea. The manner of acquiring the information first hand will necessitate their being in the ship's holds during the loading of the cargo and circulating from compartment to compartment. Knowing their ship and knowing the cargo on board their ship is a fundamental principle of safety and of efficient merchant ship operation. Any philosophy or circumstance of operation which tends to minimize the importance of the ship's officers' knowledge of their ship and her cargo or fails to encourage the acquisition of such knowledge is acting to the serious detriment of the ship, company, or merchant fleet so affected.

Cargo exceptions and damage reports. As mentioned above in discussing the receiving clerk's duties, the checker will check the cargo as it is loaded from the connecting carrier to the dock to see that it is as represented upon the dock receipt. This is one check that the shipowner's organization makes against accepting cargo that is not in good condition upon receipt. The ship's officers must always be making checks also. They must visually check cargo while it is being loaded. Obviously, they cannot check all cargo that comes on board, but they can spot check almost all shipments. Any discrepancies that appear should be reported by them on a *cargo exception* form or *cargo damage report* form. One form may be used, but the context of the remarks will vary depending upon whether the report is in fact an exception or a cargo damage report.

The cargo exception is a listing of defects of the cargo which should be excepted on the bill of lading. In other words, the cargo is received as stated in the terms of the bill of lading except for the points mentioned in the exception report. The cargo damage report is simply a statement of damage to cargo giving all details.

As mentioned above, most cargo exceptions will be taken first by the checker who visually checks the cargo when it is received on the pier. It is obvious, however, that this is not going to preclude some packages or shipments being missed by the checker in one detail or another. The officers of the ship are the next responsible members of the shipowner's organization to come into contact with the cargo. The damage or condition being excepted may have been caused while the cargo was on the pier; if so, the claims department should know this. The most important period for the ship's officers to be on the alert for exceptions is when loading cargoes in foreign ports where the shipowner's agent may not have a trained or experienced dock force available to check cargo upon receipt from the shipper. In these instances, the ship's officers' check may well be the only check. The neglect of proper exceptions could mean the loss of a great deal of money for the shipowner.

The cargo damage report is a statement of fact regarding the condition of cargo when discovered in the ship in a damaged condition. Generally there are a number of such reports to be made whenever the cargo is being discharged. During the loading of cargo, longshoremen frequently cause the damage of cargo. In such case, a report is made out and a representative of the stevedore will sign acknowledging the facts. If cargo is found in the ship during the loading procedure in a damaged condition and the cause cannot be determined, a report should be made of the facts. Some companies will require that the cargo be sent back to the dock and recoopered before being stowed under in the ship. When this is done, careful checking is required so that the bill of lading will state correctly the condition of the cargo.

The cargo exception and the damaged cargo report are similar in context. Many companies do not require the ship's officers to differentiate between them; they require a report of the damage on a standard form. Such reports can be made more meaningful, however, if the ship's officer is aware of the difference between the two reports. Both types of reports should have six essential items recorded upon them:

1. Consignee marks.
2. Commodity type.
3. Container type and number involved.
4. Stowage location when discovered.
5. Extent of the damage.
6. Remarks concerning the facts of the discovery.

The principal difference between the cargo exception and damaged cargo report will be in the context of item six. As an example, the remarks on a cargo exception concerning damaged steel rods would read as follows:

Steel rods arrived alongside the ship in a gondola car with rods bent and considerable rust in evidence.

The officer making such a notation could make the report more useful by giving a count of the number of bundles involved or an extension of the remarks in any way possible.

The cargo damage report would lack any reference to the fact that cargo was just being received from the connecting carrier. A cargo damage report on the same type of cargo would read along the following lines:

Steel rods bent by longshoremen in breaking them out of stowage. Top tiers were very rusty, probably caused by heavy condensation during the voyage.

THE MARINE TERMINAL [1]

Although a short chapter could be devoted easily to the design of marine terminals, we will limit our discussion to a brief survey of the principal factors.

[1] Based on a paper by Frank W. Herring, Modern Design of General Cargo Marine Terminals, presented at ASCE 1954 Annual Convention, New York.

One of the most common observations made by visitors to the water-front is that many of the piers or wharves seem obsolete and inefficient. This is, of course, an accurate observation, for outdated marine terminals will probably always be with us. These structures are built with a view to using them for forty or fifty years. It is little wonder then, that structures built in 1910 to accommodate ships of 5000 tons deadweight or less and to handle horse and wagon connecting carriers are not able to serve efficiently when ships of 10,000 tons deadweight are alongside and are being serviced by the large truck and trailer combinations of this period.

Function of the marine terminal. The principal function of a general cargo marine terminal is to act as an interchange point for cargo moving from land routes to the sea-going carrier. The *transit shed,* which is the only superstructure of any consequence at the terminal, gets its name from the temporary nature of the storage facilities that it is supposed to offer.

A marine terminal cannot be said to be modern or efficient unless it can accommodate with expediency the latest developments in the water and land transportation systems that it serves and also provide for full use of all modern materials handling equipment.

Two basic types of construction. The two basic types of marine terminal construction are the *pier* and the *wharf.* The pier is a long and relatively narrow structure that juts out into the harbor waters, roughly at right angles to the shoreline. This type of construction is desirable in areas where water frontage is at a premium and where there is sufficient clearance in the stream for the pier. This type of construction is the most common in American ports. Almost all terminals are constructed on piers on the island of Manhattan in New York Harbor and along the Embarcadero in San Francisco Harbor for obvious reasons. This construction affords more berths for ships per linear foot of frontage than the wharf type.

The wharf, or quay as it is called in many foreign ports, is constructed along the shoreline roughly parallel to it. It is used where there is no shortage of water frontage or where the waterway adjacent to the terminal site is too restricted to permit the use of pier construction. The wharf is well adapted to use at river ports, and this type of construction predominates at New Orleans, La.; Portland, Ore.; and Sacramento, Calif.

Basic marine terminal requirements. Because of the great increase in the use of the large semitruck and trailer as a connecting carrier, the modern marine terminal must be designed to accommodate large numbers of these carriers daily without congestion. In other words, space must be planned for expeditious ingress and egress roadways and loading and discharging areas beyond the space necessary for the temporary storage of the cargo moving over the terminal. The pier type terminal offers a greater problem here than the quay or wharf. In the case of the wharf, it is sometimes possible to provide loading platforms with a height equal to the truck platforms and designed so as to obviate the necessity of the truck entering the transit shed storage area.

Everything possible should be done to provide for adequate traffic control of the waiting lines of trucks coming to the terminal to pick up or deliver cargo. The greater the efficiency on the pier or wharf, the less the need for shoreside space and control.

Overhead clearances and floor load capacities. With the modern high stacking fork lift truck and similar equipment, the effective use of the marine terminal area has been increased three or four times. The pallet loads are frequently stacked to a height of twenty feet, thus this much overhead clearance is a minimum. The efficient use of all materials handling equipment is dependent upon a smooth roadway, hence the need for durable surfacing. One of the most efficient materials handling combinations is the tractor and trailer used in conjunction with the fork lift truck. In order to use the tractor and trailer correctly, it is necessary to have apron space extending out from the transit shed for at least 15 ft.

A floor load capacity of about 600 lb per sq ft is desirable to handle the modern fork lift truck and its load.

Space requirements. Berths for each ship should be at least 550 ft in length with a depth of 35 ft alongside at mean low water. The slip between two adjacent piers should be at least 250 ft wide, or if two or more ships are to be berthed at either pier, a greater clearance is recommended by Herring. A clearance of 300 ft would not seem excessive in view of the difficulty of maneuvering the inner ships, especially when barges are working on the offshore side of the outer ships.

A minimum shed space of 90,000 sq ft for each ship berth is recommended by Herring, based on studies made by the Port of New York Authority. In these studies it was found that the typical dry cargo ship calling at a New York terminal loads and discharges about 12,500 measurement tons.[1] Half of this cargo is discharged from the ship and the other half is loaded. Since the ship must discharge first and then load, the transit shed must be designed to accommodate both inward and outward cargoes at the same time.

[1] A measurement ton consists of 40 cu ft.

These 12,500 measurement tons occupy 500,000 cu ft, and this is the volume for which storage space must be provided within the shed. Considering the use of tiered pallet loads with the normal amount of broken lots, the need for aisles, truck roadways, truck working areas, office space, and servicing areas, in addition to the space needed for the 12,500 measurement tons of cargo, the total area requirement per ship berth of 90,000 sq ft has been proposed by the Port of New York Authority. This figure is based on data gathered under working conditions in the New York Harbor area, and it should be a reliable guide for terminals where full ship loads are loaded and discharged.

The area requirement stated above includes provision for 30 truck berths, each 40 ft by 12 ft, for loading and unloading. That number is based on the assumption that the 12,500 measurement tons of cargo are delivered to or taken from the pier in five working days. It also assumes that half the cargo moves by truck and that the average truck load is 10 measurement tons. This amounts to 1250 measurement tons a day, moving in 125 trucks. For an 8-hr day, this means that about 16 trucks must be handled every hour. Since it takes almost 2 hr on the average to load or unload a truck, about 30 available truck spots for each berth are needed.

Modifying circumstances. The terminal outlined above is not proposed as a universal standard. It hardly seems possible that there could be a universal design standard for a marine terminal. To begin with, the choice of the basic design, pier or wharf, is dependent upon factors that vary from port to port and even from area to area in the same port.

Other variable factors that may change the design features of any given terminal are: (1) The volume of cargo delivered by railroad facilities as opposed to over the road trucks. (2) Whether the terminal is primarily for loading or discharging or a combination of both. (3) Whether the terminal will handle a large amount of some uniform type of packaged or semibulk commodity.

While there are many obsolete marine terminals in operation today in all ports of the world, there are some excellent terminals that have been built in recent years or old facilities that have been modernized.

The Port of New York Authority's new pier C at Hoboken, a two berth facility, is an example. This pier is 700 ft long and 328 ft wide. One apron of this pier is 20 ft wide, whereas the other, which bears one railroad track, measures 25 ft. Another installation at Port Newark, of the wharf type construction, allows 550 ft for a ship berth; the apron measures 50 ft and bears two railroad tracks. The rear of each shed has a tail gate high freight platform abutting on a 100 ft wide paved roadway and two rail tracks laid flush with the surface.

In San Francisco, the Matson Navigation Company utilizes a modernized terminal. The old facilities included two piers which had an inside clearance of 222 ft. The inside area between the two piers has been joined by a pile-supported platform. The center portion of this joining platform between the two old piers was designed as a depressed well for truck maneuvering and backup and for rail track accommodations. The remainder of the slip was utilized for pier and shed widening. The terminal now provides three generous berths, one on each side and a third across the end.

Specialized cargo facilities. A few commodities are transported along regular routes in sufficient quantities to justify specialized facilities designed for the handling of that commodity alone. Bulk liquids, such as petroleum products, can be pumped into and out of the ship's tanks; bulk ore and grain can be gravitated into the ship's hold through chutes and unloaded by huge clamshell-type buckets and cranes or, in the case of grain, sucked out by vacuum pumps. Raw sugar is handled at Crockett, Calif., in bulk by endless bucket conveyors, being loaded in the Hawaiian Islands by gravity. Two especially interesting facilities in New York Harbor are the *Daily News* newsprint terminal in Brooklyn, and the United Fruit Company's banana unloading terminal in Weehawken, N. J.

At the newsprint terminal, a permanent crew of 28 men operates a system of conveyor belts, hoists, and specially designed fork lift trucks to handle rolls of newsprint moving to the terminal by ship, barge, and boxcar and from the terminal to the plant via truck. Longshoremen unload the ship and place the newsprint rolls on the conveyor system at shipside. All of the *Daily News'* requirements of about 1000 tons of newsprint each working day moves through this facility.

The Weehawken Interchange Terminal, as the banana unloading terminal is called, is designed to facilitate the rapid and safe transfer of stems of bananas from the ship's hold to refrigerated cars and trucks. Four specially designed traveling cranes housing endless belt conveyors transfer the stems of bananas from the ship's hold to an extensive system of horizontal belt conveyors called *curveyors*. The curveyor runs between long lines of waiting refrigerated cars and trucks and delivers the stems direct to the waiting carriers. A crew of 330 longshoremen can transfer a shipload of 60,000 stems of bananas from a ship to rail cars or trucks in one 8-hr day.

CHAPTER 2

Cargo responsibility

WHO IS RESPONSIBLE?

When speaking of ship's cargoes, the obvious answer to the question, "Who is responsible for the cargo?" is quite often not the correct answer. It would seem that whichever party held the cargo in its custody would be the party who was responsible. However, because of the peculiar provisions of the traditional ocean bill of lading as written under two controlling acts of Congress, the responsibility for cargo is a matter of *type* of damage and *cause* of damage. There are at least four parties that are interested in every cargo shipment transported by any type of carrier: (1) The shipper. (2) The carrier (shipowner). (3) The underwriter. (4) The consignee. Of these four, the shipper and the carrier have the greatest responsibility toward the safe transportation of the cargo. These responsibilities will be discussed at some length in this chapter for two reasons: first, to point up those areas where the shipowner's organization can best strengthen the carrier's position in case of litigation over damaged cargo; second, to explain the necessity and reasons behind some of the routine duties required of the ship's officers and crew members. The objective of the discussion is not to outline ways and means of circumventing the requirements of the laws governing carriage of cargo by sea, rather it is to underline the ways and means of meeting those requirements easily and completely. The more experience one has with the records of damaged cargoes the clearer it becomes that if the shipper and carrier, or their agents, would diligently carry out their responsibilities as laid down by the Harter Act and the Carriage of Goods by Sea Act, the amount of cargo damage and loss would be reduced greatly.

The Harter Act of 1893. There is no need to set forth the text of the entire Harter Act. The general provisions of the act are of interest to us. Some comments regarding their effect on the question of responsibility for cargo will be made. Prior to the passage of this act, which became effective in 1894, the shipowner was held responsible for cargo damage unless he could prove that such damage was due to one of the following causes: (1) An act of God. (2) An act of public enemies. (3) Inherent vice. (4) Fire.

With the passage of the Harter Act, the shipowner was relieved of the responsibility for damage from six additional causes: (1) Errors in navigation or mismanagement of the ship. (2) Perils of the sea. (3) Insufficiency of packaging. (4) Seizure under legal process. (5) Act or omission of shipper. (6) Saving or attempting to save life or property at sea.

In order for the carrier to enjoy the above ten immunities, the shipowner was required to fulfill certain definite responsibilities. These responsibilities were three in number: (1) He must properly stow and care for the cargo. (2) He must exercise due diligence to properly equip, man, and provision the ship. (3) He must exercise due diligence to make the vessel seaworthy in all respects.

The Harter Act applies only to vessels operating in the domestic trade. It directs the shipowner to issue a bill of lading, and it prevents him from legally not accepting the three responsibilities specified above. It does not prevent him from accepting more responsibilities. After the Harter Act became effective, the ocean bill of lading was still not standardized because under the stress of competition various shipowners would voluntarily accept greater responsibility than legally necessary. However, the carrier's position had been improved somewhat. The cargo comes under the protection of the act from the moment the ship leaves the pier until the cargo is delivered to the consignee at the port of discharge.

The Carriage of Goods by Sea Act of 1936. Forty-two years after the Harter Act became effective the Congress passed the Carriage of Goods by Sea Act, which was fashioned somewhat parallel to an act by the same name enacted by the British Parliament in 1924. This act was another attempt to standardize the ocean bill of lading and clarify the relationship of the ship to its cargo. From the provisions, it seems to aid the carrier's position for it adds seven more immunities, one more responsibility, and eases the carrier's burden with respect to seaworthiness. The Harter Act remains in effect for all vessels in the domestic trade, whereas the Carriage of Goods by Sea Act applies to American or foreign vessels carrying goods between an American port and foreign port. The 1936 act may apply to vessels in the domestic trade if the bill of lading specificly so states. Where applicable, the 1936 act supersedes the Harter Act. The 1936 act applies from the time the cargo is hoisted aboard the ship until it is discharged at the port of destination.

The additional immunities were: (1) Act of war. (2) Quarantine restrictions. (3) Strikes or lockouts. (4) Riots and civil commotion. (5) Insufficiency or inadequacy of marks. (6) Latent defects not discoverable by due diligence. (7) Any other cause arising without the actual fault and privity of the carrier.

The additional responsibility was the necessity to make all cargo spaces fit and safe for stowing the cargo.

Under the Harter Act, all the immunities of the carrier were ineffective if the shipper could prove that the vessel was unseaworthy in *any* respect at the outset of the voyage. In other words, the carrier was liable for damage if the ship was unseaworthy even though the unseaworthy aspect could not have contributed to the cargo damage. On the face of it, this seems to be ridiculous to a seaman, but that is the interpretation put on the act as written. Under the 1936 act, the carrier cannot be held liable for reasons of unseaworthiness unless the unseaworthy condition contributed to the cargo damage.

Summary of immunities. Summarizing all the immunities of the carrier as they appear in section 4 of the 1936 act we find that neither the carrier nor the ship shall be responsible for loss or damage to cargo arising from any of the following:

1. Error in navigation or mismanagement of the ship.
2. Fire, unless caused by the fault or privity of the carrier.
3. Perils of the sea.
4. Act of God.
5. Act of war.
6. Act of public enemies.
7. Arrest or seizure under legal process.
8. Quarantine restrictions.
9. Act or omission of the shipper.

10. Strikes or lockouts.
11. Riots or civil commotion.
12. Saving or attempting to save life or property at sea.
13. Inherent defect, quality, or vice of the goods.
14. Insufficiency of packaging.
15. Insufficiency or inadequacy of marks.
16. Latent defects not discoverable by due diligence.
17. Any other cause arising without the actual fault and privity of the carrier.

The carrier's responsibilities.   In order for the carrier to enjoy these immunities, the shipowner must fulfill these four responsibilities:

1. He must exercise due diligence to make the ship seaworthy.
2. He must exercise due diligence to properly man, provision, and equip the ship.
3. He must properly care for and stow the cargo.
4. He must make all cargo spaces fit and safe for stowing the cargo.

It is impossible to discuss the precise meaning and intent of all seventeen immunities as listed by the 1936 act so that ship's officers or others within the shipowner's cargo operations group can quickly and easily determine whether a given situation is in fact covered by one of them. However, a clearer understanding of practical means of aiding the shipowner in fulfilling his responsibilities to the cargo can be gained by the cargo operations group through study of the act's provisions, reviewing court interpretations of the meaning of the terms used in the act and reviewing court opinions regarding specific cases.   With improved understanding, the ship's officers will be enabled to act more intelligently in the interest of all concerned.

Viewpoint of shipper and shipowner.   One fact that becomes apparent from reviewing the accounts of past litigation pertaining to cargo damage is that the shipper generally attempts to prove that the damage was caused by improper stowage or improper care and custody.   At the same time, the shipowner generally takes the position that the damage was the result of mismanagement or an error in navigation on the part of the ship's officers or crew.   There is little wonder that this is so, in light of the obvious prejudice each would have in any case plus the extremely fine line of distinction between the two as adjudged by the courts.   Indeed, the difference is so slight that, even after reading an account of some cases and knowing how the courts decided the question and studying the court opinion, the layman will not be able to detect the slight technical difference that decided the issue.

The most outstanding example of a technical difference is that where the act says the carrier is exempt from responsibility for damage caused by mismanagement by the ship's crew but then says that the carrier is responsible for improper stowage. Stowage of cargo in an improper manner is definitely incorrect management or mismanagement, to use the terms of the act. Thus we have one form of mismanagement for which the carrier is not immune from responsibility. Another is the improper care and custody of the cargo. To try and point out salient points whereby the layman can reliably determine mismanagement as compared to improper care and custody is almost futile. The best course for members of the shipowner's cargo operations group to follow is to remember the basic responsibilities of the carrier and make every effort to see that they are fully met.

Improper stowage of the type that comes to the attention of surveyors working in the interest of the shipper is related to insufficient or improper dunnaging, lashing, or other means of securing the cargo in its stowage position. The most numerous cases of improper stowage are those wherein the cargo is found to be stowed with incompatible cargoes or in places on the ship where damage was nearly certain. The initial step in preventing this latter cause of cargo damage is a thoroughly prepared and *discussed* tentative cargo stowage plan. A secondary step is to brief the officers of the ship concerning the plan and a watchful attitude on the part of the officers during the loading operation. It is, of course, imperative that the planners and executors have extensive experience with the commodities being stowed and a thorough knowledge of the best general stowage methods.

Three other factors that need careful attention by ship's officers to prevent the claimant from being successful in his assertion that the carrier did not fulfill his responsibilities are: (1) Inspection of hold areas, refrigeration spaces, and tanks which are to receive cargo. Such inspections should be made carefully, and full and complete log book entries should be entered to support the shipowner's position. (2) Careful attention to ventilation procedures with appropriate log book entries. (3) Careful attention to all openings leading directly into the cargo spaces. If damage is caused by neglect of an opening leading directly into a cargo space, it will quite likely be adjudged as improper care and custody. However, if water enters the hold area as a result of a tarpaulin that became torn because of a loose mooring line rack being washed aft by heavy seas, the cause would quite likely be deemed mismanagement. A slight and seemingly insignificant point, however, may change the court's opinion in either case.

MARITIME CASES [1]

One of the best ways to underline what action should be taken in any given situation relative to the handling and stowage of cargo is to study the decisions of the courts in past cases. With this idea in mind, several illustrative cases are discussed below in brief. The discussions are based on actual cases and they demonstrate dramatically how a ship's officer and other operating personnel can best serve to protect the interests of the shipowner.

Improper stowage versus insufficiency of packaging. In 1942 a ship at Basra, Iraq, loaded 732 cases and 319 bags of licorice extract from open lighters. The licorice had been shipped by rail from Turkey and had been on the dock waiting for the ship for about one month. The cases were marked with the words: "Stow away from the boilers."

When loading commenced, the temperature of the atmosphere was about 115°F. The master of the ship noted that some of the cases were broken and in some instances the licorice was oozing out. He had all damaged containers recoopered and endorsed the bill of lading to the effect that the cases were badly damaged and recoopered, but that the ship could not be responsible for loss of contents or short delivery.

The entire cargo of licorice was stowed in the forward part of No. 4 'tweendecks, directly forward of which was the engine room. The cargo extended from the deck of the compartment to within 12 in. of the overhead. The cases were stowed about eight high with the bags on top. The ship proceeded to an East African port and loaded chrome ore. Some of this chrome ore was placed just aft of the licorice with a temporary wooden bulkhead erected between the two cargoes. During the voyage, no temperatures were taken of the hold spaces and no inspections made. In Baltimore, where the licorice was to be discharged, it was found that the extract had broken out of most of the cases and bags

---

[1] The basic information regarding the cases outlined in this chapter was obtained from American Maritime Cases, published under the auspices of the Maritime Law Association of the United States. References at the end of some discussions refer the reader to American Maritime Cases, the year published, and the page number; for example (1947-AMC-568). The reports of these cases are interesting to all personnel connected in any way with the operation of merchant ships. The reports are of particular importance to ship's officers as a means of learning how the courts view questions concerning damaged cargo and the causes. It gives one an opportunity to stand on the shoulders of those who have gone this way before and, probably, to acquire greater insight into better practices. AMC is published monthly in paper bound editions and yearly issues are available in book form. Digests for reference purposes are also available. These cases are accounts of actual incidents and resulting litigation and the basic causes of cargo damage are brought to light vividly.

when in a glutinous state and thereafter had become a hard mass. Many of the cases and bags were stuck together. Wood, nails, and other foreign material were imbedded in the licorice. This made it impossible to remove the cargo from the ship case by case or bag by bag. It had to be broken by picks before it could be removed from the hold. Recovery was sought for the expense of removing it, melting it down to remove the foreign material, and making it merchantable.

In court, the shipper's argument was that the damage was due to *improper stowage*. He claimed that the licorice should have been stowed in one of the lower holds, preferably in No. 1 lower hold where the temperature was less than in No. 4 'tweendecks, and also that dunnage should have been used between tiers to allow better circulation of air.

The carrier claimed that the licorice extract was not in good condition when loaded and its stowage was entirely proper. It was also claimed that any change in the condition of the licorice during the voyage was due to *inherent vice* and to the *insufficiency of packaging*.

It was developed in court that the recognized place for stowing such cargo was below the waterline of the ship where the temperatures are lower than in the upper deck. The carrier introduced temperatures of another ship that had carried licorice extract successfully in this upper deck, but the court rejected these records. It rejected them because it was purely a matter of speculation whether the temperatures on the first ship were the same as those on the second. In fact, there were two things that made it seem likely that the temperature on the second ship was probably higher. First, chrome ore in bulk will heat when damp. Such cargo was stowed adjacent to the licorice, and although there is no evidence that it did or did not heat, the court could not accept the temperatures with so much conjecture about them. Secondly, the ventilators in the after part of the 'tweendecks where the licorice was stowed led into a special locker which prevented full circulation of the air in that space. This was not the case on the first ship.

It may have been true that the temperatures on the two ships mentioned above were the same, but the ship's officers failed to take any temperature records and log them; therefore, the carrier was without proof.

The court held in favor of the shipper saying that he had proved, as he must, that the cargo was in a marketable condition when delivered to the ship, but that on arrival in Baltimore it was not marketable. The court also concluded that the proximate cause of the change was not insufficiency of packaging or inherent defect but improper stowage.

The court went on to explain its position by pointing out that, whereas there was no obligation on the part of the vessel to keep the extract after stowage from becoming *somewhat* either more soft or more hard (because it was characteristic of the extract to become more or less viscous with change of temperature), there was an obligation to *use every reasonable effort to check its viscosity* so that it would not change greatly from that which it had when taken aboard the vessel. The court was satisfied that such requirement was not met when the vessel's officers, being fully apprised of the character of the cargo, failed to stow it in that part of the vessel where it was the custom to stow it and where the temperature was indisputably lower.

Although it is true that it cannot be said with certainty that had the cargo been so placed its condition upon arrival in Baltimore would have been different, it is reasonable to believe that had proper precautions been taken its condition on arrival would not have been materially different from that when delivered to the ship in Basra.

The court went on to point out that the law requires the shipowner to use all reasonable means to ascertain the nature and characteristics of goods tendered for shipment and to exercise due care in their handling and stowage, including such methods as their nature requires.

The provision for limitation of liability contained in the bill of lading which the vessel owners might properly have asserted as a defense to the claim, had the stowage of the cargo been proper, becomes of no avail. (1947-AMC-568)

Fire, unless caused by the fault or privity of the carrier. In August 1926, a ship left New York bound for Hull, England. Six hours after departure, fire was discovered in coal in a temporary bunker in No. 3 'tweendeck. Although the ship immediately changed course and ran for the port of New York, she sank with a total loss of her cargo.

In this case the shipper charged the carrier with a breach of contract for not delivering the cargo at its destination. The carrier, of course, pleaded in defense the Fire Statute of 1851 to which the bill of lading referred. Both parties agreed that the fire was the proximate cause of the loss.

The shipper took the position that the ship was unseaworthy when she sailed because the bunker fire was inevitable and that this condition was due to the negligence of the ship's chief engineer. Therefore, they contended that the carrier could not claim exoneration from liability under the Fire Statute.

The court found that the fire was not caused by the neglect of the ship's owner but by gross negligence of the ship's chief engineer. The chief engineer had loaded new coal on top of old coal while the old coal had become so hot in some spots from spontaneous heating that it burned the trimmer's soles.

The court stated that the limited liability act of 1851 (Fire Statute) provided that the owner of a vessel should not be liable for any loss to cargo caused by fire unless the fire was caused by the *design or neglect of the owner*. The negligence of the ship's officers in causing a fire was not to be imparted to the owner so as to deprive him of the protection of the Fire Statute.

Specifically, the court held that a vessel owner is not liable for damage to cargo caused by the negligence of the chief engineer in placing new bunker coal over old bunkers. It was indicated that the court's decision was based on precedent when it was pointed out that in all cases where exoneration from liability under the Fire Statute had been denied previously, there had been proof that the fire was due to the negligence of the owner himself or of some representative of the owner other than the ship's officers and crew. (1932-AMC-1012)

Strike or lockout versus improper care and custody. This interesting case involved green salted hides that were loaded on a ship in an Australian port. Thereafter, the ship was delayed for a period of two and a half months owing to a seaman's strike. After a total of six months, the shipment was delivered to the consignee in a Belgian port but in a badly deteriorated condition. In an original suit for damages, the carrier was exonerated from liability because of the strike or lockout clause of the bill of lading. However, the case was appealed, and the cargo owner won a judgment for the damage to the cargo. The court summed up its opinion by stating that, simply because a seaman's strike occurs, the carrier cannot abandon the cargo or reduce its efforts to care for the cargo.

Some of the factors that caused the court to deny exoneration from liability to the carrier follow, and every ship's officer should keep this information fresh in his memory as he goes about his cargo duties throughout the years. Above all, these factors illustrate the need for constant diligence with respect to cargo care.

The carrier was negligent in not taking action to *avoid* damage while the ship was unable to proceed. The owner of the cargo should have been notified of the delay so that he might at least consider measures to protect his goods. No effort was made to ventilate the cargo properly while the ship was at anchor in port, such as opening the hatches and trimming all vents into the wind. No inspections of the hides were made throughout the time at anchor to see if any damage was taking place or if rehandling might be necessary. The longshoremen were not requested to unload, shift, or resalt the hides during the delay. The ship was docked for three weeks before shifting to the anchorage, yet no attempt had been made to discharge the hides which were known to be perishable. The officer who supervised the stowage of these hides was found to be incompetent, inefficient, and ignorant of the proper handling of hides. Finally, upon termination of the strike, the cargo was transshipped to another ship and stowed in the after part of No. 3 hold adjacent to the fireroom bulkhead. Thus the hides were submitted to excessive heat during the sea voyage and this aided their deterioration.

In view of all the above facts, the carrier was held guilty of *improper care and custody* and liable, notwithstanding the *strike or lockout* clause in the bill of lading.

This is an excellent example of a case that the carrier might have won if the ship's officers had exercised a minimum of initiative and been able to show a small amount of evidence of having thought about the cargo by ventilating, inspecting, and making appropriate log book entries. These things require very little effort yet are definite manifestations of proper care and custody, and the cargo owner has a right to expect at least this reasonable amount of consideration for his goods.

An act or omission of the shipper. In 1945, a shipper packed a complete wax museum in crates and barrels and described the cargo as 40 barrels and crates of wax museum pieces. The shipment was bound for Honolulu, T. H., and a bill of lading was issued.

Actually, the shipment consisted of some plaster figurines and wax pieces depicting various parts of the human anatomy. Some of these pieces were contained in glass showcases. The tariff rates in effect at that time called for $8.25 per measurement ton for wax objects as described in the bill of lading. The rate for plaster figurines of the type contained in the shipment was $11.25 per measurement ton, with the carrier assuming the risk.

Upon discharge, damage reports were made out because it was found that almost every container was damaged to some extent. When the owner of the cargo brought suit to recover the cost of the damaged pieces, the court held that the carrier was not liable because the shipper failed to disclose the true nature of the cargo and actually received a lower freight rate because of the description given the shipment. Furthermore, there was no liability because there was insufficient evidence to prove that the pieces were properly packed in the first place. (1947-AMC-1082)

The value of exercising due diligence. A case that points up the value of being able to prove that due diligence was exercised in making a ship seaworthy involves cargo damaged by sea water that entered the ship's hold through leaky flanges on four overboard drains from the ship's sanitary system. This incident occurred during the maiden voyage of the ship.

Five owners of cargo brought suit for damage to cargo stowed in No. 4 lower hold. The cargo was loaded in New York and discharged at a South American port. It was found that the cargo had been thoroughly wet by salt water about 4 ft deep in the cargo compartment. It was determined that the water had gotten there through leaky flanges on pipes of the sanitary system that ran through the compartment and that the leaks were the result of faulty construction.

During the course of her construction, the ship was subjected to constant tests by representatives of the Coast Guard, American Bureau of Shipping, Maritime Commission, and various manufacturer representatives. All of these men made various tests at various times to determine the ship's seaworthiness. She was tested further during her trials. Finally, after her delivery to the owners, the ship's officers made a visual inspection of the ship, especially of the interiors of all holds and particularly the pipes and connections within the holds. No evidence of leaking, such as water stains, was found.

The court found that the cargo in No. 4 lower hold did suffer substantial damage from sea water, but it also found that the damage did not occur through failure of the carrier to exercise *due diligence* in making the ship seaworthy at the time the cargo was loaded.

Thus we see that a *latent defect* not discoverable by due diligence was held to exonerate the ship from liability, but it is important to be aware of the fact that due diligence must be proved. Accurate and complete log book entries describing all efforts along these lines are an invaluable aid in this regard.

Peril of the sea versus improper care and custody. A point of view that the author believes may not be widely held by seafarers is expressed in the decision of the court in the following case.

A ship was loading bagged coffee at a Haitian port while at anchor. The cargo was being brought to the ship in lighters which were propelled by oars, and the lighters were fitted with hand bilge pumps. With the lighters secured to the ship at about 1600, loading commenced. The wind was northerly at about force 2, Beaufort scale. At 1635 it commenced to rain and the wind picked up to force 7. Loading operations were halted during the brief storm which lasted about 3 hr.

As a result of choppy seas and being on the weather side of the ship, the lighters shipped a good deal of water. The hand operated bilge pumps were inadequate and one lighter sank; the coffee in all lighters was thoroughly wet.

In the eventual litigation that followed this incident, the carrier claimed that the cargo loss was due to a *peril of the sea* and the inadequacy of the pumps on the lighters. However, the court held that the lighters were in the custody of the ship when alongside and the loss could have been prevented if reasonable effort to save the lighters had been made.

This decision was undoubtedly due to the testimony that established the fact that the ship could have strung the lighters out along the stern of the ship and used oil to calm the seas, whereas *nothing* had been done to aid the lighters.   (1952-AMC-1094)

Error in navigation versus improperly manned and equipped and unseaworthy condition.   This case involves a ship that had considerable trouble with her main engines prior to a grounding which resulted in the loss of her cargo of bananas either through jettisoning or rotting. It was also brought out in the testimony that the chief engineer had been drunk at the outset of the voyage.

As a result of the immediate history of engine trouble and the drunken chief engineer, the shipper charged that the ship was *unseaworthy and improperly manned and equipped.*   But, from the log and testimony, the court held that the proximate reason for the grounding was an *error in navigation* and ruled in favor of the ship.   This case went to an appellate court before the ship received the favorable ruling; a lower court held that the ship was *improperly manned and equipped and unseaworthy.*

A summary of the facts is as follows.   Six weeks before the ship left Miami for the Cuban port to pick up the banana cargo, the engines had been replaced and the ship overhauled.   The compass had been spot-checked at this time also.   The compass had been swung and compensated by an expert 15 months before the grounding.   The captain of the ship had been well recommended to the shipowner and was deemed fully competent.   On the outward voyage from Miami, Fla., to the loading port in Cuba, the ship's port engine became disabled.   However, it was decided that the return voyage could be made on one engine; therefore, the ship was loaded and sailed.

Not long after leaving the Cuban port with the load of bananas, the starboard engine also became disabled.   A tug was obtained and the vessel proceeded while repair work went ahead on the engines.   At about 2000, August 13, 1947, the ship dropped the tug and proceeded on her own power.   The log showed that the ship was steering a magnetic course of 308°.   This was the course being steered at the time of the stranding at 0110, August 14, 1947.   The log showed no allowance for wind that was blowing from the east, deviation of the compass, or current.   It was brought out in the testimony of many ship's officers that the normal *magnetic* course for the run in question was 308° with allowances for wind which would make the course anywhere from 309 to 316° depending upon the weather.

The appellate court did not believe that the history of engine trouble or the fact that the chief engineer had been drunk upon departure from the loading port were shown in any way to have been the cause of the grounding. It was decided that the grounding resulted from an *error in navigation* in the form of simply failing to allow for leeway made by the wind.

Inspection of cargo spaces. The case discussed below was taken from the records of a large insurance company and serves to illustrate the importance of *thorough inspection of cargo spaces,* the value of taking soundings (especially during fueling operations), and the dangers involved in pressing up double bottom tanks.

A claim amounting to $350,000 was filed against the shipowner for fuel oil damage to tobacco. Fuel oil from the double bottom tanks escaped into the cargo hold and came in contact with a large number of bales of tobacco. To get all the facts, the story must begin with the loading of the outward cargo in the United States.

Railroad rails were loaded in the United States in the lower hold in question for discharge at Basra, Iraq. In discharging these rails, the longshoremen first pried up the rails at one end and secured a chain sling around approximately four rails at a time. The rails were dragged across the tank tops in the process and in a few cases a rail had slipped from the load and dropped back into the square of the hatch.

Although there was no direct proof of it, it was probable that the tank covers were damaged during this discharging process. The tank lids, however, were not examined before the tobacco was loaded on board. Later, the master and chief officer signed a statement to the effect that the lids were damaged while discharging the rails.

After the rails were discharged, the hold was prepared for the stowage of tobacco. Two inches of dunnage was laid crisscross fashion on the tank tops, and mats were laid over the dunnage, around ironwork, and as a liner around all sides of the hold. There were permanent horizontal cargo battens at the sides of the hold and in addition strips of wood were fashioned vertically over the battens.

The chief officer, whose duty it was to inspect the hold, went into the hold while mats were being laid and *after* it had been cleaned up. As far as he knew, the lids may have been covered over with mats at the time he made his inspection. According to the master, who had been on the ship since she was built, the manhole lids had never been removed and no damage to them had ever been heard of or reported.

Some 3000 bales of tobacco were loaded into the lower hold. After the vessel completed loading, she proceeded to a fueling port. The chief engineer estimated he had between 650 and 700 barrels of fuel on board, all in the settling tanks. Oil was pumped on board. When the operation was completed, an oil barge man came aboard to have his account signed by the chief engineer. This man claimed 12,515 barrels had been supplied, or some 900 barrels more than the chief engineer could account for. After some verification of the barge man's records, it was decided to take bilge soundings. The mate was busy at the time and soundings were taken by the maintenance man. Four feet of oil was discovered in the cargo hold in which the tobacco was stowed.

It developed that the mate had not requested any soundings during the morning because the men were busy tying up the oil barge, and later it had been overlooked. However, the boatswain said he had been told by the mate not to take soundings while in port!

Due to war time conditions the ship sailed to join a convoy with the oil in the cargo hold. During the voyage the fuel oil was consumed but the damage to the tobacco was heavy.

Counsel representing the shipper made the following observations in arguing the case:

The following facts or circumstances appear to be established. The damage to the tank lids existed when the chief officer made his inspection and before the tobacco was loaded. It is unimportant how long before or in what manner the damage did happen. The lids and their shields were not examined or inspected prior to loading the tobacco. Based on the usual or normal standard of due diligence, we think there was a clear failure to exercise due diligence to make the vessel seaworthy with respect to cargo in not inspecting and discovering the condition of the lids before the commencement of the voyage.

It may be suggested that under existing war conditions a different or lesser standard of due diligence should be applied. While we shall keep this point in mind, we think there were not any war conditions which would furnish any excuse for those on board failing to find the damaged lids. Besides the master and chief officer, there were two other deck officers all of whom had ample time to examine the holds thoroughly. We believe that due diligence was not exercised.

Despite this unseaworthiness and lack of due diligence, the damage, or the greater part of it, would not have happened if bilge soundings had been taken during the fueling at Bahrein Island or if the tanks had not been pressed up at the time.

Even if these acts, that is, failing to take soundings and pressing up of the tanks, were negligent and, if viewed apart, would be considered acts of *management;* we think they would not constitute a defence. The Court's opinion in the case of the Elkton appears decisive on this point. The Court said: "When the owner accepts cargo in an unseaworthy ship, though the defect be such as may be neutralized by care, he imposes on the shipper an added risk; not merely that his servants may fail, insofar as she is sound and fit, but they may neglect those added precautions which her condition demands. That risk the statute does not impose upon the shipper; he bears no loss until the owner has done his best to remove all risks except those inevitable upon the seas."

On the basis of the facts in the case the shipowner paid $263,341 in damages.

LOG BOOK ENTRIES

Because the ship's officer makes a countless number of log book entries all during his career, there is always the danger that he will become careless about the manner in which they are made. Our survey of the distribution of responsibility for the cargo should make it evident that the log book entries can affect the shipowner's position materially.

When a hold is inspected to determine its fitness for receiving cargo, this fact and some details concerning it should be carefully noted in the log. The time of fueling and the time of bilge soundings reflect due diligence, or the lack of it, so definitely that the prosaic task of sounding bilges must never be overlooked, and, what is just as important, neither should the entries in the log book. All efforts to ventilate a hold properly or to determine or control conditions in a hold before or during the voyage should be clearly indicated in the log. If this is not done, the officer is jeopardizing his employer's position in the eyes of the court (in case of litigation), and his own position in the eyes of his employer. All efforts to prevent the elements from entering the hold during loading operations or from reaching cargo in lighters alongside should be logged. Every time a lashing is checked or set up or added to deck cargo, this fact should be entered in the log.

Whenever there is any doubt about whether an action to protect cargo is warranted, the decision should be in favor of doing it. But, it is just as important to log the fact that the action was in fact taken. It is well known that all such special entries should be signed and the time of the action indicated. Entries should never be erased, and it is a poor policy to add entries long after the action has taken or should have taken place in an effort to deceive a surveyor or counsel as to the true facts. Post scripts to the log can be uncovered easily, and it leaves the responsible officer in an embarrassing position. When honest mistakes are made in writing an entry, delete them by drawing a single neat line through the error and leave the mistake clearly discernible.

CHAPTER 3

Principles of stowage

The fundamental objectives when cargo is stowed in the ship are: (1) To protect the ship. (2) To protect the cargo. (3) To obtain the maximum use of the available cubic of the ship. (4) To provide for rapid and systematic discharging and loading. (5) To provide for safety of crew and longshoremen at all times.

PROTECTING THE SHIP

The problem involved in meeting this objective is the correct distribution of the cargo weight. The distribution must be correct vertically, longitudinally, and transversely. The weights must not be concentrated on any deck so that the structure's supporting strength is exceeded.

Vertical distribution of weight. *Vertical distribution* affects the stability of the ship. If too much weight is in the upper decks of the ship, the ship will have a small amount of stability and be in a condition known as *tender*. If too much weight is concentrated in the lower holds, the ship will have an excess of stability and be in a condition known as *stiff*. The tender ship has a long slow easy roll. The stiff ship has a fast whiplike roll that makes her especially uncomfortable in a heavy sea and is often the cause of cargo shifting transversely.

If a ship is excessively stiff, she will roll with such violent motion that damage to the ship can be caused by heavy wracking stresses on the hull. Some of the defects caused by these heavy wracking stresses will be apparent immediately after they occur, such as cracked porthole or window glass in the superstructure, standard compasses being whipped from their pedestals, and topmasts or antennas being shaken loose. Some defects having their basic cause in these wracking stresses will never be attributed to the improper vertical distribution of the cargo. These defects may not be discovered until the ship undergoes a thorough inspection on a drydock. These defects are cracked seams, loose rivets, leaking hull openings, and leaking tanks.

Longitudinal distribution of weight. *Longitudinal distribution* affects the trim of the ship and the hogging and sagging bending stresses that the ship's hull must withstand. The trim is the difference in the draft of the ship fore and aft. The ship should be loaded so that she has an even trim or a trim slightly by the stern, 6 in. to 1 ft. A trim by the head, if only a few inches, does not affect the speed of the ship. Trimming by the head is avoided, however, because if the ship is deep loaded and in a heavy seaway, there is more possibility that damaging green seas will be shipped on the foredeck. Hogging occurs when the ship has too much of the total weight concentrated in the ends, and the hull bends as shown in Fig. 3-1*a*. Sagging occurs when too much weight is concentrated amidships, and the hull bends as shown in Fig. 3-1*b*.

If a ship is hogged or sagged as she lies in still water, these excessive stresses will be accentuated when the ship is in a seaway, and the result may be a cracked deck or hull plate. Excessive hogging or sagging, as a result of improper longitudinal distribution of cargo or ballast, has been the cause of many ships breaking in two. But for every ship that has cracked into two pieces, there are hundreds of cases where the shipowner has had to pay for the repairs of cracks, large and small, in hull and deck plating. Many of the resulting expenses and delays could have been avoided by more intelligent longitudinal distribution of the cargo, voyage after voyage.

It must be understood clearly that a ship can be trimmed well while she is hogged or sagged dangerously. Good trim is simply a matter of correct balance of trimming moments. These can be precisely as desired, whereas the concentration can be such that great damage will be done, as explained above.

Transverse distribution of weight. *Transverse distribution* offers no problem. When stowing the cargo, the only necessity is to make sure that the weight is equal on both sides of the ship's centerline. This is accomplished by starting all loading on the centerline and stowing outboard, loading equal amounts in the wings, or in the case of heavy lifts putting them on the centerline if possible. If heavy lifts cannot be put on the centerline, then by careful planning, an equal weight must be placed on the side opposite to the heavy lift. This last problem may arise when forced to load a heavy lift on deck.

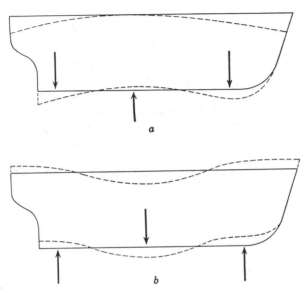

FIG. 3-1. (*a*) Hogging: too much weight in ends. (*b*) Sagging: too much weight amidships.

Although it is rarely of practical use, it is interesting to know that the period of the ship's roll can be affected by the concentration of the weight transversely. If the mass is concentrated inboard along the centerline of the ship, the roll will be very rapid and the period of the roll will be decreased. Conversely, if the weights are concentrated outboard in the wings, the roll will be slowed down and the period of the roll will be increased. Theoretically, then, this is a device that could be used to give a stiff ship a more comfortable roll. If a ship is unavoidably loaded stiff, the roll can be slowed down by concentrating weights outboard. In practice, such refinements are seldom practicable, although they are possible.

Importance of weight distribution. Improper weight distribution due to improperly loaded cargoes has cost many shipowners much time and money in the past and in all probability is still costing time and money. Ships have been lost at sea due to the shifting of cargoes or ballast caused primarily by violent rolling in a heavy seaway. For every ship lost, there are probably thousands of cases of minor but, nevertheless, costly damages. This is needless trouble for all principals concerned. The answer is simple. All responsible officers must know what is meant by correct vertical distribution of weights, and furthermore, they must know how to accomplish said distribution with positive and scientific certainty.

The problem of proper longitudinal distribution is equal in importance if not greater than that for vertical distribution. According to the findings of a Board of Investigation established by the Secretary of the Navy in April 1946, to inquire into the design and methods of construction of welded steel merchant vessels, 970 ships reported some type of structural failure during the years 1943 to 1946. The total number of structural fractures reported by these ships was 4720. One hundred twenty-seven of these ships sustained fractures that weakened the main hull structure so that the vessel was lost or placed in a serious condition. Twenty-four ships sustained a complete fracture of the main deck; one ship sustained a complete fracture of the bottom. Eleven of these ships broke in two, and of these eleven, seven were lost completely.[1]

Part of the answer to this problem of structural failures was the installation of crack arresters, modification of cargo hatch corners (where many of the fractures originated), elimination of square sheer-strake cutouts for accommodation ladders, and general elimination or modification of structural discontinuities. The rest of the answer was to give more attention to loading and ballasting of the ships. Part of the answer to the problem, then, is virtually the same as given above for vertical distribution; namely, that responsible officers must know what is meant by correct longitudinal distribution of weight and how to accomplish it when loading ships.

The point to be made here is that improper longitudinal distribution of weights does contribute to structural failures of ships. These failures are of such a nature that in many cases the shipowner's organization may not be aware of the cost in time and money that improper distribution is causing. This is because minor failures might be attributed wholly to heavy seas or the age of the ship, whereas these factors only contribute to the failure, and the principal blame should go to the improper longitudinal distribution of cargo and ballast. The operations department of every steamship line should insist that the longitudinal distribution

---

[1] Report of a Board of Investigation, *The Design and Methods of Construction of Welded Steel Merchant Vessels,* Government Printing Office, Washington, 1947, pp. 1–3.

of weights be calculated, recorded, and attested to by the master of every ship that sails. Furthermore, some tabular or mechanical means for calculation of the bending moments of the hull should be employed. A statistician should correlate the cost of repairs and the bending moments found in the ships.

In order to facilitate a complete discussion of the first fundamental objective of cargo stowage, the basic principles of stability, trim, and longitudinal stresses will be covered in this chapter. It is recommended, however, that every ship's officer, stevedore, or member of a shipping organization who has responsibility for the loading of ships consult the references mentioned in the footnotes for a more detailed explanation of the governing principles.[1, 2]

THE SHIP'S STABILITY

Stability is the tendency of a ship to return to an upright position when inclined from the vertical by an outside force. This discussion shall only be concerned with *initial stability,* which can be defined as the tendency of a ship to right itself when inclined less than 10°. Stability at large angles and damage stability are topics that every well-informed ship's officer should understand, but the discussion of them is too lengthy for this coverage and would not aid the discussion of the first objective of good stowage.

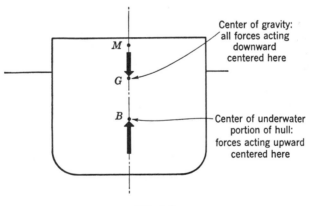

FIG. 3-2.

Three important points. For a study of initial stability we constantly refer to a diagram of a ship's midship section (see Fig. 3-2) and the

[1] La Dage and Van Gemert, *Stability and Trim for the Ship's Officer,* D. Van Nostrand Co., New York, 1947, Chaps. 1, 2, and 3.

[2] La Dage, *Modern Ships,* Cornell Maritime Press, Cambridge, 1953, Chap. 6.

relationship between three points on it. These points are known as: (1) The center of buoyancy (*B*). (2) The center of gravity (*G*). (3) The metacenter (*M*).

Archimedes' principle of buoyancy is the basis of any explanation regarding the stability of floating bodies. This principle states that a body submerged wholly or partially in a fluid is buoyed up by a force equal to the weight of the fluid displaced. On a ship, the total of the upward forces of buoyancy are considered to be concentrated at point *B*. Actually, there are hydrostatic forces acting over the entire submerged surface of the ship's hull, but the total of the upward force is the force of buoyancy and acts through point *B*.

This force of buoyancy acting through *B* is opposed by an equal force acting downward through point *G*. When a body is floating, the forces through *B* and *G* are equal. The force through *B* will never exceed the force through *G*. The force through *G* may exceed the force through *B*, in which case the body will sink. When the forces through *G* and *B* are equal, the body will float. If the floating body is at rest, that is, not revolving transversely or longitudinally (rolling or pitching), then the forces through *B* and *G* are exactly opposed. They are acting along the same vertical line. The force acting through *G* is the sum of all the weights making up the ship's structure. For convenience, we consider them as acting through this single point *G*.

Point *B* will always be at the exact center of the underwater portion of the ship's hull. Point *G* will always be at the exact center of the entire mass of which the ship is composed. This mass includes all that lies above or below the waterline, everything in the ship or on the ship. The addition of a weight, the removal of a weight, or the shifting of a weight, will change the position of *G*. The only thing that will change the position of *B* is a change of shape of the underwater portion of the hull. The underwater portion of the hull is changing shape, of course, whenever the ship rolls or pitches; thus *B* moves about as the ship works in a seaway.

The vertical position of G. First we will discuss the location of *G*. The first step is to examine the problem of determining the *position of the center of gravity of a system of weights*. We use a physical law that may be explained mathematically as follows: *If a number of weights are part of a system of weights and each weight is multiplied by its distance from a reference line or surface, then the sum of all these products will equal the sum of all the weights times the distance of the center of gravity of the system from the reference line or surface*. This is a very important concept and the reader should not proceed until he is certain that he understands it. The rule as stated above applies to masses, but it can be made applicable to volumes as well. It can be used to find the position of a center of gravity in three dimensions; however, our problem in stability is somewhat simplified by the fact that our G will always be considered to lie on the ship's centerline, and we will be concerned only with the height of G above the keel of the ship. Let us consider, then, the relatively simple problem of finding the position of the center of gravity of a system of weights stretched out along a line.

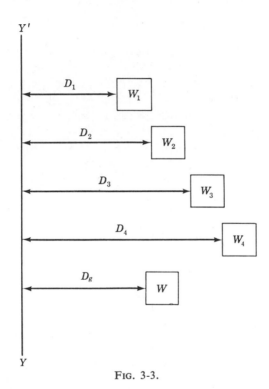

Fɪɢ. 3-3.

Figure 3-3 shows a system of four weights (W_1, W_2, W_3, W_4) with their respective distances (D_1, D_2, D_3, D_4) from a reference line yy'. The above law says that the following is true:

$$(W_1 \cdot D_1) + (W_2 \cdot D_2) + (W_3 \cdot D_3) + (W_4 \cdot D_4) = W \cdot D_g \qquad (1)$$

where D_1, D_2, D_3, D_4 are the distances of the weights from the line yy'.
    W_1, W_2, W_3, W_4 are the weights.
    W is the sum of all the weights in the system.
    D_g is the distance of the center of gravity of the weight system from the reference line yy'.

Before proceeding further, it must be pointed out that the product of a weight and a distance ($W \times D$) in each case is a *moment*. A moment is defined as the product of a force acting through a distance. The units used on ships are tons for W and feet for D, hence the units of the moment are foot-tons. Knowing this we can restate the important law given above: the sum of all the individual moments in a weight system is equal to the moment caused by the total weight of the system being concentrated at the distance of G from the reference line. It is important to remember that the product of a weight acting through a distance is a moment.

Figure 3-2 illustrates the system of weights as being referred to a vertical line outward in a horizontal direction. This was done purposely because in everyday life it is the way that weight systems are generally visualized. The seesaw is a good practical example. However, the law holds for finding the position of G with reference to a horizontal line upward in a vertical direction. This latter method also is the way we consider the problem when working to locate G on a ship. A numerical example pertaining to the vertical position of G follows. In this example, we will shift also to the terms used on board ship.

Numerical example

In Fig. 3-4 the reference line is the keel of the ship. The lower hold has 3000 tons in it with the center of this weight 8 ft above the keel; the lower

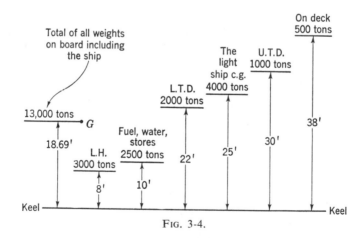

Fig. 3-4.

'tweendecks has 2000 tons centered 22 ft above the keel; the upper 'tweendecks has 1000 tons 30 ft above the keel; the deck load of cargo amounts to 500 tons which is 38 ft above the keel. There are 2500 tons of fuel, water, and stores on board with the center of weight 10 ft above the keel.

The light ship structure has a weight of 4000 tons and the vertical height of its center of gravity is 25 ft above the keel. The question we want to answer with all these data is: How far does the center of gravity of all these weights (G) lie above the keel? Referring to the general statement of the problem, we proceed to multiply each weight by its distance above the reference line. We then add all of these moments. We also add all the weights involved to obtain the total amount of weight in the system, in this case the displacement of the ship. To obtain the answer we seek, we divide the sum of all the moments by the ship's displacement.

$$
\begin{array}{rcl}
25 \cdot & 4{,}000 = & 100{,}000 \text{ ft-tons} \\
38 \cdot & 500 = & 19{,}000 \text{ ft-tons} \\
8 \cdot & 3{,}000 = & 24{,}000 \text{ ft-tons} \\
22 \cdot & 2{,}000 = & 44{,}000 \text{ ft-tons} \\
30 \cdot & 1{,}000 = & 30{,}000 \text{ ft-tons} \\
10 \cdot & 2{,}500 = & 25{,}000 \text{ ft-tons} \\
\hline
x \cdot & 13{,}000 = & 242{,}000 \text{ ft-tons}
\end{array}
$$

| Distance of G above keel | Total weight | Sum of all moments |

Dividing 242,000 by 13,000 we solve for the value of x.

$$x = 18.69 \text{ ft} = \text{Called } KG$$

Thus we see that G lies 18.69 ft above the keel of the ship.

The 13,000 is the weight of the ship and all she contains under the conditions given in the problem. This figure is the *displacement* of the ship. The displacement is indicated in formulas by the Greek letter delta (Δ). The weight of the cargo and the fuel, water, and stores, 9000 tons, is known as the *deadweight lifting capacity* of the ship if this weight puts the ship down to her maximum legal draft. The *cargo deadweight* is the 6500 tons of cargo. The weight of the ship with nothing on board, 4000 tons, is known as the *light ship displacement*.

The solution of a practical problem requires all of the data given above. The weight of the cargo in the various compartments is obtained from the stowage plan. The distances of these weights above the keel are obtained partially from data concerning each compartment given on a ship's *capacity plan* (see p. 147) and partially from estimates made by the officer. If the compartment is filled with a homogeneous cargo, the weight can be considered to be centered vertically. If loaded with heavy goods on the bottom and lighter goods on top, assume the center of the weight to be about one-third of the height of the compartment above the deck of the compartment. To find the center of all the fuel, water, and stores weights is a smaller problem solved in the same manner as the general problem. The amount of fuel and water and the tanks in which they are contained must be obtained from the ship's chief engineer. The amount of stores and their positions with reference to the keel must be estimated as closely as possible. The weight of the light ship and the position of its center of gravity must be obtained from the ship's capacity plan or stability data supplied to the ship by the builders. These data are determined through the inclining experiment.[1] Light ship weight is the light ship displacement. This is the weight of the ship without any cargo, fuel, water, or stores on board.

Shifts in position of G. The position of G is affected by addition, subtraction, or shifts of weights in the system. It is important that the reader be capable of calculating these shifts in location of G. When con-

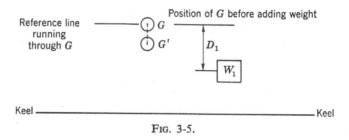

FIG. 3-5.

sidering stowage problems, it is often necessary to estimate the shift in G owing to a change in the stowage plan, or owing to the consumption of large masses on the ship, such as the burning of fuel oil from the double bottom tanks.

The first problem that we will examine is a shift in G owing to an addition or subtraction of weight to the system. Later, we will examine the shift in G caused by a movement of mass within the system. We refer to the basic law and consider a system comprised of the original total weight and the single added new weight. The reference line will be a horizontal line passing through the known position of G. The distance between our reference line and the biggest weight in our two weight system is zero, and, hence, the moment is also zero. This is important. One other moment remains. This is the product of the additional weight and its distance from the old position of G (see Fig. 3-5). The sum of these products is equal to the value of the last product. We divide the sum of the moments by the old displacement plus the newly added weight. The quotient will be equal to the shift of G. The new position is referred to as G' (G prime) and the distance of the shift is indicated by

[1] La Dage and Van Gemert, *Stability and Trim for the Ship's Officer,* D. Van Nostrand Co., New York, 1947, Chap. 4.

GG'. The shift is always toward the position of the added weight. Do not forget the formula for GG'.

$$D_1 \cdot W_1 = D_1 W_1$$

$$0 \cdot \Delta = 0$$

$$GG'(\Delta + W_1) = D_1 W_1$$

$$GG' = \frac{D_1 W_1}{(\Delta + W_1)} \tag{2}$$

where W_1 = added weight.

D_1 = distance of added weight from old center of gravity.

Δ = displacement of ship before adding W_1.

When subtracting a weight, the same reasoning applies. The shift of G is away from the weight removed and the value of the weight system is the displacement less W_1. Equation 2 for GG' becomes:

$$GG' = \frac{W_1 \cdot D_1}{\Delta - W_1} \tag{3}$$

The shift of $G(GG')$ caused by a shift of a part of the weight system, such as moving 100 tons up or down on the ship, is found by eq. 4.

$$GG' = \frac{W_1 \cdot D_1}{\Delta} \tag{4}$$

where GG' = shift of G. Always in the direction that the weight is shifted.

W_1 = the value of the weight that is shifted.

D_1 = distance that W_1 is shifted.

Δ = the ship's displacement.

Equation 4 is derived by considering the removal of a weight equal to W_1 from the position of G then replacing it at the position of rest after the shift. Using this reasoning and eq. 2 we have:

$$GG' = \frac{[(\Delta - W_1) \cdot 0] + [W_1 \cdot D_1]}{(\Delta - W_1) + W_1}$$

which becomes:

$$GG' = \frac{W_1 \cdot D_1}{\Delta}$$

which is identical to eq. 4.

Numerical example

Given: A ship displacing 15,000 tons with a *KG* of 30 ft; 2000 tons of fuel oil is burned from the double bottoms, this mass had a *KG* of 2 ft.

Required: The ship's new *KG*. (*Note:* The distance of *G* above the keel is generally referred to as *KG*. This notation will be used hereafter.)

Solution: This is a case of removing a weight from the weight system, hence we use eq. 3. W_1 equals 2000 tons. D_1 equals 28 ft. Hence, the GG' equation becomes:

$$GG' = \frac{W_1 D_1}{\Delta - W_1} = \frac{2000 \times 28}{13,000} = 4.3 \text{ ft}$$

Since *G* has moved up 4.3 ft, the new *KG* is 34.3 ft.

One more type of problem remains to be clarified with respect to the position of *G* and its shift due to the movement of weight on the ship. We have considered the solution of the shift in *G* due to adding or removing a single weight. There may be need to calculate the final position of *G* after loading several weights and discharging several weights. In this problem, it is necessary to consider each addition and removal separately and to divide all the moments into those that will move *G* up as opposed to those that will move *G* down. A net moment is obtained by adding these two sums algebraically. The net moment is divided by the *final* displacement to obtain the shift in *G*.

Numerical example

Given: A ship with a *KG* of 20 ft. The displacement is 10,000 tons.

Two weights W_1 and W_2 are loaded. $W_1 = 500$ tons and is placed 23 ft above the keel. $W_2 = 500$ tons and is placed 5 ft above the keel.

Two weights are discharged. $W_3 = 1000$ tons removed 12 ft above the keel. $W_4 = 1000$ tons removed 40 ft above the keel.

Required: The problem is to determine the ship's *KG* after the above operation. We actually would have four problems here if we solved each separately by eqs. 2 and 3. It is easier to combine the data to form one problem. The procedure is to make two columns. In one column, list all the moments resulting in an increase of *KG*; in the other, list all those resulting in a decrease.

Solution: Before adding and removing the weights, the ship had a *KG* of 20 ft. Carefully check the effect of each weight on the *KG*. W_1 is added 3 ft above the initial *G* which we are going to use as a datum level, hence, the moment of $3 \times W_1$ will increase our ship's *KG*. W_2 is added 15 ft below our datum level, and the moment will decrease the *KG*. W_3 is removed 8 ft below *G*, and *G* will move away from a removed weight; thus, this moment will increase *KG*. W_4 is removed 20 ft above *G*; thus, the moment will decrease *KG*. Next we calculate each of these moments giving a plus sign to those that increase the *KG* and a minus sign to those that decrease the *KG*. Add them algebraically. Next divide by the final displacement of the ship. The quotient is the distance in feet that G has moved up or down. If the net moment has a minus sign, the movement is down and KG has been decreased. If the sign is plus, the movement of G is up and KG has been increased. The solution of the above problem follows:

Increase of KG (+)		Decrease of KG (−)	
$500 \times 3 =$	1500 ft-tons	$500 \times 15 =$	7,500 ft-tons
$1000 \times 8 =$	8000 ft-tons	$1000 \times 20 =$	20,000 ft-tons
	$= +9500$ ft-tons		$= -27,500$ ft-tons

$$+9,500$$
$$-27,500$$

$$-18,000 \text{ ft-tons (net change in moments)}$$

A total of 2000 tons was discharged and 1000 tons were loaded; hence, the final displacement is 1000 tons less than the initial 10,000 tons.

Final step to solve for GG':

$$GG' = \frac{-18,000}{9000} = -2 \text{ ft}$$

Therefore, the new KG is $20 - 2$ or 18 ft.

Determining the position of B. The position of B can be calculated in a manner similar to that used to calculate G, except that volumes are used instead of weight values. The calculations are complicated by the fact that these volumes are bounded by curved surfaces, but they are not exceptionally difficult. The reader should refer to a standard reference if he wishes to learn exactly how these calculations are made. For practical determination of stability, there is no need to make the calculations involving the location of B. The reader needs only to be aware of the fact that B moves about as the vessel is inclined and why it moves.

Movement of B. The definition of B must be recalled before we attempt an explanation of how and why B moves about when the ship is inclined. Point B is the geometrical center of the *underwater* portion of the hull. Looking at Fig. 3-6, we note that B is on the centerline of the ship. If the ship is upright and floating, we know that G is either directly above or below B on a line perpendicular to the waterline. G is illustrated as above B on the diagram of Fig. 3-2. If the ship is inclined as shown in Fig. 3-6, a wedge of volume is removed from the underwater portion of the hull on the side away from the inclination and transferred to the side toward which the ship is inclined. What will happen to B? Obviously, B will move in the direction of the submerged side. This can be appreciated intuitively, for the center of the underwater portion now lies toward that side. The amount of the shift of B

is not too important in our explanation of factors involved in stability, but a brief exposition of the method is presented.

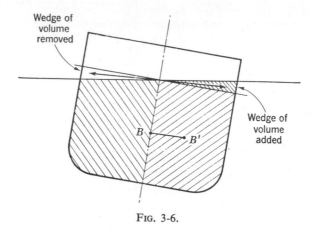

Fig. 3-6.

Calculating the shift of B. The technique involves the same principles used with respect to finding the center of a system of weights. The only difference is that, in place of weight values, volume values are used. Hence, the equations used to calculate GG' can be used to calculate BB'. In the case of the movement of B, because of a shift of the volume wedge from one side to the other, eq. 4 can be used with the units changed as necessary:

$$BB' = \frac{v \cdot d}{V} \tag{5}$$

where BB' = the distance that B shifts.

v = volume of the wedge.

d = distance that the center of the volume wedge moved.

V = volume of the entire underwater portion of the ship.

The locus of the point B as the ship is inclined to larger and larger angles will form an ellipse. This fact is of significance when studying stability at large angles of inclination.

The metacenter (M). The third and last point that is to be examined is the metacenter, M. To locate the metacenter, the naval architect takes the curvature of a circle that has the same curvature as a very small segment of the elliptical path of B. Radii of this circle are drawn. They intersect at the center of the circle and this point is where M is located. M moves about as the ship is inclined. This fact can be appreciated because the curvature of an ellipse is a minimum at the extremities of the minor axis and a maximum at the extremities of the major axis. Therefore, the radii will be changing continually, and the point M will follow. For small angles of inclination, M will fall on the centerline of the ship. As the angle of inclination approaches 10°, M moves upward and away from the side toward which the ship is inclined. When considering *initial* stability, it is assumed that M is always directly on the centerline. The distance from B to M is notated as BM and known as the metacentric radius. The force of buoyancy acting upward through B always passes through M which will always be directly over B in a vertical direction normal to the waterline.

Distance from keel to B and M. The distance from the keel to point B is known as KB and is calculated by the naval architect. BM is also calculated. The sum of KB and BM gives KM which is of great importance in the calculation of initial stability. The value of KM varies with the ship's draft. For the ship's officer to know his ship's KM, he must refer to a set of hydrostatic curves or have a table giving the KM of the ship for the various drafts. The draft referred to is the mean draft, of course. This means that KM varies with the displacement. In order to calculate the ship's stability, the KM must be known. All ships should have a deadweight scale with the KM given on it or a table of KM's by draft or deadweight. Hydrostatic curves may be used, if available, but they are more difficult to read and cumbersome to use.

Determination of stability. The three points that must be understood clearly for an appreciation of ship stability have been examined. The reader may already realize that a ship increases her stability with a lowering of G. The distance between G and M is referred to as the ship's GM. When a ship is inclined initially, B moves away from the centerline, G remains stationary, and for small angles we will assume that M remains stationary. Thus, our points would be located as seen in Fig. 3-7a if G was initially below M. The angle of inclination has been exaggerated in this diagram so that the elements of the figure can be seen more easily. Note that the force through B and through G are not opposed to each other any more. They are forces acting through a distance; thus, they create a moment. The distance through which these forces act is the line GZ. GZ is perpendicular to the line BM, the metacentric radius. This moment tends to revolve the ship in a direction opposite to the inclination. In other words, it tends to push the ship back into an upright position. This moment is called the righting moment.

Stable, neutral, and unstable equilibrium. When G is below M, the ship possesses *stable equilibrium* and tends to return to an upright position if inclined by an outside force. The tendency to right herself depends on the ship's displacement and the value of GZ, because the right-ing moment is the product of displacement and GZ.

If the points, G, B, and M, are located as shown in Fig. 3-7b, the point G has moved up until the distance GZ has become zero and there

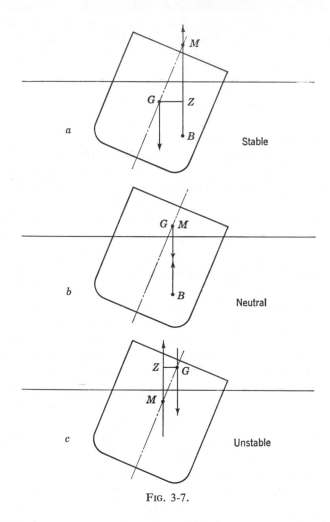

Fig. 3-7.

is no righting moment. In this position, the GM is also zero. GM and GZ vary directly. The ship is in a condition of *neutral equilibrium* when GM and GZ equal zero. When a ship possesses neutral equilibrium, she will remain in whatever position she is placed within certain limitations.

If G is moved up beyond the level of M, the points and forces involved would be acting as shown in Fig. 3-7c. In this condition, the ship possesses *unstable equilibrium*. The ship will not remain in an upright position but will assume a list either to the port or to the starboard. The angle of the list will depend upon the distance that G is above M. The greater the distance the greater the angle of list.

Listing due to negative GM. The ship will not capsize just because she has unstable equilibrium unless G is too far above M. When G is close to M, even though above it, the ship will assume a small list. This list may be increased to a dangerous magnitude by moving G up as a result of burning fuel oil from the ship's double bottom tanks. The reason why the ship assumes a small list and does not continue over is explained by pointing out that the metacenter, M, moves up as the angle of inclination varies between 0 and 20°. Thus, M moves above G if G is sufficiently close to M, for G is stationary. When M is above G, the ship obtains stable equilibrium, but she will have a permanent list that can be to the port or starboard. The list will change from one side to the other when a force is applied to the hull, such as centrifugal force when making radical course changes or from strong winds or seas.

The ship's officer should be able to recognize a ship with negative GM by her behavior in a seaway. A ship with negative GM will have a list, but the list may change from port to starboard and back again with such forces on the hull as wind and sea or centrifugal force when applying heavy rudder. The ship will always have a long, slow, sluggish roll.

Correcting a list due to a negative GM. A common mistake, and often a serious mistake, made in the field of stability is that of not recognizing a list caused by negative GM, or unstable equilibrium, and, therefore, taking corrective measures that are improper.

If a ship has a list of 5 or 6° caused by offcenter weights, that is, by G being to port or starboard of the centerline, the obvious correction is to move weights toward the high side and correct the list. However, if a list is caused by negative GM, the movement of weights to the high side would cause the vessel to right itself partially and then suddenly take a much greater list to the opposite side. The sudden rush toward the opposite side would take place after about one-half of the previous angle of list had been removed. The second list to the opposite side would be greater because it would be the result of two poor conditions: (1) Negative GM. (2) Offcenter weights.

The only way to correct a list due to negative GM is to add, remove, or shift weights so that G *will be moved down*.

In practice, the lumber carrier is frequently a victim of negative GM conditions. To prevent or correct a list due to this condition, the double bottom tanks should be kept as full of oil as possible. After a long voyage, the double bottom tanks may be so empty that the ship will have an excessive list upon arrival in port. In such a case, the lumber deck load should be carefully removed in layers. It would be a serious blunder to attempt to right the ship by discharging from the low side first. The list can be removed by pumping salt water into the empty fuel oil double bottom tanks, but this is generally avoided if possible. If salt water once gets into the fuel oil system of the ship, the engineers may have endless trouble with it.

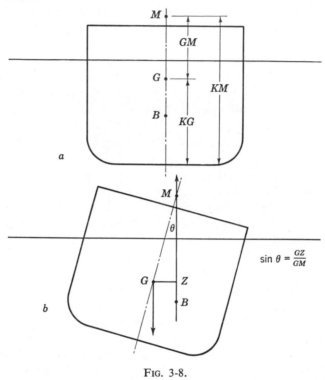

Fig. 3-8.

GM as a measure of stability. In the triangle GZM, of Fig. 3-8b, angle Z is a right angle. From elementary trigonometry we have:

$$\sin \theta = \frac{GZ}{GM} \tag{6}$$

from which we get:

$$GM = \frac{GZ}{\sin \theta} = GZ \cdot \csc \theta \tag{7}$$

From eq. 6, we see that GM varies directly as GZ. It has already been pointed out that GZ is one of two factors that determine the tendency of the ship to right herself. Because GM and GZ vary directly, GM is a measure of stability also.

Calculating GM. All of the points that we have examined are illustrated in Fig. 3-8a. They are arranged to indicate a positive GM. To calculate GM, data to calculate KG are required. In addition, a table of KM's for all the drafts from light to loaded is required. Then, $KM - KG = GM$. Once we know the GM of the ship, we have some knowledge of her stability and we know how she will react to a heavy seaway. With experience, such information gives the ship's officer basis for increasing his professional ability to make correct and prompt decisions concerning this entire field.

Numerical example

Given: A ship with a light ship displacement of 4500 tons. Light ship $KG = 25$ ft. KM for a displacement of 9500 tons = 24.5 ft. The following weights are on board: Fuel, water, stores; 2000 tons with KG of 20 ft. Lower hold cargo; 2000 tons with KG of 10 ft. 'Tweendeck cargo; 1000 tons with KG of 30 ft.

Required: The ship's GM.

Solution: We know the KM so we only have to calculate KG. KM will be obtained from a table of these values based on displacements or drafts. To calculate KG, we find the vertical moments of all the weights (including light ship), add these moments, and divide by the displacement. The result is the KG. Then $KM - KG = GM$.

$$4500 \cdot 25 \; - \; 112,500 \text{ ft-tons}$$
$$2000 \cdot 20 \; - \; 40,000 \text{ ft-tons}$$
$$2000 \cdot 10 \; - \; 20,000 \text{ ft-tons}$$
$$1000 \cdot 30 \; - \; 30,000 \text{ ft-tons}$$

$$\overline{9500 \qquad\qquad 202,500 \text{ ft-tons}}$$

$$202,500 \div 9500 = 21.3 \text{ ft} = KG$$

$$24.5 - 21.3 = 3.2 \text{ ft} = GM$$

Light and loaded displacement GM's. Stability is the tendency of a vessel to right herself. This tendency is measured in units of the righting moment which are foot-tons. Considering a constant GZ, it can be seen that when a vessel is light, say displacing 6000 tons, that the righting moment will be considerably less than when the vessel is loaded, say displacing 14,000 tons. The righting moment should be kept at a nearly constant value; hence, the GM that produces a comfortable and safe ship in the light condition will produce a very stiff ship in the loaded condition. The average *loaded* merchant ship is safe and comfortable with a GM between 2 and 3 ft. The GM of the ship with only 1000 or 1500 tons of cargo or ballast on board should be 4 to 5 ft. The important point here for the ship's officer to remember is that when the ship is only partially loaded the *GM* must be larger than when the ship is fully loaded.

As can be seen from Table 3-1, a perfectly light ship may have a *GM* from 8 to 12 ft. With some fuel, water, and stores on board, this will generally be reduced 2 or 3 ft. The resulting *GM* will generally be too large for a ship even in the partially loaded or ballasted condition. At light drafts, the *KM* is reduced rapidly as the displacement increases; thus, the addition of weight so that the position of *G* remains fixed will reduce *GM* by dropping the metacenter down closer to the center of gravity.

Distribution of partial loads. It is neither feasible nor necessary to specify the precise distribution that should be given partial loads. The important thing is to be aware that, if only 500 or 1000 tons are being carried, the load should be carried in the 'tweendeck areas. If the cargo amounts to 2000 or 3000 tons, the metacenter may drop so rapidly that some cargo will be required in the lower holds for a safe and comfortable *GM*. Each ship and her partial load will present a particular problem and should be solved on the basis of the facts available. The above is a discussion of the general case, and it is not intended to lay down any precise rules or imply what should be done in a particular case. However, it can be stated safely that if a ship capable of lifting 7500 to 10,000 tons cargo deadweight is lifting only about 1000 tons, none of that weight should be in the lower holds.

When stowing a few hundred tons of ballast or cargo in the upper deck areas to reduce the *GM* of a ship going to sea with a partial load, the ship's officers should take every precaution possible to see that such ballast or cargo is heavily shored, braced, or tommed into position. In the event of heavy weather, the ship may still roll rapidly and the cargo will be subjected to strong centrifugal forces. Ships are still likely to be lost at sea without a trace due to negligence of responsible officers in these precise matters. January 1948, the S.S. Samkey, a British steamer, was lost with all hands while on a voyage to Cuba because of the sudden shifting of ballast carried in the 'tweendecks. The shifting, of course, was caused by heavy weather. The type of ballast was known as Thames ballast, which consists of stones of various sizes mixed with sand, with an angle of repose of about 35°. A stiff ship in a heavy sea will roll to much greater angles than a tender ship, and ballast with an angle of repose of only 35° would require heavy shifting boards. On this ship, inadequate shifting boards had been installed.

Estimating vertical distribution. It is often stated with reference to the stowage of cargo that, as a general guide for proper vertical distribution of cargo when carrying full loads, about one-third of the weight should be in the 'tweendecks and about two-thirds should be in the lower holds. **This rule should not be used.** Such distribution will often give a ship an excessive *GM*. The rule also leaves much doubt as to what should be done when the ship has three decks or four decks. The only safe procedure is to calculate the correct vertical distribution by the methods outlined above. However, if for any reason it is necessary to estimate the desired vertical distribution of a full load and data for calculating the amounts are not available, the safest procedure is to place in each compartment a proportion of the total weight equal to the ratio of the individual compartment's bale cubic to that of the ship's total bale cubic. This can be expressed by the following formula:

$$\frac{v}{V} \cdot T = t \tag{8}$$

where V = total bale capacity of the ship.

v = bale capacity of the compartment or series of compartments at equal distances from the keel.

T = total tonnage to be loaded.

t = number of tons of the total load that should be placed in the compartment or compartments in question.

This method cannot be used when taking on partial loads or under ballasted conditions as is evident from the above discussion.

Numerical example

Given: On a C1-A, the bale cubic is as follows:

$$
\begin{array}{ll}
\text{U.T.D.} & = 145,805 \text{ cu ft} \\
\text{L.T.D.} & = 134,025 \text{ cu ft} \\
\text{L.H.} & = 164,550 \text{ cu ft} \\
\hline
\text{Total} & = 444,440 \text{ cu ft}
\end{array}
$$

The cargo deadweight is 8000 tons. No other information is available.

Required: The vertical distribution of the 8000 tons.

Solution: Simply multiply 8000 by the ratio of each compartment's cubic to the cubic of the entire ship.

$$\frac{145,865}{444,440} \cdot 8000 = \text{tons in U.T.D. area}$$
$$2640 = \text{tons in U.T.D. area}$$

$$\frac{134,625}{444,440} \cdot 8000 = \text{tons in L.T.D. area}$$
$$2440 = \text{tons in L.T.D. area}$$

$$\frac{164,550}{444,440} \cdot 8000 = \text{tons in the L.H. area}$$
$$2920 = \text{tons in the L.H. area}$$

Note that the weight is divided up to equal about one-third for each level in this particular case. The resulting *GM* would depend upon the tankage of the ship which can cause the *GM* to vary widely. Tankage is the distribution of the weights in numerous tanks on the ship. Free surface effect would have to be given consideration also as in any calculation of *GM* in practice.[1]

Some light ship KM's, KG's, and GM's. Some light ship *KM*'s and *KG*'s are given in Table 3-1. These are presented only as examples, they

TABLE 3-1

LIGHT SHIP DATA

Type of Ship	Δ	KM	KG	GM
Liberty	3412	30.48	19.75	10.73
Victory	4500	34.9	26.5	8.4
Mariner	7675	38.5	31.5	7.0
C1-B	4141	32.33	24.77	7.56
C2-S-AJ1	4500	36.32	27.92	8.40
C3-S-A2	4973	42.10	29.44	12.66

must not be taken as the light ship conditions for ships of the same construction. These data will vary considerably even on sister ships, and as ships are modified, repaired, or re-equipped, the conditions will vary on the same ship. When considering a particular ship, the ship's officer must have the latest inclining experiment data of that ship. Without these data, calculations concerning stability may be in error.

TRIM CALCULATIONS

Trim defined. *Trim* is defined as the difference in drafts forward and aft on the ship. The trim of a ship is a function of the moments developed by weights acting forward of the ship's tipping center as opposed to those acting aft of the tipping center. With a ship on an even keel, the points mentioned in the explanation of stability would be arranged as shown on Fig. 3-9. These are the same points except that they are analyzed on the profile of the ship instead of the midship section. The center of gravity and the center of buoyancy are in the same place vertically as before. *M* is much higher and is identified as the longitudinal metacenter. The *GM* is a few hundred feet in length and is designated as the longitudinal *GM*. It is important that the reader review the explanation of how *G*, *B*, and *M* are located and why *G* and *B* move.

[1] La Dage and Van Gemert, op. cit., *Stability and Trim for the Ship's Officer*, D. Van Nostrand Co., New York, 1947, Chap. 6.

When a ship is on an even keel and at rest, the points G and B are vertically one over the other. If they are not, the ship will revolve slightly causing B to move until it comes under G. Hence, if we take the ship on an even keel and place a weight aft of point B or G, point G will

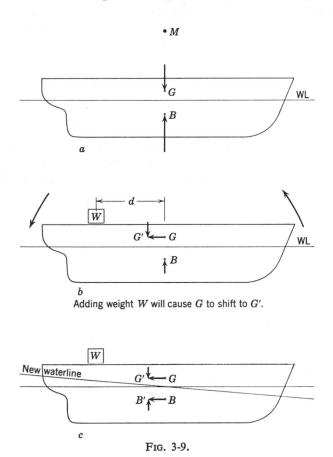

Adding weight W will cause G to shift to G'.

FIG. 3-9.

be moved aft. The situation then would be as illustrated in Fig. 3-9b. This condition cannot exist because the forces acting upward through B and downward through G are now acting through a distance, and this produces a moment. This moment will tend to revolve the ship counterclockwise as you look at this diagram. As the ship trims by the stern, a wedge of volume is shifted from the forward part of the vessel to the after part. This causes B to shift aft and eventually come directly under G again, as shown in Fig. 3-9c. When this occurs, the ship will come to rest with a change of drafts forward and aft. The ship will have changed trim.

Moments producing a change of trim. The change of trim can be expressed as a function of two completely different moments. The reader should be able to see that GG' multiplied by the displacement is one moment that causes the ship to revolve. The displacement used in this calculation is the displacement in the final condition. Another moment, which would be equal to the first one mentioned, is the product of W times D, where W is the individual weight being considered at a distance D from the tipping center of the ship. Either of these two moments may be used to calculate the change in trim, but the methods used in each solution differ slightly.

As the vessel revolves in changing trim, it does so about the center of flotation which is the geometrical center of the waterplane at which the ship is floating. This point is also known as the tipping center and is notated as T.C. The tipping center changes its position as the displacement increases, generally moving aft.

Change of trim values. When given a set of drafts for two different conditions, the change of trim between the two conditions is calculated by first noting the trim in each case. Next, if the trim is in the same direction in both cases, the change in trim is found by subtracting the smaller from the larger.

Numerical example

Given: A ship with the following initial and final drafts.

	Fwd., ft and in.	Mean, ft and in.	Aft, ft and in.	Trim, in.
Initial:	20 06	20 08½	20 11	5 aft
Final:	26 00	27 00	28 00	24 aft

Required: The change in trim.
Solution: By inspection it can be seen that 24 less 5 gives a *change of trim* of 1 ft 7 in. by the stern.

If a ship has a trim in the opposite direction, the change of trim is found by adding the two trims in both cases.

Numerical example

Given: A ship with the following initial and final drafts.

	Fwd., ft and in.	Mean, ft and in.	Aft, ft and in.	Trim, in.
Initial:	20 00	19 06	19 00	12 fwd.
Final:	20 00	20 04	20 08	8 aft

Required: The change in trim.

Solution: Inasmuch as the trim is by the head in the initial condition and by the stern in the final condition, the change in trim is found by adding the ·trim in each case. Thus, the *change in trim is:* 1 ft 8 in. by the stern.

Moment to change trim 1 in. (MT1). As stated above, the change of trim can be expressed as a function of one of either of two moments. When calculating the effect of loading, discharging, or shifting partial loads, that is, when the change of displacement is small, the moment obtained by multiplying the weight involved by the distance through which it acts is most commonly used.

When loading or discharging a weight, the moment is obtained by determining the distance between the center of flotation and the position of the weight and multiplying by the value of the weight. The change in trim is determined by dividing the above moment by a value known as the *moment to trim the ship 1 in*. This value is notated as *MT*1 and is found on the hydrostatic curves of the ship and on the deadweight scale. This value increases with displacement. If the exact position of the center of flotation is not known, the moment may be calculated about the midship section of the ship. If this is done, however, an error will be introduced. The center of flotation will generally be well forward of the midship section at light drafts. At loaded drafts, it may be slightly aft or slightly forward. The equation for the change of trim is:

$$\frac{W \times D}{MT1} = \text{Change in trim} \tag{9}$$

When shifting a weight, the moment is obtained by multiplying the weight by the distance that the weight is moved.

A typical trim problem is solved by first entering the deadweight scale with the ship's existing mean draft and picking off the *MT*1. Determine the trimming moment and divide by the *MT*1. The result will be the change in trim in inches. If the ship's tipping center is exactly at the midpoint longitudinally, the *change in draft* readings forward and aft are obtained by dividing the total *change in trim* by 2 and applying to the old draft readings. If the ship's tipping center is not precisely at the midpoint, the change of *draft* (not trim) forward can be found by multiplying the change in *trim* by the ratio of the distance of tipping center from the forward perpendicular to the total length on the waterline. In the same manner, the change in draft aft can be found. The sum of the changes in draft should equal the total change in trim. In practice, the error produced by assuming that the tipping center is at the midship section, whether it is or not, is less than the inaccuracies that enter into the actual reading of the drafts. Hence, the extreme precision obtained by multiplying by the ratio mentioned above is unnecessary.

Numerical example. A trim problem involving a shift of weight.

Given: A ship with an $MT1$ of 1200 pumps 200 tons of fuel oil from a forward tank to an after tank, a distance of 60 ft. The drafts before the shift were: fwd., 23 ft 08 in.; aft, 23 ft 04 in.; mean, 23 ft 06 in.

Required: The total change in trim and the final drafts.

Solution:

$$\frac{200 \times 60}{1200} = 10'' \text{ total change in trim by the stern}$$

Assuming the tipping center is amidships, the draft aft is increased 5 in. and the draft forward is decreased 5 in. Therefore, the new drafts would be: fwd., 23 ft 03 in.; aft, 23 ft 09 in.; mean, 23 ft 06 in.

In the above problem, if the ship was 480 ft on the waterline and the tipping center was 10 ft forward of the midship section, the exact change in drafts would be:

$$\frac{\text{Distance of tipping center from fwd.}}{\text{Length on the waterline}} \times \text{Change in trim} = \text{Change in draft fwd.}$$

$$\tfrac{230}{480} \times 10 = 4.79 \text{ in.}$$

$$\frac{\text{Distance of tipping center from aft}}{\text{Length on the waterline}} \times \text{Change in trim} = \text{Change in draft aft}$$

$$\tfrac{250}{480} \times 10 = 5.21 \text{ in.}$$

From this problem, it is seen that the error produced by assuming the T.C. to be amidships when it was actually 10 ft forward, amounts to less than a quarter of an inch.

Numerical example. A trim problem involving the addition of weight.

Given: A ship with an $MT1$ of 1000. 150 tons are loaded 100 ft aft of the tipping center. The drafts before loading were: fwd., 19 ft 02 in.; aft, 19 ft 04 in.; mean, 19 ft 03 in. Tons per inch immersion (T.P.I.) is 50.

Required: The total change in trim and the final drafts.

Solution: The $MT1$ and the T.P.I. are found on the deadweight scale. T.P.I. is defined as the number of tons required to increase the mean draft 1 in. It is obvious that to determine the final drafts, this figure would have to be known unless the deadweight scale was on hand to refer to. In practice the deadweight scale would be available, but when working problems the T.P.I. is usually stated. In this problem it is given as 50 tons.

The initial step in calculating the final drafts is to increase all the given drafts by an amount equal to the *mean sinkage*. The mean sinkage is obtained by dividing the number of tons loaded by the T.P.I. In this problem it amounts to 3 in. The reasoning used in the solution is that the weight is loaded directly over the tipping center first then shifted to the actual position. Thus, the mean sinkage is added to all the given drafts first then with these drafts the change of trim is applied exactly as in the simple shift of weight problem already solved. Therefore, applying the mean sinkage to the given drafts we obtain: fwd., 19 ft 05 in.; aft, 19 ft 07 in.; mean, 19 ft 06 in.

Calculating the change of trim:

$$\frac{150 \times 100}{1000} = 15 \text{ in.}$$

The change forward is −7½ in., and aft it is +7½ in. The final drafts would be: fwd., 18 ft 09½ in.; aft, 20 ft. 02½ in.; mean, 19 ft 06 in.

Calculating the T.P.I. The T.P.I. is found by taking the area of the waterplane for the draft in question and dividing by 420. That is:

$$\frac{\text{Area of waterplane}}{420} = \text{T.P.I.}$$

The derivation is simple. The number of tons required to sink a ship 1 ft is equal to the weight of sea water displaced by the volume of a 1-ft layer of the hull. Thirty-five cu ft of sea water weigh 1 ton. Therefore, to find the tons required to immerse a ship 1 ft, we simply divide the volume of a 1-ft slice by 35. The volume of a 1-ft slice is equal to the area of the waterplane multiplied by 1 ft. This is expressed by the equation:

$$\frac{\text{Area of the waterplane} \times 1}{35} = \text{Tons per foot of immersion}$$

But, we want to know the tons per inch which is exactly one-twelfth of a foot. Letting A.W.P. equal area of the waterplane, we have:

$$\frac{\text{A.W.P.}}{12 \times 35} = \text{T.P.I.}$$

Which is the same as:

$$\frac{\text{A.W.P.}}{420} = \text{T.P.I.}$$

Calculating MT1. When asked to calculate the $MT1$, the problem is to find the value of $W \times D$ (the trimming moment) that will produce a change of *trim* of 1 in. or, what amounts to the same thing, a change of *draft* at either end of ½ in. One-half inch can be expressed also as $\frac{1}{24}$ ft. We will say then that our problem is to find an equation for $W \times D$ that will produce a change of *trim* of $\frac{1}{12}$ ft or a change of draft forward and aft of $\frac{1}{24}$ ft. When we do this, we will designate such $W \times D$ as $MT1$. Referring to Fig. 3-10, if the weight, W, is moved aft some distance, D, then G will move aft to some point G'. A moment will be set up causing the ship to revolve counterclockwise as we look at the diagram. This will cause B to move aft until it is again under the center of gravity; that is, B will move to point G' or directly below this point and become B'.

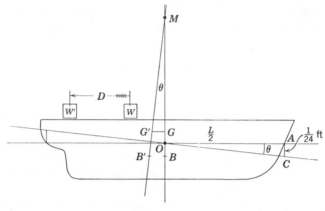

FIG. 3-10.

Starting with the ship on an even keel, the right triangle MGG' has been formed. Also right triangle OAC has been formed. AC equals $\frac{1}{24}$ ft. OA equals one-half the length of the ship, which we notate as $L/2$. The angles GMG' and COA are both equal to theta (θ).

From trigonometry:

$$\tan \theta = \frac{GG'}{GM} \tag{10}$$

$$GG' = \tan \theta \times GM \tag{11}$$

Also:

$$\tan \theta = \frac{\frac{1}{24}}{L/2}$$

$$\tan \theta = \frac{1}{12L} \tag{12}$$

From eq. 4, p. 47:

$$GG' = \frac{W \times D}{\Delta} \tag{13}$$

Solving for $W \times D$ (our trimming moment):

$$W \times D = GG' \times \Delta \tag{14}$$

Setting the right hand side of eq. 10 and 12 equal to each other and solving for GG':

$$GG' = \frac{GM}{12L} \qquad (15)$$

Substituting the right hand member of eq. 15 in 14 we have:

$$W \times D = \frac{GM \times \Delta}{12L}$$

Because $W \times D$ produced a change of trim of 1 in. and by definition $MT1$ is the notation used for this particular moment, we substitute $MT1$ for $W \times D$ and obtain:

$$MT1 = \frac{GM \times \Delta}{12L} \qquad (16)$$

Changing draft at one end of vessel only.   The application of the principles of trim calculations to determine where a given weight should be loaded on a ship so that no change in draft will occur at one end of the ship may prove useful to the ship's officer.   If the weight, W, is known and the T.P.I. is known, the mean sinkage is obtained by dividing W by T.P.I.   Let us suppose that we wish to load the given weight, W, so that no change will occur in the present draft aft.   It is immediately clear that we must load the weight at some point forward of the tipping center. It must be loaded so that the change of *draft* aft is equal to the mean sinkage due to loading the weight.   The change of draft is considered equal to ½ the change of trim; therefore, the change of trim obtained as a result of loading this weight must be equal to twice the main sinkage. Now we have two formulas which we combine and then solve for the distance, D, that the weight must be from the tipping center.

$$\frac{W}{\text{T.P.I.}} = \text{Mean sinkage}$$

But, we have said that mean sinkage must be removed from the draft aft in order not to have any change aft.   In other words, the change of trim must be equal to twice the mean sinkage or $2W/\text{T.P.I.}$
From eq. 9, p. 61, we have:

$$\frac{W \times D}{MT1} = \text{Change of trim}$$

Knowing that our change of trim must be equal to $2W/\text{T.P.I.}$, we substitute in the above equation:

$$\frac{W \times D}{MT1} = \frac{2W}{\text{T.P.I.}}$$

Solving for D:

$$D = \frac{2 \times MT1}{\text{T.P.I.}} \tag{17}$$

Numerical example

Given: A ship with a draft of: fwd., 19 ft 00 in.; aft, 19 ft 06 in.; mean, 19 ft 03 in. must load 200 tons. $MT1$ is 1400. T.P.I. is 50.

Required: Where shall the weight be loaded so that there will be no change aft?

Solution: Using eq. 17:

$$D = \frac{2 \times 1400}{50}$$

$$D = 56 \text{ ft forward of the tipping center}$$

If this problem is stated without mentioning the weight involved, the solution is the same with the exception that the weight may be found by knowing the mean sinkage required and the T.P.I. For example, supposing the problem had asked for the position and the amount of the weight needed to give the ship an even trim with a mean draft equal to the present maximum draft. The present mean draft is 19 ft 03 in., and the problem states that it must be 19 ft 06 in. when the weight is loaded. Therefore the mean sinkage must be 3 in. Now, from our equation for mean sinkage:

$$\frac{W}{\text{T.P.I.}} = \text{Mean sinkage}$$

We have:

$$W = \text{T.P.I.} \times \text{Mean sinkage}$$
$$W = 50 \times 3$$
$$W = 150 \text{ tons}$$

Thus, we know the weight required; the solution for the remaining part of the required data is the same as the first problem. The final draft in the final problem would be: fwd., 19 ft 06 in.; aft, 19 ft 06 in.; mean, 19 ft 06 in.

Calculating trim with large changes of displacement. When a ship is laid out during the planning stage of the cargo operation, the weights should be so distributed longitudinally that the final trim will be within an acceptable range. The methods of calculating trim and changes of trim discussed above have assumed comparatively small parts of the ship's total cargo capacity being used; therefore, small changes in displacement were envisioned. When loading a complete shipload or even a half or quarter, there will be a large change in displacement. A large change in displacement makes it very important that the correct $MT1$ and tipping center be used. T.P.I. will not be used for finding mean sinkage. Mean sinkage is determined accurately only by referring to a deadweight scale and picking off the correct drafts for the different deadweights involved.

First method: moments about the tipping center. Two methods may be used to calculate the trim when large changes of displacements are involved. The first method is based on the concepts already discussed. Care must be used to choose the $MT1$ for the final condition and the average position of the tipping center between the initial and final condition. In this first method, the trimming moments are taken about the tipping center.

Table 3-2 illustrates a form that may be used to record the data when loading a large number of weights throughout the ship so that the net effect of all the trimming moments can be calculated. The first question

TABLE 3-2

FORM FOR CALCULATION OF CHANGE IN TRIM ABOUT TIPPING CENTER (T.C.)

Com-part-ment	Weight, tons	Distance from Amidships, ft	Distance Fwd. of T.C., ft	Distance Aft of T.C., ft	Trimming Moments	
					Fwd., ft-tons	Aft, ft-tons
		This fact is needed because T.C. position is given from the midship section of the ship as a reference line.				

Total weight_____   Total trimming moments   Fwd._____   Aft_____

$$\frac{\text{Net trimming moments either fwd. or aft}}{\text{Mean } MT1} = \text{Change of trim}$$

Mean $MT1$ = _____
Mean position of T.C. = _____

With large changes of displacement, use deadweight scale to obtain *final* mean draft. Apply this to original condition and then apply change of trim to obtain *final conditions.*

that arises in the use of this form when determining the moments about the tipping center is one regarding the position of the tipping center. Data from the hydrostatic curves of the Mariner type ship appear in Table 3-5. It can be seen that the tipping center (column G) is constantly changing its position. The best that can be done is to pick the tipping center for the average position. It must be pointed out that the geometrical centers of all compartments and tanks must be known rela-

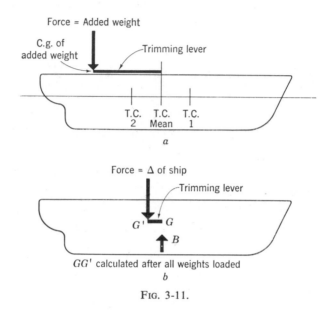

FIG. 3-11.

tive to the midship section. The centers of such compartments and tanks must then be computed relative to the tipping center that has been calculated.

The T.P.I. is not used to determine the final mean draft. Using a mean T.P.I. would introduce a large error in the calculations. The mean sinkage is determined by referring to the deadweight scale as mentioned above.

The final $MT1$ value must be used. This is obvious because it has already been pointed out that we assume all the weight to be loaded over the position of the mean tipping center first. After calculating the effect on mean sinkage, we imagine the weight is shifted so as to produce the trim. The reader should study the elements of the solution of the problem represented by Fig. 3-11a.

Second method: moments about longitudinal B. A more accurate and more commonly used method of calculating trim involving large changes of displacement will be explained next. Before attempting this explanation, however, the reader is reminded that all of the previous methods involving trim considered moments about the tipping center, or longitudinal center of flotation, of the ship. However, it was stated at the beginning of the discussion on trim that trimming moments may be considered also to act about the center of buoyancy. In the first method, we considered the total weight involved as acting through a distance from the tipping center. In this second method, we consider the weight as causing a shift of G. This shift of G creates the trimming lever GG' as illustrated in Fig. 3-11b. The weight acting through the distance GG' is the *displacement* of the ship, and, thus, the *trimming moment* is formed. Figure 3-11 shows two diagrams. Diagram a points out the trimming moment of the first method. Diagram b points out the trimming moment of the second method. The reader should not proceed without being clear on these points.

The second method requires that the final longitudinal position of G be calculated along the same lines as the vertical position of G was calculated in the study of transverse stability. From hydrostatic curves or suitable tables, the longitudinal position of B is obtained for the condition of even keel. The distance of G from B is the trimming lever, and the weight involved in the trimming moment is the displacement. Once we have the trimming moment, we simply divide by the $MT1$, as before, to obtain the change of trim.

Inasmuch as the longitudinal position of G must be calculated, it is obvious that the location of the geometrical center of every cargo compartment and tank must be known with reference to some longitudinal point. The midship section can be used as the reference point, but if this is done, it is necessary to bring plus and minus quantities into the calculations which unnecessarily complicate the solution. It is recommended that either the forward or after perpendicular be chosen as the reference point.

This method is thoroughly discussed under the section dealing with the trim and stability booklet for the Mariner type ships.

Change of trim with second method and partial loads. The second method of calculating trim may be used for calculating change in trim for partial loads as well as the first method. Suppose a ship capable of lifting 10,000 tons deadweight has all but 3000 tons on board, and the problem is to plan the loading of the last 3000 tons so that a suitable trim is obtained. The procedure is the same as that for starting with a light ship except that the longitudinal position of B and G must be determined in a different manner. If the ship is on an even keel, the location of B can be determined by looking it up on suitable tables or from the hydrostatic curves for the ship. However, if the ship has a trim by the head or stern, the location of B (and therefore of G also) is obtained by using the equation for determining the change of trim by the second method. We have:

$$\frac{GG' \times \Delta}{MT1} = \text{Change of trim}$$

Solving for GG':

$$GG' = \frac{MT1 \times \text{Change of trim}}{\Delta}$$

All of the factors in the right hand term are known. The value of GG' is applied to the position of B as if the ship had been on an even keel at the mean draft. B must be either forward of or aft of the latter position, depending upon whether the ship has a trim by the head or stern respectively. The distance that it is forward or aft will be equal to GG'.

A record of the distances forward and aft of G' that the 3000 tons are disposed is kept, and the final position of G', call it G'', is calculated. Thus $G'G''$ becomes the trimming lever, and the weight involved is the final displacement. The change of trim and final draft is determined as outlined previously.

Trim and stability booklet for Mariner type ships. Some of the data contained in a trim and stability booklet prepared by the Maritime Administration, Division of Preliminary Planning, is presented below in a series of tables and one curve, Fig. 3-12. Most of these tables are self-explanatory to the officer with a basic knowledge of trim and stability concepts. However, a brief explanation will be set forth here with a rather detailed summary of the final solution for GM and the calculated draft as it appears in Table 3-10.

All ships should have information of this type available to the operating personnel afloat and ashore. The main lack in the past has been complete hydrostatic data such as appears in Table 3-5. The reader should note that this is simply an extension of the familiar deadweight scale to the point where it contains some really valuable information about the ship. That is, it is valuable if used consistently and correctly.

Table 3-3: A list of the ship's principal characteristics.

Table 3-4: A trimming table for quick solutions of effect on trim when loading, discharging, or shifting small weights.

Table 3-5: The hydrostatic properties of the ship. The usual deadweight scale given on most capacity plans includes only the information appearing in columns A, B, D, and E. Without the information con-

TABLE 3-3

TABLE OF PRINCIPAL CHARACTERISTICS

Length, overall	563 ft 7¾ in.
Length, between perpendiculars	528 ft 0 in.
Length, 20 stations	520 ft 0 in.
Beam, molded	76 ft 0 in.
Depth to main deck, molded at side	44 ft 6 in.
Depth to 2nd deck, molded at side	35 ft 6 in.
Bulkhead deck	2nd deck
Machinery	Turbine
Designed sea speed	20 knots
Shaft horsepower, normal	17,500
Shaft horsepower, maximum	19,250
Full load draft, molded	29 ft 9 in.
Full load displacement	21,093 tons
Light ship	7,675 tons
Light ship vertical position of center of gravity	31.5 ft
Light ship L.C.G. aft F.P.	276.5 ft
Passengers	12
Crew	58
Grain cubic	837,305 cu ft
Bale cubic	736,723 cu ft
Reefer cubic	30,254 cu ft
Fuel oil (double bottoms + settlers)	2,652 tons
Fuel oil (deep tanks)	1,156 tons
Fuel oil, total	3,808 tons
Fresh water	257 tons
No. of holds	7
Gross tonnage	9,215
Net tonnage	5,367

tained in columns *C, F,* and *G,* it is not possible to make many trim and stability calculations.

Table 3-6: Tank capacities and free surface effects of individual tanks are listed. Instructions for obtaining the total free surface correction are included. Note that the correction is always subtractive from the *GM.*

Table 3-7: This is a very useful table giving the gain in *GM* by ballasting any given tank at various displacements.

Figure 3-12: The required *GM* curve. The *required GM* may be defined as that *GM* which will prevent the ship from having a negative stability in case any one compartment has been flooded and prevent heeling which might result in flooding any other undamaged compartment. Normal operating conditions are assumed. It should be obvious that actual conditions on a given ship can modify the value of the required *GM.* For example, the required *GM* for a fully loaded Mariner type ship (mean draft 29.9 ft), according to the curve, is 2.2 ft. However, if

TABLE 3-4

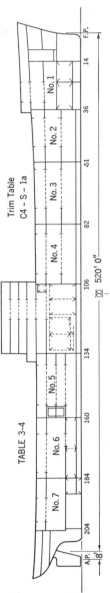

Trim Table
C4 - S - 1a

Table of Corrections in Inches to Draft Foward and Aft for Each 100 Tons Loaded at Any Distance from Amidships

Example: Find the change in trim after loading 100 tons in No. 2 hold (160 ft forward amidships)

	Forward	Aft
Initial draft	19'6"	20'6"
Correction	+7.6"	−4"
New draft	20'2"	20'2"

30'0" draft

Fwd	Aft
+9.0	−5.3
+9.6	−5.0
+8.5	−4.8
+8.8	−4.6
+8.2	−4.3
+7.9	−4.1
+7.6	−3.8
+7.4	−3.6
+7.1	−3.4
+6.8	−3.1
+6.5	−2.9
+6.2	−2.7
+6.0	−2.4
+5.7	−2.2
+5.4	−1.9
+5.1	−1.7
+4.8	−1.5
+4.6	−1.2
+4.3	−1.0
+3.7	−0.8
+3.4	−0.5
+3.2	−0.3
+2.9	0
+2.6	+0.2
+2.3	+0.4
+2.0	+0.7
+1.8	+0.9
+1.5	+1.1
+1.4	+1.4
+1.2	+1.6
+0.9	+1.9
+0.6	+2.1
+0.4	+2.3
+0.1	+2.6
−0.2	+2.8
−0.5	+3.0
−0.8	+3.3
−1.1	+3.5
−1.3	+3.8
−1.6	+4.0
−1.9	+4.2
−2.2	+4.5
−2.5	+4.7
−2.7	+4.9
−3.0	+5.2
−3.3	+5.4
−3.6	+5.7
−4.1	+5.9
−4.4	+6.1
−4.7	+6.4
−5.0	+6.6
−5.3	+6.8
	+7.1

20'0" draft

Fwd	Aft
+11.1	−7.2
+10.8	−6.9
+10.4	−6.6
+10.1	−6.2
+9.7	−5.9
+9.4	−5.6
+9.0	−5.3
+8.7	−4.9
+8.3	−4.6
+8.0	−4.3
+7.6	−4.0
+7.3	−3.6
+6.9	−3.3
+6.6	−3.0
+6.2	−2.7
+5.9	−2.3
+5.5	−2.0
+5.1	−1.7
+4.8	−1.4
+4.4	−1.0
+4.1	−0.7
+3.7	−0.4
+3.4	−0.1
+3.0	+0.3
+2.7	+0.6
+2.3	+0.9
+2.0	+1.2
+1.6	+1.5
+1.3	+1.9
+0.9	+2.2
+0.6	+2.0
+0.2	+2.8
−0.1	+3.2
−0.5	+3.5
−0.9	+3.8
−1.2	+4.1
−1.6	+4.5
−1.9	+4.8
−2.3	+5.1
−2.6	+5.4
−3.0	+5.8
−3.3	+6.1
−3.7	+6.4
−4.0	+6.7
−4.4	+7.1
−4.7	+7.4
−5.1	+7.7
−5.4	+8.0
−5.8	+8.4
−6.2	+8.7
−6.5	+9.0
−6.9	+9.3
−7.2	+9.6

Notes: (1) The corrections have been computed for the two drafts 10 ft apart to facilitate interpolation, but in practice it will be accurate enough to refer to the table nearest the ship's draft. (2) When discharging, use the table as loading and change the plus and minus signs.

0   50   100 feet

TABLE 3-5

Deadweight Scale

Hydrostatic Properties, C4-S-1a

A	B	C	D	E	F	G	A
Mean Draft Bottom of Keel	Total Displacement, Salt Water tons	Transverse KM- Molded, ft	T.P.I.	MT 1, ft-tons	L.C.B. Aft F.P., ft	L.C.F. Aft F.P., ft	Mean Draft Bottom of Keel
30		31.4		1950		282	30
	21,000		70		269		
29		31.3		1900		281	29
	20,000			1850		280	
28		31.2	69				28
				1800	268	279	
27	19,000	31.1	68				27
				1750		278	
26	18,000			1700		277	26
		31.05	67		267		
25	17,000			1650		276	25
24		31.1	66			275	24
	16,000			1600			
23		31.2			266	274	23
	15,000	31.3	65	1550		273	22
22		31.4					
		31.5	64			272	21
21	14,000	31.6		1500			
20		31.8			265	271	20
	13,000	32.0	63				
19				1450		270	19
		32.5					
18	12,000					269	18
		33.0	62		264		
17	11,000	33.5		1400			17
16		34.0	61			268	16
	10,000	34.5					
15		35.0		1350		267	15
		35.5					
14	9,000	36.0	60		263	266	14
		37.0					
13	8,000	38.0	59	1300		265	13
12	7,800 7,600 7,400	Light ship					12

TABLE 3-6

FREE SURFACE CORRECTION AND TANK CAPACITIES

C4-S-1a

Tank		Frames	97% Fuel Oil, tons	100% Salt Water, tons	Column A i slack	Column B i 97%	Vertical Center of Gravity	L.C.G. F.P.
Double bottom 1	₵	14–24	48.2	52.8	106	67	4.5	39.9
Double bottom 1A	₵	24–36	81.9	89.8	464	204	4.8	64.9
Double bottom 2	P	36–57	71.2	78.1	428	158	2.7	106.6
	S	36–57	71.2	78.1	428	158	2.7	106.6
Double bottom 3	₵	57–82	227.6	249.5	3777	944	2.5	161.6
	P	57–82	55.6	61.0	300	120	3.0	169.2
	S	57–82	55.6	61.0	300	120	3.0	169.2
Double bottom 4	₵	82–106	224.1	245.7	3626	943	2.5	222.0
	P	82–106	128.1	140.5	1138	364	2.6	223.8
	S	82–106	128.1	140.5	1138	364	2.6	223.8
Double bottom 5	₵	106–127	196.2	215.1	3173	825	2.5	278.3
	P	106–134	178.0	195.2	2048	676	2.6	288.3
	S	106–134	180.0	197.4	2048	676	2.6	288.3
Double bottom 6	₵	134–160	242.3	265.7	3928	1021	2.5	354.4
	P	134–160	87.0	95.4	615	221	2.8	348.2
	S	134–160	87.0	95.4	615	221	2.8	348.2
Double bottom 7	P	160–184	94.6	103.7	768	269	2.7	412.4
	S	160–184	94.6	103.7	768	269	2.7	412.4
Deep tank 1	₵	14–24	125.3	137.4	134	130	16.5	40.3
Deep tank 1A	₵	24–36	257.6	282.5	945	680	16.8	65.1
Deep tank 2	P	106–113	100.7	...	20	20	19.1	260.8
	S	106–113	100.7	...	20	20	19.1	260.8
Deep tank 3	P	113–119	86.1	...	17	17	19.1	277.0
	S	113–119	86.1	...	17	17	19.1	277.0
Deep tank 6	P	160–172	201.2	220.7	1242	634	11.4	401.2
	S	160–172	201.2	220.7	1242	634	11.4	401.2
Deep tank 7	P	172–184	128.8	141.2	618	358	11.7	430.7
	S	172–184	128.8	141.2	618	358	11.7	430.7
Deep tank 8	P	184–190	50.5	55.4	68	58	9.6	454.0
	S	184–190	50.5	55.4	68	58	9.6	454.0

Tank		Frames	100% Fresh Water, tons	100% Salt Water, tons	Column C i slack	Vertical Center of Gravity	L.C.G. F.P.
Fore peak	₵	Stem—14		110.8		11.7	17.1
Aft peak	₵	204–218		93.0		24.9	506.8
Deep tank 4	P/S	120–127	123.7	...	5575	21.3	296.0
Deep tank 5	P/S	127–133	108.4	...	4789	20.9	312.0
Dist. water	₵	106–109	24.9		59	39.5	255.8

Notes: Fuel oil at 37.23 cu ft per ton, 97% full. Fresh water at 36.0 cu ft per ton, 100% full. Salt water at 35.0 cu ft per ton, 100% full.

Free Surface Correction Procedure: (1) Add quantity in column A for tanks slack. (2) Add quantity in column B for tanks 97% full. (3) Add quantity in column C for fresh water tanks. (4) If any tank is empty, or pressed up with water, use zero for that tank. (5) Divide sum total by the ship displacement in tons to obtain free surface correction in feet.

L.C.G.—F.P. = distance between the longitudinal center of gravity and the forward perpendicular.

    ₵ = symbol for centerline of ship.

    P = port.

    S = starboard.

    i = moment of inertia of the free surface waterplane divided by 35.

TABLE 3-7

GAIN IN GM BY BALLASTING (FEET)

C4-S-1a

Displacement 100 tons	D.B.*1 52	D.B. 1A 89	D.B. 2 156	D.B. 3 371	D.B. 4 526	D.B. 5 607	D.B. 6 456	D.B. 7 207	D.T.†1 137	D.T. 1A 282	D.T. 6 441	D.T. 7 282	D.T. 8 110
85	0.05	0.05	0.20	0.40	0.60	0.65	0.55	0.20	−0.10	−0.15	0.05	0.0	0.0
90	..	..	..	0.45	..	0.70	..	..	−0.05	−0.10	0.10	0.05	..
95	..	0.10	..	..	0.65	..	..	0.25	..	..	0.15	..	..
100	..	..	..	0.50	0.70	0.75	0.60	..	0.0	−0.05	..	0.10	0.05
105	..	..	..	..	..	..	..	..	..	0.0	0.20	..	..
110	..	..	..	..	..	0.80	..	..	..	..	0.25	0.15	..
115	..	..	..	..	..	..	..	..	0.05	0.05	0.30	..	0.10
120	..	..	..	..	..	0.85	..	..	..	..	..	0.20	..
125	..	..	..	..	..	..	0.65	..	..	0.10	0.35	..	..
130	..	..	..	..	..	..	..	0.30	..	..	..	..	..
135	..	..	..	..	..	..	..	..	..	0.15	..	..	..
140	..	..	..	..	..	..	..	..	..	..	..	..	..
145	..	..	0.25	..	..	..	..	..	..	0.15	..	0.25	..
150	..	..	..	..	..	..	..	..	0.10	..	0.40	..	..
155	..	..	..	..	..	..	..	..	..	..	..	..	..
160	..	..	..	..	..	..	..	..	..	..	..	..	..
165	..	..	..	..	..	..	..	..	..	..	..	..	..
170	..	..	..	..	..	..	..	..	..	..	..	..	..
175	..	..	..	..	..	..	..	..	..	0.20	..	..	..
180	0.10	..	..	..	..	..	..	..	..	..	..	..	..
185	..	..	..	..	..	..	..	..	..	..	..	..	..
190	..	..	..	..	..	..	..	..	..	..	..	..	..
195	..	..	..	..	..	..	..	..	..	..	..	..	..
200	..	..	..	..	..	..	..	..	..	..	..	..	..
205	..	..	..	..	..	..	..	..	..	..	..	..	0.15
210	..	..	..	..	..	..	..	..	..	..	..	0.30	..
213	..	..	..	..	..	..	..	..	..	..	..	..	..
215	..	..	..	..	..	..	..	..	..	..	..	..	..

* D.B. = double bottom.
† D.T. = deep tank.

the ship were loaded completely with lumber below decks, this *GM* is in excess of what might be considered a minimum safe *GM*.

Table 3-8: This table provides a simplified means of determining the proper amount of double bottom tankage to meet the requirements of

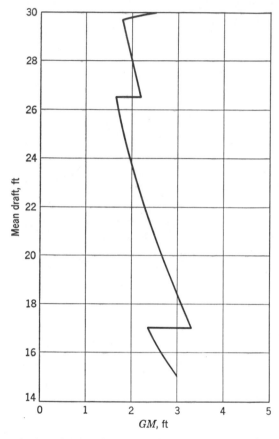

FIG. 3-12. Required *GM* curve for the C4-S-1a. The required *GM* values given in this diagram must be maintained in order to enable the ship, under *average* operating conditions, to sustain damage in any one compartment without reaching a condition of negative stability after damage and without heeling which might result in flooding any other undamaged compartment.

one compartment damage for any indicated condition of loading. Interpolation should be made between the figures given to obtain the required double bottom tankage.

Table 3-9: These are four working forms to be filled out to obtain data necessary to calculate the *GM* and trim conditions. They have been

TABLE 3-8

DOUBLE BOTTOM TANKAGE REQUIREMENTS IN TONS TO MEET ONE COMPART-
MENT DAMAGE FOR NORMAL CONDITIONS OF LOADING

Total Cargo Plus D.T. 1, 1A, 6, 7 & 8 (Column 1 + 2 + 3)	Excess of Hold Weight over Upper 'Tweendeck Weight in Tons (Column 3 − Column 1)						Additional D.B. Tank-age per 100 tons of Deck Cargo
	+1500	+1000	+500	0	−500	−1000	
1,000		0	0	75	475	850	150
2,000	0	0	0	800	1225	1600	140
3,000	0	150	550	950	1350	1750	130
4,000	0	325	675	1050	1400	1775	120
5,000	50	400	750	1100	1425	1775	110
6,000	100	400	725	1050	1350	1650	100
7,000	50	350	650	950	1275	1600	90
8,000	0	200	500	800	1100	1400	80
9,000	0	0	325	650	1000	1600	70
10,000	0	250	500	800	1050	1325	60
11,000	0	50	325	575	825	1100	50
12,000	0	0	0	275	625		

The forms shown below may be used to determine the required double bottom tankage.

From the above table

Upper 'Tween-deck Layer	Col. 1, tons	Lower 'Tweendeck Layer	Col. 2, tons	Hold Layer	Col. 3, tons
No. 1 main deck	160	No. 1 3rd deck	130	No. 1 deep tank centerline	
No. 1 2nd deck	180	No. 2 3rd deck	369	No. 1A deep tank	
No. 2 2nd deck	291	No. 3 3rd deck	621	No. 2 tank top	271
No. 3 2nd deck	418	No. 4 3rd deck	641	No. 3 tank top	546
No. 4 2nd deck	401	No. 5 26′ 6″ flat, dry and reefer	349	No. 4 tank top	650
No. 5 2nd deck	416	No. 5 3rd deck, dry and reefer	321	No. 5 tank top	406
No. 6 2nd deck	384	No. 6 3rd deck	703	No. 6 deep tank P/S	127
No. 7 2nd deck	250	No. 7 3rd deck	366	No. 7 deep tank	
				No. 8 deep tank	
Total	2500	Total	3500	Total	2000

Note: D.B. = double bottom; P/S = port and starboard.

Summary

Item	Tons
Total column 1	2500
Total column 2	3500
Total column 3	2000
Total columns 1 + 2 + 3	8000
Total column 3 − column 1	−500
Required tankage (from table)	1100
Deck cargo in tons	200
Required D.B. tankage for deck cargo	160
Total required D.B. tankage	1260

TABLE 3-9

LOADING TABLE

Voyage No. *Example*

Dry Cargo

Hold	Bale Cubic	Tons	*KG*	Moment	L.C.G. F.P.	Moment
No. 1 main deck	16,085	*160*	55.6	*8,896*	59.2	*9,472*
No. 1 2nd deck	18,140	*180*	45.2	*8,136*	54.8	*9,864*
No. 1 3rd deck	12,210	*130*	31.9	*4,147*	56.6	*7,358*
No. 2 2nd deck	29,255	*291*	43.0	*12,513*	104.4	*30,380*
No. 2 3rd deck	34,592	*369*	29.1	*10,738*	105.3	*38,856*
No. 2 tank top	25,476	*271*	13.1	*3,550*	106.2	*28,780*
No. 3 2nd deck	42,000	*418*	41.3	*17,263*	161.3	*67,423*
No. 3 3rd deck	58,150	*621*	28.3	*17,574*	161.6	*100,354*
No. 3 tank top	51,375	*546*	12.7	*6,934*	162.7	*88,834*
No. 4 2nd deck	40,255	*401*	40.3	*16,160*	221.5	*88,822*
No. 4 3rd deck	60,020	*641*	27.7	*17,756*	221.9	*142,238*
No. 4 tank top	61,140	*650*	12.5	*8,125*	223.1	*145,015*
No. 5 2nd deck	41,775	*416*	40.5	*16,848*	356.5	*148,304*
No. 5 26′ 6″ flat centerline	16,388	*175*	30.8	*5,390*	350.2	*61,285*
No. 5 3rd deck centerline	16,022	*171*	21.4	*3,659*	351.0	*60,021*
No. 5 tank top	38,135	*406*	10.9	*4,425*	353.6	*143,562*
No. 6 2nd deck	38,610	*384*	41.0	*15,744*	416.5	*159,936*
No. 6 3rd deck	65,850	*703*	26.9	*18,911*	415.5	*292,097*
No. 6 deep tank P/S	11,930	*127*	11.2	*1,422*	402.6	*51,130*
No. 7 2nd deck	25,095	*250*	41.8	*10,450*	469.6	*117,400*
No. 7 3rd deck	34,220	*366*	28.4	*10,394*	469.4	*171,800*
Total	736,723	*7676*	28.5	*219,035*	255.7	*1,962,931*

Reefer Cargo

Hold	Reefer Cubic	Tons	*KG*	Moment	L.C.G. F.P.	Moment
No. 5 26′ 6″ flat P/S	16,256	*174*	30.7	*5342*	354.4	*61,666*
No. 5 3rd deck P/S	13,998	*150*	21.8	*3270*	353.4	*53,010*
Total	30,254	*324*	26.6	*8612*	353.9	*114,676*

TABLE 3-9 (*Continued*)

Loading Table

Fuel Oil or Ballast

Tank	F.S.	Tons F.O., S.W.	KG	Mo-ment	L.C.G. F.P.	Moment
No. 1 D.B. centerline			4.5		39.9	
No. 1A D.B. centerline	204	82	4.8	394	64.9	5,322
No. 2 D.B. P/S			2.7		106.6	
No. 3 D.B. centerline			2.5		161.6	
No. 3 D.B. P/S			3.0		169.2	
No. 4 D.B. centerline	943	224	2.5	560	222.0	49,728
No. 4 D.B. P/S			2.6		223.8	
No. 5 D.B. centerline	825	196	2.5	490	278.3	54,547
No. 5 D.B. P/S ½	4096	179	2.6	465	288.3	51,606
No. 6 D.B. centerline	1021	242	2.5	605	354.4	85,765
No. 6 D.B. P/S	442	174	2.8	487	348.2	60,587
No. 7 D.B. P/S	538	189	2.7	510	412.4	77,944
No. 1 D.T. centerline			16.5		40.3	
No. 1A D.T. centerline			16.8		65.1	
No. 2 D.T. P/S ⅔	40	134	19.1	2559	260.8	34,947
No. 3 D.T. P/S ⅔	34	117	19.1	2235	277.0	32,409
No. 6 D.T. P/S			11.4		401.2	
No. 7 D.T. P/S			11.7		430.7	
No. 8 D.T. P/S			9.6		454.0	
Fore peak			11.7		17.1	
After peak			24.9		506.8	
Total	8143	1537	5.4	8305	294.6	452,855

(*1286 tons F.O. in double bottom*)

Fresh Water

Tank	F.S.	Tons F.W.	KG	Mo-ment	L.C.G. F.P.	Moment
No. 4 D.T. P/S	5,575	124	21.3	2641	296.0	36,704
No. 5 D.T. P/S	4,789	108	20.9	2257	312.0	33,696
Distilled water	59	25	39.5	988	255.8	6,395
Total	10,423	257	22.9	5886	298.8	76,795

Note: D.B. = double bottom; D.T. = deep tank; S.W. = salt water; F.O. = fuel oil; P/S = port and starboard.

TABLE 3-10

Voyage No. *Example*

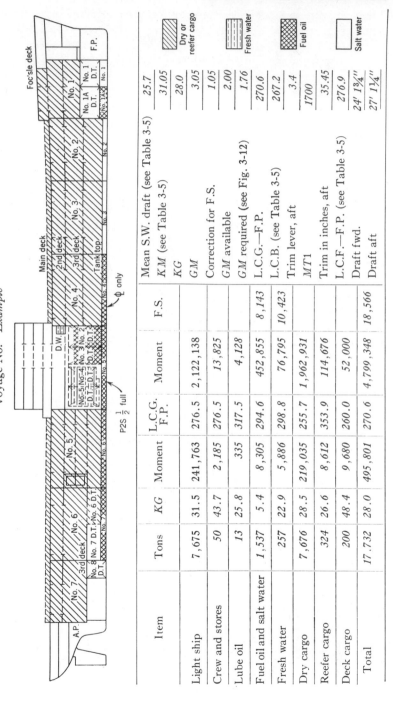

Item	Tons	KG	Moment	L.C.G. F.P.	Moment	F.S.
Light ship	7,675	31.5	241,763	276.5	2,122,138	
Crew and stores	50	43.7	2,185	276.5	13,825	
Lube oil	13	25.8	335	317.5	4,128	
Fuel oil and salt water	1,537	5.4	8,305	294.6	452,855	8,143
Fresh water	257	22.9	5,886	298.8	76,795	10,423
Dry cargo	7,676	28.5	219,035	255.7	1,962,931	
Reefer cargo	324	26.6	8,612	353.9	114,676	
Deck cargo	200	48.4	9,680	260.0	52,000	
Total	17.732	28.0	495,801	270.6	4,799,348	18,566

Mean S.W. draft (see Table 3-5)	25.7
KM (see Table 3-5)	31.05
KG	28.0
GM	3.05
Correction for F.S.	1.05
GM available	2.00
GM required (see Fig. 3-12)	1.76
L.C.G.—F.P.	270.6
L.C.B. (see Table 3-5)	267.2
Trim lever, aft	3.4
$MT1$	1700
Trim in inches, aft	35.45
L.C.F.—F.P. (see Table 3-5)	276.9
Draft fwd.	24' 1¾"
Draft aft	27' 1¼"

filled out with an example. The amount of dry cargo, reefer cargo, fuel oil or salt water, and fresh water is entered in the appropriate table. The summary of each item is entered in the correct space on Table 3-10.

Table 3-10: This is a form for summarizing all the data and solving for estimated *GM* available, item 6, and the drafts forward and aft, items 14 and 15 respectively.

Explanation of solution given on Table 3-10

1. The mean salt water draft is obtained from Table 3-5 entering with the ship's displacement, 25.7 ft.

2. The *KM* for the displacement is also taken from Table 3-5, 31.05 ft.

3. The *KG* is obtained by calculation. Divide the total vertical moments (495,801 ft-tons) by the ship's displacement (17,732 tons); *KG* equals 28.0 ft.

4. *KM* less *KG* equals the calculated *GM* before correcting for any free surface. Thus: $31.05 - 28.0 = 3.05$ ft.

5. The virtual rise of *G* due to free surface (F.S.) is obtained by taking the sum of the free surface moments, each moment being taken from Table 3-6 and entered on Table 3-10, and dividing this sum by the ship's displacement. Thus: $18,566/17,732 = 1.05$ ft.

6. The correction for free surface is subtracted from the *GM* to obtain *GM* available. Thus: $3.05 - 1.05 = 2$ ft.

7. Compare the *GM* available to the *GM* required. The latter is obtained from Fig. 3-12 and found to be 1.76 ft. The *GM* available is adequate. The *GM* available may be too great in some cases; if it is, the rolling period will be short and this is undesirable (see the discussion on magnitudes of *GM*'s, p. 56).

8. The longitudinal position of the center of gravity of the ship is calculated. It is obtained by taking the sum of the longitudinal moments about the forward perpendicular (F.P.) and dividing by the ship's displacement. Thus: $4,799,348/17,732 = 270.6$ ft aft of the F.P.

9. The position of the longitudinal center of buoyancy (L.C.B.) is obtained from Table 3-5 for the ship's displacement. In this case it is 267.2 ft aft of the F.P.

10. The trimming lever is the distance between the longitudinal center of gravity (L.C.G.) and the L.C.B.; thus, in this case it is: $270.6 - 267.2 = 3.4$ ft. The trim will be by the stern if the L.C.G. is *aft* of the L.C.B. or by the head if *forward*.

11. The *MT*1 is obtained from Table 3-5. In this case: 1700 ft-tons.

12. The actual trim or change in trim from an even keel is obtained

by dividing the trimming moment by the $MT1$. The trimming moment is equal to the product of the trimming lever times the ship's displacement. In this case: trimming moment $= 17,732 \times 3.4 = 60,288.8$ ft-tons. The change in trim then becomes: $60,289/1700 = 35.45$ in.

13. It is assumed that the ship started with an even keel with the mean draft of 25 ft 8.4 in. To obtain the draft forward and aft, the change in trim must be applied to this mean draft. Inasmuch as the trim in this case is by the stern, we add part of the 35.45 in. to obtain the draft aft and subtract to obtain the draft forward. If the longitudinal center of flotation (L.C.F.) was located exactly amidships, we could find the *change of draft* forward and aft by dividing the change of trim by 2.[1] But, if the L.C.F. is not amidship, the change of *draft* forward is equal to the change in trim times the ratio of the L.C.F.–F.P. to the length of the ship between perpendiculars (L.B.P.). In this case the L.C.F.–F.P. is found to be 276.9 ft which is 12.9 ft aft of the midship section of the ship.

14. The change of draft forward is equal to: $(276.9/528) \times 35.45 = 18.6$ in. (subtracted). Thus: 25 ft 08.4 in. less 1 ft 06.6 in. = 24 ft 01.8 in. draft forward.

15. The change of draft aft is equal to the difference between the change of trim and the change of draft forward, and it is additive. Thus: $35.45 - 18.60 = 16.85$ in., and 25 ft 08.4 in. plus 1 ft 04.85 in. = 27 ft 01.25 in. draft aft.

The use of trimming tables. Trimming tables constructed as illustrated in Table 3-4 are generally found below the profile view of the ship on the capacity plan. The tables are constructed to show the change in *draft* forward and aft when a weight of 100 tons is placed on the vessel. The effect on the draft forward and aft can be determined by looking in the box directly below the point on the ship where the weight is placed. If the weight being considered is more than, or less than, 100 tons, the effect is increased or decreased proportionately. For example, if a 300 ton weight is loaded, the figures in the box are increased three times.

In each box there is a plus or minus sign. These signs indicate how the values in the boxes are to be applied to the initial draft figures. These signs are for a loading process. Therefore, if the weight is discharged the signs must be changed. The changes in draft set down in the boxes takes into consideration the change in mean draft due to mean sinkage.

---

[1] The longitudinal center of flotation is the tipping center of the ship and corresponds to the center of the area of the water plane at which the ship is floating. As the ship trims it rotates about a transverse axis passing through this point. It is abbreviated L.C.F.

Because the $MT1$ changes with draft, a set of numbers for each draft in increments of 1 ft would be better than the two drafts illustrated. It will be noted that the two drafts are 10 ft apart. This makes it possible to interpolate in calculating the change in drafts for a mean draft lying in between or slightly beyond the two drafts listed. Choosing the table for the nearest draft generally yields sufficient accuracy for most operating conditions.

LONGITUDINAL STRESSES

The following discussion is not intended to be a thorough presentation of the involved subject of strength calculations as applied to the hull of a ship. A summation of the elements of the problem and their relationship to the responsibilities of the ship's officer is our prime objective. It is hoped that the discussion will also clarify the approach to the problem that the ship's officer should take in meeting it on the ship.

The strength equation. Let us say that we have the problem of determining the stress in pounds per square inch on a ship's deck or bottom under a given set of conditions, wherein the type of sea that is running is specified and the distribution of weight in the ship is specified.

Without deriving the equation here, we will accept the following mathematical statement as truth, for we need to use it in our solution of the above problem.

$$M = \frac{I}{y} \times p$$

where M is defined as the bending moment of the hull girder.

I is defined as the moment of inertia of the hull girder.

y is defined as the distance from the neutral axis of the hull girder to the most remote member of the hull girder.

p is defined as a measure of the resistance offered by the material of which the hull girder is made; hence, it is given in units of *stress, pounds per square inch.*

THE SECTION MODULUS. The ratio of I to y is also known as the section modulus of the hull girder. It depends upon the form and distribution of material in the construction of the hull girder. I/y may be notated as S. The *section modulus* of the ship is calculated by the naval architect, and if we are to have the necessary data to calculate the answer to the problem stated above, we must know S for the hull of the ship.

BENDING MOMENT AND·STRESS OF MATERIAL. Two other factors remain in our equation: the bending moment of the hull under our so-called specified conditions of sea and load and the stress of the material p. The latter is what we must find ultimately; hence, our discussion will now revolve around the problem of determining the bending moment or M in our equation.

FINDING THE BENDING MOMENT.   The first step is to determine the weight of the ship per linear foot starting from one end of the vessel. This is the weight in tons of each foot of length and includes the weight of the ship's structure and all the deadweight items aboard her, such as cargo, fuel, water, and stores.   This is a difficult task.

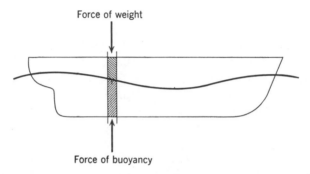

FIG. 3-13.   If a particular slice of the ship's hull is considered as indicated in this diagram, it becomes obvious that unless the weight and buoyancy forces are equal this slice is resisting a shearing stress tending to push it upward or downward. The ship profile is depicted as floating in a trochoidal curve with the height $\frac{1}{20}$th of the length of the ship; this is the so-called *standard sea* as defined by the naval architect.

The next step is to calculate the buoyancy of the ship per linear foot of length.   This is a relatively easy task.   All that must be done to obtain the buoyancy of a linear foot is to calculate the volume of the underwater portion of the hull for a 1-ft slice longitudinally, and divide by 35.   At this point, let us note that *total* weight must always equal the *total* buoyancy; however, the weight at any one point may exceed or be less than the force of buoyancy acting on that point of the hull.

Let us consider a single slice of the hull as illustrated in Fig. 3-13.   If the force of buoyancy on this particular slice exceeds the weight or vice versa, the edges of the slice will experience a shearing stress.   If the next and each succeeding slice experiences this shearing stress, we have a force acting through a distance which exerts itself on the hull of the ship.   A force acting through a distance is termed a moment, and in this case it is called a *bending moment* because as the hull girder resists the force, it bends.   If the shearing stress is large or acts over a considerable distance, the bending moment will be large.

The strength curves. The buoyancy and weight in tons per linear foot are plotted as curves as shown in Fig. 3-14a. Next, the difference between the weight and buoyancy values at every point is plotted. Excess of weight is assigned a negative value and plotted below the base line; excess of buoyancy is assigned a positive value and plotted above the base

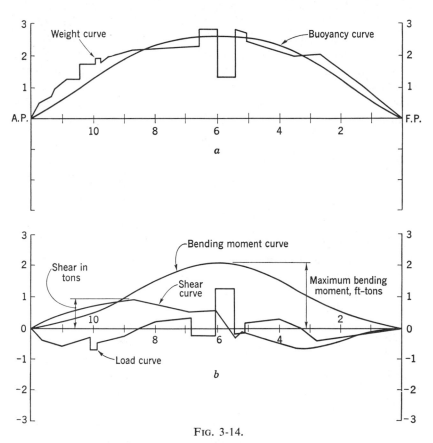

Fig. 3-14.

line. The curve resulting from this plot is known as the load curve, see Fig. 3-14b. The total area under it should be equal to zero.

Next, the integral of the load curve is plotted and called the shear curve, see Fig. 3-14b. Finally, the integral of the shear curve is plotted and called the *bending moment curve,* see Fig. 3-14b.

All of the curves shown in Fig. 3-14 are simply for purposes of illustration. The conditions depicted parallel those of a ship in still water. The strength curves for a ship in a standard wave with crest amidships would have more buoyancy amidships and less at the ends. Conversely, if the ship were in a wave with the trough amidships, the buoyancy amidships would be reduced while it would be increased at the ends. The weight curve would, of course, remain the same, unless the load conditions on the ship were changed.

The abscissas on all five curves are in units of length. The ordinate on the weight and buoyancy curves is in units of tons per linear foot. The ordinate on the shear and load curves is in tons, and the ordinate of the bending moment curve is in units of foot-tons.

Going through this process, the maximum bending moment as well as the bending moment at any given point may be obtained. With this value, the stress, tension, and compression on the hull bottom and deck plating can be calculated, providing we know the section modulus, because:

$$p = \frac{M}{S}$$

where M is the bending moment which we have calculated.

S is the section modulus for the hull which we must obtain from the design naval architect.

The naval architect specifies structural members for all decks and other parts of the hull to withstand the tension and compression stresses that are found to exist in them when the ship is placed in a standard sea and under a standard load condition. This is done for a hogging and a sagging condition.

Standard sea and standard load. The standard sea is one in which the height is one-twentieth the length of the ship and in the form of a trochoidal curve. For a hogging condition, the crest of the sea is assumed to be amidships. The buoyancy amidships would be at a maximum then. For a sagging condition, the trough of the sea is assumed to be amidships. The buoyancy would then be a minimum amidships.

The standard load for a ship with machinery spaces amidships assumes the midship tanks empty and the end tanks full with all cargo compartments full. This is a poor loading pattern for such a ship for it results in an initial hogging tendency.

The standard load for a ship with machinery spaces aft assumes the cargo spaces full and the end tanks empty. This will create an initial sagging tendency in such a vessel.

Obviously, the load and the sea can be exaggerated so as to produce excessive stresses; however, the naval architect does not design the ship to withstand the worst possible conditions but, rather, what might be termed reasonably bad conditions. Then a suitable safety factor is worked into the calculations for determining the final scantlings used to construct the ship.

It should be apparent that if the ship is loaded with an extreme concentration of weight in the center hatches or in the end hatches and subsequently the ship meets with extremely heavy seas, the stresses on the hull girder will become dangerously high.

The beam theory. We have been referring to the hull of the ship as a beam or girder. The ship is really a complicated built-up shape, and much of the theory of stresses on the hull is based on the assumption

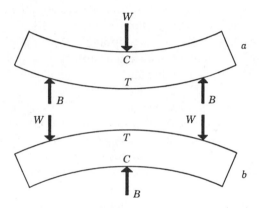

FIG. 3-15. W = excess of weight. B = excess of buoyancy. C = steel in this area under compression. T = steel in this area under tension.

that hull stresses are quite similar to beam stresses. Experience of naval architects has proved that this assumption is a reasonable one to make. Figure 3-15a illustrates a beam heavily loaded on its midlength. This parallels a ship in the sagging condition. Note that the steel of the upper decks is under a compression stress, and the bottom is under tension. Figure 3-15b illustrates a beam supported at its midlength and loaded on its ends. This parallels a ship's hull in the hogging condition. Note that the steel of the upper decks is under tension stresses, and the bottom is under compression. If these tension or compression stresses become greater than the ship is designed to withstand, the plating will fail. Under tension, the plating will crack or tear apart. Under compression, the plating will buckle.

Practical approach to the problem. The ship's officer must make certain that his ship is never loaded so that extreme hogging or sagging will occur. In actual practice, however, it is difficult for the ship's officer to obtain data to make calculations concerning the bending moments of the vessel as she sails each voyage. What, then, should be the practice to remove this blank spot of the average ship's officer in his knowledge of his ship. Three solutions are set forth below:

1. The shipowner should see that every ship is supplied with necessary data, such as strength curves, section modulus, geometrical locations of all spaces, and other information to facilitate the calculations of bending moments and possibly the stresses. Then, instructions in how to use the data should be provided where necessary. All ship's officers should then prepare tabular methods of calculating the hogging and sagging moments under conditions of loading for each voyage. Such a tabular method has been worked out and publicized by the American Bureau of Shipping and is presented below. This method has been worked out for the T-2 tanker by the American Bureau of Shipping. With the proper data and background, any ship's officer can make up a similar set of tables and diagrams to work out the hogging and sagging tendencies for his particular ship.

2. If a tabular method has been devised for the ship upon which he is sailing, the ship's officer should work with it until he is thoroughly acquainted with it. Then he should use it consistently. The hogging and sagging tendencies of his ship in waves of standard proportions should become as familiar to the ship's officer as the sailing drafts of his ship.

3. If his ship is equipped with a mechanical device for the calculation of hogging and sagging bending moments, the ship's officer should be thoroughly familiar with its use and the significance of the data it provides him. A mechanical device for such computations is now on the market and is manufactured by the American Hydromath Company. A slide rule type device for accomplishing the same thing was devised by Ensign A. V. Divino in 1951 while a student at the U.S. Merchant Marine Academy.

Approximating the longitudinal distribution. Lacking the time, the data, or the materials to take advantage of any of the previously mentioned suggestions, an estimation of correct longitudinal distribution for ships with their engine room spaces amidships can be made. The method is based on the same premise as the method for roughly estimating the vertical distribution. The amount of weight that should be placed in each longitudinal compartment is equal to the ratio of the cubic of that compartment to the cubic of all the cargo compartments. This may be expressed by the following equation:

$$\frac{v}{V} \times T = t$$

where v = the volume of the compartment in question.

V = the volume of all cargo compartments.

T = the total weight to be loaded.

t = the weight to be loaded in the compartment in question.

Caution must be exercised with such a method. In the case of ships with the engine room spaces aft, it would lead to excessive sagging moments.

Tabular method for checking on longitudinal load distribution. The method presented here was developed by the American Bureau of Shipping to determine the adequacy of any load distribution, with respect to satisfactory design conditions, for the T-2 tanker on a hogging and sagging wave of standard proportions.

The results obtained from this simplified method are approximate. It has been determined by comparison with numerous direct bending moment calculations that the degree of approximation is of an acceptable magnitude with a range of displacements from 10,000 to 22,000 long tons and trims varying from 30 in. forward at the deep displacement to 170 in. aft at the light displacement.

The light ship weight with crew and stores and the longitudinal distribution of these weights for the purposes of this study are average for this class of vessel.

The method consists of determining *numerals* based on the longitudinal distribution of weight along the hull. These hogging and sagging numerals are obtained by multiplying the load in each space on the vessel by a factor depending on the longitudinal location of the weight, adding the product to the numeral for light ship with crew and stores, and deducting three times the deadweight divided by 100. To get the maximum benefit from this method, these calculations of hogging and sagging numerals should be made not only for the completed loading but should also be made through the entire range of proceedings with the loading of either cargo or ballast as the loading progresses or as changes in loading are made.

The numerals should be determined for both hogging and sagging. In the event either numeral exceeds 100, it indicates that the structure is subject to conditions which are more severe than the standard conditions. In many conditions of operation, especially those less than full and homogeneously loaded, it will be possible to distribute the load in such a manner as to give a value much less than 100. For the purpose of operation, particularly in heavy weather, it is desirable to obtain the lowest possible numeral.

The diagram in Fig. 3-16 gives the hogging and sagging factors for an added load of 100 tons at any longitudinal location on the vessel.

Table 3-11 lists the hogging and sagging factors for each tank space on the vessel as read from the diagram in Fig. 3-16 and should be suitable for most conditions of load distribution. Should an appreciable item

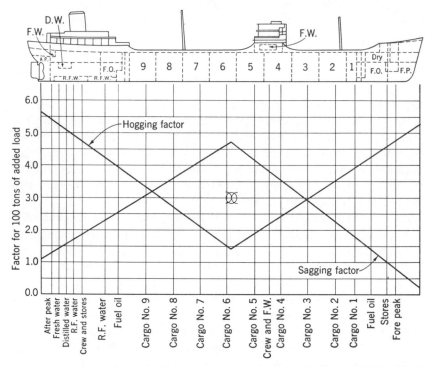

Fig. 3-16.   Diagram for determining numeral from load distribution (T-2 tanker).

of weight, such as a deck load, be added to the vessel with a longitudinal center considerably removed from any of the tank centers, the hogging and sagging factors for this weight should be read from the diagram in Fig. 3-16 and inserted in the table along with the weight of the item in long tons divided by 100.

Table 3-12 is an example worked out for a vessel with a cargo distribution which gives an *unfavorable* numeral.

Table 3-13 is an example worked out for the same vessel with the same cargo redistributed to give a favorable numeral.

A second tabular method for calculating stresses.   This is a variation of the previous method.   It is a method for estimating the stresses on the T-2 tanker due to hogging and sagging.   Table 3-14 illustrates

TABLE 3-11

TABLE FOR DETERMINING HOGGING AND SAGGING NUMERALS
FROM LOAD DISTRIBUTION

Blank Form (T-2 tanker)

Line No.	Item	Weight, long tons 100	Hogging		Sagging	
			Factor	Numeral	Factor	Numeral
		(a)	(b)	(c)	(d)	(e)
1	Light ship and crew and stores	54.12	...	88.8	...	29.7
2	F.P. tank	...	4.82	...	0.65	...
3	F.O. forward	...	4.31	...	1.26	...
4	F.W. amidships	...	2.21	...	3.77	...
5	F.O. aft	...	3.90	...	2.52	...
6	R.F.W. forward D.B.	...	4.20	...	2.27	...
7	R.F.W. after D.B.	...	4.86	...	1.68	...
8	Distilled water	...	5.06	...	1.52	...
9	F.W. aft	...	5.19	...	1.40	...
10	A.P. tank	...	5.37	...	1.25	...
11	Cargo No. 1	...	3.92	...	1.73	...
12	Cargo No. 2	...	3.54	...	2.18	...
13	Cargo No. 3	...	3.00	...	2.82	...
14	Cargo No. 4	...	2.46	...	3.47	...
15	Cargo No. 5	...	1.91	...	4.11	...
16	Cargo No. 6	...	1.49	...	4.65	...
17	Cargo No. 7	...	2.08	...	4.11	...
18	Cargo No. 8	...	2.69	...	3.59	...
19	Cargo No. 9	...	3.29	...	3.06	...
20	Subtotals (lines 2 through 19)	...		...		...
21	Subtotals (line 1 + line 20)			...		...
22	Deadweight correction = 3 × (line 20 in column a) enter in columns c and e			...		...
23	Displacement ÷ 100 (lines 1 + 20)	...				
24	Resultant numerals (lines 21 − 22)			...		...

TABLE 3-12

TABLE FOR DETERMINING HOGGING AND SAGGING NUMERALS
FROM LOAD DISTRIBUTION

Example Showing Unfavorable Distribution

(T-2 tanker)

Line No.	Item	Weight, long tons 100	Hogging Factor	Hogging Numeral	Sagging Factor	Sagging Numeral
		(a)	(b)	(c)	(d)	(e)
1	Light ship and crew and stores	54.12	...	88.8	...	29.7
2	F.P. tank	...	4.82	...	0.65	...
3	F.O. forward	...	4.31	...	1.26	...
4	F.W. amidships	0.70	2.21	1.5	3.77	2.6
5	F.O. aft	5.60	3.90	21.8	2.52	14.1
6	R.F.W. forward D.B.	1.56	4.20	6.5	2.27	3.5
7	R.F.W. after D.B.	0.70	4.86	3.4	1.68	1.2
8	Distilled water	0.30	5.06	1.5	1.52	0.5
9	F.W. aft	0.30	5.19	1.5	1.40	0.4
10	A.P. tank	...	5.37	...	1.25	...
11	Cargo No. 1	...	3.92	...	1.73	...
12	Cargo No. 2	13.72	3.54	48.6	2.18	29.9
13	Cargo No. 3	22.84	3.00	68.5	2.82	64.4
14	Cargo No. 4	23.21	2.46	57.1	3.47	80.5
15	Cargo No. 5	23.23	1.91	44.4	4.11	95.5
16	Cargo No. 6	23.23	1.49	34.6	4.65	108.0
17	Cargo No. 7	23.21	2.08	48.3	4.11	95.4
18	Cargo No. 8	23.08	2.69	62.1	3.59	82.9
19	Cargo No. 9	3.00	3.29	9.9	3.06	9.2
20	Subtotals (lines 2 through 19)	164.68		409.7		588.1
21	Subtotals (line 1 + line 20)			498.5		617.8
22	Deadweight correction = 3 × (line 20 in column a) enter in columns c and e			−494.0		−494.0
23	Displacement ÷ 100 (lines 1 + 20)	218.80				
24	Resultant numerals (lines 21 − 22)			4.5		123.8

Even Keel

TABLE 3-13

TABLE FOR DETERMINING HOGGING AND SAGGING NUMERALS
FROM LOAD DISTRIBUTION

Example Showing Distribution to Obtain Favorable Numeral

(T-2 tanker)

Line No.	Item	Weight, long tons 100	Hogging Factor	Hogging Numeral	Sagging Factor	Sagging Numeral
		(a)	(b)	(c)	(d)	(e)
1	Light ship and crew and stores	54.12	. . .	88.8	. . .	29.7
2	F.P. tank	. . .	4.82	. . .	0.65	. . .
3	F.O. forward	. . .	4.31	. . .	1.26	. . .
4	F.W. amidships	0.70	2.21	1.5	3.77	2.6
5	F.O. aft	5.60	3.90	21.8	2.52	14.1
6	R.F.W. forward D.B.	1.56	4.20	6.5	2.27	3.5
7	R.F.W. after D.B.	0.70	4.86	3.4	1.68	1.2
8	Distilled water	0.30	5.06	1.5	1.52	0.5
9	F.W. aft	0.30	5.19	1.6	1.40	0.4
10	A.P. tank	. . .	5.37	. . .	1.25	. . .
11	Cargo No. 1	6.77	3.92	26.5	1.73	11.7
12	Cargo No. 2	20.74	3.54	73.4	2.18	45.2
13	Cargo No. 3	22.84	3.00	68.5	2.82	64.4
14	Cargo No. 4	22.21	2.46	54.6	3.47	77.1
15	Cargo No. 5	17.03	1.91	32.5	4.11	70.0
16	Cargo No. 6	2.00	1.49	3.0	4.65	9.3
17	Cargo No. 7	19.91	2.08	41.4	4.11	81.8
18	Cargo No. 8	22.08	2.69	59.4	3.59	79.3
19	Cargo No. 9	21.94	3.29	72.2	3.06	67.1
20	Subtotals (lines 2 through 19)	164.68		467.8		528.2
21	Subtotals (line 1 + line 20)			556.6		557.9
22	Deadweight correction = 3 × (line 20 in column a) enter in columns c and e			−494.0		−494.0
23	Displacement ÷ 100 (lines 1 + 20)	218.80				
24	Resultant numerals (lines 21 − 22)			62.6		63.9

Even Keel

TABLE 3-14

TABLE FOR ESTIMATING HOGGING AND SAGGING STRESSES

| | | | | Hogging | | Sagging | |
	Full Load (1)	Any Condition (2)	Change Hundreds of Tons (3)	Change per 100 Tons (4)	Change in Stress, psi (5)	Change per 100 Tons (6)	Change in Stress, psi (7)
Full load			217.70		10.500		14.600
A.P. tank	0			+470		−350	
F.W. aft	29			+432		−318	
Distilled tank	36			+410		−296	
R.F.W. aft	73			+370		−263	
Crew STS aft	40			+330		−232	
R.F.W. fwd.	166			+238		−148	
F.O. aft	692			+175		−97	
Cargo No. 9	1714			+50		+10	
Cargo No. 8	1803			−65		+112	
Cargo No. 7	1813			−182		+218	
Cargo No. 6	1814			−302		+322	
Cargo No. 5	1814			−218		+218	
Cargo No. 4	1812			−110		+98	
Cargo No. 3	1784			0		−25	
Cargo No. 2	1620			+102		−142	
Cargo No. 1	529			+178		−230	
Crew and F.W.	81			−160		+155	
F.O. fwd.	728			+236		−317	
Stores fwd.	20			+330		−402	
F.P. tank	0			+355		−430	
Totals							

the form to be used. Some comments regarding the form will clarify its use. At the top of the form in column 3, the number 217.70 is entered. This is the displacement of the ship assumed for design purposes. The numbers 10,500 and 14,600 in columns 5 and 7 respectively indicate the stress in the deck when loaded under the design conditions. The distribution of the 21,770 tons is as shown in column 1.

The steps to be followed in using the table are as follows:

1. In column 2, list the actual distribution of the weights in the problem ship being considered.

2. Subtract column 1 from column 2. If column 1 is greater than column 2, place a minus sign before the result in column 3; if column 1 is less than column 2, place a plus sign before the result in column 3.

3. Observing rules for algebraic signs, multiply column 3 by column 4 and place the result in column 5.

4. Observing rules for algebraic signs, multiply column 3 by column 6 and place the result in column 7.

5. Add algebraically the numbers in columns 5 and 7. These sums will be the stresses in the weather deck in pounds per square inch.

The maximum allowable stress is 18,000 psi. If the sum in either column 5 or 7 is above 18,000, some changes should be made in the longitudinal distribution of the weights.

CHECKING ON THE HULL DEFLECTION

Simply noting where the actual waterline amidships is as compared to the true mean draft affords a check on the amount that the hull is deflected. Draft marks amidships are found on many bulk carriers, therefore a check on the waterline's position can be made by inspection from the dock. A practical check on hull deflection for all ships may be made

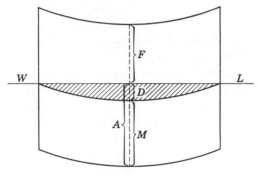

FIG. 3-17.

by subtracting the mean draft amidships from the hull's depth to obtain the freeboard. Next, a plumb line is prepared to equal the freeboard in length. With the upper end of the plumb bob at the statutory deck line, the position of the lower end is noted. If the lower end of the plumb line is in the water, the ship is sagged. The amount of the deflection is equal to the difference between the actual freeboard and the calculated freeboard. It can be determined by noting the number of inches the line must be shortened to make the plumb bob level with the waterline. This should be done on both sides of the ship, using the mean of the data received. The ship is hogged, in the above test, if the end of the plumb line is out of the water.

Figure 3-17 is a diagram of a barge in a sagging condition. Observe that the vessel is floating on an even keel with waterline WL. If we read the drafts forward and aft and divide by 2, we obtain a mean draft equal to M. The draft amidships is equal to A because of the sagging condition. In the method outlined above for checking on hull deflection, our plumb bob would be immersed in the water to the depth of D. If the plumb bob were above the waterline this distance, the hull deflection would be due to hogging.

Numerical example

Given: A tanker has the following drafts: fwd., 13 ft 00 in.; aft, 18 ft 00 in. The depth of the ship is 40 ft. After measuring the freeboard on both sides of the ship and taking the average, the mate arrives at a figure of 24 ft 00.0 in.

Required: Is the ship hogged or sagged? If so, how much?

Solution: The mean draft *amidships* is equal to 15 ft 06.0 in.; therefore, the freeboard amidships should be 24 ft 06 in., providing no hull deflection exists. But, our actual freeboard is 6 in. less than it should be, so we conclude that the ship is sagging 6 in.

True Mean Draft and True Displacement. In the numerical example given above, reference was made to the mean draft *amidships*. It should be noted that the mean draft amidships may *not* be the true mean draft of the ship if we define the *true mean draft* as the draft used to enter the deadweight scale for purposes of picking off hydrostatic data about the ship. Since this is the most common purpose of obtaining the mean draft, methods of obtaining the true mean draft should be discussed.

The corrections that we will show as necessary to consider will be: (1) Correction for trim. (2) Correction to perpendiculars. (3) Correction for hull deflection. (4) Correction for density.

CORRECTION FOR TRIM. This correction can best be considered by referring the reader to a diagram such as Fig. 3-18. First we consider

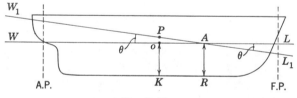

FIG. 3-18.

the ship on an even keel with waterline WL and with the mean draft KO. We will consider the center of flotation at some point other than on the midship section, because if the center of flotation is on the midship section, there is no correction to the mean draft for out of trim conditions. Therefore, we assume the tipping center of the ship to be at A.

Now, if weights on the ship are moved so that the ship trims by the stern, she will assume a new waterline W_1L_1 which passes through point A. Her displacement will not have changed, but it is obvious that the mean draft amidships has increased to KP. However, the true mean draft for purposes of entering the deadweight scale or hydrostatic curves is still equal to KO which is also equal to RA. Hence, it can be seen that the distance OP is the correction that must be applied to the mean draft obtained in the usual manner in order to obtain the true mean draft. In this case the correction would be subtracted.

From the above discussion and the diagram of Fig. 3-18, it becomes apparent that it is important to know where the tipping center lies with respect to the midship section of the ship. It will be noted that the correction may be added or subtracted, depending upon where the tipping center is (forward or aft of the midship section) and upon the trim of the ship, that is, by the head or by the stern.

Calculating the correction for trim. In Fig. 3-18 the following is evident from trigonometry:

$$\tan \theta = \frac{\text{Trim of the ship}}{\text{Length of the ship}}$$

Also:

$$\tan \theta = \frac{OP}{OA}$$

where OP = difference between mean draft amidships and true mean draft or, in other words, the correction.

OA = distance of tipping center from midship section.

Solving for OP:

$$OP = \frac{OA \times \text{Trim of ship}}{\text{Length of ship}}$$

Length of ship used in this equation is the length between perpendiculars notated L.B.P. OP will be subtracted from the mean draft amidships to get the true mean draft if the tipping center is forward of the midship section and ship is trimmed by the stern or if the tipping center is aft of the midship section and the ship is trimmed by the head. The correction (OP) is added when the inverse of the two above situations exists. OP, as calculated above, is in feet and should be changed to inches by multiplying by 12 to obtain the effect on displacement as shown in the example.

Numerical example

Given: A ship has 500 ft between perpendiculars. The tipping center is 12 ft forward of the midship section. Drafts: fwd., 16 ft 00 in.; aft, 20 ft 00 in.

Required: True mean draft.

Solution: Let x equal the correction to the mean draft to obtain the true mean draft. This correction is subtractive.

$$x = \frac{12 \times 4 \times 12}{500} = 1.15 \text{ in.}$$

As can be seen from the above example, the correction will not amount to much unless the ship is badly out of trim. Assuming a T.P.I. of 50 tons, the error in displacement would have been $50 \times 1.15 = 57.5$ tons. The true mean draft would have been 17 ft 10.85 in.

Change of displacement for 1-ft trim. Using the same idea as before, we can use the following equation for calculating the *tons* of correction to the displacement for 1 ft of trim:

$$c = \frac{\text{T.P.I.} \times 12 \times d}{L}$$

where c = correction to displacement in tons.
L = length of ship between perpendiculars in feet.
d = distance of tipping center from amidships in feet.

The sign given the correction depends on the trim and position of the tipping center.

	Tipping Center Aft.	Tipping Center Fwd.
Trimmed by the stern	Add	Subtract
Trimmed by the head	Subtract	Add

Accuracy of correction for trim equation. The above equation is only an approximation of the true correction. The error lies in assuming the hull form below the waterline to be the same *with trim* as it is on an *even keel.*

There is no simple solution to obtaining a true displacement correction for badly out of trim conditions. If the correction for 1 ft of trim is multiplied by the number of feet of trim, an error will result. Up to 5 ft this error will not be significant.

Shift of the tipping center. When a ship trims by the stern, the tipping center actually shifts aft of the location where it appears if on an even keel at the given true mean draft; if trimmed by the head, it shifts forward. This shift becomes significant only when a ship is trimmed heavily one way or another. For tankers, which sometimes operate with large trims, the naval architect frequently calculates the exact corrections for 5 and 10 ft of trim. Table 3-15 shows such data for the T-2 tanker. As can be seen in this table, the error that would result by multiplying the 1-ft trim correction by 10 to obtain the correction for a 10-ft trim is so much that it is best to ignore the correction for such abnormal trim conditions, unless, of course, such a table is available. For intermediate trims and drafts, it is necessary to interpolate to obtain the exact correction.

TABLE 3-15

Hydrostatic Data

(T-2 tanker)

Draft, ft	Tipping Center from Amidships, ft	T.P.I.	Change in Displacement for 1-ft Trim by the Stern, tons	Change in Displacement for 5-ft Trim by the Stern, tons	Change in Displacement for 10-ft Trim by the Stern, tons
8	5.8 fwd.	59	8.2 (minus)	31 (minus)	40 (minus)
10	5.3 fwd.	60 ½	7.6 (minus)	32 (minus)	39 (minus)
12	4.8 fwd.	61	7.0 (minus)	30 (minus)	37 (minus)
14	4.1 fwd.	61 ½	6.0 (minus)	26 (minus)	31 (minus)
16	3.2 fwd.	62	4.7 (minus)	19 (minus)	24 (minus)
18	2.3 fwd.	62 ½	3.4 (minus)	10 (minus)	13 (minus)
20	1.2 fwd.	63	1.8 (minus)	1 (plus)	8 (plus)
22	0.2 aft	64	0.3 (plus)	12 (plus)	34 (plus)
24	1.8 aft	64 ½	2.8 (plus)	22 (plus)	57 (plus)
26	3.6 aft	65 ½	5.6 (plus)	33 (plus)	74 (plus)
28	5.5 aft	66	8.7 (plus)	43 (plus)	88 (plus)
30	7.6 aft	67	12.1 (plus)	54 (plus)	100 (plus)

CORRECTION TO PERPENDICULARS. Another source of error when seeking the true mean draft is caused by the draft marks being placed along a line other than the true perpendiculars of the ship. It is assumed by many operating personnel, when taking the drafts forward and aft, that these marks are on the true perpendiculars. This is manifested by the fact that they add the draft values as read, divide by 2, and call the result the mean draft. On a ship with a raked bow, it is impossible to put the draft marks along the perpendicular. Hence, when the ship is *not on an even keel,* the true draft at the position of the perpendicular is something other than what is read.

The correction that must be applied to the draft as read to obtain the draft at the perpendicular is a function of the ratio of trim of the ship to the length of the ship and the distance of the draft mark from the perpendicular in question. Thus, the correction may be determined by the following equation:

$$c = \frac{T \cdot d \cdot 12}{L}$$

where c = the correction to the draft as read in inches.

T = trim of the ship in feet.

L = length of ship between perpendiculars.

d = distance from perpendicular to the draft mark in feet.

Figure 3-19 illustrates the elements of this problem. The sign of the correction is as follows:

Trimmed by the Stern   Trimmed by the Head

Add correction aft   Subtract correction aft
Subtract correction fwd.   Add correction fwd.

Because the signs change at either end, if the draft marks at both ends are equidistant from their respective perpendicular no correction need be made.

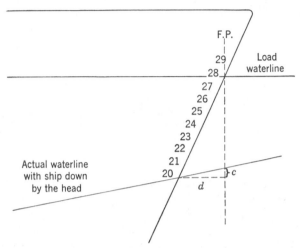

FIG. 3-19. Diagram illustrating correction to perpendicular. The actual waterline has been given an exaggerated trim by the head to accent the correction to the perpendicular. The correction c should be added to the draft to obtain the draft at the forward perpendicular. d equals the distance from the draft mark to the forward perpendicular; note that it is the length of a perpendicular dropped from the intersection of the actual waterline and the ship's stem to the F.P.

All ships should be equipped with tables showing these two corrections for various conditions of trim and draft so that officers reading the drafts and recording the mean drafts in the log book can record accurate data. The correction for trim and the correction to perpendiculars are not required if the ship is on an even keel. In the majority of cases they would not be significant, but their values should be known.

EFFECT OF HULL DEFLECTION ON DISPLACEMENT READING. As a result of checking on the hogging and sagging as outlined above, deflections of the hull of 2 or 3 in. will be found to be quite common. Occasionally, deflections of 6 to 8 in. will be experienced. Deflections of 1 ft or more have been reported.

In the face of these facts, the question of what is the ship's true displacement when hogged or sagged arises. Entering the deadweight scale with the mean draft corrected for the errors already mentioned will not give the true displacement when the hull is deflected. Figure 3-19 clearly illustrates that if we take the drafts fore and aft and correct as outlined for the mean, the draft will be above the true mean if hogged and below if sagged. When the hull is deflected, the real mean draft lies somewhere along the distance D, still referring to Fig. 3-17.

Displacement correction for hogged or sagged condition. A practical means of obtaining a very close approximation of the correction for displacement due to hog or sag is to first correct for the mean draft as outlined above. Then use this mean draft to enter the deadweight scale and pick out a displacement correct for everything except hull deflection. The correction for hull deflection is then calculated with this equation:

$$c = 9.6 \cdot \text{T.P.I.} \cdot D$$

where c = correction in tons.

  D = hull deflection in feet.

T.P.I. = tons per inch immersion for mean draft.

The correction is added if the ship is sagging and subtracted if it is hogging.

The theory of this approximate correction is based on calculating the volume of the cross hatched portion of Fig. 3-17, assuming that the hull is deflected in a parabolic curve and that the curvature of the hull bounding the outer surface is also a parabolic curve. With the volume obtained divided by 35, the result is the displacement correction.

CORRECTION FOR DENSITY. When a ship is floating in water that is brackish, another correction to the displacement as read from the deadweight scale must be made. This is called the *correction for density* and is necessary because the deadweight scale is prepared assuming the ship is floating in salt water. The correction amounts to the displacement as read from the deadweight scale multiplied by the difference between the specific gravity of the water in which the ship is floating at the time of reading the drafts and the specific gravity of sea water, which is taken as 1.026. This can be expressed in the following equation:

$$c = \Delta \cdot (\text{S.G.}_1 - \text{S.G.}_2)$$

where c = the correction in tons.

  S.G._1 = specific gravity of sea water (1.026).

  S.G._2 = specific gravity of the water in which the ship is floating.

  Δ = displacement as read from the deadweight scale using the true mean draft.

The density correction would always be subtractive.

Obviously, the ship must be equipped with a suitable hydrometer for measuring the density of the water in which the ship is floating.

Draft correction for density.   Because of the differences in the densities between pure sea water and fresh or brackish water, the ship's mean draft will change when going from one to the other.   This change in draft or correction may be found by a number of equations.

To obtain the fresh water draft if the salt water draft is known, multiply the latter by the ratio of 36/35.   If the fresh water draft is known, the salt water draft can be found by multiplying the fresh water draft by 35/36.   The results will be approximate, but accurate enough for most practical purposes.[1]

A general equation based on the specific gravity differences and the T.P.I. concept is as follows:

$$c = \frac{\Delta \cdot \text{Difference in specific gravity}}{\text{T.P.I.}}$$

From this equation, assuming a specific gravity of 1.026 for salt water and 1.00 for fresh water, an equation for the difference in draft between fresh and salt water is:

$$c = \frac{\Delta}{40\text{T.P.I.}}$$

where Δ = displacement in tons.
$\quad\quad c$ = difference in draft in inches.
$\quad$ T.P.I. = the tons per inch immersion.

CONCENTRATION OF WEIGHTS

The weights may be distributed transversely, vertically, and longitudinally so that no damage can be caused to the ship, yet there remains one aspect of the problem of handling weight distribution on the ship that has not been discussed.   This is the problem of loading weights so that the total weight on any deck, or part of any deck, is not so great that damage will be done to the ship structure.

Deck load capacities.   The deck load capacities of all decks of the ship must be known in order to make a decision concerning this problem. The deck load capacity is given on most capacity plans.   If it is not recorded thereon, the ship's officer should make every effort to find these values and place them upon the plan.   The data are given in pounds per square foot and may be defined as the average load that the deck can support.   This does not mean that, if the value of the deck load capacity is exceeded on any single square foot, the deck will fail to support it.

---

[1] 35 cu ft of salt water weigh 1 long ton; 36 cu ft of fresh water weigh 1 long ton (approx.), hence the source of this useful ratio.

It is a figure that can be used to determine the design load of the deck of a given compartment or part of a compartment. For example, the deck load capacity of the weather deck of the average merchant ship is in the order of 350 lb per sq ft. This means that if a heavy lift is being loaded on deck that has a base 100 sq ft in area, the lift could weigh as much as 35,000 lb without endangering the structure. In other words, divide the area over which the load will be spread into the number of pounds in the load; if the result is equal to or less than the deck load capacity, there is no reason for shoring up. If the result is greater than the deck load capacity, shoring up under the deck may be necessary.

Although the foregoing indicates that only the area over which the load is actually resting should be used in determining the deck load, this allows for a considerable margin of safety. The load is distributed over an unknown area extending out beyond the precise limits of the container. Some engineering data suggest that it is safe to assume that the supporting area extends out from the container one-half the length and breadth all around. Thus the area that contributes to the support of the load is four times the area of the base of the container. Obviously, this assumption will lead to trouble when carrying loads that extend over very large areas of the deck, such as over the entire beam of the ship. The assumption may be used with caution, however, when considering single small containers.

Height limitation. When loading small dense units of cargo, such as steel billets, lead ingots, or tin plate, the height of the stowed cargo block must be limited. If such cargo is loaded too high, the deck load capacity will be exceeded and the ship structure will be damaged.

Two things must be known in order to calculate the height in feet that it is safe to load any given cargo. First, the deck load capacity must be known. Second, the stowage factor of the cargo must be known. The stowage factor is defined as the number of cubic feet required to stow 1 long ton of the cargo without any broken stowage. Knowing these values, the following equation may be used:

$$h = \frac{c \times f}{2240}$$

where h = the maximum height to load the cargo.

c = deck load capacity.

f = the cargo's stowage factor.

2240 = a constant equal to the number of pounds in 1 long ton.

Utilizing free space over dense cargo. Obviously, if the cargo is very dense it cannot be stowed very high. Cargo with a stowage factor in the order of 10 can be stowed only 2 or 3 ft high in 'tweendeck areas, while in the lower hold the height will be limited to about 7 ft. This leaves several feet of free space over such cargoes which cannot be used if the dense cargo is stowed to the limit of the deck load capacity.

When two cargoes are available, one with a very low stowage factor and the other with a high stowage factor, it may be desirable to limit the height of the heavy cargo below the full limit of the deck so that the free space on top can be filled with the lighter cargo. If general cargo is to be stowed over such heavy concentrated cargo, an average stowage factor may be estimated and the height of the dense cargo limited accordingly.

Calculating the height limit of dense cargo when overstowing with light cargo. We consider a column 1 ft square and equal in height to the cargo compartment. This column must be filled with a mixture of light and heavy cargo such that its total weight equals the deck load capacity of the compartment. Note that the cubic capacity of this column is equal to the height of the compartment. Hence, we have a problem somewhat similar to the full and down loading problem.

In this problem, we may work with densities or stowage factors. In the general solution that follows and the numerical example, densities are used because the values are considered easier to work with. Our problem is to determine the number of cubic feet that each cargo type must occupy out of the total cubic in the 1-ft column. The cubic feet is also the height limit of each cargo type in order to fill the space and use up all the deck load capacity.

Deriving a general solution

Let: a = density of light cargo.

b = density of heavy cargo.

h = number of cubic feet in a 1-ft square column in the compartment.

c = number of pounds of deck load capacity.

x = cubic feet of light cargo in the column h.

y = cubic feet of heavy cargo in the column h.

Then:

$$x + y = h \qquad (1)$$

and

$$ax + by = c \qquad (2)$$
$$(-)\ \underline{ax + ay = ah} \qquad (3) = a \times (1)$$
$$by - ay = c - ah$$
$$y = \frac{c - ah}{b - a}$$
$$x = h - y$$

But since h is 1 ft square, x and y may also be read as units of height alone.

Numerical example

Given: Steel billets with a stowage factor of 12 are to be stowed in a compartment 12 ft high with a deck load capacity of 400 lb per sq ft. General cargo with an average stowage factor estimated at 160 is to be stowed over the steel.

Required: How high should the steel be tiered to allow the free space over the steel to be filled with the general cargo and not exceed the deck load capacity?

Solution: First solve for the density of the steel billets and the general cargo.

$$2240/12 = 186 \text{ lb per ft}^3 \quad \text{density of the steel}$$

$$2240/160 = 14 \text{ lb per ft}^3 \quad \text{density of the general cargo}$$

Let x = cubic feet of general cargo and y = cubic feet of steel. Then:

$$x + y = 12$$

$$\begin{aligned} 14x + 186y &= 400 \\ (-) \ 14x + \ 14y &= 168 \end{aligned}$$

$$172y = 232$$

$$y = 1.35 \text{ cu ft steel}$$

$$x = 10.65 \text{ cu ft general cargo}$$

Therefore, the steel should be tiered 1.35 ft high; thus, the general cargo would be 10.65 ft high.

PROTECTING THE CARGO

The first objective of good stowage has been thoroughly discussed and it should be apparent that to meet the objective a ship's officer must **know his ship.** The second objective of good stowage can only be met fully by officers who **know their cargo.** Knowing your ship is an easier task than knowing your cargo. In the first body of knowledge there are certain fundamental, unchanging, and consistent principles of mathematics and physics to be mastered. This takes a little time and effort, but once understood there is an end to the required effort for practical operating purposes. In the second body of knowledge, many of the factors involved change from shipping route to shipping route and even from ship to ship. The problems may vary from time to time on the same ship. The ship's officer, in order to know his cargo, must always be alert to the changing commodities received on board. The changing commodities bring new problems, and it is an absolute necessity continually to seek information of an empirical nature in order to know what is permissible.

To know what is the *best* thing to do under a given set of conditions is not always possible; in some cases the true answer to a question may not be known by anyone.   There is no organized program of research to determine the exact answers to many of the problems met with in practical cargo operations.   Each ship is a laboratory of a sorts, but the facts that emerge from company investigations of poor out-turns of cargoes are not publicized through any medium; indeed, in some cases the facts are guarded with great care.   The most skillful cargo officers are those with years of worthy experience and gifted with good judgment.   But, the best experience and the best judgment will pay higher dividends if backed with a good foundation of facts gained from the experience and the judgment of those who have passed the same way before.

SEGREGATION OF CARGO

One of the fundamental requirements in the protection of the cargo is the proper segregation of the various types.   This also is one of the most difficult requisites to meet when carrying full loads of general cargoes. It offers almost no problems on ships carrying only one or two items.

Segregation refers to the stowage of cargoes in separate parts of the ship so that one cannot damage the other by its inherent characteristics. Wet cargoes must be kept away from dry cargoes.   Generally certain areas of the ship will be specified for the stowage of wet items when the ship is laid out during the planning stage of the cargo operation.   In the same way, other areas will be specified for dry cargoes, dirty, or clean.

Although segregation is called for in the case of odorous and delicate cargoes, special sections are not specified for their stowage.   Each time the ship is laid out, care must be taken not to make a gross error in this respect.   Segregation of light and heavy cargoes is necessary with respect to their vertical position.   Heavy items must always be given bottom stowage in any compartment.   Refrigerated cargoes must be given stowage in spaces especially equipped to handle them, and segregation among items under this single category must also be given attention.   Finally, the stowage of any of the classified items covered by the publication CG-187, Explosives and Other Dangerous Articles, must be in strict accordance with the segregation required by the provisions of the regulations contained in this book.

Wet cargo, as used in this discussion, refers to items that are liquid but in containers.   The implication is that with such cargo comes the possibility of leakage, and the stowage should be such that in case of any leakage the liquid will find its way to the drainage system without damaging any other cargo.   Wet cargo does not refer to bulk liquid commodities; the latter require obvious special stowage in deep or peak tanks.

Examples of wet cargoes are canned milk, beer, fruit juices, paints, lubricating oil, and so on.

Dry cargo refers to the general class of items that cannot possibly leak and furthermore can be damaged by leakage from the wet cargo. This category includes flour, feed, rice, paper products, and many more items.

Dirty cargoes are those commodities that are exceptionally dusty and always tend to leave a residue behind them. The residue, of course, will *contaminate* other cargoes. Examples are cement, antimony ore, charcoal, lamp black, and many similar items.

Clean cargoes are those that leave no residue, are not likely to leak, and generally will not cause any damage to any other cargo, but are themselves highly vulnerable to contamination.

Odorous cargoes are those commodities that give off fumes that are likely to *taint* certain susceptible cargoes if they are stowed in the same or even in adjacent compartments. Examples are kerosene, turpentine, ammonia, greasy wool, crude rubber, lumber, casein, and many others. Some odorous cargoes may taint more delicate cargoes and yet are susceptible to tainting themselves.

Delicate cargoes are those that are highly susceptible to damage by tainting from the odorous types. Examples are rice, flour, tea, cereals, and many others.

To thoroughly discuss segregation, a discussion of commodities is necessary. A worthwhile coverage of commodities cannot be undertaken in this book. The intention here has been to point out the necessity of giving segregation the serious consideration it warrants when planning the stowage. The ability to adjudge correctly whether cargoes need segregation comes only with experience.

DUNNAGING

A second requirement in the stowage of cargo so as to protect it is the correct use of dunnage. The word dunnage as it is used in relation to modern cargo stowage refers to the wood that is used to protect the cargo. The common dunnage board is a 1 by 6 in. piece with a length of 10 to 12 ft. The lumber used for dunnage is classed technically as number 4 or 5 stock in the board or rough merchandise grades. For special uses when stowing heavy lifts or steel products, heavier lumber will be used, such as 2 by 10 in. deals, 6 by 8 in. timbers, or split pieces of cord wood. Refrigerated cargoes require strips of the common building lath as dunnage, which measure $\frac{3}{8}$ by $1\frac{1}{2}$ by 48 in. In all cases, the dunnage should be dry and clean. Dunnage that has been contaminated by previous cargo or is wet from any cause should not be used. If it is badly contaminated, it should be discarded. If once wet by salt water, its use may cause more damage than any savings made by attempting to salvage it.   Green wood is a very poor risk for use as dunnage.

Type of wood. For some uses, it makes little difference what type of wood is used.   For example, any wood can be used if the dunnage is to be used in stowing steel rails or providing drainage under bags of antimony ore.   However, for dunnaging sugar, hides, marble, and certain other commodities, only well-seasoned dry clean pine, spruce, or fir should be used.   If oak, redwood, or mahogany is used with the latter group of commodities, staining will result.   Generally it is poor practice to accept anything but dry clean pine, spruce, or fir, because the dunnage is used for various cargoes and the operation cannot depend upon what type of dunnage is in the hold.

Amount of dunnage on the ship. The average general cargo carrier requires approximately 100,000 board-ft of dunnage which will weigh about 150 tons.   Depending entirely on the type of cargo being stowed, the amount specified above may be increased or decreased by 25%.   In some cases, the amount of dunnage may be much less than 75,000 board-ft, but it will rarely be over 125,000.   The average general carrier will require replenishment of her dunnage to the amount of about 25,000 board-ft after each voyage because of the need for condemnation of part of the supply during the voyage.   Dunnage control should be regulated by the operations department and not left up to each ship entirely. Ship's officers should give dunnage the same care as the cargo for two reasons: first, the dunnage is stowed with the cargo so that unless the dunnage is clean and dry the cargo will be damaged by it; second, the cost of dunnage wood has increased to the extent that the average supply mentioned above is worth from $4000 to $5000.   It sells currently for approximately $42.50 per 1000 board-ft on the Eastern seaboard (see .Fig. 3-20).

The use of dunnage. Dunnage is used to protect cargo by preventing:

1. Contact by free moisture.
2. Condensation.
3. Crushing.
4. Chafage.
5. Spontaneous heating.
6. Pilferage.

Dunnage is also used to facilitate rapid and systematic discharge.   The discussion will include an explanation of how each of the above six results are obtained through the use of dunnage.

(a)

(b)

Fig. 3-20. (a) Shows bag stowage on a floor of dunnage three tiers high. One dunnage board has broken at a knot, seen in the lower right hand corner. Before bags are stowed over this floor, this break in the floor should be made solid. Another interesting point in this view is the bag on bag stowage which clearly shows the spaces left between the bags for ventilation purposes. Finally, the bags have "dog ears" which enable easy handling without the necessity of hooks. (b) Shows a floor of dunnage over two different levels of cargo making a level platform on which to start the stowage of a different type of cargo. This dunnage is being used to strike a level which will reduce crushing from uneven pressures both on the cargo being stowed and the cargo below. Courtesy Cadet-Midshipman T. M. Ward, U.S. Merchant Marine Academy, class of 1955.

PREVENTING CONTACT BY FREE MOISTURE. The term *free moisture* has been used in this category to eliminate confusion with damage caused in some instances by the transfer of hygroscopic moisture (see p. 438). No amount of dunnaging will prevent the latter type of trouble; the only effective means of preventing such damage in general cargo is by proper segregation. Free moisture refers to water in the liquid form that might be present in a cargo hold as a result of a leak in the hull plating, an adjacent tank, deck, or openings into the hold, or heavy condensation. Also included in this category, insofar as dunnaging is concerned, is liquid from any wet cargo.

The first dunnage used in the stowing of most cargoes is in this category. This is the dunnage laid on the deck upon which the first tier of cargo is stowed. To provide for drainage under the cargo, the first dunnage should be laid with the length toward the drainage system and spaced about 6 in. There should be at least two tiers of dunnage, the bottom tier laid to provide the drainage and the top tier to support the cargo. Thus, on the modern ship with drain wells aft and running transversely, the first tier of dunnage would be laid fore and aft. The second tier should always be perpendicular to the first and may be spaced 2 or 3 in. On ships with side bilge systems, the first dunnage laid in the lower holds should run diagonally, slanting aft from the centerline.

If bags are being stowed on top of such a floor, the dunnage should be spaced not more than 1 in. Wide spacing of dunnage floors upon which bags are to be stowed results in the bottom bags being split and heavy loss of contents through leakage. If the commodity in the bag requires ventilation, spacing the dunnage a little is advantageous. If the commodity does not require ventilation, the floor will be better if made solid.

Necessity for multiple layers of dunnage. When laying the bottom tier of dunnage under circumstances that include the high probability of drainage from some source, the tiers of dunnage running toward the drainage system should be increased. Five tiers may be laid with a sixth tier on top as a floor with some cargoes that need maximum circulation of air as well as drainage. The ship's officer should not be timid about requiring dunnage to be laid correctly. *It is a basic requisite of proper care and custody,* and it can prevent costly damage in many instances. Longshoremen the world over are very apt to lay dunnage floors in a slipshod and highly inadequate manner. Common deficiencies are laying it so that the best drainage is not provided, laying insufficient tiers, and improper spacing. The ship's officer must be in the hold of the ship to prevent gross negligence in this initial step in stowing cargo.

Vertical dunnage. To prevent contact with steel members of the ship and thereby preclude the possibility of wetting with condensation, vertical dunnage is installed between the cargo and all steel members. The members referred to are the stanchions, frames, ladders, transverse bulkheads, partial longitudinal bulkheads, and ventilator shafts running through the space. This dunnage may be put into position by standing it up against the vertical member and temporarily held in place by one container of cargo being stowed against the bottom. Another way is to stand the dunnage up in place and tie with rope yarn, then wrap heavy paper around the dunnage and member together and tie with more rope yarn. The rope yarn serves the purpose of holding the dunnage in place until the cargo is safely stowed.

The dunnage drainage floor and the vertical dunnage to separate the cargo and the steel members complete the dunnage used to prevent contact with free moisture.

DUNNAGE TO PREVENT CONDENSATION. The dunnage that prevents condensation is the dunnage that is placed in the cargo to facilitate the circulation of air currents. It is by thorough ventilation that high dew point air is removed from hold interiors, and this is necessary to prevent condensation. When laying the floor upon which to stow certain cargoes, such as fish meal in bags, deep tiering is utilized to help circulation under the cargo and thus remove moisture laden air. Such floors may be five tiers deep with a sixth layer on top upon which to stow the cargo. Blocks of cargo may be separated vertically by laying crisscross dunnage separation at convenient intervals, normally about 5 ft. Venetian ventilators, which are made from dunnage wood, may be worked into some cargoes for ventilation purposes. The venetian vent is made with two pieces of dunnage measuring 1 by 6 in. and about 10 ft. long. These two boards are separated by slanting pieces of lumber measuring about 1 by 2 in. and nailed to the side to form a support and separation for the two solid pieces and openings along the vent's entire length. Figure 3-21 is an illustration of a venetian ventilator. This type of fitting is used so frequently with rice cargoes that occasionally they are referred to as *rice ventilators*.

Use of the venetian vent or rice ventilator. The venetian vent is inserted within bagged cargoes. At 5-ft intervals, the vents are laid longitudinally and transversely to form continuous air channels in both directions. Generally two longitudinal lines are laid running in the same vertical plane as the hatch carlings (fore and aft hatch coamings), and two transverse lines are laid in the same vertical plane as the hatch end beams. These four lines intersect at the four corners of the hatch, and at these points a vertical vent is fitted. This arrangement continues for the full depth of the cargo. When the cargo is stowed, such a system provides for continuous internal movement of air and is an effective aid in the prevention of heavy condensation. If the ship is operating on a route where the outside temperatures may fluctuate between two extremes or if the hatch is extremely long, the vents may be inserted at more frequent longitudinal and transverse intervals.

Sweat battens. The permanent dunnage attached to the frames of the ship is also an aid in ventilation. This dunnage is known as cargo battens or sweat battens. It is generally made of 2 by 6 in. lumber held in place

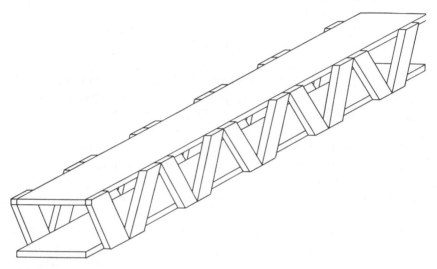

Fig. 3-21. A venetian vent or rice ventilator made out of dunnage.

by clips that are bolted to the inboard flange of the frame. The sweat battens prevent the cargo from filling up the frame spaces and hence these spaces are reserved to act as vertical air ducts.

Deep dunnage floors, crisscross dunnage floors, venetian ventilators, and the sweat battens complete the dunnage used to prevent condensation.

DUNNAGE TO PREVENT CRUSHING. Dunnage that is used to prevent crushing of cargo is that which is placed in the hold to prevent the cargo from shifting, to spread weights evenly so that pressure is equalized on lower tiers in deep holds, and to maintain levels.

Eliminating voids. Cargo seldom fits exactly into a hold. When stowing athwartships, there is nearly always a void that will appear at either side or along the centerline of the ship into which no container will fit. It is a standard rule never to leave a void in a stowed cargo block. Such voids must be filled with something. The best thing to place in such voids is cargo that is small and durable, known as *filler cargo*. However, if filler cargo is not available, dunnage must be used. The dunnage may be used to build up bracing between the two sides to pre- vent movement of the cargo or dunnage may be piled directly into the void. The need for dunnage to fill in such voids often occurs in the wings of compartments where there is much curvature, such as the end

FIG. 3-22. Dunnage to fill wing voids. This view shows dunnage being used to fill up a triangular void in the wings to form a level surface upon which the next tier of drums will be stowed. Also shown here is a really well laid dunnage floor. Athwartship stripping has been laid down first, and then longitudinal pieces over the first layer form a solid bed. These longitudinal pieces tie the stowed block together and reduce the probability of the bulkhead being constructed falling over. This is well-stowed cargo.

lower holds. This dunnage is used for two reasons: first, for filling in the void; and second, for maintaining a level tier. Figure 3-22 illustrates such use of dunnage. Filling voids is a precaution against shifting which results in crushed cargo.

Toms, shores, and braces. Large pieces of cargo that stand alone or blocks of cargo that are not supported on one of their sides require shor- ing or bracing in order to prevent shifting and possible crushing.

Shoring is the process of using 6 by 8 in. timbers or similar pieces known as shores to secure cargo. The shore runs from a low supporting level *up* to the cargo at an angle.

Bracing is the process of using timbers to secure cargo by running the brace horizontally from a support to the cargo. The timbers used for this purpose are known as braces or more correctly as *distance pieces*.

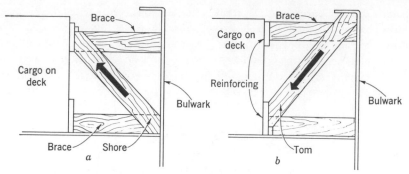

FIG. 3-23. This is a sketch of deck cargo being secured with shores (*a*) and toms (*b*). Bracing (or distance pieces) are used in both cases. Note that when a force, as from a sea striking the opposite side, pushes the cargo against the shore, the shore tends to lift the cargo up. If the cargo is lifted upwards, the shoring itself, braces, and lashings may be loosened and eventually cause the cargo to shift. The tom, on the other hand, forces the cargo downward toward the deck. The tomming is better than the shoring, but a combination of both should be used. Lashings should always be used also. Wherever a brace, shore, or tom exerts pressure against the cargo, reinforcing should always be used.

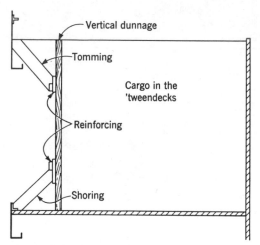

FIG. 3-24. Tomming and shoring of cargo stowed in the wings of the 'tweendeck space. It is important to reinforce wherever pressure will be exerted by the toms or shores, and it is also important to cut the vertical dunnage so that it fits snugly between the deck and overhead in the space or to use wedges to take up any slack. If the cargo being shored up is not in lengths, such as cartons or cases, the reinforcing shown here should run longitudinally to exert pressure all along the face of the cargo block; also, the vertical dunnage pieces should be more frequent although each vertical piece may not need to be secured with a shore and tom. Initiative and resourcefulness must be displayed by the carpenters and the officers to erect good shoring with a minimum of time and materials.

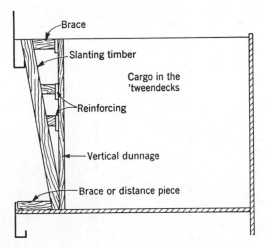

Fig. 3-25. This is an easy way of shoring a bulkhead of cargo in the 'tweendecks, providing timbers of about 4 by 6 in. are available. The slanting timber should be put in place, being cut to just fit with the greatest dimension running athwartships. The braces are not likely to be displaced because they will work downward with the working of the cargo and tend to tighten themselves.

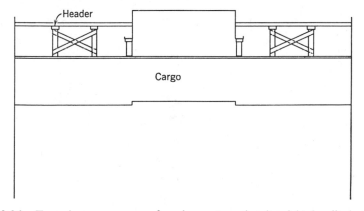

Fig. 3-26. Tomming over cargo of such a nature that it might be displaced by heavy working of the ship in a seaway, such as cylinders, bombs, pipe, steel billets. It is important to tie the toms together with dunnage wood as shown and to use cleats on either side of the upper end of the tom nailed to the header. Wedges should be driven under the lower ends of the toms to make them fit tightly. This view is looking forward or aft. The headers run longitudinally with the toms spaced on approximately 6-ft centers.

Tomming is the process of using timbers to secure cargo by running the timber from an upper support *down* to the cargo either vertically or at an angle. The timbers used for this purpose are known as toms.

FIG. 3-27. The Peck and Hale shoring net. This is a view of the Peck and Hale shoring net in place. The cables are adjustable and apply tension to the net at any position safely and securely (see Fig. 3-40). Courtesy Peck and Hale, Inc.

Tomming is used to secure top tiers of cargo that are not secured by other cargo being stowed over them. Cargoes that need tomming, especially in the 'tweendeck areas, are steel products, such as rails or billets, pipe, bombs, and similar items. In the lower holds, tomming may be employed but the overhead clearance may be so great that it is better to use lashings.

Shoring and bracing are usually all that can be done when securing deck cargo. Tomming can be used on deck only when the cargo is below the level of a mast house or other deck structure and a tom can be fitted into position. Whenever possible tomming should be used even if shoring is also used.

FIG. 3-28. This is a view of the Peck and Hale shoring net in place showing the method of stowing the net when not in use. Note the vertical corner protecting piece. The net has provided a wall that will support the stowed cartons without the use of lumber, hammer, nails, or carpenters. Courtesy Peck and Hale, Inc.

Below decks, bracing or tomming is preferable to shoring. Shoring transmits a lifting effect to the cargo that is undesirable. Shoring may loosen in heavy weather unless carefully wedged and supported. Tomming presses downward against the cargo and when the ship is heaving in a heavy seaway the rise of the cargo only presses the tom more tightly against the overhead support. The shore, however, works with the sea and the cargo may be lifted upward. When it settles, the shore may fit loosely and eventually its supporting effect may be completely lost.

Examples of shoring, tomming, and bracing are illustrated in Figs. 3-23 to 3-26.

Peck and Hale shoring net. The shoring or tomming of cargo shown in Figs. 3-23 to 3-26 clearly shows interference with the free space which might be more convenient if left clear. It is also quite obvious that a good deal of lumber is consumed along with the labor of constructing the shoring. It may also happen that cargo may be stowed next to a block of cargo in the wings for part of a voyage but during another part the adjacent cargo will be removed. In such a case, shoring must be erected at an intermediate port or the cargo broken down by shifting some of it into the hatch square. This requires labor and materials, and in some parts of the world the materials for erecting the shoring may not be available.

The Peck and Hale shoring net, as illustrated in Figs. 3-27 and 3-28, is an answer to these problems. It provides a means of support for the cargo bulkheads without the use of shoring or tomming.

Determining the length and cutting a shore properly. The length along the center of the stock can be calculated by trigonometry, of course, if measurements *A* and *B* are known. A more rapid and very practical method using a carpenter's square is as follows:

1. Measure distance *A* from the center of the reinforcing to the deck, or to whatever height the lower end of the shore may extend. In this example we are assuming that the lower end is supported on the brace or

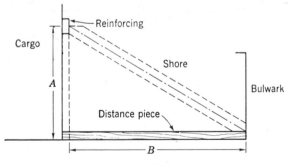

Fig. 3-29.

distance piece. Measure distance *B* from the edge of the anchorage to the face of the reinforcing. In this example we will assume *A* = 4 ft and *B* = 6 ft 09 in. (see Fig. 3-29).

2. Lay off on a carpenter's square, using the ratio of 1 in. to 1 ft, measurements A and B as shown in Fig. 3-30.

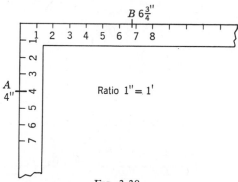

FIG. 3-30.

3. Measure the distance between points A and B in inches and convert to feet. This is the length of the shore along the center of the stock. In this case $7\frac{7}{8}$ ft (see Fig. 3-31).

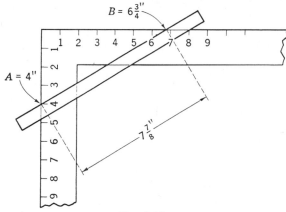

FIG. 3-31.

Cutting the shore. The shore should be cut so that flat bearing surfaces are provided and so that sharp points are avoided. The shore should not be cut to the desired length until after one end has been cut to the proper angle as described below.

1. Lay the square along the shore as indicated in Fig. 3-32, making sure that the measurements 4 in. and $6\frac{3}{4}$ in. lie along the same line. Mark and cut the shore as shown in the figure.

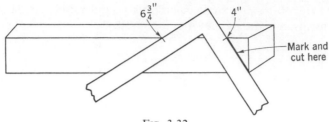

FIG. 3-32.

2. Measure the center of the stock and mark a line at right angles to the cut just made, starting at the center of the stock (Fig. 3-33). When

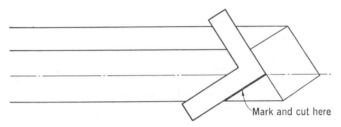

FIG. 3-33.

this last cut has been made, one end of the shore has been cut. The length of the shore is now reckoned from the point at this end and along the center of the stock (see Fig. 3-34).

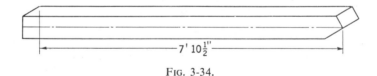

FIG. 3-34.

3. Along the center of the stock measure the length of the shore, $7\frac{7}{8}$ ft or 7 ft $10\frac{1}{2}$ in., and mark off a perpendicular at the other end of the stock.

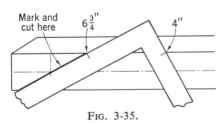

FIG. 3-35.

4. Place a carpenter's square at the center point with the same measurements on the same line as before. This time make the cutting line on the *other side of the square* (see Fig. 3-35).

5. Mark a right angle from the center point of the last cut (Fig.

3-36) and cut along the line indicated in the figure. This is the last cut. The shore is now properly cut to a length of 7 ft 10½ in. to fit the measurements shown on Fig. 3-29.

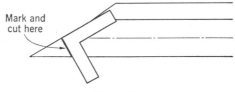

FIG. 3-36.

Steel strapping as shoring. Blocks of cargo may be secured in any desired position without the use of shores or toms by using steel strapping that virtually lashes the block to the ship's side or to a bulkhead, as shown in Fig. 3-37a and b.

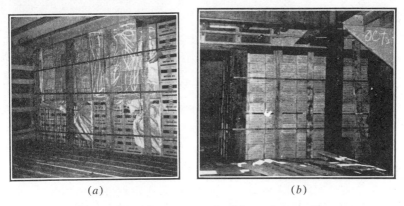

(a) (b)

FIG. 3-37. Cargo secured with steel strapping.

Figure 3-38a shows three steel straps secured behind dunnage to three separate portable beam clamps. These clamps can be set into position on frames, beams, or stiffeners within a few minutes and removed easily. This is the preparation necessary prior to loading cargo that will be secured with the steel strapping. Another preparatory step would be to do the same thing at another and opposite bulkhead, as shown in Fig. 3-38b.

With the preliminary steps completed, the cargo is stowed. Vertical dunnage strips are placed along the face of the stowed cargo block at 3- or 4-ft centers. Other lengths of steel strapping are spliced to the ends previously prepared. Finally, the ends are brought together and set tightly against the block by using the stretcher and secured by use of the crimper (see Fig. 3-43).

This procedure will secure a block of cargo of any size or shape in any position so long as a bearing surface is available and the preliminary steps are taken. No shores, toms, or braces are needed.

Dunnage floors. Dunnage floors, solid or spaced, are laid between tiers of cargo in cardboard containers in deep lower holds. This is very important if the inside containers are known to be fragile or liable to leakage. A floor is not needed between every tier. It is recommended that the first floor be laid after three tiers, the second floor after another

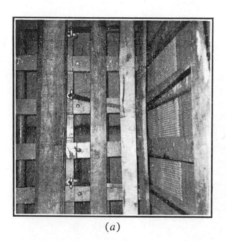

(a)   (b)

Fig. 3-38. Steel straps secured to frames with the opposite ends left slack until after the cargo has been stowed.

three tiers, the third floor after six additional tiers, then a fourth floor after still another six tiers. No more than four floors will be needed. The first two floors are the most necessary. The purpose of all these floors is to prevent the spread of damage in case one of the inside containers fails. For example, if a bottle or can of beer begins to leak in a carton stowed in the third tier up from the bottom of a hold in which cartons were stowed from the deck all the way up, what would happen if no dunnage floor were used? The beer would wet the carton and reduce its strength, and in all probability the adjacent inside containers would be called upon to support the entire weight of all the cases between them and the surface of the stow. Without the support of the outside container and with one inside container gone, the adjacent bottle would break and the one adjacent to that would break in turn. This procedure would be accelerated in heavy weather. Eventually, a large amount of damage would be caused in the area of the first broken bottle or collapsed can. The stowed block would sag in toward the damaged area, and damaged cargo would be found throughout the bottom layers. The inside containers would not stop failing until the upper layers were reached where the superimposed weight would be lessened.

Now, if dunnage had been laid between the third and fourth tiers, the weight on the bottles adjacent to the broken bottle would have been partially taken up by the bridge of dunnage over the third tier. In fact, an entire carton can be left out of the third tier without causing any damage. The floor of dunnage over the third tier would simply bridge the gap, and there would be a negligible increase in pressure on other containers in the tier. Thus, it is seen that floors of this type prevent crushing.

As the stowage progresses vertically when stowing odd sized and shaped cases and crates, steps will be formed in the cargo block. If dunnage is not placed in the stow so as to spread the pressure of the upper tiers equally on the lower tiers, there is danger of some containers being crushed. What this amounts to is the use of dunnage to maintain a level surface upon which to stow the next crate or case. When stowing small crates on top of a larger crate, dunnage is needed to transmit the weight to the edges of the large crate instead of to the area inside the perimeter of the crate. This is of importance in lower holds that are deep more than in 'tweendeck spaces (see Fig. 3-20b).

The dunnage used to fill voids, maintain levels, floor off, shore, brace, and tom the cargo completes the dunnage used to prevent crushing.

PREVENTING CHAFAGE. Chafage of cargo is a source of damage when containers rest against the edges of structural members or other dunnage. Vertical dunnage placed against the permanent sweat battens is used to prevent small containers from hanging up on the upper edges of the battens. If this should happen as the ship works in a seaway, the sides of the cardboard containers may be sheared off or bagged cargo may be torn. In general, the dunnage placed in the cargo to prevent chafage is not extensive. The use of dunnage for the other purposes set forth herein precludes chafage. There are exceptions, however, as mentioned above, and the ship's officer should be on the alert for situations that call for additional dunnage to prevent chafage.

PREVENTING SPONTANEOUS HEATING. Some cargoes require dunnage to provide air channels through the stowed cargo block in order to carry away heat generated by the cargo. If such heat is not carried away, the temperature will gradually rise and serious damage may result. Refrigerated cargoes of fruit that is ripening are the best example. Ripening fruit creates a large amount of heat, and cool air currents must pass through such cargoes or areas will become comparatively warm and the ripening process will be accelerated with resulting damage in the form of overripe product at the discharge port. Dunnage placed between every tier of the cargo in the form of strips of building lath provide the necessary air channels. It is important that the length of the strips lie in the direction of the air currents.

Other examples of cargoes requiring such dunnaging are onions, fish meal, and charcoal. These latter cargoes do not use the building lath for stripping. They may use stripping of 1 by 6 in. dunnage, crisscross floors, or even the venetian ventilator. As can be seen, the dunnaging used to prevent spontaneous heating is the same as that used for the prevention of condensation. In most cases, the dunnage used to aid circulation of air fulfills both objectives.

ADDITIONAL DUNNAGE USES. Dunnage for the protection of cargo from pilferage is mentioned for the sake of completeness. The use is in the form of a rough fence or barrier around cargo that is subject to pilferage but cannot be stowed in a special locker for some reason.

Dunnage is also used to separate cargoes. In this form it is aiding the discharge process rather than protecting the cargo as in all of the above examples. When used as separation, strips of dunnage or solid floors are laid between layers of the cargo. Separation is necessary when the same type of cargo is destined for separate ports or for different consignees at the same port. Being clearly and definitely separated makes the cargo easier to discharge in consignee blocks. In the same way the separation lessens the probability of overcarrying the cargo.

LASHINGS

Cargo becomes damaged when it is not secured in its stowed position. Dunnage may be used for this purpose as outlined in the preceding section. Another means of securing cargo, and one that is especially useful when securing on deck cargo, is by the use of lashings.

Lashing should be of steel chain, wire rope, or steel strapping. Lashings of fiber rope should never be used when attempting to secure cargo on the deck of a ship for a long voyage. Fiber rope stretches when under stress and chafes easily. In emergencies or under some circumstances it may have to be used. If used, it should be checked often, and when slackness appears additional line should be used to frap the original lashings tighter. Never remove the original lashings with the idea of replacing them.

Regardless of the material used, the first requisite is the installation of pad eyes at points along the deck which will afford the best leads for securing cargo. This is a requirement that the ship's officer should take care of as soon as he knows where the cargo is to be stowed. This ap-

plies whether the cargo is being stowed below deck or on deck, so long
as it is going to be necessary to lash it down.

Chain lashing is secured by using a shackle at the lower or deck end
of the chain, passing the chain over or around the cargo in whatever
manner seems to be most appropriate for the job on hand, and securing
the other end by the use of a pear link, pelican hook, and turnbuckle.
The pear link provides a movable link to which the turnbuckle can be

FIG. 3-39. The turnbuckle in this photo has a pelican hook on one end and a
pear link directly attached to the other end. The pear link is at the upper end
with the chain set in the narrow end. To eliminate the possibility of the chain
links pulling past the pear link, the slack should be led back and tied with rope
yarn. After the lashing has been set up by twisting the barrel, the wood should
be left in the barrel. Courtesy Cadet-Midshipman R. Butler, U.S. Merchant
Marine Academy, class of 1955.

attached without having to use the opposite end of the chain. The chain
will not always be the exact length and it is too expensive to cut it to
fit each time it is used; hence, it is necessary to have this adjustable
method of securing one end. The use of a pear link is illustrated in
Fig. 3-39. After securing the pelican hook and the pear link, the turnbuckle is set up by inserting a piece of wood in the barrel and twisting.
Once the lashing is tight, the wood should be left in the barrel and lashed
to something to prevent the turnbuckle from backing off and becoming
slack. For the same purpose, a short stick should be inserted through
the pear link on one side of the turnbuckle.

Chain is used when securing extremely heavy objects on deck and for
lumber deck loads. The most common size is ¾ in. in diameter, with
a 36-in. turnbuckle, and shackles of 1 or 1½ in.

Wire rope is secured by using clips to form eyes where needed, and the eyes are secured to the pad eyes with shackles. The wire rope is passed between the deck and the cargo or over the cargo and finally to a turnbuckle with a pelican hook. Wire rope is more workable than the chain and can be pulled hand tight very easily after which the clips can

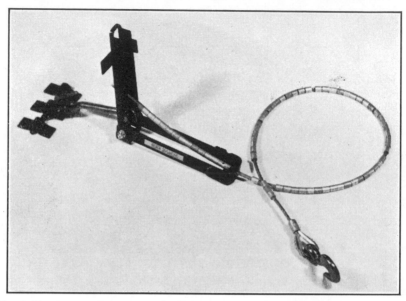

Fig. 3-40. Peck and Hale adjustable cable. The adjustable cable consists of only two parts, a toggle and a beaded wire rope. The toggle has a jaw for receiving the beads. When the handle is closed, tension is applied and the beads are locked in position. The beaded assembly with movable ½-in. beads provides a means for immediate adjustment to any length desired. Any number of beads may be furnished, depending upon the amount of adjustability needed. Courtesy Peck and Hale, Inc.

be applied. When the clips are on, the rope is seized then cut. The turnbuckle is set up to tighten the lashing and the same precaution against backing off that was mentioned in the case of chain lashings must be taken.

The most common type of wire rope used for this purpose is 6 by 19, ⅝-in., plow steel wire. Old cargo falls should be saved for use as lashings of this type. Three-quarter inch wire rope will be used whenever the object being secured is heavy enough to warrant it.

Peck and Hale device. A patented device for lashing automobiles or trucks in position is manufactured by Peck and Hale, Inc. (Fig. 3-40). This device is an adjustable cable secured to the bumper Y brackets at the front and to spring shackles or Y brackets at the rear of the car. A deck ring is required to which the lower hook of the cable is secured. All attachments are made from underneath to the car and no tools are required. Four cables are used to secure each car, as shown in Fig. 3-41. The cable is ¼-in. diameter. Cars secured with this device require no 4 by 4 lumber for chocking. This is a very important fact, not only because of the expense of the lumber but because of the labor re-

Fig. 3-41. Automobiles secured with the Peck and Hale adjustable lashing. Note the absence of all lumber cribbing. Courtesy Peck and Hale, Inc.

quired to set the chocking in place during the stowing process and the additional labor of breaking up the chocking when discharging. Also eliminated is the confusion and congestion caused by the workmen during the installation or removal process. There is also the danger of damage to the automobiles as the carpenters work in the closely stowed areas. Figure 3-42 shows a method of providing anchorage for deck end of lashing when stowing automobiles over bulk cargoes.

Steel strapping. Steel strapping during the past ten years has become a widely used type of lashing on ships. Such strapping was used by railroads for many years prior to its use on board ships. The Signode Company manufactures a number of special fittings that enable quick, safe, and easy application of steel straps as lashings on ships. The straps for use below decks are 1¼ in. wide and 0.05 in. thick with a breaking strength of 7500 lb. A heavy duty strap for use on deck is 2 in. wide and 0.05 in. thick with a breaking strength of 11,000 lb. This compares with a breaking strength for ¾-in. carbon steel chain of 28,000 lb, ⅝-in. wire of 13,000 lb, and of ¾-in. wire of 47,000 lb on the average for improved plow steel.

The strapping comes in rolls that are kept in specially built frames which make it easy to transport the strap supply about the ship and easy

Fɪɢ. 3-42. Peck and Hale adjustable cable. Here we see an automobile that has been stowed on a dunnage floor over cargo stowed in a deep lower hold. Because of the lack of pad eyes or ring bolts in the deck, a ¾-in. chain has been stretched from one frame across the ship to its opposite number. With the chain stretched tight by the use of a turnbuckle, connecting links have been used to provide a place for securing the lashing cable. Courtesy Peck and Hale, Inc.

to remove the required amount during installation. The strapping may be rove through a *triangular link,* an *offset hook,* or a portable *beam* or *frame clamp.* All of these fittings present a flat bearing surface to the strap. The strap is rove through the eye of whatever fitting is being used, then over the cargo to another fitting and back up to the middle of the cargo block where the ends are secured. Or, two ends may be secured to fittings and then brought together over the cargo. It depends entirely on the judgment of the officer in charge of the operation.

Before securing the ends, tension is applied with a hand tool known as a *bulkhead stretcher* or with socket wrenches (see Fig. 3-43*b*). With suitable tension on the strapping, *seals* are placed over the joint and then crimped together with the *sealer*.   A tool known as the *cutter* is used to cut the strapping at convenient lengths.   A fitting known as a *winch tightener* or *anchor spindle* used in conjunction with a removable socket wrench is used to set up the tension in case of slack during the voyage. To prevent the winch from backing off when under stress, the socket

(*a*)   (*b*)

Fig. 3-43. (*a*) Coil box and cutter. (*b*) Tension is being applied to strapping with rachet socket wrenches on the spindle of the winch tightener. When these wrenches are removed, the socket wrenches seen in Fig. 3-46 will be put on.
Courtesy Signode Co.

Fig. 3-44. Two wire clips and a piece of ⅝-in. wire form a short strap which is used to anchor the offset hook. Two-inch steel strapping is passed around the hook.

wrench is placed on the rotating spindle so that the handle bears against the strap. Figure 3-44 shows the use of an offset hook as an anchoring device. Figure 3-45 shows the application of the seals with the crimper, the type of turnbuckle used, and the winch tightener with socket wrench can be seen by the tin can. Figure 3-46 shows steel strap lashings applied to secure a deck load of a diesel locomotive, note also the distance pieces and cribbing used to assist in securing the carriage.

Fig. 3-45. Securing steel strapping. The man who is standing is using the crimper to secure seals that have been placed over the two parts of the lashing. The cutter is seen in the lower left hand corner. The man kneeling has his right hand on the stretcher. The winch tightener and socket wrenches are near the tin can, the lashing in the background has a spindle in place. The lashing being worked on has a turnbuckle in place. Both serve the same purpose. Courtesy Signode Co.

The use of the winch tightener is not necessary if the turnbuckle is inserted in the lashing.

MAXIMUM USE OF AVAILABLE CUBIC

Controlling broken stowage. The stowage of cargo so that the greatest possible amount of the cubic capacity of the ship contains cargo is primarily a matter of controlling the *broken stowage*. Broken stowage has been defined as that space within a loaded ship that is not occupied by cargo. Therefore, the space that contributes to the broken stowage is space between containers of irregular shape, containers with curvature, space filled with dunnage, and the space over the last tier into which no cargo can be fitted for one reason or another. Broken stowage is expressed as a percentage of the total available cubic. Broken stowage on uniform packaged commodities will average about 10%, that on general cargo will average about 25%. Both of these values may be affected by a number of variables. Some of these variables, as shall be seen, are

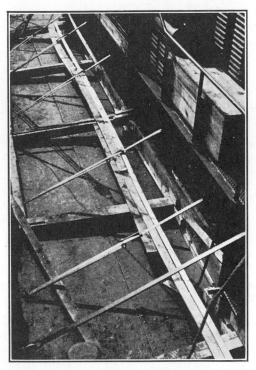

FIG. 3-46. Locomotive carriage lashed with 2-in. steel strapping. The winch tightener with socket wrench has been used instead of turnbuckles. Courtesy Signode Co.

within the control of the shipowner's organization, some are not. The control of broken stowage starts with the laying out of the ship and continues throughout the actual stowage process. A formula for the calculation of broken stowage was given on p. 4.

Use of filler cargo. Filler cargo is defined as small durable packages or pieces of cargo that may be stowed in the interstices or voids between larger pieces. As has already been pointed out, it is a violation of basic principles to leave a void anywhere within a stowed cargo block. Hence, if a void occurs, it either must be filled with dunnage, braced or shored with dunnage, or filled with filler cargo. Unless the filler cargo is used, the broken stowage is increased.   The expression *small* pieces of durable cargo is meant to be taken on a comparative basis with the cargo in which the voids appear.   For example, when stowing large frames of structural steel, wooden boxes of foodstuffs may fit in and around the pieces of steel in such a way as to qualify as filler cargo.   On the other hand, when stowing the cases of foodstuffs in the wings of a lower hold and a row has to be shut out because of the curvature, smaller pieces of boxed merchandise or bundles of pipe may be used as filler cargo.   Thus, whatever an officer judges to be suitable for stowage in void spaces becomes filler cargo.

The efficient use of filler cargo is dependent upon the terminal manager's administrative policies with respect to it.   The first step is to have all personnel alerted to the need for spotting shipments that are suitable for such use.   Next a system must be set up whereby such cargo is assembled to be ready for use when needed during the loading process. This must be organized or the use of filler cargo will be haphazard. For example, when a given gang has stowed a tier out to the wings, the gang boss will either have to fill in the triangular wing space with dunnage or call for filler cargo.   This is assuming that the curvature has not yet been stowed under.   If the gang boss contacts the walking boss or dock personnel and they have to make a decision then and there as to what may be suitable or available, time is sure to be lost and in all probability the filler cargo may never be located.   All the gang boss should find it necessary to do is send word via his hatch tender for some filler cargo for the same port as that being stowed.   The filler cargo should be used until the tier has been leveled out and the gang boss calls for the regular commodity.   If the initiative is not taken by the gang boss, then the ship superintendent (walking boss) must see that the correct thing is done.

Choosing cargo to fit the hold.   When laying out the ship, decisions are made relative to what cargoes go where.   During this stage of the cargo operations, a ship may be "blown up" (given an excessively high broken stowage percentage).   This can be caused by the decision to stow large crates and cases in the end lower holds where small curved items should go.   Planning to stow drums for the first port of call in a 'tweendeck where only nine-tenths of a drum can be stowed in the space remaining over the last tier, will result in much broken stowage.   The latter mistake could be rectified during the actual loading process (as many of them are), providing a readjustment is possible, or additional cargo can be obtained for stowage over the drums.   Generally this cause of broken stowage is pretty well controlled in practice, however, the principle of choosing cargo to fit the hold should always be kept in mind.

Skill of the longshoremen. The final factor in the control of broken stowage is probably the most variable. The skill, industry, and interest of the longshoremen are definitely important factors in whether a ship is stowed compactly. The use of excessive amounts of dunnage in lieu of filler cargo and the failure to stow some items in neat and uniform rows and tiers are two ways that longshoremen can do the greatest amount of harm, insofar as the control of broken stowage is concerned.

When stowing drums or crates and cases of odd sizes, the extra effort needed to two-block adjacent containers may prevent many longshoremen from doing the job right. A large number of loosely stowed containers not only will increase the broken stowage but may set the stage for disastrous shifting during heavy weather. When stowing bagged goods that are flowing into the ship through chutes, longshoremen may step aside and allow a large number of the bags to fall at random; after a time, and before the chute becomes jammed, a few of the uppermost bags can be set straight. There may be no indication of the improper stowage except as reflected in the rise in broken stowage percentage for the compartment. The poor stowage will come to light, of course, when the cargo is discharged.

During the actual stowage of the cargo, the walking boss and gang boss can do much to affect the value of the broken stowage. The judicious use of dunnage, filler cargo, and the manner in which individual containers are placed in stowage are all ways that broken stowage is affected. Still another is the measuring of the holds before stowage of bales or any items that may be stowed in such a way that more than one vertical dimension can be obtained from the container. If the hold measurements are taken and compared with the container's measurements, a decision can be made quickly regarding how the containers should be placed in the hold so that the last tier will come as close as possible to the top of the hold. Inasmuch as the space over the last tier contributes to broken stowage, it can be seen that this results in better control of the value.

In summary, the best use of available cubic is obtained by paying attention to three factors: (1) The use of filler cargo. (2) The choice of cargo to fit the hold. (3) The skill of the longshoremen.

RAPID AND SYSTEMATIC LOADING AND DISCHARGING

Prevent the long hatch. The rules for providing for rapid and systematic loading and discharging are few. One of the first rules is to prevent the stowage of a disproportionate amount of cargo in any one hatch for any one port. A hatch that is so stowed is known as a *long hatch*. The ship's time in port is controlled by the maximum number of gang hours in any one hatch, therefore the work should be divided evenly among all hatches. For example, if a five hatch ship has 3000 tons for a given port and hatches 1, 3, 4, and 5 have 400 tons apiece whereas hatch number 2 has 1400 tons, the ship will be in port just as long as if all hatches had 1400 tons. In other words, it would take as long to discharge the 3000 tons as it would 7000 tons, provided the 3000 was stowed as stated above and the 7000 was divided evenly in all five hatches. If a given hatch is double rigged, as most large hatches are, that hatch can handle more than a single rigged hatch.

Prevent overstowage. Another obvious rule is to prevent cargo from being overstowed. *Overstowed* does not mean that the cargo necessarily has cargo stowed directly over it, but simply that cargo is blocking the discharge in one way or another. Overstowage is prevented by thorough preplanning before the loading operation commences. If cargo is over-stowed, it necessitates the shifting of the blocking cargo before any discharge can take place. It may require that some cargo will have to be completely discharged and then reloaded. All of this activity is costly in time and money and should be avoided.

Prevent overcarriage. The third rule for obtaining rapid and systematic discharge encompasses three factors all of which may be described as means of preventing *overcarried* cargo. Overcarried cargo is cargo that is inadvertently left in the ship and taken beyond the port of discharge on the ship's itinerary. Thus, it is obvious that overcarried cargo is a symbol of the antithesis of rapid and systematic discharge operations. It will be seen that the three devices that reduce the possibility of overcarried cargo are also natural aids to rapid discharge.

PORT MARKS. The first device is the use of *port marks*. Port marks are geometrical designs placed on cargo in various colors so that the destination can be noted at a glance without the necessity of reading carefully all the printing upon the case. These port marks are in the form of green circles, blue diamonds, red crosses or other such markings. When blocks of cargo are so marked in the hatch, the ship's officer at the port of discharge can more easily and with more certainty check on the completeness of the discharge. This check is necessary every time a port is discharged. The longshoremen never should be allowed to cover up a hatch until a ship's officer has personally inspected the hold to make certain all cargo for the port is out. This check must be made sometimes under adverse conditions, such as during foul weather in the middle of the night. The ship's officer in charge of the deck should be aware, of course, of the approximate time that the discharging is to be completed. He should be on hand to check the hatch at the time of completion. If the cargo is well marked with port marks, the check will be more definite.

In most cases, the port marks are placed on the cargo by a member of the dock force. During the stowage, these marks may be stowed so that they are not visible in the hold and this makes them useless for the above purpose. The remedy is to place additional marks on the cargo after stowage or to put the marks on the cargo so that they will always be visible.

BLOCK STOWAGE. The second device is to provide for block stowage insofar as possible. This means to eliminate small segments of cargo in several locations in any one hatch and to make some attempt to assemble large blocks at one level in one compartment. This may not be possible because of the need for segregation, but an effort should be made to attain such stowage. Block stowage is accomplished by thorough preplanning.

Related to this problem is the need for keeping consignee marks in blocks within any one port block. This is mainly useful to the dock force in segregating the cargo as it is being discharged. When discharging, the necessity of spotting the cargo on the dock by consignee for organized delivery may prove to be a difficult and time consuming problem, especially if the cargo comes out of the ship with several consignee marks being discharged simultaneously. The segregation is a simple task if one mark comes out at a time until all of that mark is completed. The planning and stowing of the cargo should provide for consignee marks being kept together and marked off in the hatch by some separation system.

PROPER SEPARATION. The last device to be mentioned with regard to the prevention of overcarriage is the proper separation of cargoes. *Separation* refers to the material used to separate blocks of cargoes by port and/or consignee. If blocks are separated, the longshoremen are directed, more or less, through the block of cargo. If the separation is omitted or incomplete, confusion is the result, and some cargo may be inadvertently left in the ship.

Some cargoes need no separation because they are different in nature and mistaking a container is impossible. For example, when discharging bags of rice for one port and the adjacent cargo for the next port is barrels of flour, there is no possibility of mixing the rice and the flour. This may be termed natural separation.

Separation between cargoes of the same type with different consignee marks and in bags is obtained by the use of strips of burlap. Heavy paper may be used. Dunnage boards widely separated are used, but dunnage worked into the stowage of bags may lead to chafage and tearing of the bags with a consequent loss of contents.

When separating general cargoes, heavy paper is used with appropriate marks on the exterior. This refers to the separation of miscellaneous containers, such as small cartons and cases containing general merchandise bound for different ports but stowed adjacent to each other. Such stowage is most likely to result in the overcarriage of a few containers if port marks and separation are not given proper attention.

Lumber needs careful separation of consignee marks. This cargo may be separated by laying strips of rope yarn athwartship spaced about 6 ft longitudinally over the stowed mark. Painting stripes across the stowed block is also used, but should not be used when working with milled or surfaced lumber in the finishing grades. Wire and staples are used but this method of marking off is not desirable because the staples left in the lumber obviously are liable to cause trouble when the lumber is being worked. The wire and staples are not as easy to handle as the rope yarn or paint, and the efficiency of marking off is no greater.

Wire may be used when separating structural steel, steel pipe, or steel rails. Paint and dunnage strips may also be used for separating steel products.

In summary, the provision of rapid and systematic loading and discharging depends upon three factors: (1) Preventing long hatches. (2) Preventing overstowed cargo. (3) Preventing overcarried cargo.

SAFETY OF CREW AND LONGSHOREMEN

Cargo should be stowed so that during the discharging process it is unlikely that unsafe areas will develop for the men working the cargo or the men working about the ship. Sometimes it happens that the cargo may be discharged in such a way that unsafe areas actually are created by the process. An example is in the case of a block of cargo being totally discharged before moving to another block even though high and perhaps unstable bulkheads are formed all around the square where the longshoremen are laboring. This objective is so obvious that it may, in many cases, be ignored. It is mentioned because it has come to the author's attention on several occasions that cargo is stowed in such a way that unsafe conditions exist during the discharging process. Instances have occurred also where the manner of discharging either aggravated the situation or actually created it needlessly.

CHAPTER 4

Planning the stowage

PLANNING COMPLICATIONS

When faced with the problem of planning for the stowage, the officer drawing up the plan must deal with a number of factors that directly or indirectly complicate his task. It may help to clarify the entire problem to list these factors so that the reader can consider each in its proper relation to the others and be more aware of where the troubles really lie.

Diversity of the cargo. The diversity of the cargo, as to its inherent characteristics as well as its shape and weight, is first and foremost on the list. If all cargoes could be stowed together in any compartment or in any order vertically and longitudinally, the problem of planning would be reduced in difficulty by over fifty per cent. The fact that cargoes must be separated in definite ways complicates their segregation. When there is only one cargo or even several that can be stowed together, the planning for good stowage is greatly simplified.

The number and sequence of ports. If all the cargo is going to one port, it is obvious that the planning problems are greatly reduced. Under such conditions, it is impossible to overstow or to overcarry cargo and long hatches are impossible.

It is interesting to note, however, that a situation making it difficult, if not impossible, to satisfy all the objectives of good stowage can be created by an itinerary of just two ports with just two cargoes. The reader might consider, for example, a ship booked to carry a full and

FIG. 4-1. View of the curvature of the 17-ft flat at hold number 7 on the Mariner type ship. This is above the level of the shaft alley, but it can be seen how much more complicated the stowage of cargo in this space would be with a shaft alley also running down the center longitudinally.

down load of steel rails for port *A* and cartons of packaged cereals for port *B* with the ship to call at port *A* first. How would such a cargo be stowed? Remember the necessity of correct weight distribution, segregation of light and heavy cargoes vertically, control of broken stowage, and rapid and systematic discharge. The booking of such a cargo would be a gross error, of course, on the part of the freight traffic department.

The shape of the hold. This factor must be considered in regard to the question of control of broken stowage. All factors of stowage may be well satisfied, but if the plan calls for large cases to be stowed in the lower holds of the end hatches, the broken stowage percentage will be high. If possible, bagged cargoes or smaller curved items should be stowed in such areas. This is an example of the give and take that must go on when planning the stowage of any cargo (see Fig. 4-1).

OBSTRUCTIONS IN THE HOLD. Obstructions in a hold should be kept to a minimum by the designers. If obstructions are in the hold, otherwise perfect stowage may have to be changed because the cargo will not go in around the obstructions or, if it will, the broken stowage may rise an unwarranted amount. In this respect, some of the areas in the

FIG. 4-2. Mariner type ship No. 3 second deck space, illustrating types of obstructions.

Mariner type ship are badly designed. For an example of a 'tweendeck area with a number of complicating features see Fig. 4-2. This figure shows the 4½-in.-coaming, a requirement that may some day be eliminated by the design of a watertight flush hatch covering. This 4½-in.-rise with the inclined platform reaching out into the wings and fore and aft bays makes the stowage of the cargo very difficult. Also, it reduces by 4½ in. the height of the largest packages that can be stowed in the wings. These facts reduce the commercial value of any ship. The fore and aft ventilation ducts running below the beams are an obstruction common only to the Mariner type. Athwartship ducts running up in the beam spaces and discharging the air in a fore and aft direction make the latter obstruction unnecessary. Other obstructions protruding into the cubic of the compartment can be seen.

Heated bulkheads. Bulkheads that are heated may make it necessary to stow cargo such as lard, wattle bark extracts, and similar items in other spaces when all other factors are best satisfied by placing them in the heated compartment. This fact, of course, requires a change in the plan and results in a complication.

Optional cargo shipments. Optional cargo is cargo that is loaded for discharge at any one of several ports at the option of the shipper. Such shipments are sometimes difficult to keep from being overstowed. They must be ready for discharge at all of several ports instead of only at one. Only a limited amount of optional cargo can be stowed without the necessity to shift cargo for its discharge in some cases. The complicating feature should be readily appreciated.

Unavailability of cargo. Cargo may be booked and planned for stowage but the shipper may fail to deliver it to the dock when it is time to load as planned. Such a situation makes it necessary to change the entire plan. The degree of the change depends on the amount of the cargo involved and other conditions. It should be clear that the unavailability of cargo may cause much trouble during the stowage operation.

THE TENTATIVE CARGO PLAN

Importance of tentative cargo plan. With only two cargoes and two ports creating difficult problems, as illustrated in the above hypothetical case, the reader can appreciate more readily the problems that may arise on occasion when stowing a hundred commodities for several ports. General cargo carriers operate under the latter conditions consistently. The operation may be further complicated by the need to load cargoes as well as discharge them at intermediate ports on the itinerary.

The correct way to prevent costly mistakes from occurring during the loading process is to lay out the ship as far in advance as possible. The preliminary laying out of the ship is the plan for stowing the vessel made up from the engagement sheet or recapitulated data from such a source. This first plan is called the tentative plan to eliminate confusion with another plan known as the final stowage plan. There are terminals in operation where large cargo liners are loaded without the benefit of a formal tentative plan. However, to do so is contrary to the best operating principles. It is true, of course, that when the same type of ship is loaded in regular and frequent intervals over runs that are almost identical year in and year out, the importance of the tentative plan will be less than when a ship is being loaded for the first time on a new run. With years of experience with the same ship, same cargo in general, and the same run, the loading methods will be very similar; but, they will never be identical. The differences will always warrant a rough tentative plan at the least. With respect to weight distribution, the same mistake might be made for years and quite unnecessarily it may cause gradually increasing costs for repair and maintenance. The latter mistakes would be rectified only if the final stowage plans were analyzed. Lacking this check and the continual loading of the ships by intuition, the shipowner may operate his fleet with less efficiency than possible.

Preparation of the tentative cargo plan. The pier superintendent is generally the individual responsible for laying out the ship. As mentioned above, he will obtain the data for preparing the plan from copies of the engagement sheet kept by the booking clerk. The booking may not be complete when he starts to make up the plan. This will complicate the task to some extent and require a number of changes during the actual loading process. The object is to have some basis for making initial decisions when starting the loading operation and to have an instrument with which to brief all supervisory personnel about the operation.

As mentioned above, when the same ship receives similar shipments voyage after voyage to be loaded for the same consignees in approximately the same amounts, the tentative and final stowage plans, if analyzed constantly, should reflect the best answer for stowing the cargo on board in accordance with the five objectives of good stowage. The development of new products and changes in demand for the old will cause a gradual change in the types and amounts of cargoes found on old and established runs. The change will be so gradual that there will be little difference in the tentative plan between one voyage and the next, but there will be change. The need for analyzing the stowage from time to time will always be present on the general cargo carrier.

Provisions of the tentative plan. The tentative plan provides for loading cargo bound for the last port of call first, that is, on the bottom *tiers*. The layers of cargo are referred to as tiers. The athwartship and fore and aft lines of stowage are referred to as *rows*. The plan will show limitations to the stowage as to height and bulkheads fore and aft and athwartship. The approximate amounts in tons and numbers of containers expected to be placed in the indicated spaces will also be shown. All of these data may be changed during the actual stowage in order to expedite the total operation.

Heavy cargoes must be loaded on the bottom tiers. A complication arises immediately when a heavy item must be loaded so that it can be discharged at one of the early ports on the itinerary. There are several ways to meet this problem. One of the most common is to split the hold transversely leaving at least one section of the hatch available to the hook and, if necessary, to further subdivide the two parts longitudinally. A second solution is to save a part of or the entire hatch square for the first port.   A third device is to use the upper decks for the heavier pieces bound for the early ports.   A fourth is to resort to on-deck stowage if it is allowable by the terms of the bill of lading.   A fifth, solution and the least desirable is to stow the heavy item under cargo bound for a later port.   This may be the only possible answer under some conditions, but it requires the shifting of cargo to get the load discharged and means added time and expense for the cargo operation.   It should never be used without having exhausted every other possibility.

The tentative plan will provide for the correct distribution of weight vertically and longitudinally.   This problem was discussed in detail in the preceding chapter.

The tentative plan will reflect the correct segregation of the cargo. The problem of segregation is that of stowing the cargoes so that one cannot cause damage to another, and this may be the most difficult problem to solve.   Compromises will have to be made in this regard at times.

Finally, the tentative plan will provide for an amount of cargo in each hold so that no one hold will require an unproportional number of gang hours of work to discharge the cargo.   This calculation will take into consideration the number of sets of cargo gear at each hatch.

Using the tentative plan.   The use of the tentative plan insofar as the pier superintendent is concerned should be quite obvious.   Once prepared, he can use it to judge whether the finished ship will be in accordance with the best principles of stowage.   He can analyze it and discuss it with the members of the dock force which insures that all personnel of a supervisory capacity will be briefed about the operation. If for any reason a change is required, the old plan is a beginning point. A very important use of the plan is so that the pier superintendent can tell how many gangs are needed from day to day and what gear is required.   Many daily decisions will be more quickly and accurately made if based upon a good tentative plan.

The ship superintendent or walking boss needs it to see how the ship is to be stowed.   Instead of having to continually seek the pier superintendent, he can make more intelligent decisions on his own.   If changes must be made, he can always consult with the pier superintendent.   Having the tentative plan, however, makes the entire operation run much more smoothly and guarantees more positive results.

Whereas the use of the tentative plan as outlined for the above officers within the shipowner's organization is fairly uniform from company to company, the use of the plan with regards to the master of the ship and his officers varies from the full use of it to a complete lack of its use.

The ship's officers and the tentative plan. The cargo operations are the most expensive operational costs for a general cargo carrier. Every effort should be expended to make the procedure as efficient as possible under practical operating conditions. One of the things that can be done in this respect, but is neglected in many cases, is the briefing of the ship's officers regarding all the plans for loading the ship.

To begin with, a copy of the tentative plan should be presented to the master of the ship so that this officer can make a preliminary analysis of it. The approximate draft, metacentric height, bending stresses, and segregation should be clearly notated upon the plan. These are the bases for judging whether a given layout is good or bad. The master of a ship should know whether the ship he is to take to sea is going to be loaded as he would load her. It is the responsibility of the operations department to see that every ship master has the data needed to ascertain the above fact. In some instances, the master of the ship has little if any influence on the way his ship is to be loaded; regardless of the reason, this is not right. This may stem from the method of operation by the company, or from the laissez faire attitude adopted by the master himself.

In every case, the master of the ship should make some analysis of the tentative plan for the stowing of his ship. He should either approve or disapprove of the stowage. If there are things of which he disapproves, there should be a clarification of the issue with the pier superintendent. In the final analysis, the master of the ship is the officer responsible for the way the ship is stowed. This fact must not be forgotten by anybody.

The master should brief all of the ship's officers in regard to the loading operation. This should be in the form of a conference on the ship with the pier superintendent and walking boss present if possible. The chief officer should have a copy of the tentative plan, and after the loading conference the other deck officers should carefully note those items that will require checking during the actual operation.

Under this system, the ship's officers will be able to stop serious mistakes in the loading before they occur. The shipowner will be able to utilize the years of experience of the officers with the cargoes they carry. Too frequently, the officers are completely un-informed about the operation taking place on their ship. All information about the proceedings is often held by the pier superintendent and walking boss, and it is not systematically passed on to the officers. Direct questions may be answered readily, but not enough complete information is given to enable the officers of the ship to bring their full potential to assist in the cargo operation. Lacking full and complete data, the officers feel unfamiliar with current problems that in many cases could be handled better if they were properly briefed.

The practice of briefing subordinates concerning any operation in which they are going to take part is a fundamental principle of leadership. Conducting a briefing makes all hands feel more as if they have a personal stake in the outcome and gives them a feeling of participation that is very important for the attainment of efficiency. This policy of thorough briefing, of course, should be set by the operations manager. If he fails to do so, the master of each ship should do what he can to enforce it. Under a cooperative relationship, any ship will function in a more efficient manner than under an impersonal and un-informed relationship between the master and his officers.

THE CAPACITY PLAN

When laying out the ship, certain information concerning the ship must be readily available. The data needed is incorporated on a plan of the ship known as the capacity plan. A full and complete capacity plan answers the question of whether a given cargo shipment can be stowed in any given compartment or part of a compartment and what the effect on the ship will be.

The information that a capacity plan should have upon it is tabulated below.

Compartmentation. An inboard profile view of the ship showing all of the compartments of the ship; the holds, tanks, store rooms, quarters, and working spaces are shown.

Volumes. The volumes of all the above spaces are not specified. The volumes of the tanks and the cargo holds are given. The *bale* capacity and the *grain* capacity of each cargo compartment capable of receiving dry cargo is given. The bale capacity is the cubic capacity measuring vertically from below the beam flanges down to the upper side of the tank top plating or the spar ceiling if any exists. Transversely the measurements are from inside the sweat battens, and longitudinally from inside any stiffeners or insulation on the bulkheads. The grain capacity is the cubic capacity measuring from inside the plating of all six sides less the volume taken up by the structural members extending into the hold. In other words, the bale capacity is the volume of the hold that can be utilized when stowing bales and the grain capacity is the volume that can be utilized when stowing grain. The bales cannot go in between all the frame and beam spaces, but the grain will flow around such members.

The volumes of the complete hold may be recapitulated in a table on the plan, but the profile plan of the ship should be broken up into units of space as they are often done in actual stowage of cargo. Figure 4-3 is an illustration of how the profile plan of the ship may be subdivided to make this part of the capacity plan more useful.

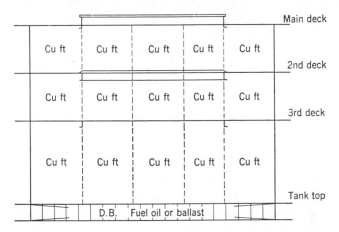

FIG. 4-3. Subdivision of the profile. Subdividing the profile plan as shown here makes it easier to obtain data needed when making calculations relative to the stowage of cargo. This subdivision is not made by the naval architect, but will have to be done by the ship's officer.

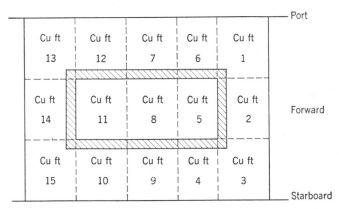

FIG. 4-4. Subdivision of the plan view. The plan provided by the naval architect may have too much detail on it to allow a clear subdivision as shown here. If so, the ship's officer should draw a plain outline and subdivide it for use with the planning of the cargo stowage. The shaded area is a 3-ft safety area in which cargo should not be stowed if, while such cargo is in this space, the compartment below will be open.

Below the profile plan of the ship, plan views of the various decks appear. On these plan views, the cubic of the compartments should be broken up into smaller units. On a hatch that has three sections, the plan view of the decks should have the space divided up into fifteen separate parts. Such a division is shown in Fig. 4-4. When speaking or making written notations of these spaces, the terms applied to 1 and 3 are *forward winged out* or simply *forward wings*. If the position refers to only one wing, it should be designated by name, such as *forward port wing*. Area 2 is *forward amidships*. Areas 13, 14, and 15 are referred to in the same manner except that they are aft. The entire area on each side of the hatch in the wings is referred to as *wings abreast*. More explicit designation may be given by reference to the section of the hatch. For example, wings abreast would mean the cargo was stowed in areas 6, 7, 12 and 4, 9, 10. If cargo was stowed only in the approximate limits of area 10, this may be designated verbally as *starboard wing abreast aft*. Areas 5, 8, and 11 are designated as the hatch square. It should be emphasized that there is no universally accepted terminology for designating all of these areas. These areas simply may be given numbers or referred to as "bays," a term used on many piers to designate certain stowage areas. The terms used need only to be descriptive of the position to be acceptable.

Safety area. When cargo for one port is stowed in a 'tweendeck space and it will remain there while it is necessary to work the hatches below, this cargo should not be stowed too close to the edge of the hatch opening. Cargo should be kept 3 ft back from the edge of the hatchway in this case. It is a good practice to paint a white or red line this distance from the edge as a guide line for longshoremen. The space between this line and the edge of the coaming may be called the *safety area* or, in some cases, it is appropriately named *no-man's land*. The cubic of this space may sometimes be included in the hatch square cubic figure and sometimes in the appropriate areas surrounding the hatch. Just how it is handled is not too important, but the area in which it is included should be known.

This no-man's land serves to prevent longshoremen falling into the open hatch when working around this space when opening or closing hatches and also provides room for the ship's personnel to pass safely. Also, when cargo is being loaded or discharged, it lessens the probability that the cargo stowed in the 'tweendeck area will be struck with the result that a container is damaged or knocked below so that a longshoreman is injured.

Clearances. The distance between the bottom of the hatch coaming and the deck plus the lengths, widths, and heights of all the compartments should be notated upon the capacity plan. The distance from the forward edge or after edge of a hatch coaming to the opposite lower end of the compartment below should be included, because this measurement will tell the planning officer at a glance whether a given length of pipe or timber will go into the compartment in question. It should be kept in mind that if a given length will just squeeze by the obstruction when being stowed in the beginning, then only one tier will be possible. As the cargo builds up, the drift, as this measurement is called, will be reduced. The length of clear deck run on the weather deck is also an important clearance and should be indicated on the plan. This measurement controls the size of single items that can be stowed on deck.

Deck load capacities. To enable the planning officer to know whether a given cargo can be stowed on a given deck, insofar as the structural strength of the deck is concerned, all decks of the ship should have their capacities in pounds per square foot notated upon them. The need for this data was discussed earlier, see pp. 102–104.

Geometrical centers. To make the capacity plan useful for calculation of trim and stability problems, the distances of the geometrical centers of all cargo compartments and tanks above the keel and from one of the perpendiculars should be given. The center of gravity of the contents of the compartment above the keel will not coincide with the figure given on the plan unless the compartment is filled with a homogeneous mass. When not filled with a homogeneous mass or only partially filled, an estimate must be made of the location of the center of gravity. For example, if the compartment is filled with a general cargo with the heavier items on the lower layers, the center can be assumed to be about one-third of the height of the compartment above the deck of the compartment. If half of the compartment's capacity is filled with one cargo, the center of the mass will be one-fourth of the height of the compartment above the deck of the compartment, and so on. For an explanation of the need for such data see Chapter 3.

Trimming table. Below the profile view of the ship, a trimming table will be found. This table enables the quick solution of the effect of a small change in longitudinal weight distribution on the trim of the ship. When calculating the final trim after loading a large amount of cargo, it is just as simple and more accurate to use the methods outlined in Chapter 3. The use of the trimming table is explained on p. 82. Most of these tables are based on a unit of 100 tons, it is important to keep this fact in mind (see Table 3-4).

Deadweight scale. (See Table 3-5.) The deadweight scale is found on all capacity plans; however, the data given with the scale is often incomplete for all the needs of the planning officer. This scale is simply a diagram of the draft of the ship marked off in increments of 1 in. Corresponding to the draft, the displacement of the ship and deadweight carrying capacity are always given. To make the deadweight scale more complete, the T.P.I., *MT*1, and *KM* of the ship should also be given. All of these data vary with the draft. The *deadweight carrying capacity* for any given draft is the *displacement* of the ship for the given draft less the *weight of the light ship*. The cargo deadweight carrying capacity cannot be recorded upon this scale, because this value varies with the amount of fuel, water, and stores on board. Under any given set of conditions, the cargo deadweight carrying capacity may be calculated if the tons of fuel, water, and stores on board is known. The total of the latter value is subtracted from the deadweight carrying capacity taken from the deadweight scale to obtain the *cargo deadweight capacity*.

Also reflected upon the deadweight scale is the freeboard of the ship. As explained in Chapter 3, the freeboard of the ship, as derived by taking the mean of the forward and after drafts, will only coincide with that reflected on the deadweight scale if the ship is neither hogged nor sagged. If the ship is hogged, the actual freeboard will be greater than that taken from the scale. If the ship is sagged, the actual freeboard will be less. This fact can be used as a check on whether a ship is hogged or sagged.

Capacities and arrangement of cargo gear. The capacity of each boom should be notated on the capacity plan so that the planning officer will have these important data at hand. Often a question regarding whether a given gear can take a given load rigged in one way or another must be answered. For similar reasons, the length of each boom and rigging itself should be depicted upon the plan.

Miscellaneous data. Besides the data mentioned above, which is needed to plan quickly and thoroughly for the stowage of cargo, the capacity plan is also a source for such information as the principal dimensions of the ship, pitch of the propeller, boiler and engine data, and a recapitulation of some of the information included on the profile and plan views of the ship.

With all these data, the original plan can be made up and the resulting *GM*, trim, and layout of the ship can be obtained. Furthermore, in the case of a need for changing the stowage, the effect on the *GM*, trim, or bending stresses can be readily obtained.

It should be pointed out that the *KM* is omitted on almost all deadweight scales by the naval architects. However, the *KM*'s for each draft can be obtained from other sources and placed on the available plan of every ship by the ship's officers. If a capacity plan with these data already recorded on it is available from the builders, it should be requisitioned. If the capacity plan found on a ship when an officer joins her is discovered to lack many of the details mentioned above, one of the first jobs that should be done is to seek the missing data and place them upon the plan.   The officer doing this will know his ship much better and be able to function in a far more efficient and competent manner.

THE FINAL STOWAGE PLAN

The tentative stowage plan is a guide to load the ship.   When the ship is completely loaded, the stowage of the cargo will resemble the tentative plan but will never be precisely in accordance with it.   The numerous changes large and small cannot be kept on the tentative plan so that it will serve as a final plan.   It is necessary to construct a final stowage plan as the ship is loaded compartment by compartment.   This plan must show in great detail the actual stowage of the ship.   It must depict the vertical, longitudinal, and transverse limits of all ports and of as many of the individual marks as is practicable.

Use of the final plan.   The final plan is used by the stevedore of the discharging port to plan the discharging operation.   It is used by the ship's officers to know the stowage of their ship so that in case of any emergency they can estimate the seriousness of the situation and more intelligently plan for action necessary to cope with it.   Also, it is analyzed by the master to determine the metacentric height, the appropriate bending moments, what might have been done to better the trim if it is extreme in any way, and to judge the 'quality of the stowage generally. Later, if he deems it warranted, the master may recommend to the operations department a change in past methods or offer constructive suggestions.   He can do none of these things unless he has a good final stowage plan and unless he analyzes it thoroughly.

Without an accurate, complete, and clear final stowage plan, there can be no efficiency in the discharging operation and the safety of the ship and crew is impaired greatly.

Construction of final plan.   The construction of the tentative and final stowage plan is almost identical except that the tentative plan will not be so detailed.   The construction of a final plan will be described in this section and an explanation of some of the notation will be given. It must be pointed out that the notation is not standardized throughout the merchant marine.   The variations are minor and once the reader has a general idea of the way these plans are laid out, he can read all plans after a few minutes given to study the notation.

The stowage plan is generally constructed on a profile plan of the ship with bow depicted to the reader's right.   The stowage of all 'tweendeck areas is presented as a plan view, that of the lower holds as an elevation. Now, inasmuch as a profile view of the ship is used upon which to draw the plan, a plan of the 'tweendeck hatchways must be drawn in on the plan to be used as a reference in locating the cargo stowed therein.

Figure 4-5 shows the blank form for one hold, assuming the ship has two decks and three sections to the hatchway. Obviously, nothing is proportional or to scale on the blank form. As the limitations of the stowage are drawn on the plan, some approximation of proportion should be attempted. For example, if a mark runs one half the distance from the forward bulkhead aft to the hatch edge, the plan should show that mark as running half the distance. This may not be possible to do when a

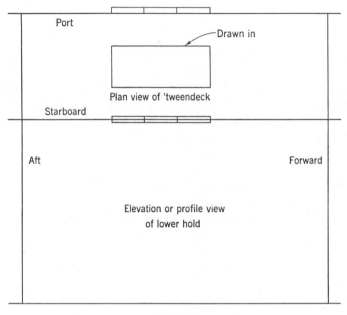

Fɪɢ. 4-5.

number of marks or ports are stowed in the same area. The reason it becomes impossible is because the space between marks, when the division bcomes small, is not large enough for legible printing on the actual plan.

Commodity type plan. Two types of plans are found in use. One of these may be described as the *commodity plan* and the other as the *block plan*. The commodity plan shows as much of the detail of the stowage as possible upon the profile of the ship. That is, the limitation of all cargo is outlined on the plan. In the spaces prepared, the name of the commodity, the marks, the tons, and the number of packages are recorded. This is usually all the data that will be needed to plan for the discharge of the cargo or plan for action when fighting fire or in case of any emergency. This type of plan presents a *picture* of the stowage that is readily interpreted. The officer sees the segregation immediately upon viewing the plan.

Block type plan. The block plan shows the limitation of the cargo, but in the spaces on the profile of the ship a number is placed. This

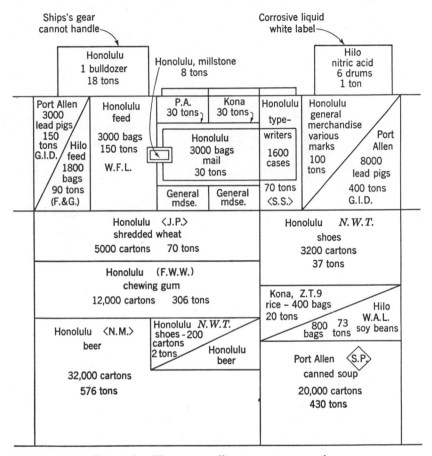

Fig. 4-6. The commodity type stowage plan.

number refers the reader of the plan to a line on a table or list placed on the plan below the profile of the ship or on a separate sheet of paper. On this line, the cargo represented by the number is fully described. The block plan makes it possible to give more detail concerning the stowed cargo if it is desired. All the room needed on the face of the plan is the room necessary to print a number which is small indeed. Then almost as much detail concerning the cargo as appears on the manifest may be written on the line opposite the reference number. There is generally some system to the numbering of the cargo blocks. All the numbers in No. 1 hold will be in the 100's, all those in No. 2 hold in the 200's and so on. To make the identification of items more easy and less susceptible to mistakes, the initials or first syllable of the port of destination may follow the number. Furthermore, the number may be underlined in a distinctive color representing the port of discharge. Both types of plans should be colored to make the reading of them easier and more foolproof.

Example

To illustrate some of the methods of showing the stowage on a plan, the reader is referred to Fig. 4-6. The reader should follow step by step the stowage and recording of the stowage on the plan. The lower hold has a depth of 25 ft and the 'tweendecks 11 ft.

Stowage 1: Port Allen, 20,000 cartons of canned soup in the forward part of the lower hold.

Comments: Stowed 11½ ft deep from the forward bulkhead aft to take in one section of the hatch and all the way across the ship. The mark is S.P.

Stowage 2: Honolulu, 32,000 cartons of canned beer in the after part of the lower hold.

Comments: Stowed 12½ ft deep up to the edge of the hatch then it drops down about 4 ft at the square of the hatch and continues forward taking up two sections of the hatch. In the wings, it continues at a level of 12½ ft. The mark is N.M.

Stowage 3: Honolulu, 200 cartons of shoes stowed in the square of the hatch only over the beer 4 ft deep.

Comments: This view is an elevation, hence the wing stowage is separated from the hatch square stowage on the plan by the use of a slanting line through the common athwartship area. The cargo in the square of the hatch should come out first and therefore it is shown above the slanting line which is supposed to indicate this fact. The mark is N.W.T.

Stowage 4: Hilo, 800 bags of soy beans.

Comments: These soy beans are in the two wing bays and must come out after the Kona rice, hence the stowage is shown below the slanting line. The mark is W.A.L.

Stowage 5: Kona, 400 bags of rice.

Comments: Stowed in the way of the hatch square for a depth of 4½ ft. Same depth as the soy beans except that it is amidships. It comes out first, hence it is on top of the slanting line. One section of the hatch is used. The mark is Z.T. (9).

Stowage 6: Honolulu, 12,000 cartons of chewing gum.

Comments: Stowed 6 ft deep all the way across and including two sections of the hatch. The mark is F.W.W.

Stowage 7: Honolulu, 5000 cartons of shredded wheat.

Comments: Stowed 6½ ft deep all the way across including two sections of the hatch. The mark is <J.P.>.

Stowage 8: Honolulu, 3200 cartons of shoes.

Comments: Stowed 9 ft deep all the way across to include one section of the hatch. The mark is N.W.T.

The stowage of block number 8 completes the lower hold.

The following stowage refers to the 'tweendeck.

Stowage 1: Port Allen, 8000 pigs of lead.

Comments: These lead pigs would have to be stowed not more than 20 in. high; this would leave considerable space above them for lightweight cargo. But the 'tweendeck stowage is shown on the plan view. This corresponds to the problem of showing the stowage of a lower hold on an elevation when the cargo is not the same all the way athwartships. The slanting line is used; forward of the line, we place the cargo that is to come out last. This is to be taken as showing that the Port Allen cargo is overstowed by the Honolulu. In 'tweendeck storage this is not done very often. Generally the cargo blocks run from the deck to the overhead. The mark is G.I.D.

Stowage 2: Honolulu, 100 tons of general merchandise.

Comments: Stowed forward of the hatch over the Port Allen lead. No marks have been listed because they are so numerous the space doesn't permit it. The hatch list or manifest would have to be consulted in order to know exactly what the cargo comprised. The term *general merchandise* denotes less than carload lots of drugs, hardware, furniture, appliances, canned goods, dry goods, shoes, clothing, and tools. Note that with the general merchandise, the cargo stowed forward of the hatch in the 'tweendecks weighs 500 tons. Unless the area of the deck multiplied by the deck load capacity equaled 500 tons or more, this stowage would quite likely cause damage to the ship.

Stowage 3: Port Allen, 3000 lead pigs.

Comments: Stowed over a large area about 20 in. high as those forward. Total weight amounts to 150 tons. Since the Port Allen lead is aft of the slanting line and the stowage is aft of the hatch, it is read as being overstowed by the Hilo feed. The mark is G.I.D.

Stowage 4: Hilo, 1800 bags of feed.

Comments: These bags of feed come out before the Port Allen lead. They are stowed over the lead in the same way that the Honolulu general merchandise is forward. The mark is F. & G.

Stowage 5: Honolulu, 3000 bags of feed.

Comments: Stowed from the edge of hatch aft to the Port Allen lead and Hilo feed from the deck to the overhead and all the way across the ship. The mark is W.F.L.

Stowage 6: Port Allen, 30 tons of general merchandise.

Comments: Stowed in the port and starboard wing bays of the third section of the hatch. Space limits even an abbreviated description on both sides, so the two sides are used for a short notation of the cargo. The arrow on the port side refers the reader to the other side for more information.

Stowage 7: Kona, 30 tons of general merchandise.

Comments: Same stowage as given the Port Allen general.

Stowage 8: Honolulu, 1600 cases of typewriters.

Comments: These are stowed in the wing bays of the forward section and in the square of the hatch of the forward section from the deck to the overhead. The mark is <S.S.>.

Stowage 9: Honolulu, 3000 bags of U.S. mail.

Comments: One or two sections of the 'tweendeck square are usually saved for mail which is received during the last hours of loading. Mail may be placed over other cargo in the square. It makes good beam filler cargo when space is at a premium.

Stowage 10: Honolulu, one millstone.

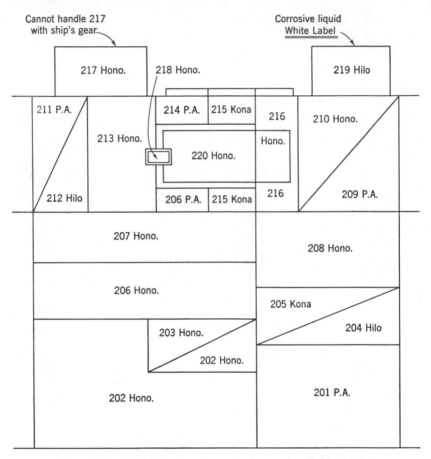

Fig. 4-7.   The block type stowage plan.   (See Table 4-1.)

Comments: This is an eight ton lift and as such it requires special rigging for handling and must be conspicuously entered on the plan. It is only one item and the space on the plan is far out of proportion to what it occupies, but it is necessary to draw such items to the attention of all who use the plan so that rapid discharge is assured.

Stowage 11: Honolulu, one bulldozer.

Comments: On-deck cargo is shown in whatever way it is most convenient with full notation. Heavy lifts must always be well marked. If ship's gear cannot handle the lift, some statement should inform the reader of the facts.

Stowage 12: Hilo, 6 drums of nitric acid.

Comments: The stowage of explosives and other dangerous articles must be clearly and accurately illustrated on the final cargo plan. Besides the ordinary data for other cargo, such cargo must have its classification, as given by the Coast Guard publication 187, and the label required clearly printed on the plan and underlined. Thus, nitric acid which is classified as a corrosive liquid and carries a white label is recorded as shown on Fig. 4-6.

The plan in Fig. 4-6 is of the commodity type. A hatch list is made up which gives more complete data about every shipment stowed in each compartment. Thus, with the commodity type plan and the hatch list, the stevedore discharging the ship knows all that is necessary.

If the plan is a block plan, the plan itself would be as illustrated in Fig. 4-7. Below the profile drawing of the ship and stowage, a table such as Table 4-1 would be placed. By cross reference between the plan and

TABLE 4-1

201 Port Allen, 20,000 cases of canned soup, 430 tons for S.R.
202 Honolulu, 32,000 cartons canned beer, 576 tons, for N.M.
203 Honolulu, 200 cartons shoes, 2 tons, for N.W.T.
204 Hilo, 800 bags of soy beans, 73 tons, for W.A.L.
205 Kona, 400 bags rice, 20 tons, for Z.T. (9).
206 Honolulu, 12,000 cartons chewing gum, 306 tons, for F.W.W.
207 Honolulu, 5000 cartons shredded wheat, 70 tons, for J.P.
208 Honolulu, 3200 cartons shoes, 37 tons, for N.W.T.
209 Port Allen, 8000 pigs lead, 400 tons, for G.I.D.
210 Honolulu, general merchandise consisting of: 20 cases drugs for F.G.; 12 bags pipe fittings and 5 bundles of pipe for J.S.; 400 cartons shoes for Y.P.; 8 cases household effects for C.L.S.; 1000 cartons dry groceries for K.K.; five refrigerators for H.A.; 17 cartons radios for H.P.; and miscellaneous Sears and Roebuck packages. Total: 100 tons.
211 Port Allen, 3000 pigs lead, 150 tons, for G.I.D.
212 Hilo, 1800 bags feed, 90 tons, for F. & G.
213 Honolulu, 3000 bags feed, 150 tons, for W.F.L.
214 Port Allen, general merchandise: 32 cases dry goods for Z.T.; 64 cases hardware for P.A.H.; 160 cases typewriters for G.I.S.; 400 cartons dry groceries for D.S.L.; 16 cases drugs for R.X.; and miscellaneous Sears and Roebuck packages. Total: 30 tons.
215 Kona, 2000 bags feed for G.G.; 200 cases typewriters for K.S.; 1500 cases of drugs for K.G.H. Total: 30 tons.
216 Honolulu, 1600 cases typewriters, 70 tons, S.S.
217 Honolulu, 1 bulldozer, 18 tons. **Ship's gear cannot handle.**
218 Honolulu, 1 large millstone with sling attached, 8 tons. Readily accessible in square of hatch aft.
219 Hilo, 6 drums nitric acid, 1 ton. **Corrosive liquid, white label.**
220 Honolulu, 3000 bags mail, 30 tons.

the table, the same information would be obtained as from the other type plan. The numbers all being in the 200's means that the hold we have been discussing is No. 2 hold.

Preparation of the final plan. The final stowage plan is prepared by a member of the receiving clerk's staff known as the *plans clerk* or by the ship's officers. The procedure varies from company to company. In some companies, the ship's officers keep no records and accept the plan made up by the dock force. In others, a plan is made up by the ship's officers and another by the plans clerk. In certain cases the officers may keep only a rough copy of the stowage and use it to check the plan from the dock. In a third method of operating, only one plan is maintained and this by the officers. Whenever a plan is kept by the officers, the second or third officer will have the direct responsibility of entering the data on a master plan. The chief officer will confer with the officer keeping the plan from time to time. In this way he can keep abreast of the operation while taking care of other duties. In case of a change in the tentative plan or a development of any kind that is not in accordance with the best principles of stowage, the chief officer would be notified. Then he would attempt corrective measures. If the chief officer is not satisfied with the corrective measures, he may make an appropriate log book entry, notify the master, and/or write a formal report concerning the incident.

Of the three means of keeping the final stowage plan, the second system is superior. The least desirable, of course, is the first which places complete reliance upon a plan kept by a member of the dock force. In spite of their experience and sincerity, plans clerks will from time to time make mistakes in the construction of the plan. Some of these mistakes may be serious.

One reason for the plans clerk making mistakes is that the data for making the plan is taken from notations on tally slips to a large extent, and the actual stowage is not witnessed. As a result, the precise limitations of the stowage are not accurately depicted on the final plan. At times the notation on the tally slip may be in error; if so, the stowage shown on the plan will also be in error. Errors of this sort lead to embarrassing situations for the ship's officers. The officers are expected to know all about the stowage of the cargo on their ship. When they don't they are automatically and justly judged as incompetent.

The best way for a final stowage plan to be made for the use of the ship is to have the officers prepare it from actual observation of the stowage in the holds and data received from the receiving clerk's office. Thus the officer noting the stowage of cargo block number 201 in Fig. 4-7 would make a rough notation on a blank plan showing the limitations of the stowage. If the plan was of the commodity type, he would enter the type of cargo and probably the marks. Obviously, he would not

know the exact number of cartons or the total weight, this data he
would have to obtain from the receiving clerk's office.

Keeping a plan as outlined above guarantees that the officer will know
the stowage well. It is not a difficult task, although it may seem difficult
to anyone who has not actually performed it. But, difficult or easy, the
advantages are great. The ship's officers will have a clearer knowledge
of the stowage, and in gaining it they will have been circulating from
hold to hold keeping a watchful eye on the entire operation. The actual
procedure in keeping the plan requires that the officer start in No. 1 hold
and, after observing the stowage activities there, to proceed to No. 2 hold
and finally all the way aft to the last hold. He should carry with him a
small book with a cargo compartment drawn on each page. The book
should be small enough to fit into a pocket. In this book, notations of
what is observed will be made. When the ship has been completely observed, the officer transfers these data to a master rough plan. The blank
that forms this plan may be kept in one of the officer's cabins or in the
chart room. All officers should observe the progress of the plan's
construction and check back in the holds from time to time to ascertain
its accuracy.

One officer should be responsible for making hourly trips through the
holds as described above and entering the information on the rough
master plan. On some of the rounds through the ship, there may be no
change from the last observation. But, when a change does occur, the
officer should be on hand to see where the old mark left off and the new
mark started. If a tentative plan is available, all officers will know
approximately when changes are to be made, and they can plan their
work more intelligently. They can be on hand to check on the security
of the cargo that is going to be stowed under, the laying of dunnage or
separation, and in general see how the stowage of the last cargo is finished
off and the next cargo commenced.

If a plans clerk is also keeping a plan, it may be used to check the plan
kept by the ship's officers. This is the second system mentioned above
as being extant. This is the best because it provides for a check on the
accuracy of each.

Disposition of final plan. When the ship has been completed, a
smooth plan is made up from the rough original, duplicated, and the
copies distributed. Copies should be sent ahead of the ship to all the
discharging ports, and copies should also be distributed to the operations
department, and to all deck officers of the ship. During the final stages
of the loading, the ship's officer keeping the plan may be unable to complete a smooth copy and duplicate it before the ship sails. If this is the
case, there will be no copy to send ahead of the ship. In the first port

of call, a plan may be dispensed with for the first half day's work if a brief recapitulation of the top stowage is sent by wireless from the ship a few days before the ship arrives. This message can give the agents at the first port of call enough information to organize the first day's operation. Upon arrival, copies of the complete stowage can be distributed to port officials and other copies sent ahead to the ensuing ports on the itinerary.

If a plan is kept by the plans clerk, it will be finished a short time after the ship sails and can be sent ahead by air mail.

CHAPTER 5

Stowage of the cargo

PREPARATION OF THE CARGO SPACES

Cargo is stowed in the holds and tanks of the ship. In the hold areas, special compartments may be built, such as cargo lockers for valuable or easily pilfered items, magazines for the stowage of explosives, and insulated compartments for refrigerated cargoes. Prior to the loading of any cargo in any compartment, be it tank, magazine, reefer space, special locker, or plain hold, the compartment must meet minimum standards of cleanliness. In some instances, the cleanliness of the hold is not of major importance. For example, when loading bagged cement. In most cases, however, an improperly prepared hold may result in heavy damage claims due to tainting and/or contamination. If the shipper can prove that the attention paid to the preparation of a hold area was below that warranted by good seamanship and thereby create grounds for claiming improper care and custody, he has a good chance of collecting damages. It is the duty of the chief officer to have all cargo compartments prepared for the receipt of cargo and to make log book entries concerning the efforts expended along these lines.

Standard procedure of cleaning holds. Holds may be cleaned by the ship's crew or by ship service company gangs hired on a contract basis. The choice of the type of labor to be used is most commonly made by a member of the operations department on an economical basis. When ships are in places where cheap labor is available, then such labor should be used. However, when the choice is between the ship's crew members and a shoreside contractor in a port of the United States, the differential in cost may be in favor of using the ship's crew. Another factor in favor of using the ship's crew may be good labor relations on board the ship; the decision should be given careful consideration.

The actual process of cleaning a general carrier's holds is simple and routine, providing no special problem of cleaning is created by the carriage of extremely odorous or dirty cargoes. The equipment needed for each hatch is as follows: 1 dirt sling, 2 endless rope slings, enough brooms for all hands in the cleaning gang, rope yarns, and some cluster lights. The cleaning starts in the upper 'tweendeck. The first task is to clear a small space of all debris and start piling all the clean dunnage in a neat stack over two 2 by 4 in. battens spaced about 6 ft apart. If 2 by 4 in. battens are not available, a double height of 1 by 6 in. boards will suffice. After the usable dunnage has been salvaged, the condemned dunnage should be slung up in the rope slings. If two rope slings are not enough, use more. All the paper and other debris should be rolled up and placed in the dirt sling. This dirt sling consists of an ordinary rope net sling with a lining of canvas to prevent the dirt from falling through. Every ship should have at least one dirt sling for every hatch with perhaps one or two extra.

If the ship is at sea, the dunnage in the rope sling and debris in the dirt sling can all be discharged over the side. This is accomplished by slinging the load up in the conventional manner except that one part leading to the blacksmith (cargo hook) is removed and a rope yarn is used as a connecting device. The load is then swung out over the side and the rope yarn is cut with a knife. Thus, the load is safely dropped into the sea, but the sling is retained on the hook. In this manner, each compartment can be completely cleaned up before shifting to the next lower one.

If the ship is in port or in an area where such material cannot be dropped over the side, the debris, including the condemned dunnage, must be dumped on the weather deck of the ship. This should be done in such a way that the safety of crew members walking fore and aft is not impaired. If the pile of debris on deck gets too large, the loads should be merely slung up and left in the hold ready to be hooked up and dumped over the side when the opportunity presents itself. If the working circumstances are such that the decks and the holds must be cleared, the mate must make arrangements for trucks or railroad cars to come alongside and receive the debris to be discharged from the hold being cleaned (see Fig. 5-1).

After the good dunnage is stacked up in one wing where it is available as needed for the next cargo, the condemned dunnage slung up ready for discharge, and the paper, debris, and dirt swept up and placed in a dirt sling ready for discharge, then the cleaning process is completed.

FIG. 5-1.   Debris on deck from hold cleaning operation.

Washing the interiors of dry cargo holds.   Occasionally it may be necessary to wash the interior of a dry cargo hold.   Washing is always done *after* having cleaned the hold according to the system described in the standard procedure of cleaning holds, p. 160.   After carrying cargoes that leave behind a heavy dust or glutinous residue, the simple sweeping outlined above would be insufficient to clean the hold if the next cargo were a delicate or clean type of commodity.

The washing procedure is simply using a wash deck hose below decks to direct a solid stream of water over all the surfaces of the hold and toward the drainage well.   If possible, the washing should be done along-side of a dock where fresh water can be used directly from a dock outlet.

If the washing is done at sea, the preliminary wash may be with salt water with a thorough rinse with fresh water.   If the washing is done with salt water without a rinse of fresh, the salt residue left after drying is completed will pick up moisture from the air and may damage the cargo coming in contact with it.   Probably the worst feature of allowing the salt water to dry on the hold interior is the increase in the corrosion rate that would result.

A period of two or three days should be allowed before attempting to load another cargo in a freshly washed hold.   This time is needed for drying purposes.   If the outside atmosphere is relatively dry and windy and a good stream of air is directed into the hold with the hatches removed for a maximum exhaust circulation, the drying process should not take more than 36 hr.   However, in the case of high outside humidity or heavy rain, the drying period may extend to several days.   If the ship is equipped with a dehumidifying system, the hatches can be closed and the system placed on recirculation with dry air (see p. 460) which will result in one hatch being well dried out in 3 hr.   If an exceptional condition were to arise where every hatch of the ship had to be washed, the drying of all hatches could be accomplished in one day.

Deodorization methods.   If drain wells or parts of a given hold become contaminated by odorous cargo residue, they may have to be treated with a simple deodorizing wash.   A solution consisting of $\frac{1}{2}$ lb of chloride of lime mixed with $2\frac{1}{2}$ gal of fresh water is quite effective. If the area is only slightly affected, it may be simply swabbed down with this solution.   If it is very dirty, it should be washed with a solid stream from a wash deck hose using fresh water and then swabbed down with the chlorated lime solution.   If the odor persists, sprinkle some of the powder over the area.   High test hypochlorate, abbreviated HTH, is a more powerful deodorizing agent which also comes in the powder form.   When compared with chlorated lime, smaller amounts of HTH are used when making up solutions for deodorizing holds.   A tablespoonful of HTH to a bucket of fresh water makes a fairly strong solution; no more than this should be used.   This powder should not be left in the area where it might contact cargo directly.   If the solution is too strong, it may eradicate the odors of the past cargo but the odor from the HTH may cause damage itself.

Preparation for bulk commodities.   The preparation of a dry cargo hold for the loading of bulk commodities generally involves more than the simple cleaning described above.   One thing that always must be done is to prepare the drainage system to pass water but to retain the bulk commodity.   In the case of the drain well plates in the lower hold, this involves covering the opening with two layers of burlap and cementing the edge down. The cement that is applied to the edge should be flattened and not built up. If the cement is rounded off or built up in any way, there is more danger of its getting knocked loose and allowing the bulk commodity to fill up the drain wells. If this occurs, there is no way of pumping water out of the compartment in case of a leak from any source. Such a detail could mean the loss of the ship.

Additional protection for the burlap covering is afforded by placing a small wooden box about 6 in. high and with the bottom removed over the drain well opening. This covering is referred to as a *high hat* in some trades. It is not absolutely necessary but the added protection may be well worth the trouble.

In the case of bulk copra, the interior of the hold is entirely covered with fiber mats. Bulk coal requires no interior covering, but pipes must be inserted in the hold *before* the coal is loaded so that temperatures can be taken in the interior of the stowed cargo. In the case of bulk grain, a longitudinal bulkhead must be built along the centerline of the ship in the lower holds if more than a specified amount is loaded. If the grain is loaded so that it completely fills the hold, special feeders must be built in the 'tweendeck spaces. These shifting boards and feeders are built in accordance with regulations published by the U.S. Coast Guard.

The above examples are presented to show the type of special preparations that may have to be taken before loading certain cargoes.

Standard procedure for cleaning tanks. Machines are used on tankers almost exclusively for the washing of the tanks. Hand washing methods are used for washing tanks on most dry cargo ships, but machines are used in some instances. A brief description of washing by machine will be given below.

When washing by hand, the temperature of the water cannot be as high as when using a machine. Consequently, the tanks are heated by steaming. Washing by machine eliminates the need for this prolonged steaming. The fact that steaming is not necessary is one of the principal advantages of washing by machine. Steaming a tank causes expansion and later contraction of the hull which may result in hull damage, especially after being repeated many times. Steaming also accelerates corrosion of the tank interior. If a machine is used, the ship must be capable of delivering at least 180 gal of salt water per minute to the machine at a temperature of 185°F under a pressure of about 180 lb per sq in. This will supply one machine. If two machines are to be run simultaneously, the ship must have a heat exchanger and pump capable of doubling the above supply. Two types of machines are used. One is the Butterworth machine pictured in Fig. 5-2 and the other is the Pyrate machine. They operate on the same principle. The water is discharged under high pressure and high temperature and as it strikes the surface of the tank it cleans the surface of all oil, wax, and dirt. The

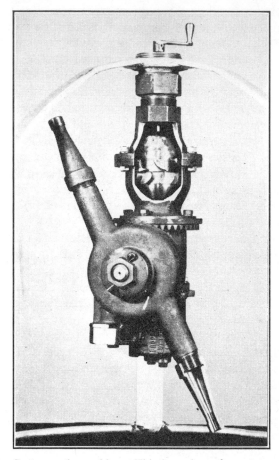

FIG. 5-2. The Butterworth machine. This is a view of a cutaway model of the Butterworth tank washing machine. The hose connected to the threaded upper end hangs free in the tank. The water turbine is connected to a shaft which in turn rotates an eccentric crank. The eccentric crank operates a pawl which rotates a worm. This rotating worm meshes with a worm gear and by this means the nozzles are rotated in a vertical plane; at the same time a stationary gear rotates the entire assembly in a horizontal plane.

machine rotates in two planes and the stream from each nozzle covers every inch of the tank that can be reached by a straight line from the machine's position in the tank during its operation. From this last statement, it can be seen that surfaces behind beam knees, bilge brackets, and web frames will not be struck by the solid stream of hot water. Therefore, these surfaces must be reached by repositioning the machine so that they are struck by the solid stream or by hand hosing and cleaning after the machine has been removed.

The machine may be lowered into a tank through a special hole cut through the deck for this specific purpose or through a manhole from one side. If lowered through a manhole, a block with a bull line or single whip to hold the machine in the center of the tank must be rigged. If the special hole is used, it will be cut through the center of the tank. Regardless of the method used to suspend the machine in the tank, the cleaning routine is the same. A recommended method is to lower the machine to within 5 feet of the bottom of the tank and run for about 30 min, draw the machine up to within 5 ft of the top of the tank and run for about 15 min, lower 5 ft and run for another 15 min. Continue lowering and washing at 5-ft increments until within 5 ft of the bottom again. Run the machine at this lower level for 30 min to complete the process.

All the time that the machine is running, the pumps should be slowly pumping out the wash water. This keeps a steady stream of water running toward the suction foot and carries away some of the sludge and dirt that would otherwise be floating on the surface of the water in the tank. This sludge would adhere to the sides of the tank at the lower levels and make the cleaning job much more difficult. The reason for operating the machine at the lower position first is to warm up the tank and knock down the worst of the scale and dirt at the beginning of the operation.

The length of time and number of drops may be increased or decreased depending upon the condition of the tank and the degree of cleanliness desired. Figure 5-3 shows the method of rigging up a machine to wash from different positions by the use of blocks and single whips. The machine is assumed to be entering the tank through a manhole, but the same thing can be done if it is lowered through a tank washing hole.

After washing as outlined above, the tank is opened and ventilated by a mechanical blower. On dry cargo ships the rigging of wind sails, as done on tankers, is not always practicable.

After ventilation, men must be sent into the tank to muck out. *Mucking out* may be defined as the process of scraping up scale and sediment left in the tank and placing it in a bucket which is hauled out of the tank and dumped over the side or on deck to be shoveled over the side when the ship is at sea. This process is done entirely by hand and is a slow going job. It should be done thoroughly. The mucking out process is followed by wiping down the interior, spotting the dirtier areas by using a hand hose, or by wiping with a solvent and rags.

The entire process of washing by machine can be divided into these three stages: (1) Washing. (2) Ventilating. (3) Mucking out. The first and last stages vary in length of time and care taken in carrying them out depending upon the condition of the tank at the beginning and the cleanliness desired in the end.

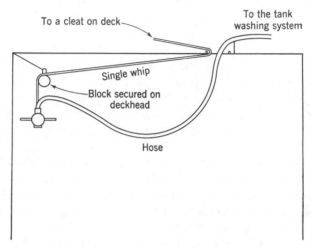

Fɪɢ. 5-3.   Rigging for an improved wash.   The objective here is to place the machine in a more advantageous position for washing than that afforded by being lowered straight through the deck opening.   Instead of rigging a block as shown here, a ¾-in. hole may be bored through the deck at suitable points and a ⅜-in. wire on a reel attached to the washing machine.   This is a system recommended by the Navy for positioning the machine to obtain a better wash.   After the wash, the holes are tapped, plugged, and welded over.

Washing by hand hose.   The majority of dry cargo vessels still are not equipped with the machines, pumps, and heat exchangers for cleaning tanks mechanically; therefore, the tanks must be washed by hand. Washing by hand starts with the steaming of the tank by turning on the steam smothering line.   The steaming period may run from 4 to 8 hr depending upon the condition of the tank before the process starts.   If the tank has been carrying black fuel oil and is to be prepared for a product that is easily contaminated, the tank will require at least 6 hr of steaming.

After the steaming period, the tank must be allowed to cool for 1 or 2 hr.   The cooling time will depend upon the outside temperature and no definite time limit can be specified.

As soon as it is possible, a man should be sent into the tank with a wash deck hose and washing by hand should commence. This man should have a line around his shoulders and under his arms and be tended by one man from the deck. A vapor proof light should be lowered into the tank so that the man in the tank can see where he is directing the stream of water from the hose. This man must work from the top of the ladder leading into the tank which is an awkward and dangerous position to handle a hose. To prevent an accident, he should lash himself to the ladder before the hose is passed down to him. At the first stage of the washing process, this man's head should be no farther down into the tank than a foot or so, just enough to enable him to see the interior. The blower should be rigged and a supply of fresh air should be supplied to him continuously. He will start washing the overhead and continue down the bulkheads and sides of the tank. At the beginning, the heat will be intense and the man should be relieved after not more than 10 min of washing. Gradually, the time for each man in the tank can be increased as the tank cools down. It is important to start the hand washing before the tank cools excessively, because as the tank cools the waxy elements in the oil tend to coagulate and become difficult to wash away. The steaming period should melt most of the wax and grease and make it easier to wash the tank. The hand hose cannot be handled with the high pressures and temperatures used with a machine. The temperature of the water when washing by hand should be 125°F and the pressure 125 lb per sq in. This is about as much pressure and as high a temperature as a man clinging to a slippery ladder can handle. If started while the tank is still warm, this washing procedure will be effective. While the washing process is being carried out, the tanks should be slowly stripped by operating the pumps steadily. This is for the same reason as mentioned in the case of machine washing, to have a steady stream of water running toward the suction foot and prevent a rise in the dirty water level in the tank.

As the washing continues the tank will be cooling down and the man handling the hose in the tank will have to go farther and farther down. After he has done all the washing possible with the hose, the tank should be well ventilated with a mechanical blower. Following the ventilation process, all hands should be sent into the tank for wiping down and mucking out. When the tank has been wiped down and mucked out, it should be clean, dry, and ready for the next cargo.

Whether washing a tank by hand or by machine, if the tank is not cleaned sufficiently well after the regular washing process there is no other alternative except to repeat the process. However, if only certain spots are found to be dirty, the interior may be cleaned in those localized areas only.

If a tank has been used for dry cargo for some time and the principal defect in the tank's condition is heavy rust and dirt accumulation, the interior may have to be scraped and chipped before the washing process. This depends upon the type of cargo that is to be loaded into the tank. For example, when loading latex in bulk in Malaya it is imperative to have every square inch of the tank free of rust and dirt. The interior surface of the tank is coated with wax before the latex is loaded and there must be no trace of rust under the coating of wax. Luckily, in that part of the world labor is not costly, and sufficient workers can be engaged to cover the interior surface literally foot by foot. Each worker labors all day long on a few square feet, but in the end the tank is scaled clean without any further washing or preparation being necessary. The wax can be applied after removing all the scaffolding and equipment, and then the latex is loaded.

Before any tank is loaded, the interior is inspected by a representative of the shipper, the shipowner, and one of the ship's officers. The shipowner will generally have a surveyor certify the tank as being clean for his own protection. The surveyor being a qualified representative of the cargo underwriters, probably from an organization such as the National Cargo Bureau, Inc.

CHECKING THE CONDITION OF THE CARGO HOLD

To the casual observer, glancing down into a ship's cargo hold, it does not appear that there are many things that could go wrong with the space below. It has the appearance of a big steel container with spaced wooden lining against the frames and little else. Yet, before an officer can make an entry in the ship's log relative to the condition of the cargo spaces, he must have checked in one way or another a long list of items. Some of these things must be checked each time the ship empties her holds, others, such as the striking plate under the bilge sounding pipe, need to be checked very infrequently. These items are tabulated below and commented upon briefly.

Permanent dunnage. The term *permanent dunnage* refers to the sweat battens secured to the frames, the spar ceiling laid over the tank tops, the wooden sheathing sometimes secured to the transverse bulkheads separating boiler rooms or engine rooms from adjoining cargo holds, and any wooden casings around pipes or conduits going through the cargo spaces. These items can be inspected as the ship is being discharged. That is to say, there is no need to make a special inspection trip through the ship to keep informed about their condition. The policy should be set by the chief officer for all officers to take note of the condition of these things as they travel from hatch to hatch during their normal day's work of observing the cargo operations. If something is noted to be missing or broken, the chief officer should be given the information as soon as possible. In the case of sweat battens, the chief officer should order the ship's carpenter to replace the missing sweat batten during the lunch hour or whenever there will be no longshoremen in the hold. In this manner, the ship's sweat battens will always be in first class condition. If casings or spar ceiling is noted in damaged condition, it may be repaired by the ship's force but more than likely a requisition to the company's construction and repair department will have to be made. The sweat battens can usually be taken care of by the ship's force in the manner described above, and the work and trouble is negligible. If the batten is missing above a height that can be easily reached from the tank tops, the cargo provides a convenient platform upon which to work.

Limber system. The term *limber system* refers to the drain pipes and drain holes that comprise the method for carrying off all liquids to the drain well in a hold. In other words, limber is a synonym for drainage. The limber system or drainage system must be checked each time a ship has been discharged. If a ship is on a run where the cargo is always coming in and going out, the check must be made whenever it is practicable.

In the 'tweendecks, the principal thing to be checked is the drain pipe leading down to the ship's drain well in the after end of the hold. This drain pipe can be checked by pouring water from a bucket down the pipe and observing whether the water flows through or not. Obviously, two men are needed to see if the flow is obstructed or not.

If the flow is obstructed, the carpenter should clear the pipe with an ordinary wire snake or by using a rubber plunger. If the pipe cannot be cleared by these methods, it must be removed and either renewed or cleaned out. Cargo should not be stowed in a 'tweendeck space where the scupper drains are plugged up. There are cargoes that must be stowed so that leakage from them is prevented from reaching these drains, but the drains themselves should never be plugged. One reason for this is because of the tremendous effect on stability that the free surface in the upper levels of a ship has. The free surface effect itself is the same whether high or low in the ship, but the added weight of the liquid trapped in the upper levels adds to a poor situation. If it becomes necessary to use a fire hose in the 'tweendeck where there are no drains, the water will create a condition that endangers the ship. One of the contributing causes to the capsizing of the Normandy in 1941 at a dock during the fighting of a fire in her in New York City was the fact that the water from the fire hoses collected in the upper decks and *remained* there. If the water could have drained to the lower levels through freely running pipes, the ship might be afloat today.

These drains from the upper decks to the drain well are located in the after end of the hatch. This fact must be kept in mind when stowing certain cargoes. Cargoes that are known to drain heavily should normally be loaded near these drains. There are exceptions; for example, if the cargo is of such a nature that it would obstruct drainage from other cargoes, then it should be stowed away from the drains. In the latter case, however, it would be highly important to see that the dunnage was laid to form an efficient drainage system under the cargo stowed near the drain pipes. Lack of attention to such details on the part of stevedores or ship's officers might be the cause of costly damage to cargo.

SIDE BILGE AND DRAIN WELLS. In the lower holds, two types of drainage systems may be found. On older vessels, those built prior to World War II, the side bilge system is almost always found. The Victory ship built during World War II also has side bilges in No. 2 and No. 3 holds and in the deep tanks of No. 4 hold. When using the deep tanks for dry cargo, they should be stowed as lower holds with side bilges. In side bilge construction, the double bottom stops a few feet inboard from the hull plating and then continues downward at an angle of about 45° from the horizontal to join the hull plating at about the middle of the turn of the bilge.

In most of the modern ships, the tank top plating continues outboard in a horizontal plane and connects with the hull plating. A drain well is provided for draining off any water or other liquids that might find their way into the ship's hold. The drain well is located between the last two frames and floors of the hold. It drops down below the level of the tank tops to within about 18 in. of the outer bottom, runs athwartship for several feet, and stops about 18 in. inboard from the turn of the bilge. Figure 5-4 is a midship section illustrating the side bilge construction; Fig. 5-5 illustrates the modern construction.

In the case of the side bilge construction, it is important to check all of the limber (drainage) holes that are through the bilge bracket where the hull and tank top intersect. These holes should be clear. This bilge system is not open to the hold. It is usually covered with boards of 2 by 12 in. dimensions. These boards are known as the limber boards and their purpose is to keep dirt and cargo residue from entering the limber system. They are removable for inspection purposes. It is necessary, therefore, to open up the bilges and check them by removing these boards each time.

In the case of holds equipped with the drain well system, there is a perforated plate that covers the drain well which must be kept clean. If these holes become plugged, no water or liquid cargo can drain into the well. Hence, if the hull plating is pierced or water finds its way into the compartment in any way, there will be no way for it to be removed.

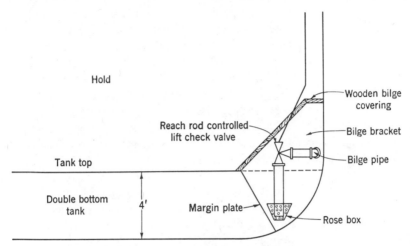

FIG. 5-4. Side bilge system. The rose box and bilge suction is located in the after end of the compartment. To seal off the side bilge system, it is necessary to cover the wooden bilge covering laid over the face of the bilge bracket so that the bulk commodity cannot leak through. This requires a good deal more care than sealing off the entrance to a drain well. More burlap is required and it must be carefully secured in place by use of battens laid over the burlap and nailed down.

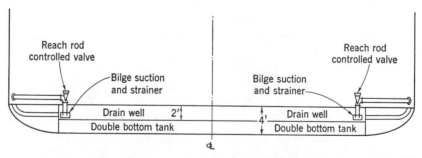

FIG. 5-5. Drain well. The drain well may run almost all the way across the ship as shown here or it may be only about 4 ft transversely. Its depth is about 2 ft and it is located just forward of the after bulkhead of the compartment, extending forward about 2½ ft. The opening into the drain well from the hold is from 2 to 4 ft long in a transverse direction. It is this opening that must be made dust tight but not water tight when preparing for bulk commodities.

It will back up into the hold and cause free surface, which will impair the stability, or rise vertically and damage the cargo.

The liquid that finds its way into either the drain well or into the after part of the side bilge is removed from the compartment through a bilge suction pipe that is connected to a bilge pump manifold in the engine room. The ship's officer when checking the limber system should always check the wire cage or perforated box covering the suction foot in the well or bilge. The wire cage or perforated box acts as a strainer of the liquid being picked up by the suction and it must be clean and clear. This strainer is known as the *rose box*. The pipe used to pump out the well or bilge is 3 in. in diameter and the end is not fitted with a bell. It terminates about $1\frac{1}{2}$ in. above the lowest point in the well or bilge. The rose box keeps rags, bits of wood, and other debris from being sucked into the bilge suction pipe. If the rose box is neglected, it will eventually become clogged; this will result in making it impossible to pump out the hold in case of leakage.

STOP-LIFT-CHECK VALVES. The bilge suction pipes have valves inserted in them just above the level of the suction foot. These valves are known as stop-lift-check valves. The action of this valve is as follows: If the valve stem is turned clockwise as far as it will go, the valve is closed. If the valve is opened one and a half turns, its action is the same as any lift-check valve. If the valve stem is turned counter clockwise for several turns, the valve is raised off its seat and it acts as an open valve.

Ordinarily, this valve should be set to operate as a lift-check valve. That is, it should be backed off about $1\frac{1}{2}$ turns. In this position, if suction is lost when pumping the bilges, the contents of the pipe will not be vomited back into the well. This fact makes it easier to regain suction again and to retain suction when pumping liquids at low levels which is almost always the case when pumping out the bilges and drain wells of cargo ships.

The valve should be closed when there is danger of flooding an adjacent compartment through the bilge system, as in the case of a collision. This may not be necessary unless the pipe is broken by the impact, but it should be done as a safety precaution. Part of every ship's collision drill should include the closing of these valves by crew members instructed in the procedure.

The valve will have to be opened wide in case it becomes necessary to pump water into the hold through the bilge system. This may be the only way to extinguish some types of fires.

This valve should be checked to see that it turns freely each time that it becomes accessible after discharging cargo. It is important to reset it, however, as required by the chief engineer. It may be opened wide in some cases so that the lift-check feature is not utilized.

REACH RODS. Obviously, these valves cannot be reached when the hold is filled with cargo. To operate them from the deck, they are fitted with *reach rods*. These are simply extensions of the valve stem running up through the main deck through water tight glands and fitted with a wheel for turning. They must be checked to see that they are not broken and that they turn freely. If they are rusted and frozen, the ship may be placed in a dangerous condition in case of an emergency. It is recommended that the reach rods and bilge suction valves be checked at the same time. This can be accomplished by one man turning the reach rod from the weather deck level while another man observes the action in the hold.

The 'tweendeck drains, side bilges or drain wells, rose boxes, bilge suction valves, and reach rods comprise an important group of items all related to keeping the drainage system of the ship functioning in the best manner. These items should be checked each voyage and if anything is not working correctly it should be repaired before cargo is loaded.

BILGE SOUNDING PIPE. In order to determine whether a given compartment is taking water, each one is equipped with a pipe running from an accessible upper deck down to the drain well or bilge called the *sounding pipe*. At regular periods, an iron or brass rod is lowered down this pipe until it strikes the bottom of the well or bilge. The rod is coated with chalk, and if any water or other liquid is in the bilge its presence and depth will be indicated on the rod. This chore is performed by the ship's carpenter and is called *sounding the bilge*. It should be done at least twice a day under ordinary circumstances, every half hour when taking on fuel oil or other liquids in the ship's tanks, and right after a period of heavy weather. There may be times when the bilges cannot be sounded because of heavy seas with water on deck continually; during such times, orders to the watch engineering officer should be given to pump all the bilges at least once a watch. Such orders would generally be given by the master of the ship through the chief engineer.

THE STRIKING PLATE. After several years of daily sounding, the steel directly below the bilge sounding pipe will wear away. If a pinhole develops in this spot from wear and corrosion, oil or water from the tank below can enter the hold. The amount of oil that can enter the hold might be sufficient to cause damage to cargo in the lower tiers, especially if the tank were pressed up and the ship had a large trim by the stern. Another bad feature of such a hole is the possibility of contaminating the drinking water if carried in the tank below.

To guard against the possibility of the steel directly below the bilge sounding pipe wearing out, this area is covered with a small doubling plate which is called the *striking plate*. This plate does not wear out quickly and hence need not be inspected every time the drainage system is checked. However, every officer joining a ship should satisfy himself that this plate on both sides of every compartment is not worn through. This can only be done by opening up the drain well and sighting the plate or running a finger over it to feel the amount of wear. If it is badly worn, it should be renewed at the first opportunity. It is not necessary to renew the entire plate. The worn spot can be filled with a bead of weld.

Electrical conduits and outlets. Conduits and outlets can also be checked as the cargo is being worked. Whenever a defect is noted, a repair requisition should be sent in immediately or the defect should be taken care of by the ship's force.

Ladders. As a safety measure, a broken rung in a ladder should be repaired as rapidly as possible. If a ladder is damaged during the cargo operation and it cannot be repaired immediately, the longshoremen must be provided with a Jacobs ladder or other means of climbing into and out of the hold. Rungs can be replaced very easily by the ship's force. The uprights of the ladder can be bored with a ⅝-in. hole and a ½-in. steel bar, threaded at both ends, secured in place with nuts. This can be used as a temporary repair measure, providing the uprights are not bent out of line. Ladders are frequent casualties in ship's holds and their repair goes on continually.

Rivets, seams, and pipes. The rivets and seams of the hull plating, tank top plating, deck plating, and the plating of the transverse bulkheads forming one side of a tank should be constantly surveyed by the ship's officers as they make their frequent visits to the holds. Prior to loading cargo, a special inspection should be made for evidence of leaks. Leaks may be spotted by rust streaks or oil traces. This also applies to pipes running through the compartment and especially the flanges of such pipes.

Manholes and side ports. These openings into the hold should be checked more frequently than any of the other items mentioned. Obviously, they should be checked when they are closed and made ready for sea. If any of the dogs are difficult to turn, they should be made free at the first opportunity, which may not be at the time of closing. The gaskets should be kept clean and intact. If gaskets are flax or woven fiber material of any kind, they should be oiled and free of paint. If they are made of rubber, they should be kept clean and free of oil, grease, and paint. The knife edges against which the gasket presses when the door of the opening is closed should be clean and free from broken or jagged places.

While at sea, side ports should be checked twice daily. This is not of great importance when the ship is light and the weather is fair, but if the ship is loaded and the seas are running up the hull and placing a hydrostatic pressure over the side port as the ship works in the seaway, it is extremely important. If possible, some means of gaining access to the side port should be made without having to open a manhole on the weather deck. This can be accomplished by building crawl holes in the cargo in the shelter deck spaces leading from entrances other than the manhole openings on the weather deck, if such openings exist.

If a side port is found to be leaking while at sea, it should be caulked with oakum. Directly in the way of most side ports, a drain will lead to the drainage system of the hold. This drain should be kept clear so that in case of leakage the entering sea water can be drained off quickly. In such a case, it would be common sense to have the bilges serving the compartment pumped frequently by the engineer officer on watch. In very bad weather it may be impossible to have the bilges sounded periodically because of water on deck and generally unsafe conditions in the exposed area of the bilge sounding pipe opening on the weather deck.

Fire fighting equipment. The steam smothering or carbon dioxide outlets should be checked to see that they are not broken and are clear. The inlets to the smoke detecting system should be checked also to see that they are clear and in good working order.

Hatch covering equipment. It may not be necessary to place this item on the check off list; however, it is important to have all this equipment in good order. If tarpaulins are used, there should be at least three and they should be without holes or weak seams. Sufficient hatch boards should be on hand to cover the hatch opening completely. The practice of spacing hatch boards to take up space produced by a missing board is likely to lead to trouble.

Ventilation ducts. The most important thing that needs checking in the case of the ventilation ducts leading into the holds is that the system of closing them from the outside atmosphere is in good working order. In the case of fire, it is imperative that all openings to the atmosphere be closed and kept closed. In some instances, it may be necessary to close these openings in case of heavy seas coming on board. It should be seen, of course, that these same openings into the hold are clear so that the hold can be correctly ventilated during the voyage.

THE STOWAGE OF CONTAINERS

This chapter is entitled the Stowage of Cargo, but it is impossible to deal with the stowage of all types of cargo in this single work.   In the remaining pages of this chapter we will discuss the stowage of a number of common container types and some important cargo types.   We will also deal with the problem of calculating space consumption using the stowage factor.   The discusison will be based on the principles already covered and should serve to illustrate their application.   The cargoes selected for discussion are not necessarily any more important than hundreds of others that might have been chosen; however, some selectivity had to be exercised and those covered do bring out a number of interesting points.   A full discussion of a large number of commodities will have to await the writing of a book with that objective.   Such a discussion cannot be an adjunct to a book dealing with fundamental principles.

The stowage of bags.   The preparation of the hold for the stowage of bags commences with the laying of a dunnage platform upon which to stow the bottom tier.   This platform is primarily for drainage purposes although in some cases it is equally important to keep bagged cargo from contacting the steel deck.   If the ship is equipped with side bilges, the first layer of dunnage should be laid down running athwartships or preferably at an angle to the keel.   If laid at an angle to the keel, the forward end of the dunnage should be inboard.

If the ship is equipped with drain wells in the after end of the hold, the first tier of dunnage should be laid down running fore and aft.   The dunnage should be spaced not more than 1 ft apart.

The second tier of dunnage should be laid at right angles to the first, except that in the case of the first tier being laid diagonally the second tier may be laid either fore and aft or athwartships.   For bagged cargoes, the second tier should be spaced not more than 1 in. apart.   If the dunnage is too widely spaced, the pressure of the top tiers will cause the bags on the bottom tiers to split.

If ventilation is not a major problem with the commodity in the bags, the dunnage of the second tier should be placed flush together.   This eliminates any possibility of splitting the bottom bags and requires very little additional dunnage.   If sufficient dunnage is available, the drainage tiers of dunnage should be 2 or 3 in. high if the commodity requires maximum ventilation, such as rice and soy beans.   This provides for a series of ventilation ducts under the cargo.

The stowage of the bags may be in any one of three ways depending upon the nature of the commodity in the bags.   If the commodity requires maximum ventilation, the best stowage is one bag directly on top of the one below, laid with the length fore and aft (see Fig. 3-20*a*). This stowage will provide small air spaces throughout the stowed cargo block and help in the circulation of air. It is difficult to get the long-shoremen to do this consistently as the stowage proceeds. It generally requires careful explanation of the need and desirability of care in placing the bags in the hold and the presence of an officer after the stowage commences. Stowage in this manner is known as bag on bag stowage.

If the commodity does not require maximum ventilation, the best stowage is to place the upper bags between two lower ones which results in a brick work style of stowage. This stowage results in the elimination of the spaces between rows and tiers and the broken stowage percentage is reduced. If a full hatch is being stowed, it might mean that one complete additional tier can be stowed. This type of stowage is referred to as *half bag* stowage (see Fig. 5-6).

When stowing bagged cargo in small blocks where the stability of the block is a factor, it may be advisable to stow one tier of bags fore and aft and the next tier athwartship. This stowage ties the tiers together so that the stowed block is less likely to fall over while working the cargo in port or when the ship is rolling and pitching in a heavy sea. Such blocks would not depend entirely on this cross tiering for their security; they would be shored up or blocked up by adjacent cargo as well. It may not be necessary to cross tier the bags throughout the stowed block, but simply to do this on the last two rows of the block. Still another way to add to the security of a bulkhead of bagged goods is to place a strip of dunnage along the outside edge of every other tier as the loading progresses vertically. This will tend to tip the bulkhead toward the stowed block or at least lessen the tendency for the face of the bulkhead to lean away from the stowed block.

Although there are exceptions, generally no dunnage is used between tires of bagged cargoes. Venetian vents are sometimes used *within* a stowed block of commodities needing heavy ventilation air currents (see p. 111).

The only other dunnage used besides the drainage floor is vertical dunnage laid against the transverse bulkheads, against the sweat battens, and against all vertical structural members, such as stanchions, ladders, and ventilator ducts. This vertical dunnage is used to keep the bags from contacting the steel members of the ship. For additional protection and cleanliness, the vertical members may be wrapped with heavy paper and the entire thing tied with rope yarns.

If the bags contain coffee, cocoa beans, or any other commodity that may have leakage of contents and these contents must not touch the ship's deck, the bags should be stowed over separation cloths. Any

Fig. 5-6. Bag stowage. This is a view of bag stowage extending out into the hatch square for a little more than one section. It is not the best stowage. The bulkhead has been carefully built vertically and looks fairly stable; however, by running every other tier of bags along the bulkhead face with their lengths athwartship and tying the bulkhead bags into the stow, a much more stable bulkhead could have been made. The effort to do this would have been no more than building the bulkhead as shown here. Almost all of the bags in this bulkhead are running longitudinally and are built up half bag style. Thus, these bags are more or less a unit and can more easily fall away from the rest of the stow in case of really heavy weather. Of course, if other cargo will always be bearing against this bulkhead or if no bad weather is encountered, no damage will be experienced. However, cargo should not be stowed so that a good outturn depends upon so many factors that are not a certainty, especially when there is no difference in the amount of effort required. Courtesy U.S. Maritime Commission.

leakage will be caught in the cloth and can be rebagged before being contaminated. The use of these separation cloths is also advisable when stowing bagged commodities over other cargoes. The most efficient covering for this purpose is made of burlap. The burlap comes in strips about 4 ft wide which must be cut to reach the entire distance across the stowed block with enough slack to enable tucking it down the sides of the ship about 2 ft. These cloths should never be stretched tightly over the cargo but should be left with some slack.

Hooks used on some bags will result in tears that allow the contents to leak out. On loosely woven bags a hook can be used without tearing the bag. The hook will slip through the fibers and out again without actually leaving a hole for the contents to leak through. The commodity type must be large enough to allow the use of such bags, such as cocoa beans. If a bag is tightly packed and heavy (over 100 lb), there is little doubt that the longshoremen will use hooks on it. They cannot get a grip on such a bag with their hands and to handle it they are forced to use a hook. If the shipper packs the bags with corners tied to form a place for the longshoremen to grab, known as *dog ears,* hooks will not be used as readily. Paper bags of cement or plaster are very vulnerable to the hook, but they are often small enough and light enough to allow the longshoremen to lift them easily. Every effort should be made to prevent hooks being used on such cargoes. A hook with several small slightly curved prongs known as a *bag hook* may be issued to longshoremen when handling fiber bags if it is desired that they do not use their larger cargo hooks. This will help reduce hook damage in some cases. The bag hook should not be used on paper bags.

In the outboard tiers, bags may be stowed athwartships or placed on end, providing the vertical dunnage cannot be used. The reason for placing the bags athwartship is to present the relatively small surface at the end of the bag to possible damage from contact with the frames. Standing the bags on end presents a surface to the sweat battens that is too large to protrude through them and is a device that may be used in lieu of vertical dunnage. If the dunnage is available, it should be used.

The bags must not be allowed to rest on the edges of the sweat battens, stringers, upper ends of vertical dunnage, or other surfaces that might present themselves along the periphery of the hold. If they rest on these surfaces, they will be torn as the cargo settles during the voyage.

In spite of all precautions, some bags will be torn in almost every shipment; hence, it is important to use separation cloths as mentioned above in order to catch leakage. If the contents that leak out are caught in the separation cloths and rebagged, they are known as *ship fills.* If the contents are not caught but allowed to reach the deck of the ship

or dock and are swept up and rebagged, they are known as *sweepings*.
Ship fills or sweepings are distributed to the consignees having cargo in
the hold in proportion to the total amount they had originally. Ship
fills may be handled by the consignee in the same manner as the rest of
the original shipment. Sweepings must be condemned as food and used
either for the oil content or re-exported.

The stowage of bales. A drainage floor is prepared as described for
bags. Vertical dunnage is not as important in the wings as with bags,
but it should be used against transverse bulkheads and vertical structural
members in the manner described for bags. Bales contain either un-
processed fibers or strands of a commodity or a flat material shipped in
layers. Examples of the former are cotton, sisal, jute, wool, and manila.
Examples of the latter are cotton piece goods, tobacco, skins, and dry
goods.

Bales are generally parallelepiped in shape (Fig. 5-7). If they contain the fibrous commodities, they may be placed in the ship on their
flats, edges, or crowns and no harm will come to them. They stow more
securely, however, if stowed on their flats in a fore and aft direction.
All cargo should be stowed to conform with the shape of the ship unless
there is a good reason for not doing so. One good reason for deviating
from continuous flat stowage in the case of bales is to use up as much
of the cubic as possible in the compartment. Therefore, it is important
to measure the hold clearance vertically and stow the bales so that the
top of the last tier will come as close as possible to the underside of the
beams. It may be that all the bales should be on their flats, or edges, or
all but the last tier which may have to be placed on their crowns.

If the contents of the bale are in layers, the first tier is laid down on
the dunnage platform on their flats. The outboard bales in each tier
should be placed on their edges so that their flats will be presented to
the sweat battens. This precaution is necessary to lessen the damage in
case of chafage. If the bales chafe or become wet on their flats, only
one or two layers will be damaged. If the edges or ends are damaged,
every item in the container is affected. After the bales in the periphery
are stowed, it is not necessary to stow the remainder on their flats. In
fact, the remaining distance should be measured and the bales should be
stowed so that the greatest amount of space is consumed by the cargo
and there is a minimum of lost space over the last tier. The bales that
bear against stanchions and vertical ventilation ducts should be placed
with their flats against these members with dunnage between them and
the structural members.

Some of the fibrous commodities may be potentially dangerous from
fire. Two apparent causes of fires in such commodities are: (1) Spon-

taneous heating until the kindling point is reached; this results in *spontaneous combustion*. (2) Sparks caused by friction of metal bands used on bales against steel parts of the ship. The first cause of fire can be eliminated by being certain that all bales are dry when stowed and remain that way. They must also be free from oil. The second cause

FIG. 5-7. Wool bales in stowage and on the sling. Wool bales do not need to be carefully stowed on their flats because the contents are fibers and also because this type is almost a cube and does not have a pronounced flat area. These bales are mostly stowed on their flats nevertheless. Note that the clearance between the top bales and the deckhead is very small, this is good for the lost stowage has been reduced. Note the special type of sling consisting of eight snorters with two bale hooks in the eye. Each bale is picked up by the two hooks, eight bales being hoisted at once. Courtesy Boston Port Authority.

can be eliminated by making certain that dunnage always stands between a bale and the metal parts of the ship.

Carelessness in the use of matches and smoking in the hold is undoubtedly the cause of some fires. Sparks from electrical fixtures in the hold or carelessly placed cluster lights are also responsible for some fires. These causes, however, are simple safety violations and not a direct result of the stowage.

When baled commodities are received, exceptions should be taken if the bands holding them together are broken or missing or if the covering is ripped off and part of the contents exposed or hanging from the bale in loose strands. The cotton bale, for example, is supposed to have at least three quarters of its surface, including the ends, covered by burlap or other suitable cloth covering. The bands are spaced about 8 in. During the handling process from the warehouse to the ship, some bands may be broken and the covering ripped and tattered. If this happens, the possibility of fire from all sources mentioned above is increased.

The stowage of cardboard cartons. The dunnage platform on which the stowage of cardboard cartons commences is the same as for bags except that the spacing of the second tier may be up to 4 in. The stowage of cartons may start at the centerline and proceed outboard or vice versa. Probably one of the most important points to make, relative to the stowage of cartons, is the care needed to maintain the level in the wings. As the stowage proceeds outboard in the lower holds, care must be taken not to stow a carton beyond the level portion of the tank tops. That is, a row should not be stowed upon reaching a point where the next carton when placed in position will rise above the level of the rest of the tier. In place of this carton, dunnage must be laid to fill in the triangular space on the outboard side. The next tier can then be stowed. This procedure must be used in the wings until all of the curvature has been stowed under.

The cartons are placed in the hold so that each carton rests on two cartons below it. This results in stowage that is known as *brick fashion*. The dunnage in the wings should be placed against the sweat battens in a vertical position. Dunnage should also be used to separate the cargo from the transverse bulkheads and vertical structural members. If the vertical dunnage is not used in the wings, some of the cartons may become hung up on the sweat battens and as the ship works in a heavy seaway the side of the carton will be sheared off from chafing and superimposed weight from above.

The need for dunnage floors between cartons in deep lower holds is explained on pp. 122 and 123.

The tiers must be kept level. This requirement is important. Dunnaging in the wings is one of the ways that this is accomplished. Obstructions in the compartment, such as the inclined plane in open shelter deck vessels from the 9-in. hatch coamings, require care in the use of dunnage to keep the tiers level.

The stowage of crates. The term *crates* as used here refers to wooden containers that are built as a framework with open sides and tops. These crates are generally stiffened by the use of diagonal pieces but are, for the most part, open so that the contents are exposed. Crates without the diagonal stiffeners are insufficient for ocean transportation. Refrigerators, stoves, and light machinery are shipped in crates. The bottoms are solid with well built foundations for supporting the contents. The crate is a poor container because it lacks strength and it lacks protection for the contents. Crates require a layer of dunnage between every tier. The dunnage may be spaced up to about 4 in. If a shipment consists entirely of crates, the best place to stow it is in the 'tweendecks. Top tiers in the lower hold are suitable providing, of course, that the contents of the crates are not liquid. If a shipment of crates is stowed in the lower hold and it is necessarily placed on the tank tops, the height to which it is stowed should be limited to 12 ft or about half the depth of the lower hold. Cargo stowed over these crates should be lightweight merchandise.

Because of the dunnage layer between each tier of crates, it is not necessary to stow them brick fashion. This is an advantage because it means that in the wings the crates will rise vertically without the stepping in and out resulting from brick fashion stowage.

The stowage of cases. The word *case* as used here refers to the wooden box that is sheathed to form a tightly closed container. A wide variety of commodities is shipped in the case. Besides refrigerators, stoves, automobiles, and machinery; paints, drugs, beverages, and foodstuffs are also shipped in the case. Uniform sized cases may be stowed brick fashion in the same way as cardboard cartons without the dunnage floors between tiers in the bottom of lower holds. The wooden case depends upon its contents for part of its strength, as do all containers, but unlike the cardboard carton, dampness will not weaken it.

Depending entirely upon the contents, cases and cartons may at times be placed on their ends or edges if this procedure will facilitate the stowage without endangering the safety of the cargo. Another important point to make with respect to the stowage of cases and cartons is that, when their length is twice as long or approximately twice as long as the width, security of the stowed block is obtained by placing one tier with the length fore and aft and the next tier with the length athwartships. The pattern of the stowage would be as in brick fashion stowage but the stepping in and out of the outboard edges would be avoided. This is usually the manner that such items are stowed, because most containers are not constructed with a square base. In some cases the direction of the containers in any one tier will be changed so that the division of the containers is staggered.

Most of the comments above refer to shipments of crates or cases in uniform sizes. If a cargo lot consists of a number of variable sizes, the stowage precautions include some additional points. First of all, those containers with the heaviest items should be stowed in the lower tiers. Secondly, a smaller size crate or case must never be stowed within the perimeter of a larger one below it without dunnage to support the upper crate. Such dunnage should extend from at least one side of the lower case to the other but preferably the dunnage should extend over two or more cases. The upper crate or case is best stowed over two lower ones.

As the stowage of variable sized crates and cases proceeds, the longshoremen should note the variations in height of the top of the stow and use dunnage to level off small or large sections, whichever is possible. The use of dunnage in the stowage of such cargo should be extensive. Piling additional cargo on top of irregular platforms of cargo in the lower tiers invites heavy crushing damage. The crates and cases may be fitted together in much the same manner as a set of odd size blocks, but in so doing the probability that uneven pressures will cause failure of containers and damage to contents is greatly increased. The use of ample amounts of dunnage to fill in slight steps and floor off large sections is mandatory for the safest stowage. The lack of such dunnage is improper stowage.

The stowage of casks. The word *cask* refers to a type of container. The words barrel, puncheon, pipe, butt, and tun refer to sizes of the cask type of container. The term barrel often is used to mean all containers of the cask type. The actual amount of liquid contained in the various types of casks varies widely depending upon the type of liquid being carried and the trade in which it is being handled. To give some idea of the relative size of a few of the commoner casks and the names used, the following table has been prepared:

Cask	Capacity in U.S. Gallons
1 barrel	31½
1 hogshead	63
1 pipe	126
1 butt	126
1 tun	252

It must be emphasized that these volumes are not universal. For example, the English barrel of beer has a volume of 36 U.S. gal whereas the 31½ gal shown in the table is the volume of a barrel of wine. A butt of beer in England has a volume of 108 gal whereas a butt of wine has 126 gal. The volumes of the various casks are so variable that there is little point in trying to remember any of them. When concerned with the stowage of such items, the officer should be certain he determines correctly the volume of cask listed on the manifest or bill of lading before calculating the space required to stow it.

The U.S. gallon is the equivalent of the English wine gallon, 231 cu in. The Imperial gallon consists of 277.418 cu in. or 1.2 U.S. gal. One U.S. gallon is equal to 0.8331 Imperial gal.

Because of the frequency that the barrel is used when speaking of the capacity of tank ships, it should be pointed out that the barrel used in the petroleum industry has a volume of 42 U.S. gal.

The stowage of cask type containers is the same whether they are barrels or tuns except that the height limitation is less as the container grows larger. There are also two broad classifications of casks. There is the wet or tight cask made of oak. The construction of this type of cask must be done with great care. The scarfed joints of the staves must be precisely cut and the staves must narrow from the bilge out to the head with great precision. This cask is used to ship beer, wine, spirits, and olives.

The other type of cask is the dry or slack type cask. This type is usually made of softer wood than the former, fir being widely used. The joints and other construction details do not require the care and precision of the tight cask. This type of container is used to ship flour, cement, and other dry products.

The weakest part of the cask is the bilge (see Fig. 5-8). The weight should never be placed on this part of the cask when stowed. The strongest part of the cask is the quarter. The stowage of the wet or tight cask, if in small lots and when there is no need to overstow them with heavy cargo, may be on end with a layer of dunnage between the tiers. The same stowage should always be given to the dry or slack cask. When stowing casks on end, the most important things to remember are to protect the chimes of the lower tiers by using strips of dunnage between tiers and to prevent excessive weights by limiting the weight of cargoes stowed over the casks. In most lower holds it is possible to stow barrels about seven tiers high. This height is too great if stowed on end. Six tiers is maximum. This type of stowage may open up the seams of the casks beginning along the bilges. The lower tiers of casks will leak first because they will be supporting the most weight.

When carrying large numbers of the wet or tight casks, or when the best possible stowage is desired, the casks should be stowed as described below. The cask is laid in the ship with the length running fore and aft and in regular athwartship rows. The bilge of the cask is raised off the deck by dunnage at least 2 in. thick laid under the quarters. The cask is secured in position to some extent by the use of small wedges placed on either side of each barrel at both ends (Fig. 5-9). If dunnage and wedges are not used, a more elaborate and safer method is to use *quoins*. These are chocks or supports cut to fit the curvature of the cask at the

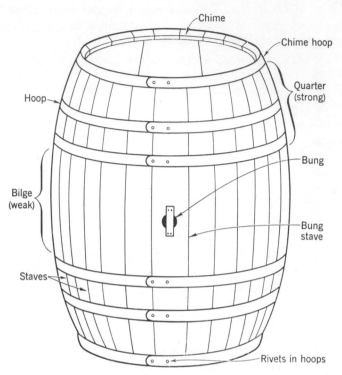

FIG. 5-8. The nomenclature of a cask. Note that the bung is in line with rivets on the hoops and that the head staves are vertical when the bung is up.

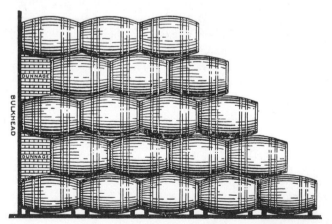

FIG. 5-9. The use of quoins. The quoins are placed under the first tier at the quarters of each cask. Courtesy U.S. Dept. of Commerce.

quarters and raise the cask vertically to clear the bilge from the deck. This type of stowage results in what is sometimes referred to as *bilge free* stowage.

In the wings, great care must be given to wedge the outboard cask securely into position with dunnage and bracing. Assuming that we are starting the stowage in the after part of the hold, the next cask forward must be precisely in line with the adjacent cask. Their chimes should fit together. One must not be inboard or outboard of the other nor up or down. As the stowage proceeds longitudinally, the curvature of the hull in the entrance or run of the ship will make it necessary to drop a cask from the outboard longitudinal rows and fill in with dunnage. The longitudinal rows should run precisely in line fore and aft.

The second tier should be stepped one half the length of the cask away from the bulkhead against which the bottom tier was stowed and a half diameter athwartship. No dunnage need be used between the first and second tier. The movement of the second tier forward and athwartships will place the bilge of the second cask over the intersection of four lower casks and the quarters of the upper cask will rest on the quarters of the lower cask. Hence, the bilge of the upper casks will be free without the use of dunnage (see Fig. 5-10).

Before stowing the third tier, dunnage should be placed in the space between the bulkhead and the chime of the second cask. This dunnage should be installed to support the quarter of one end of the third cask while the other quarter is supported by the second cask. Thus the stowage proceeds upward. It is of great importance to stow the bottom tier securely and to pay careful attention to dunnaging the wings and ends of the hold.

The curved intersection of two casks is known as the cantline of the stowed cargo. Hence, this system of stowage is referred to as *bilge and cantline*. But, the casks are stepped one half of their lengths fore and aft which gives the more descriptive phrase of *bilge and cantline half cask stowage*. If the casks are stowed bilge and cantline *full cask,* the bilges would not be free without additional dunnaging. Full cask stowage is easier, however, because it obviates the need for the dunnage every other tier at the ends. It may be safely used if the casks are empty.

The bung on a cask is placed at the bilge in line with all the rivets holding the hoops together. The rivets and bung are always along a side stave in line with the direction of the head staves. Hence, if the end staves are vertical, the bung is either directly up or directly down. A glance to see if the rivets are on top will tell whether the bung is down or up. The bung should always be up in stowage.

If the casks are properly stowed in this bilge and cantline half cask style with the bung up, the stowage results in what may be described as *bung up and bilge free* stowage. However, this phrase tells only *the result* of proper stowage not the method.

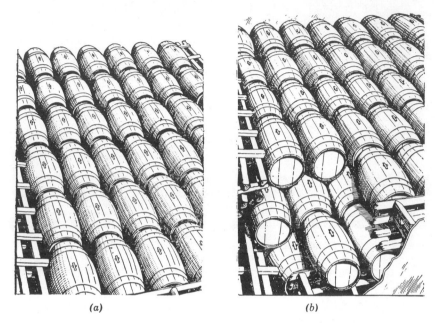

(a)   *(b)*

Fig. 5-10. Stowage of casks. (*a*) The stowage of the first tier with dunnage on the sides and one end as necessary, with all bungs up. The safety of the entire stow depends upon this first tier. These casks are resting on athwartship pieces with bilges raised off the deck and quoins to keep them secure. (*b*) The stowage after the second and third tier have been stowed, with dunnage being used to chock and fill in. All of the upper casks rest in the cantlines of the lower casks with four lower casks supporting an upper cask. Courtesy U.S. Navy.

Occasionally, shipments of casks will be in two or three sizes. If it is desired to give these shipments the best possible stowage, they should be stowed bilge and cantline half cask style with necessary modifications. It may be necessary to use dunnage and wedges between tiers to give proper support and security when smaller casks are stowed on top of larger ones. Also, instead of being able to step the third tier back against the bulkhead, it may be necessary for expediency to continue upward forming a pyramid with dunnage and bracing or suitable filler cargo being used to fill in the space left between the casks and the bulkhead. It is recommended that pyramiding be avoided by providing a platform of dunnage for stepping the third tier back against the bulkhead.

The stowage of cylinders. Flammable and nonflammable compressed gases are shipped in steel bottles commonly referred to as cylinders. These containers are under pressures of 2000 lb per sq in. and over. They must be handled carefully and stowed securely to preclude disastrous accidents.

If cylinders have nonflammable compressed gas in them, they must be stowed no closer to the side of the ship than 3 ft. Cylinders of flammable gas must be at least 8 ft from the ship's side. They may be stowed on deck or under deck, but the distance from the side of the ship is regulated. Also, certain cargoes must not be in the same hatch with flammable gases, see p. 220. In general, they should not be stowed with cargoes that are liable to give off heat.

Cylinders should be stowed on their bilges in a fore and aft position; the second tier should rest in the cantlines of the lower tier, reversing the direction of the ends in each tier. They should be placed over dunnage and, inasmuch as the cargo is fore and aft, the dunnage should be laid diagonally if stowed on deck with only one tier being used. When stowed below deck, two tiers of dunnage should be laid with the first tier fore and aft or diagonal and the second tier athwartships. For on-deck stowage, 2 by 4 dunnage spaced every 4 in. is suitable.

Cylinders are shipped in three forms with respect to the way the inlet valves are protected. They are equipped with a screw cap cover, a dished head, or they are boxed. The inlet valves must be given protection during shipment by one of these three forms.

Under certain conditions, it may be more convenient to stow cylinders standing up instead of lying down bilge and cantline style, for example, when clear deck run is lacking or is at a premium and needed for other deck cargoes. Standing cylinders on end is only permissible when extremely sturdy racks are built out of 2-in. lumber and thoroughly lashed down with wire rope, chain, or steel strapping with turnbuckles on every turn over the stowed block. The clear deck run can be saved by building these racks just forward or abaft the hatches and set well inboard to clear the deck run. If it can be prevented, however, these cylinders should not be stowed on end. They are long, narrow, and extremely unstable. They stow very naturally in a fore and aft bilge and cantline fashion and that is the way they should be placed if it is possible.

When stowed in the bilge and cantline manner, they must be securely lashed, braced, and tommed. Tomming, of course, is only possible when stowed in the 'tweendecks. Tomming is not necessary if the cylinders are extremely well lashed, but if there is any doubt as to their security, it is recommended that plans be made for setting in some toms. Tomming is also not necessary if sufficient heavy cargo is stowed over the cylinders and this cargo is well secured.

When handling these cylinders, it is important that the valves be protected as much as possible in spite of the protection afforded by caps or construction. At a pier in New York during 1952, a sling load of these cylinders was carelessly discharged from a hold. One cylinder's cap was extending beyond the edge of the platform sling and was struck a blow sufficiently strong to break the cap and the valve. The cylinder immediately took off in flight, propelled like a rocket by expelling the gas under pressure. Fortunately it went up instead of down. It spent itself rapidly, but not before it had gained enough velocity to carry it down the waterfront and land it on the roof of a pier warehouse two piers from where it took off. This gives an idea of the power and potential danger in these charged cylinders.

As mentioned before, these cylinders are under pressure of 2000 lb per sq in. and over at normal temperatures. If the temperature rises alarmingly because of fire, direct sunlight on a tarpaulin lying next to them, heating copper concentrates, or other possible causes incident to water transportation, the pressures will be increased. It is quite possible for the pressure to be raised so high that the cylinder will blow a safety plug or, if that fails, that the entire cylinder will blow up. The point here is to emphasize the need for preventing an undue rise in temperature. If carried on deck, cylinders should have dunnage between them and any tarpaulins over them to provide for circulation of air. They should never be stowed near cargoes likely to heat in stowage. If fire breaks out, these cylinders should be jettisoned if they are in danger of being affected by the heat. The latter action would be especially important if the cylinders contained hydrogen or other flammable gases. The action would be for the safety of the ship and all the other cargo on board.

The stowage of drums. Drums may be stowed directly on the deck of a ship if stowed below deck; however, a single layer of dunnage to provide better drainage and to offer more friction in case of heavy rolling is strongly recommended. Drums are stowed on end with the end bung up and as closely packed together as possible. If the distance athwartship allows for a given number of drums plus a fraction of one, they should be spaced at regular intervals instead of being close together except for the end drum. The next row should be set in the oversized cantlines formed by the above action. The third row should again be set tightly into the cantlines (vertical) of the second row and so on. This eliminates the need for any bracing or additional dunnaging in the wings, providing the wings are vertical themselves. If the wings have curvature, the triangular space in this part of the stowage should be filled in with filler cargo, bracing, or dunnage (see Fig. 3-22). Dunnage stripping should be placed between every tier. It is not necessary to use solid dunnage floors. Two strips of dunnage over a single row of drums is sufficient. These two strips will tie the stowed cargo block together, spread the weights satisfactorily, and prevent the bending of the drum chimes.

In the wings, plenty of dunnage should be used to fill in the space left between the last outboard drum and the ship's side if there is curvature such as found in the entrance and run of the vessel. A level must be provided for laying the dunnage strips for the next tier of drums. The drums are usually the 55-gal size, and the height to which they can be stowed depends upon their contents and their construction specifications. For example, the National Cargo Bureau limits 55-gal drums built according to the Interstate Commerce Commission 5E specifications to a height of six tiers if the contents have a flash point over 20° and under 80°F. On most ships, this height limitation is naturally enforced by the limit of vertical drift in the lower holds. Four tiers is the maximum height that such drums can possibly be stowed in most 'tweendeck compartments. This particular drum is usually stamped with the letters S.T.C. on the head, meaning single trip container and usually meaning single trip with flammables. Such containers are often used a second time for the shipment of vegetable oils.

The stowage position on the ship is often limited because of the contents. For example, if the contents are classed as flammable liquids within the meaning of the definition given by the Coast Guard publication 187, Explosives and Other Dangerous Articles on Board Vessels, the drums must all be stowed on the same side of the ship if on deck. There are also a number of commodities that cannot be in the same hold. These are discussed later.

The stowage of reels. What is mentioned hereafter with respect to reels also applies to any heavy cylindrical object, such as millstones. The stowage of such items should always be on their sides unless they are light enough to be easily capsized by one or two men. The type of reel envisaged here is the extremely heavy reel with some type of cable on it, sheathed, and generally marked to be rolled in one direction only. Such a reel should always be stowed with its axis running athwartships. Thus, the curvature is fore and aft. This requirement is simply to lessen the possibility of the reel exerting sufficient force to break its lashings during heavy and continuous rolling in a seaway. A ship will roll, pitch, and yaw in a seaway, but the rolling motion will be the most violent. The reel could work loose with long periods of continual stress due to extended bad weather. It might chafe lashings in two or pulverize blocking cargo. This may happen when stowed with the axis in either direction but the probability is less with the axis athwartships.

The safest level at which to stow reels is in the lower holds. This is because the rolling motion is not as violent here as in the upper decks. The reels should be blocked in place with 8 by 8 in. balks on both sides. It is preferable to have the timbers cut to fit the curvature of the reel. The timbers should be tied together by nailing 2 by 6 in. battens between them. Besides this chocking, the reel should be braced, shored, and lashed into position. If suitable cargo is available, the reel may be blocked in with cargo. Some examples of suitable cargoes are bales of wood pulp, rags, hay, or certain types of lumber. Cargoes that cannot stand some chafage without being damaged should never be used. If suitable cargo for stowing around the reel is not available, a bulkhead of dunnage should be provided against which other cargoes can be stowed adjacent to but safely protected from the potentially dangerous reel. Reels should be given about 6 in. clearance by such bulkheads.

Reels generally are well marked with precautionary measures that the shippers want taken to protect the contents. One of the most important of these, often seen on sheathed reels, is to be careful when using nails to build bracing or shoring around the reel. Some of the cable contained on these reels is enclosed in a tube that is filled with a gas to cut down corrosion and general deterioration. If the cable exterior is punctured by a nail, the entire reel is ruined, and this will result in a very costly claim. This type of damage would almost certainly be adjudged improper care and custody. Arrows are stenciled on the hub of the reel to indicate which way it should be rolled.

The stowage of uncased automobiles. Automobiles that are shipped in the assembled form may be divided into two broad classifications, namely, the new car and the secondhand car. There is little difference in the actual stowage of the two types, although there is more preparation required and possibly more potential danger when carrying the old car.

One of the points needing emphasis when discussing the handling and stowage of this commodity is the importance of checking very carefully for exceptions. Here again, the older car will give the most trouble because there are more dents, scratches, and broken parts to take exceptions on. Many companies provide forms with various views of an automobile on it where marks can be made to point out accurately where deficiencies are found. In addition, written statements are made regarding the extent of the deficiencies.

Cars may be stowed in any of the 'tweendecks facing in any direction that allows the greatest use of the available cubic. If carried in the lower holds on the tank tops, they preclude the use of all the clearance over them. Unless the space is not needed, they should never be stowed on the tank tops.

If cargo is stowed to within 7 ft of the beams in the lower hold, leveled off, covered with at least two layers of crisscrossed 1-in. dunnage without spacing, and a third dunnage layer of 2-in. deals, automobiles may be stowed over this platform. The lost space is practically eliminated.

Automobiles are sometimes safely carried on deck. If carried on deck, they should be securely lashed on top of the hatches and provided with protective light canvas covers. Even if the weather is fair during the voyage, paint from the sailors working aloft might ruin the finish of a car. Stowage on deck should be avoided if the ship is a full scantling type and loaded to her marks. Such a ship is likely to be extremely wet on deck.

The best method of securing automobiles is by the use of the Peck and Hale type of adjustable cable, as described on p. 126 and shown in Fig. 3-41. As explained on p. 127, it is possible to use these fittings without special deck fittings. It is not as convenient, but they may be attached to chains stretched athwartships and secured by the use of frame clamps and turnbuckles. This would be the only possible way to use these cables to secure automobiles that were stowed over cargo in the lower holds on a platform of crisscrossed dunnage.

Without these adjustable fittings, a large amount of 4 by 4 in. and 2 by 4 in. lumber must be on hand to secure the automobiles. A 4 by 4 in. balk is cut to fit in front of and behind the front and rear tires. The balks should be long enough to extend beyond both sides of the car about 6 in. Two 2 by 4 in. battens are then cut to run the length of the car on each side from the forward balk to the after balk. The 2 by 4's are nailed down securely to all the 4 by 4's. This forms a chock in which the automobile will ride. In addition, some lashings should be attached for greater security. The lashings are needed if the car is not new because the springs may not be compressed. The spring action during heavy weather may cause the auto to move out of its cribbing unless it is lashed. The brakes should be set and the car placed in gear.

Automobiles should not be stowed closer together than 6 in. nor should they be stored closer than 6 in. to any obstruction in the hold. The clearance overhead should be 6 in. also. The possibility of a heavy sea causing the car to rise above its stowed level is greater, of course, if it does not have its springs compressed. It is advisable when setting up any lashings that tend to place a downward strain on the car's frame to have several men stand on the bumpers. The weight of the men will compress the springs and the lashings will be tighter and hold the car down much better.

Prior to loading the automobiles, they should be prepared for stowage. Preparation includes disconnecting the battery terminals and draining the gasoline tank and radiator. All removable items should be taken off and locked in the trunk of the car; this includes hub caps, outside rear view mirrors, and search lights.

After stowage, each car should be secured by one of the methods mentioned above. The windows should be closed and the doors locked. The keys for all the cars should be collected and placed in the custody of one officer. The officer accepting the keys will be required to sign a receipt for them, and when he releases them to a member of the agent's office in the port of discharge, he should obtain a signed receipt also. Each key is identified by a key number, the make and model of the car, and a bill of lading number.

Under older cars, it is advisable to spread a few thicknesses of heavy paper to catch any oil drippings from the crankcase or transmission. Finally, cars should be covered with light weight canvas covers if there is any possibility of heavy dust from other cargoes during any stage of the voyage. These covers fit over the entire automobile and reach the deck. They are coveted items and should be issued and checked very carefully. When the cars are discharged, these covers should be gathered up, folded, and stored away in a locked compartment to be discharged at the ship's home port. The chief officer may have to sign a receipt for them when they are provided at the loading port, and he should be sure to obtain a receipt when delivering them after the voyage is completed.

The stowage of deck loads in general. Prior to World War II, deck loads were not as likely to approach the volumes seen all during the war and occasionally since the war. During the war, there was so much cargo waiting on every dock, that ships began carrying more and more on deck. On occasion, the deck loads were so large that the amount of cargo was almost equal to the cargo that would have been stowed if the ship had been provided with an additional 'tweendeck space. Besides the tremendous call for deadweight, some of the built up units that were shipped had to go on deck because they would not fit anywhere else on the ship. Units that are shipped on deck are those that are not permitted below because of their dangerous characteristics, those that will not fit below, those that if placed below consume a tremendous amount of cubic and can be safely carried exposed to the weather, or those that are difficult to stow below and can be safely carried on deck. Large deck loads are less frequent when cargo offerings are light.

The two principal concerns of the ship's officers when deck cargo is carried are: (1) The security of the cargo. (2) The accessibility of the equipment needed to safely operate the ship.

The security of the cargo begins with making thorough plans about how the cargo is to be lashed, braced, and shored. A scale drawing of the ship's deck and a scale model of the cargo enable greater accuracy when making such plans. The details of such plans should include the size and number of all braces, the under-deck shoring, the number and position of all pad eyes, and the cribbing required between the load and the deck. If pad eyes are not numerous enough or are placed so that they afford poor leads for the lashings, it is an easy matter to have them relocated. All this should be done long before the cargo is scheduled to be loaded. After the cargo is placed on the ship as per plan, the lashings and bracings should be installed as directed by the chief officer. In some companies, regular gangs of workmen are employed to do the actual work, but the chief officer should not hesitate to insist on a different arrangement or additional lashings if he is dissatisfied. Lashings and bracing should be applied with the assumption that during the first night at sea the ship will pass through a full hurricane. Using this philosophy, the ship will generally be stowed safely.

Keeping the equipment accessible is a matter of marking off with chalk everything that should be left clear for working the ship. The things to be left clear are the bilge sounding pipe openings, cleats, fairleads, reach rod valve control wheels, bitts, fire hydrants, and fire hose racks. Large clearances should be indicated and the words "KEEP CLEAR" printed on deck. To insure that these notices are respected, the ship's officers should be on deck when preparations are commenced. Furthermore, at least one officer should be on deck all during the actual process.

The type of lashings should be either chain with pear links, pelican hooks, and turnbuckles; wire rope with shackles, clamps, and turnbuckles; or steel strapping with turnbuckles. Manila or other fiber rope lashings should not be used except for frapping purposes during heavy weather or emergency use in general. Fiber rope will stretch and loosen up in time and so many turns are required for strength that setting up such lashings is a long and arduous task.

The place of stowage of deck cargoes is dictated by the nature of the container and the cargo. For example, uncased automobiles should be stowed on top of the hatch and preferably on the hatch just abaft the midship house for greatest protection. Carboys of acid should be placed on the after deck as far inboard as they can be bunched. As mentioned before, drums of flammable liquids must all be placed on the same side of the ship. A 65-ft motor launch may fit in only one or two spots on the ship's deck, hence the choice of where to stow it is automatically dictated.

SHORING UP A DECK. When the deck load is excessive, the main deck may have to be shored up. Shoring will be required whenever the deck load is greater than 350 lb per sq ft on the average ship. The shoring

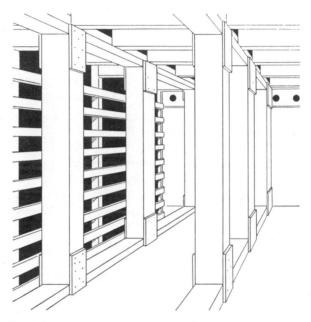

FIG. 5-11.   Shoring up the main deck from the 'tweendeck.   Courtesy U.S. Navy.

up of the main deck may not have to go farther than the 'tweendeck; however, if the load is excessive, the shoring will have to extend all the way down to the tank tops. It is a mistake to load a ship so that shoring is required in all hatches. This stiffens the hull girder and places stresses where the naval architect that designed the ship did not intend them to be concentrated. The possible result in extremely heavy weather is for structural failures in the deck or bottom plating.

The size of the shoring depends upon the total strength needed. For loads up to 1200 lb per sq ft, use a 12 by 12 in. balk spaced at 6-ft centers. This means that such shores would be under every other beam on the average ship and about two rows would be needed between the hatch carling and the side of the ship. The spacing between the hatch carling and the side of the ship should be such that the three divisions thus formed are approximately equal.   If the load is actually equal to 1200 lb per sq ft over the area it rests upon, shores would be required all the way to the lower hold.   This is because the 'tweendeck load capacity is seldom over 700 lb per sq ft.   It should be obvious that smaller shores can be used if the spacing between them is reduced or the load is less than 1200 lb per sq ft.

Fig. 5-12.   Here is a view of a Liberty ship being used to carry lumber.   It is the S.S. F. E. Weyerhaeuser and it is carrying a deck load consisting of about 1,368,000 board feet net measure.   The total load on this ship during this particular voyage was 6,148,394 board feet net measure.   The gross amount was 7,500,000 board feet, believed to be the largest load ever carried on a Liberty type ship.   With this load, 515 tons of magnesite ore was carried in the bottom of the lower holds.   The deck load shown here is 10 ft high on the fore deck and 11½ ft aft. Note the spacing of the deck lashings and how the cargo booms are secured for sea.   The forward booms at No. 2 and 4 hatches are cradled in the lumber, while all the others are stowed in collars and made fast aloft.   Note also how the mast shrouds are stowed in the deck load.   Courtesy Weyerhaeuser S.S. Co.

The shores are placed in position so that the lower end rests on a 6 by 12 in. *stringer* running longitudinally.   The upper end bears against a *header* that runs longitudinally under all the beams.   The shores are cut slightly shorter than the distance between the header and the stringer and any slack is removed by driving soft wood wedges between the lower end of the shore and the stringer.   Fish plates are used on both sides of each shore at the upper and lower ends.   The fish plates are made of 2 by 12 in. planks cut about 24 in. long and securely nailed to the shores and the stringer and header.   The space above the header between it and the deck above should be filled with 4-in. timbers cut to fit.   This means that the width of this beam filler piece will be equal to the outside measurement of the beam. The length would be equal to the distance between the beams. These pieces offer additional support to the deck plating under the load and prevent the beams from tipping. Figure 5-11 shows this arrangement of shores in a 'tweendeck.

THE STOWAGE OF LUMBER

Lumber in sawed form is shipped in full loads from several parts of the world, the largest exporting volume being from the Pacific Northwest Coast of America. The lumber shipped falls into two broad classifications: (1) Deals, battens, and boards, which are the smaller pieces, such as the 2 by 4 in. batten and the 1 by 8 in. board used for light construction work. (2) Balks, flitches, and squares, which are the larger timbers, such as the 6 by 10 in. flitch and the 16 by 16 in. square used for heavy construction work or intended for resawing at the country of destination for use in light construction work.

Lumber is shipped in loose board lots and also in packaged lots. Packaged lumber is not a new idea. Full shiploads of lumber in standard sized units were carried on the Pacific Coast before 1930. Packaged shipments are now carried on the intercoastal route between the west and east coasts of the United States. The package unit has been standardized by one major lumber carrying company at 2 ft high by 4 ft wide. The lengths in any one package are all the same (see Fig. 5-13).

The two most important problems in the stowage of lumber are the protection of the higher grades of lumber and stowage so as to combat tenderness in the ship. The first of these requisites is met by keeping the surfaced and kiln dried lumbers in the wings, using fiber rope slings, being careful not to stain the lumber, using no hooks on milled or surfaced lumber, and taking other common sense precautions.

The means used to combat tenderness in the lumber carrier, not including the obvious method of eliminating or drastically limiting deck loads (which would cut into the ship's earning power) are three in number: (1) Place the heaviest woods in the lower holds. (2) Distribute lumber types so that those stowing most compactly per unit of weight are in the lower holds. (3) Pack the ship's frame spaces.

The lumber below decks, if in loose lots, is stowed piece by piece and packed in carefully by the longshoremen. Uneven surfaces are dunnaged with lath, the broken stowage is reduced by using *ends* as filler cargo. Ends are pieces of lumber less than 6 ft in length with the same cross section as the rest of the shipment. When a lot is stowed, it is marked off with rope yarn or by painting stripes across the top of the block.

FIG. 5-13. Here we see the Weyerhaeuser full unit lot 4 ft high and 4 ft wide being hoisted on board. The standard package size is 2 ft high by 4 ft wide. The lot shown here is not strapped because it is planned to stow the lumber by hand. Wire snorters with sliding hooks comprise the sling. The bolsters upon which the load was built and transported to the pier apron can be seen lying on the dock under the load. The straddle truck to the right is standing by with another load. The empty bolsters are stacked as shown on the left. When enough empties have accumulated, a straddle truck will pick them all up and take them to the place where the loads are built up. Courtesy Weyerhaeuser S.S. Co.

Arrow heads are used to indicate a change in vertical direction of the stowed cargo.

The lumber deck load is always found on ships carrying full or large amounts of lumber. While the deck load is being started, an officer

FIG. 5-14. This shows some packaged lumber in the hold of the ship. The units on the right are 4 by 4 ft, but this company has changed its standard size package to a unit 2 ft high by 4 ft wide. Two by two inch battens separate the lots; this affords room for passing slings and to insert and remove the forks of the truck used to stow the packages in the hold. Note the large voids that unavoidably occur when working with packaged lots. Loose lumber of various lengths will have to be brought in and stowed by hand to fill up such broken stowage spaces. Courtesy Weyerhaeuser S.S. Co.

should be on deck continuously, and the building of the deck load should be watched all during the process. The sides of the load and the ends must be shaped to afford the least resistance to heavy seas. The deck load must also be stowed in accordance with the basic requirements for deck loads in general, see p. 194.

The deck load is secured by use of $\frac{3}{4}$-in. chain spaced not more than every 10 ft. The lower ends of the lashings are shackled to pad eyes; the upper ends are brought together approximately amidships and secured by the use of turnbuckles, pear links, and slip hooks. The deck load, for maximum security, should be solid from side to side where it is possible to build it like this.

Lumber shipped in packaged lots is packed into the ship with surprisingly little lost space by filling the bigger voids with loose pieces as necessary. The technique of stowing packaged lumber in the hold with the use of the fork lift truck is clearly depicted in Figs. 5-14 to 5-16.

FIG. 5-15. Here the longshoremen are shown filling in the voids and butting the loose lumber together very carefully so that a firm and smooth floor is provided on which a fork lift truck can work to stow additional tiers of packaged lumber. Note the peaveys in the background, an indispensable tool for the handling of lumber. The last few loads in the square of the hatch are stowed with the slings remaining on them. This is necessary in order to remove the first few key loads at the port of discharge and give the men working room in which to pass slings around the remaining loads. Courtesy Weyerhaeuser S.S. Co.

The calculations relative to the amount of lumber that will go into a given space or the inverse of this problem are presented under the section dealing with stowage factors.

THE STOWAGE OF BULK GRAIN

Grain in bags offers no special problems other than those of other bagged products requiring stowage to prevent damage from sweat and loss of contents through damage to the container itself, namely the bag. Grain in bulk, on the other hand, has proved to be dangerous during transportation due to the possibility of shifting and thereby rendering the ship unseaworthy. Bulk grain is also interesting in that it is handled by methods that exploit the use of gravity.

(a)

(b)

(c)

FIG. 5-16. Here are three views showing the care and planning that must go into the preparation of the loads of packaged lumber in order to prevent an excessive amount of lost cubic. (a) The load on the right ready to be placed in the vacant space on top of the two previously stowed 2 by 4 ft units. Note that the top has been stepped so as to fit the load next to the beam knees with minimum clearance. (b) The fork truck placing the load in place. The man in the center is just shoving a 2 by 2 in. batten under the load before the truck operator sets the load in place. (c) The stowage of this unit as seen from the ship's centerline. Note the minimum clearance from the overhead which can only be obtained by correct flooring off before starting to handle packaged lumber. Courtesy Weyerhaeuser S.S. Co.

Preparation for loading grain in bulk. The compartment in which the grain is to be stowed should be clean, dry, and have its drainage system prepared as outlined on p. 162.

The most important part of the preparation of the hold for bulk grain is the building of centerline shifting boards and feeders in accordance with the regulations contained in U.S. Coast Guard publication 266, The Stowage of Bulk Grain. The Coast Guard will accept certificates of loading of the National Cargo Bureau as prima facie evidence of compliance with the minimum requirements of CG-266. These rules should be studied by every officer of a ship scheduled to lift a cargo of bulk grain.

Settling of grain.   During the voyage, grain in bulk will settle down so that its depth is reduced 6% or more.   Thus, when carrying full compartments of grain in bulk, it is necessary to provide feeders in the compartment immediately above.   If no feeders are provided, the top of the

FIG. 5-17. A ship being loaded with bulk grain at a grain gallery.   Four spouts lead into the ship.   The grain is brought to the spouts from the elevator by conveyor belt.   Courtesy Port of New York Authority.

grain will drop nearly 1½ ft in the average lower hold.   This, of course, would leave the grain unsecured to some extent.   It would be similar to a liquid in a slack tank, and the ship can be placed in a dangerous condition if she encounters heavy weather.

Angle of repose of grain.   The *angle of repose* of a bulk cargo is an important fact to know about it.   It may be defined as that angle to which the surface may be rotated from the horizontal before the cargo commences to flow like a liquid. The angle of repose for wheat is 23°. Therefore, as a ship loaded with bulk wheat rolls to an angle greater than 23° when the surface of the grain is not secured properly, the grain will move slowly to the low side. This will create an offcenter weight

Fig. 5-18. Self-propelled floating grain elevator.

that may assume proportions sufficient to capsize the ship or cause her to founder eventually.

Loading grain. Grain is loaded almost universally by the use of gravity. The grain is run into the ship's hold through long telescopic chutes from elevators. The elevators are either permanently erected storage structures on the dock as shown in Fig. 5-17 or of a floating type that takes the grain from a barge, raises it, and lets it fall through chutes into the ship. Some of these floating elevators are self propelled (see

Fig. 5-18).   Figure 5-19 shows grain being loaded on a Liberty type
ship from two barges by the use of a floating grain elevator.   This elevator utilizes a vertical bucket conveyor to raise the grain to the top from
which it falls through the chute into the ship's hold.

Pneumatic elevators use large capacity vacuum pumps to suck the
grain into a receiver at the top of the elevator.   Here the grain is tem-

FIG. 5-19.   Grain elevators loading a ship with bulk wheat.

porarily stored before being discharged through the bottom of the elevator to a chute leading into the receiving vessel.   These elevators can
be used to discharge grain from the ship as well as to load.   Some of the
pneumatic elevators work at the rate of 250 tons per hr.   The grain may
be weighed during the discharging and loading process.

HANDLING AND STOWAGE OF BULK ORE

The stowage of ore on the ship built especially for the bulk trade is
accomplished by placing the ship under a series of chutes that may be
lowered into the ship's hatches and the ore allowed to flow into the
holds.   The ship has a large number of hatches but usually only four

compartments. A typical arrangement provides four hatches in two end compartments and five hatches each in two middle compartments. The engine room always is aft. The ore weight is distributed 30% in each end compartment and 20% in each center compartment.

The average loading time for 12,000 tons of ore is about 4 hr. The loading can be accomplished in less time but there is danger of causing structural damage to the ship. A test case was made on September 7, 1921, to demonstrate how quickly a ship could be loaded by these methods. The S.S. D. G. Kerr arrived at Two Harbors, Mich. ore docks at 1623½ on this day and cleared at 1700 the same day. Thus, from arrival to departure the time interval was 36½ min. Sixteen and a half minutes of this was for loading 12,506 tons of iron ore at a rate of 758 tons per minute.

Discharging operations. Discharging is accomplished by either a transporter type crane with a cantilever runway that supports a trolley on which a clam shell bucket is mounted or by use of the giant Huelett unloaders. These two crane types are illustrated in Figs. 5-20, 5-21 and 5-22.

Bulk ore on the general carrier. When carrying bulk ore on the general cargo ship, the precautions with respect to preparation of the drainage system discussed on p. 162 must be taken. Consideration also must be given to the weight distribution as discussed in Chap. 3. If a general cargo carrier is used to carry a full load of bulk ore, the distribution in any given hold should be in proportion to the given hold's cubic to the total cubic of the ship including deep tanks and refrigerated spaces if they remain empty. If these latter spaces are not empty, the weight of the material in them should be subtracted from the weight found by the proportional method.

The cargo in each hold should be trimmed so that the bulk of it lies toward the after bulkheads in the forward holds and toward the forward bulkheads in the after holds.

The above is a general rule for use only on ships with engine room spaces amidships. It should be used with caution. A check of what the ship is actually doing should be made continually as described in Chap. 3 under the discussion of hull deflection. The concept of loading by proportionality should not be used in the case of ships with their engine rooms aft. On these latter ships, the cargo spaces should be divided into four sections and the two end sections should receive about 30% of the cargo while the two middle sections should each receive about 20% of the cargo. The problem on the ship with the engine room spaces amidships is to prevent hogging, while the ship with engine room spaces aft tends to sag with full loads.

Shifting boards as mentioned for bulk grain are not needed with bulk iron ore. The angle of repose of iron ore is about 45°. In some trades

FIG. 5-20. The transporter type cranes used for unloading iron ore at Lorain, Ohio. This type crane uses the offshore and inshore cantilever boom to support a runway for the man-trolley and bucket. The entire structure can move up and down the length of the dock and is similar to the installation described later. Courtesy Pittsburgh Steamship Co.

FIG. 5-21. The S.S. Governor Miller lying at the Pittsburgh and Conneaut Dock of Conneaut, Ohio, with five hulett unloaders working. Courtesy Pittsburgh Steamship Co.

the iron ore is allowed to remain in a cone, much as it appears when finished running into the hold through the chutes. This is done for two reasons: (1) To raise the weights somewhat and prevent a stiff ship. (2) To minimize the cost of handling by eliminating the cost of trimming the ore. This practice may produce a dangerous condition if the ship runs into heavy weather and the violent working of the ship in a seaway causes the cone to fall off to one side. It is much better management always to trim down this cone and if it is necessary to raise the weights

FIG. 5-22. This is a closer view of hulett unloaders at work. The arrow points to the operator of the unloader. The operator rides with the bucket as it oscillates between ship and dock and has an excellent view of the operation.
Courtesy Pittsburgh Steamship Co.

to do it by placing some ore in the 'tweendecks. Even in fairly recent times, ships have been listed dangerously from the very cause mentioned here and a few ships have been lost at sea with many seamen. The cause, it must be emphasized, is poor judgment in loading the cargo.

Distribution on a C2-S-B1. Using the idea of distributing by volume proportionality, the distribution of 7000 tons of iron ore on a C2-S-B1 type ship would be as indicated in Table 5-1.

TABLE 5-1

Hold	Grain Capacity *	Per Cent of Total	Part of the 7000 Tons
No. 1	115,274 ft³	19%	1330 tons
No. 2	143,771 ft³	24%	1680 tons
No. 3	107,221 ft³	17%	1190 tons
No. 4	148,807 ft³	25%	1750 tons
No. 5	92,759 ft³	15%	1050 tons
Totals:	607,842 ft³		7000 tons

* Including deep tank and refrigerated cargo spaces.

The final condition of the ship would also depend upon the tankage of the ship (distribution of fuel and water), and it would probably be best to have the peak tanks empty and the tanks around the midship section full.

Specialized iron ore carriers. For many years large ocean going ore carriers that operate somewhat like the Great Lakes carriers, have been carrying bulk iron ore from Cruz Grande, Chile, to the port of Baltimore. With the recent discovery of rich iron ore deposits in Venezuela and other overseas areas, the ocean going bulk ore carrier will increase in number and in importance.

The ore from Venezuela comes from two mountainous regions, one called El Pao and the other Cerro Bolivar. In both of these developments, the ore must be moved to the ocean terminal via railroad and small feeder boats through mountainous and tropical terrain. From the Venezuela coast, the ore is carried in large ore carriers for a voyage of about 2000 miles. The principal port for delivery of this ore on the east coast of the United States is Baltimore, Md. The carriers transporting this ore have surpassed the size of those found on the older Chilean run. Before World War II, the Ore Steamship Company operated five 20,000 ton deadweight ore carriers between Chile and Baltimore. A larger carrier was built after the war capable of carrying 24,000 tons.

The National Bulk Carriers have developed an ore carrier that rivals the big trans-Atlantic liners in size. These carriers are capable of carrying 60,000 tons deadweight, and have displacements of 80,000 tons.

These ships have four large holds; the forward hold is served by four hatches. The last three holds have three hatches each. The bridge and deck officer's quarters lie between No. 1 and 2 hold. Like all ore carriers, the ship has very deep double bottom tanks, in this case about 22 ft deep. The wing tanks on either side of the hold compartment are 17 ft in breadth each. These extremely deep double bottom and wing tanks are needed on these carriers to afford a convenient method of raising the weights and preventing a stiff ship when carrying ore, and for carrying ballast water on one leg of the voyage.

Ore and oil carriers. It may occur to the reader that these ore carriers have a large tank volume. This fact has led to the recent development of ore and oil carriers. A carrier of this type is the Bomi Hills, built for the Liberia to the east coast of America trade. This particular ship carries about 24,000 tons deadweight when in ore and 21,000 tons when in oil. The oil is carried in the double bottom and wing tanks. In some carriers of this type, oil may be carried in some of the center tanks ordinarily used for ore. These ships do not carry oil and ore simultaneously; this would violate many safety regulations. They must enter a shipyard for conversion from one function to the other and this takes about two days.

STOWAGE OF REFRIGERATED CARGOES

Preparation of the refrigerated space. The preparation of the refrigerated cargo space to receive cargo includes some special steps in addition to the steps required in the case of regular general cargo spaces. The specialized nature of this preparation is evident from the discussion that follows.

CERTIFICATION OF SPACES. When loading any cargo on a ship in any compartment, a surveyor may be called in by the shipowners to have the space certified as being in all respects in good condition and ready to receive the cargo. This survey is also frequently made in the case of refrigerated spaces. Whether any cargo survey is made is entirely at the option of the shipowner. Most large companies do have surveys made before and after stowage and during the stowage of cargoes. These surveys are not costly, running between $15.00 and $75.00 depending upon the type of survey being made.

With respect to the survey of the spaces of a refrigerated ship, the survey includes the parts of the refrigeration system plus the insulation and equipment in the actual compartment. The machinery survey includes tests to insure that:

1. All controls are reacting properly.
2. Correct pressures can be maintained on both sides.
3. System is fully charged.

The survey of the insulation of the compartment in an inspection of this type is superficial. Little more than a visual check to determine whether the insulation has any breaks in it can be made; a check of insulation plugs and their condition is also made. The coils of the evaporator should be carefully tested for leaks. The interior of the reefer space must be adequately equipped with gratings and battens to protect the inside surface of the insulation sheathing. The space must be exceptionally well cleaned and all drains clear; a reefer compartment will be equipped with two to four drains instead of only one. Surveys of machinery and insulation are made by the American Bureau of Shipping and similar organizations. Surveys of the actual cargo stowage, in the United States, are made by the National Cargo Bureau.

CLEANLINESS OF THE SPACES. Although the cleanliness of the space is mentioned as a requisite for practically every item that may be discussed when speaking of the stowage of commodities on a ship, there is nothing that requires a greater degree of cleanliness than that needed in the reefer space. Improperly cleaned spaces may cause heavy mold to develop on commodities despite optimum conditions of temperature, humidity, and air motion. Fungus growths and rotting may be caused on fruits and vegetables infected by imperfectly cleaned spaces; however, it should be understood that the appearance of such damage on chilled or cooled products is not proof that the space was improperly cleaned. The product can be infected during its handling prior to loading in such a way that the outturn will show the same effects that it would if infected by unclean conditions in the reefer compartment. In fact, the most frequent cause of infected fruit is from improper handling prior to stowage on the ship. The point to be made here is that damage can be caused by an improperly prepared space, damage which can be eliminated only by effective cleaning. If the fruit shows evidence of being unclean or already having developed mold or disease spots of any kind, thorough exceptions should be taken and written up for submittal to the claims department. To make this cleaning procedure completely practicable is a problem for the shipowner. A recommended procedure is as follows:

1. Remove all gratings and sweep up the compartment.

2. Any residue from past cargoes that cannot be removed by sweeping must be scraped off or washed off the interior surface.

3. Spray the interior with a light antiseptic solution that will kill mold spores and bacteria or at least tend to retard their growth. Such a spray must not be so powerful that it will leave odors behind which might taint the cargoes to be loaded. There are many such solutions; three are given here: (1) A solution of ½ lb of chloride of lime to 3 gal of water. (2) One-quarter teaspoon of high test hypochlorite (HTH) to 3 gal of water. HTH is very powerful and the solution must be made carefully and tested by smelling the mixed solution. If the odor of chlorine is too strong, the solution is too strong. Do not allow the powder to lie around

carelessly. If the powder in full strength comes in contact with dunnage, the dunnage should be condemned. (3) A solution of sodium hypochlorite. This solution is made by adding sodium hypochlorite to fresh water, but it should also be very weak. Recommended strength is 0.8% solution; this means adding 0.8 lb of sodium hypochlorite to 99.2 lb of water.

4. Replace the gratings after washing them with one of the above solutions and allowing them to dry in the sun. If they cannot be allowed to dry, wipe them off as much as possible.

If spraying or washing thoroughly is not possible, the next best step is to wipe down the interior, including the gratings, with rags or hand swabs that have been dampened in the solution.

The interiors of reefer spaces are usually sheathed with surfaced tongue and groove spruce, pine, or fir plywood in such a manner that the cleaning is made easier than when working with general cargo spaces. All frame spaces are eliminated, corners are coved, edges are chamferred, and the entire surface is painted with several coats of a high grade varnish. The finish on the inside should not be allowed to deteriorate; revarnish the interior at least annually.

It should be understood that a thorough cleaning may not be necessary every time the spaces are to be prepared for a new reefer cargo. However, if in the judgment of the master or mate of the vessel the space is dirty and needs such a cleaning, the recommended procedure is as described. The exact procedure to be followed should be carefully outlined by the shipowner's operating department and incorporated in the company manual. With some cargoes, such as chilled meats, the cleaning should be frequent and thorough. The final decision rests with the ship's master or mate, a company shoreside refrigeration expert, or with the cargo surveyor who is retained to survey the cargo space as ready for loading a given reefer cargo.

PRECOOLING. Besides the above preparations there is also the matter of *precooling* the compartment before loading commences. There are many procedures that may be followed to insure that the space is ready when the cargo is ready. The important thing is to have the ship's chief engineer notified well in advance of the need for the space with the temperatures specified. Such notification should be given to the chief engineer at least 24 hr prior to the actual loading of the commodity. This officer will then place the refrigeration machinery in operation and commence to pull the temperature down. During this period, all of the dunnage that will be needed to stow the cargo securely should be stacked in the compartment in such a way that its heat load can be picked up easily along with that of the interior of the space. Considerable damage may be caused by using warm dunnage between the containers of refrigerated cargoes. Precooling of cargo spaces is universal, precooling of the cargoes is not. Bananas are never precooled before stowage.

TEMPERATURE RECORDS. Hourly recordings of the temperatures maintained in all reefer spaces are made and logged in the engineering log book. These temperatures are read at a remote station on modern ships. The refrigeration engineer simply has to close an electrical circuit including a galvanometer set to read degrees of temperature instead of ohms of resistance. The electrical circuit is closed by pressing a button at the centrally located recording station. On other installations the refrigeration engineer must make periodic rounds of all spaces and read a recording thermograph on the outside of each refrigerated compartment. On older arrangements, it is necessary for the engineer first to unscrew a cap and remove an ordinary mercurial thermometer from a container extending into the space. On modern ships, there is nearly always a recording thermograph regardless of the method used to obtain periodic temperature readings during the voyage. This thermograph chart can be used by the shipowner to ascertain whether the ship's operating personnel actually do maintain temperatures as requested. In the case of claims, these same charts can be used to prove that the temperatures required were, in fact, maintained.

A portable type of recording thermograph is frequently used. These can be secured in a centrally located position in the space at the beginning of the voyage and removed by properly designated personnel just prior to discharging.

Stowage of reefer cargoes. The stowage of refrigerated cargoes is a task that requires careful attention to many details on the part of the ship's officers. The officers must be with the cargo from the time the cargo is received on the dock until it is safely stowed on the ship. Refrigerated cargo, commonly referred to as reefer cargo, requires the time of two officers during some phases of receiving and caring for it.

INSPECTIONS. All cargoes should be observed by the ship's officers as they are received by the dock force and as they are loaded on the vessel. In the case of refrigerated cargoes, this observation should take the form of a continuous inspection of the cargo to ascertain whether there is any evidence that would make it doubtful that the cargo could stand the voyage. The form of this evidence will be presented in the context of this and the following sections; it is important to note, however, that the officer who is not aware of what to look for cannot protect the shipowner's interest or his ship's interest regardless of how conscientious his inspections may be. The ship's officer's check should be a double check following inspection by the receiving clerk's staff or a specially appointed company expert. Regardless of the number and type of inspections made by dock force personnel, the master of the vessel should require a thorough inspection by at least one of his officers and a written report should be submitted to him. The written report is an excellent educational device for the junior officers and it will tend to make the officer pay greater attention to what he is actually doing. The need for writing about what he finds and evaluating it will also build up an accurate vocabulary concerning the damaged conditions found. The inspection commences when the refrigerated cargo is received on the pier. At this time a ship's officer must carefully inspect the containers as they appear in the connecting carrier. The connecting carrier will be either a refrigerated railroad car or truck. Infrequently some leafy vegetables are carried to a ship only having been iced before leaving the hinterland and transported in an unrefrigerated truck. Such facts should be noted and included in a report to the master and claims department. If there are outward signs of improper handling or evidence of any type that might cause the cargo to be suspect, exceptions should be taken. If conditions warrant, the cargo may be rejected. Inspection by simply sighting the containers in their connecting carrier is not sufficient. Individual units of the commodity, such as an apple or a pear should be picked out of the lot and sampled. They should be cut in half to inspect for brown heart or other signs of internal breakdown. They should be tasted and smelled carefully. Many troubles, such as soggy breakdown in apples, manifest themselves only in the condition of the flesh without any external symptoms. The appearance of the skin should be checked for signs of mold, freezer burn, scald spots, or other diseases that may be common to the particular type of fruit in question. The types of diseases and their symptoms are so numerous that they cannot be covered completely here. It is strongly recommended that just prior to receiving a given type of refrigerated commodity, a reference should be consulted to ascertain the possible sources of trouble and the manifestations of the troubles. One such reference is the *Refrigerating Data Book,* Refrigeration Applications Volume, published by the American Society of Refrigeration Engineers in New York. This reference is published in new editions every one or two years because of the rapid changes in this field. Finally, if the product is supposed to be precooled, insert an appropriate thermometer into the pulp of the commodity and take its temperature. Such thermometers are ordinary in their construction except for a strong steel tip that makes it possible to insert the instrument into a chilled quarter of beef or a green and firm apple or pear. It is important to note this temperature and either reject the shipment or take exceptions if the temperature is not down. The need for this is twofold: (1) If not precooled, the commodity will have ripened much faster than it should have since being harvested, and it may not be able to last for the voyage without complete loss. Most fruits will not keep well under cold storage conditions unless they are precooled within 24 hrs after being picked. (2) The requirement of cooling the commodity after stowing on the ship may be more than the refrigeration system of the ship can handle in the time allowed. In this case, even if the commodity could stand the voyage if brought down, the trouble lies in the fact that the temperature cannot be reached and maintained by the facilities on hand. In this instance also, there is danger of losing the entire shipment. The fact that pulp temperatures were taken and a record of the temperatures should be included in a log book entry. These temperatures are required for any refrigerated product that is supposed to have some low temperature when arriving at the ship.

The operating departments of some companies require that refrigerated products be inspected by a competent surveyor and a report made to the company claims department. Fresh fruit shipments out of the United States should be inspected by a representative of the U.S. Dept. of Agriculture. If the shipment is found suitable, the inspector will issue an inspection certificate which will certify that the shipment is clean and contains no disease. In many foreign ports such a certificate must be on hand before the shipment can be landed.

When inspecting refrigerated cargoes as received, frozen or otherwise damaged fruit should be set aside. This fruit must not be mixed with fruit in good condition. Damaged fruit mixed with sound and healthy fruit may be the cause of the entire shipment going bad.

STOWAGE OF CONTAINERS. The basic principle to be followed when stowing refrigerated products is to build suitable air channels throughout the stowed cargo block. There are a few exceptions to this general requirement which will be mentioned later. In the case of baskets and bulge-top fruit cases, the container can be stowed so as to provide excellent air passageways without using dunnage expressly for this purpose. Dunnage used with such containers is for the purpose of binding the load together for more secure stowage. The size of the strips of dunnage used varies considerably between one ship or one company and another. One inch by 2 in., 1 in. by 1 in., ½ in. by 1 in., and the common building lath of ⅜ in. by 1½ in. by 48 in. have all been used extensively. The common building lath, according to Mr. Westling, is highly recommended because it provides ample clearance for air flow and is low in cost.[1] In placing the containers in stowage, take care to see that the contents of the crates do not take the weight of the succeeding tiers, but that the crate supports this weight. Crates that have cleats at the ends only should be stacked in the reefer compartment one on top of the other with dunnage running at right angles to the cleats between every tier. If these crates are staggered in the recognized brick fashion used on many ordinary cargoes, the load would be taken up by the contents which would become bruised and damaged. Crates that have a supporting transverse member dividing the crate into two equal parts and are provided with a center cleat can be safely loaded in the so-called brick fashion. Brick fashion, of course, makes for a more securely stowed cargo block. Vertical air channels can be provided by placing pieces of dunnage between the rows on their forward and after sides. Crates of citrus fruits, melons, apples, and similar products have containers with a bulged top. Such containers can be stowed on their ends with the bulged tops together. This arrangement provides ample air channels and the crate will carry the weight of top tiers instead of the contents. It is recommended that no higher than five tiers high be allowed with this type of container with possibly a sixth tier lying down longitudinally with the bulge up; this arrangement will aid in tying the entire stowed block together.

Refrigerated cargo types. The commodities received for refrigerated stowage are numerous and increasing every year. Most of these are well known and include meats, fish, poultry, dairy products, fruits, and vegetables. It is impossible, in this limited discussion, to formally set forth precise methods of handling and stowing each commodity type that may be classified as refrigerated. Besides the space limitations there exists the fact that the methods used in any one instance may vary from nation to nation, trade route to trade route, company to company, and even from ship to ship. Thus far there has been no effort on the part of any group, whether specifically interested in the welfare of the shipping industry or otherwise, to investigate thoroughly and determine the truths in extant practices found within the marine industry. Shipper, consignee, shipowner, consumer, and underwriter alike would benefit from research leading toward a determination of what are the best practices.

Apples, grapes, and pears constitute the greatest amount of fruit shipments in partially refrigerated vessels and offer some interesting problems. Bananas are carried almost exclusively on one type of ship and in one trade route. The methods used in handling and stowing the banana are interesting and reflect how efficient the process can become

[1] L. L. Westling, Handling and Stowing of Ship's Perishable Cargoes, Refrigeration Engineering Application Data, Sect. 43, ASRE, 1948, p. 7.

when efforts of all interested parties are coordinated. Meat carriage is done on a large scale only in the merchant marines of nations other than American, principally on British ships.

EXPLOSIVES OR OTHER DANGEROUS ARTICLES

The U.S. Coast Guard regulates the handling and stowage of a number of commodities generally referred to as "dangerous goods." Many nations have regulations of a similar nature and there is activity at the present time within the United Nations to establish some basic international code, especially relative to labels, that will assist in the safe handling of this type of cargo.

The regulations of the United States are contained in a book, *Explosives or Other Dangerous Articles on Board Vessels.* This book is published by the Coast Guard and is given the designation of CG-187. Hereafter, we will refer to it as simply CG-187.

There is no need to reprint here all the regulations; however, it is deemed of value to summarize some of the general information and to describe the type of information that the ship operator will find in this book.

Scope of the regulations. These regulations do the following:

1. They define all terms and the definitions relating to the types of classifications are of special importance. In other words, they explain just what is meant by *hazardous article* as compared to a *flammable solid.*

2. They set forth the packing requirements.

3. They prescribe the correct name to be used on all shipping papers.

4. They prescribe the marking and labeling needed on containers.

5. They set forth the requirements that must be met in order to transport the various classifications. The word *transport,* as used here, means the entire process of receiving, handling, stowing, and delivering the cargo.

6. They set forth the conditions of rejection, disposition of faulty containers, and inspections.

Vessels to which the regulations apply. In general these regulations apply to all vessels, domestic and foreign, regardless of their employment or condition. However, there are some exceptions. The most notable exceptions of the large seagoing ships are just two in number: (1) The bulk oil carrier. (2) Public vessels not engaged in commercial service.

Bulk oil carriers need no further explanation. An example of a ship in the second category is a warship of any type. A ship that is owned by the government, thus making her a public vessel, but operated in commercial service must comply with the regulations. The cargo ships operated by the Military Sea Transportation Service fall into this category.

There are many small working or pleasure craft that do not have to operate by these rules, such as yachts, fishing vessels under 500 gross tons, any vessel under 15 gross tons not carrying passengers, cable vessels, pilot boats, and others. Most of these last mentioned craft must comply with the regulations insofar as the carriage of high explosives is concerned.

Supervision of stowage. A licensed deck officer must be present at all times to supervise the loading or discharging of any of the classifications mentioned later.

Enforcement of the regulations. The primary enforcing agency is the U.S. Coast Guard. A Coast Guard officer known as the captain of the port will generally have direct responsibility for local enforcement. Enforcement officers may at any time and any place within the jurisdiction of the United States board any vessel for the purpose of enforcing these regulations.

The collector of customs and the officers under him assist in enforcing these regulations. This officer may detain a ship violating the regulations.

Inspections and log entries. The regulations require certain inspections to be made. Whenever an inspection is carried out in compliance with these regulations, it is a wise policy to log the facts with all possible details. Some of the inspections that must be made are:

1. At reasonable intervals during the voyage, the stowage of any of these dangerous goods should be inspected.

2. Prior to entering a port, a final inspection should be made.

3. Temperature readings must be taken in every space containing any of the various classifications of dangerous goods. These temperatures must be recorded in the ship's log and retained as a record for each voyage.

The time interval that might be considered reasonable would be at least once a day during good weather but at least twice daily during bad weather or when, because of the nature of the cargo, it seems wise to keep an eye on the cargo. When taking temperatures, any unusual rise between two consecutive readings would be the signal to increase the frequency of the inspections.

In case something is found wrong during an inspection, the decision of what to do with any cargo that is damaged or appears to be deteriorating is entirely up to the master of the ship. He may jettison it or correct the trouble in such way that he judges to be most suitable. Speaking practically, it is obvious that the master is in a much better position to

	Low explosives or black powder	High explosives and over 50 lb smokeless powder for small arms	Initiating or priming explosives, wet: Diazodinitrophenol, fulminate of mercury, guanyl nitrosamino guanylidene hydrazine, lead azide, lead styphnate, nitro mannite, nitrosoguanidine, pentaerythrite tetranitrate, tetrazene	Blasting caps, with or without safety fuse (including electric blasting caps) [1]	Ammunition for cannon with explosive projectiles, gas projectiles, smoke projectiles, or incendiary projectiles, ammunition for small arms with explosive bullets [4]
	1	2	3	4	5
Dangerous explosives:					
1 Low explosives or black powder	..	..	X	..	..
2 High explosives and over 50 lb smokeless powder for small arms	..	..	X	X	..
3 Initiating or priming explosives, wet: diazodinitrophenol fulminate of mercury, guanyl nitrosamino guanylidene hydrazine, lead azide, lead styphnate nitro mannite nitrosoguanidine, pentaerythrite tetranitrate, tetrazene	X	X	..	X	X
4 Blasting caps with or without safety fuse (including electric blasting caps) [1]	..	X	X	..	X
5 Ammunition for cannon with explosive projectiles, gas projectiles, smoke projectiles or incendiary projectiles, ammunition for small arms with explosive bullets [4]	..	..	X	X	..
6 Explosive projectiles, bombs, torpedoes, or mines, rifle or hand grenades (explosive) [4]	..	..	X	X	..
7 Detonating fuses, boosters (explosive)	..	X	X	..	X
Less dangerous explosives:					
8 Ammunition for cannon with empty sand loaded or solid projectiles, or without projectiles	..	..	X	..	..
9 Smokeless powder for cannon or not exceeding 50 lb smokeless powder for small arms			X		
10 Fireworks	X	X	X	X	X
Relatively safe explosives:					
11 Small arms ammunition	..	..	X	..	..
12 Primers for cannon or small arms, empty cartridge bags, black powder igniters, empty cartridge cases, primed, empty grenades, primed, combination primers or percussion caps, toy caps	..	..	X	..	..
13 Percussion fuses or tracer fuses	..	..	X	..	..
14 Time or combination fuses	..	..	X	..	..
15 Cordeau detonant, safety squibs, fuse lighters, fuse igniters, delay electric igniters, electric squibs or instantaneous fuse	..	..	X	..	..
Other dangerous articles:					
16 Inflammable liquids or compressed inflammable gases, red label	X	X	X	X	X
17 Inflammable solids or oxidizing materials, yellow label	X	X	X	X	X
18 Acids or corrosive liquids, white label	X	X	X	X	X
19 Compressed noninflammable gases, green label	X	X	X	X	X
20 Poisonous gases or liquids in cylinders, poison gas label	X	X	X	X	X
21 Combustible liquids	X	X	X	X	X
22 Hazardous articles	X	X	X	X	X

[1] Blasting caps or electric blasting caps in a quantity not exceeding 1000 caps may be stowed or stored with all articles above named except those in columns (2), (3), (5), (6), (10), (16), (17), (18), (19), and (21).

[2] Corrosive liquids (white label) shall not be stowed with inflammable solids and oxidizing materials (yellow label), or with any explosives.

[3] Cyanides or cyanide mixtures shall not be stowed or stored with corrosive liquids.

EXPLOSIVES AND OTHER DANGEROUS ARTICLES

Explosive projectiles, bombs, torpedoes or mines, rifle or hand grenades (explosive) 4	Detonating fuses, boosters (explosive)	Ammunition for cannon with empty sand loaded or solid projectiles, or without projectiles	Smokeless powder for cannon or not exceeding 50 lb smokeless powder for small arms	Fireworks	Small arms ammunition	Primers for cannon or small arms, empty cartridge bags: Black powder igniters, empty cartridge cases, primed, empty grenades, primed, combination primers or percussion caps, toy caps	Percussion fuses or tracer fuses	Time or combination fuses	Cordeau detonant, safety squibs, fuse lighters, fuse igniters, delay electric igniters, electric squibs or instantaneous fuse	Inflammable liquids or compressed inflammable gases, red label	Inflammable solids or oxidizing materials, yellow label	Acids or corrosive liquids, white label	Compressed noninflammable gases, green label	Poisonous gases or liquids, in cylinders, poison gas label	Combustible liquids	Hazardous articles
6	7	8	9	10	11	12	13	14	15	16	17	18	19	20	21	22
..	..	..	..	X	..	..	..	..	..	X	X	X	X	X	X	X
..	X	..	..	X	..	..	..	..	..	X	X	X	X	X	X	X
X	X	X	X	X	X	X	X	X	X	X	X	X	X	X	X	X
X	..	..	..	X	..	..	..	..	..	X	X	X	X	X	X	X
..	X	..	..	X	..	..	..	..	..	X	X	X	X	X	X	X
X	X	..	..	X/X	..	..	..	..	..	XX	X	X	X	X	X	X
..	..	..	..	..	..	..	..	..	..	..	..	2X	..	..	..	..
X	X	..	..	..	..	..	..	..	..	..	..	2X	..	X/X	X	X
..	..	..	..	..	..	..	..	..	..	..	..	..	..	..	..	..
..	..	..	..	..	..	..	..	..	..	..	..	..	..	..	..	..
..	..	..	..	..	..	..	..	..	..	..	..	..	..	..	..	..
X	X	..	X	X	..	..	..	..	..	..	..	..	..	..	..	..
X	X	..	X	X	..	..	..	..	..	..	..	2X	..	..	..	..
X	X	2X	2X	X	..	..	..	..	..	..	2X	..	..	3X	..	..
X	X	..	X	X	..	..	..	..	..	..	..	3X	..	..	..	..
X	X	..	X	X	..	..	..	..	..	..	..	..	..	..	..	..
X	X	..	X	..	..	..	..	..	..	..	..	..	..	..	..	..

4 Projectiles, bombs, grenades, or other forms of ammunition containing incendiary charges, either with or without bursting charges, must not be stowed with any dangerous explosives, class *A*, or less dangerous explosives, class *B*.

Note: Charged electric storage batteries shall not be stowed or stored with explosives class *A* or class *B*.

Consult detailed regulations of other dangerous articles for provisions regarding on-deck stowage of such articles on board vessels transporting explosives.

explain the loss of jettisoned cargo if he has a complete and proper record all during the voyage in accordance with the regulations.

Damaged cargo brought into port. If damaged containers of dangerous goods are brought into port, they are not to be delivered to the consignee directly. A report must be made to the nearest officer in charge of a marine inspection office with a request for instructions as to disposition. A report must also be made covering any cargo jettisoned during the voyage.

Repairs to vessels. If a ship has explosives *A* or *B* on board, she cannot enter a dry dock. She cannot undertake any repairs unless they are *emergency* repairs on the main propulsion plant. When loaded with other classifications of dangerous goods, there are less stringent restrictions on repair work. The regulations should be consulted to insure compliance. Regardless of all these restrictions, the master may approve and order repairs of an emergency nature at any time if he deems them necessary for the safety of the vessel, passengers, or crew.

Stowage of dangerous goods. The regulations set forth requirements regarding stowage with reference to segregation of the various types of dangerous goods and with reference to the location in the ship.

A stowage chart such as shown in Table 5-2 is used to determine the segregation requirements quickly. The location that is permissible can be determined by referring to the listing given the commodity in the table devoted to information on the given item. Table 5-3 is a sample page from CG-187 that shows the manner of presenting this stowage information along with other valuable information. This page was chosen because it presented data on carbon disulfide, a very dangerous flammable liquid.

Note the important data listed in the second column which gives characteristic properties, required precautions, and markings. The label required is given in the third column. The fourth column gives information on the stowage. In this example, the only stowage permissible is "on deck protected." The stowage on passenger, ferry, and railroad car ferry vessels is given in the next three columns respectively. In this example, the commodity is not permitted on board.

In the fourth column, under the stowage permitted, the type of containers allowed are also specified. These data simply refer the reader to a type of container. The exact specifications are given in another publication. In order to know the specifications of the container mentioned, the reader would have to consult a copy of the Interstate Commerce Commission publication giving full information. The initials WIC mean *with inside container.*

TABLE 5-3

CLASSIFICATION OF FLAMMABLE LIQUIDS

Descriptive Name of Article	Characteristic Properties, Precautions Required, Markings Required	Label Required	Required Conditions for Transportation			
			Cargo Vessel	Passenger Vessel	Ferry Vessel, Passenger or Vehicle	R.R. Car Ferry, Passenger or Vehicle
Carbon bisulfide Carbon disulfide	*A heavy, clear, colorless to yellow liquid having a very offensive odor* Highly inflammable. *Protect from all sources of heat. Vapor is capable of igniting without presence of naked light, as from the temperature of a warm steam pipe* Mixtures of vapor and air are highly explosive over a range of 1 to 50% in air *Self-ignition occurs at about 215°F in air* *Boiling point about 115°F* *Vapor is poisonous* *Immiscible with water* Keep cool *Stow well away from oxygen, and oxidizing materials (yellow label)*	Red	Stowage: "On deck protected" Outside containers: Steel barrels or drums: (ICC-5, 5A) not over 55 gal capacity (ICC-17E) STC not over 5 gal capacity (ICC-17C) STC not over 55 gal capacity Wooden barrels or kegs. WIC (ICC-11A, 11B) not over 16 gal capacity Wooden boxes. WIC (ICC-15A, 15B, 15C, 16A, 19A) not over 8 gal capacity Fiberboard boxes. WIC (ICC-12B) not over 65 lb gross weight Tank cars. (ICC-103, 104, 104A, ARA-II, ARA-III, ARA-IV, ARA-IVA)	Not permitted	Not permitted	Not permitted
Carbon remover, liquid (When possessing a flash-point at or below 80°F)	*Products usually added to motor fuels to dissolve out deposited carbon in cylinders of gasoline-fired engines*	Red	Outside containers and stowages as for "Compounds, cleaning, liquid," which see	Outside containers and stowages as for "Compounds, cleaning, liquid," which see	Outside containers and stowages as for "Compounds, cleaning, liquid," which see	Outside containers and stowages as for "Compounds, cleaning, liquid," which see
Case oil			See under proper shipping name as; "Benzene," "Benzine," "Gasoline," etc.	See under proper shipping name as; "Benzene," "Benzine," "Gasoline," etc.	See under proper shipping name as; "Benzene," "Benzine," "Gasoline," etc.	See under proper shipping name as; "Benzene," "Benzine," "Gasoline," etc.
Casinghead gasoline			See: "Natural gasoline"	See: "Natural gasoline"	See: "Natural gasoline"	See: "Natural gasoline"

Stowage terms used in tables.   Most of the terms used in the tables to describe the stowage of these cargoes are self-explanatory.   However, they are defined below to eliminate all possible confusion.

ON DECK IN OPEN.   On the open weather deck: the cargo may be protected from the elements if deemed necessary.

ON DECK PROTECTED.   On the open weather deck: in this case the cargo must be protected from the elements by awnings and dunnage.

ON DECK UNDER COVER.   May be stowed on the weather deck under covered erections, such as the mast house or fo'c'sle extension.

CARGO HATCH TRUNKWAY.   Self-explanatory except to add that the trunk must be constructed of steel without openings and the lower end must be closed securely from the cargo hold proper.

'TWEENDECKS READILY ACCESSIBLE.   Uppermost cargo spaces and stowed so as to be accessible from the cargo opening but not on the hatch square unless it is made of steel.

'TWEENDECKS.   The upper cargo spaces.

UNDERDECK AWAY FROM HEAT.   Any cargo compartment on the ship capable of being ventilated and not subject to any artificial heat source.

UNDER DECK.   Any place on the ship capable of being ventilated.

UNDER DECK BUT NOT OVERSTOWED.   Any compartment capable of being ventilated, but no cargo can be placed on top.

Classification, definitions, labels, and examples.   In this section we will present all of the various classifications, give a brief summary of their definitions, state the label requirements, and offer a few examples. Every ship's officer and member of the dock force should know at least this much about this important group of cargoes.   Having this information as background, he will be aware of the potential problems and dangers inherent in transporting these cargoes and be less likely to create a serious condition on the ship inadvertently.

EXPLOSIVES CLASS A.   Defined as a dangerous explosive, detonating or otherwise of maximum hazard.   No label.

Examples: Dynamite, picric acid, ammunition with war heads or explosive bullets, black powder.

EXPLOSIVE CLASS B.   Defined as simply less dangerous explosives including most fireworks.   There is no label except for fireworks.

Examples: Ammunition with empty or solid projectiles, smokeless powder, fireworks.

EXPLOSIVE CLASS C.   Defined as relatively safe explosive.   No label.

Examples: Ammunition for small arms without explosive bullets, toy caps, fuses, primers.

FLAMMABLE LIQUID.   Any liquid that gives off a flammable vapor at or below a temperature of 80°F.   Red label.

Examples: Alcohol, gasoline, carbon disulfide.

FLAMMABLE SOLID.   A solid substance, other than an explosive, that is liable, under conditions incident to transportation, to cause fires through friction, absorption of moisture, or spontaneous chemical change. Yellow label.

Examples: Burned cotton, matches, motion picture film, charcoal.

OXIDIZING MATERIALS. Any substance that yields oxygen readily which might stimulate the combustion of organic material. Yellow label.

Examples: Sodium nitrate, calcium chlorate.

CORROSIVE LIQUIDS. A strong mineral acid or other corrosive fluid which is liable to cause fire when mixed with chemical or organic matter or to damage materially other freight on contact. White label with black printing.

Examples: Nitric acid, sulfuric acid.

NONFLAMMABLE COMPRESSED GAS. Any material having a vapor pressure exceeding 25 lb per sq in. at a temperature of 70°F. Green label.

Examples: Oxygen, nitrogen, helium.

FLAMMABLE COMPRESSED GAS. Any flammable liquid material having a Reid vapor pressure exceeding 25 lb per sq in. at a temperature of 100°F. Red label.

Examples: Hydrogen, carbon monoxide, acetylene.

CLASS A POISONS. Extremely dangerous poison gas or liquid: very small amounts of the vapors, when mixed with air, are dangerous to life. White label with red printing.

Examples: Mustard gas, phosgene.

CLASS B POISONS. A liquid or solid substance of such a nature that it is chiefly dangerous by external contact with the body or by its being taken internally. White label with red printing.

Examples: Arsenic, cyanide, motor fuel antiknock compound.

CLASS C POISONS. Liquids or solids which on contact with fire or when exposed to air give off intensely irritating fumes but excluding any poisonous article. White label with red printing.

Examples: Tear gas grenades, chloracetophenone.

CLASS D POISONS. Radioactive materials above a specified level of activity. White label with red printing.

COMBUSTIBLE LIQUIDS. Any liquid which gives off flammable vapors at or below a temperature of 150°F and above 80°F. No label.

Examples: Turpentine, kerosene, paints.

HAZARDOUS ARTICLES. Any substance other than an explosive or other dangerous article which, when subjected to a test for 3 hr continuously at or below a temperature of 212°F, may liberate vapor susceptible to ignition by spark or by open flame. No label.

Examples: Coal, copra, sulfur.

Listing on the manifest. On the manifest and other shipping papers, these dangerous articles should be recorded with all the usual information plus the classification given the cargo and the label requirements. The classification should be shown in enlarged letters and underlined. For example:

Gasoline . . . . FLAMMABLE LIQUID . . . . Red Label

Notation on the cargo plan. The cargo stowage plan must show, in all necessary detail, the exact location of the stowage of explosives or other dangerous articles. The shipping name given by the regulations and the classification must be used.

General regulations governing explosives. There are a number of requirements that must be met when transporting explosives. Some of these are briefly outlined below.

MAGAZINES. All class *A* explosives must be stowed in magazines. The regulations are very clear regarding the location and some of the construction specifications of these magazines.

Location of magazines. Magazines should be located in a hold, preferably in an upper 'tweendeck. They should not be constructed bearing against a collision bulkhead nor against a heated bulkhead, such as the boiler room or galley. If it is necessary to construct the magazine in the proximity of these bulkheads, a cofferdam space of at least 4 ft should be provided and no cargo should be stowed in such spaces.

The doors of these spaces must be easily accessible from the hatchway. The magazine must not be in horizontal proximity nor below the crew or passenger accommodations.

Construction of magazines. Magazines may be constructed of steel, iron, or wood; if of steel or iron, the entire interior should be sheathed with surfaced wood at least $\frac{7}{8}$ in. thick. When completed, the interior of the magazine must be smooth and without projections. Only copper or cement coated nails should be used. The doors must be well built and provided with a lock.

If the entire hold is used for a magazine, it must be boarded over completely. This sheathing need not be applied to the overhead if the explosives are stowed not closer than 12 in. to the beams.

The compartment must be capable of being ventilated, and the vents must be covered with a fine wire mesh screen.

CHUTES FOR EXPLOSIVES. Steel roller conveyors cannot be used when handling explosives. A wooden chute must be used when taking advantage of gravity to move such commodities. This chute must have guard rails at each side at least 4 in. high. Brass screws may be used for assembly of the chute but not steel. The upper surface of the slide itself must have D shaped wooden runners fastened to it with glue and wooden dowels; these should be spaced 6 in. apart.

MATTRESSES FOR EXPLOSIVES. Landing mattresses must be provided for loading or unloading explosives. These mattresses must be at least 4 in. thick and 4 by 6 ft in width and length.

STOWAGE ON DECK. Explosives class *B* or *C* that are stowed on deck must not be within 25 ft on a horizontal plane of a lifeboat station or within 25 ft of the entrance to the crew's quarters.

LOADING OR DISCHARGING EXPLOSIVES. Class *A* and *B* explosives must not be loaded until all other cargo has been placed on board. Generally, local regulations prevent the handling of explosives at piers near a port's concentration of facilities. The ship will usually proceed to an anchorage and pick up the explosive shipment from a barge. The space for stowing the shipment must be left accessible.

At intermediate ports of call during the voyage, explosives must not be worked at the same time as other cargo. They should be discharged first at the port of destination.

The maximum load in a sling of explosives is 2400 lb.

Transfer trucks used in handling explosives must be powered by some means other than electricity.

Before loading or unloading explosives, the cargo gear must be inspected by the master or another officer. A log entry of this inspection should always be made.

Smoking is prohibited *on* or *near* any vessel loading or unloading explosives. "NO SMOKING" warning signs must be posted during such operations.

Persons under the influence of liquor or drugs must not be permitted on board a vessel while loading or unloading explosives.

Permission from the district commandant of the U.S. Coast Guard must be obtained before loading or unloading shipments of class *A* explosives in amounts exceeding 500 lb.

Flammable liquids: general requirements. Flammable liquids, when stowed on deck, must all be on one side of the ship's centerline. The 25-ft clearance from lifeboat stations and entrances to quarters is also required. If explosives are on the same ship, below or on deck, the machinery spaces must be between such cargo and the flammable liquids on deck. Flammable liquids must not be stowed closer than 20 ft to bulkheads that are heated, such as the boiler room or galley bulkhead. This requirement does not prevail if the heated bulkhead is efficiently insulated. Insulation may be a standard insulating material 3 in. thick, a temporary wooden bulkhead of 2-in. material constructed 6 in. off the heated bulkhead and the space filled with bulk asbestos or mineral wool, or a tongue and groove bulkhead 3 ft off the heated bulkhead and filled with sand to a depth of 6 ft.

Corrosive liquids: general requirements. Stowage of containers of corrosive liquids must be in such a manner that the cargo can be observed easily. When corrosive liquids are stowed on deck, any leakage must be able to drain into a scupper leading directly over the side. When they are stowed on deck and the ship also has explosives on board, the two commodities should be separated by the engine room spaces.

Glass carboys of such liquids must not be stowed more than two tiers high.

Segregation required for this type of cargo should be obvious. It must not be stowed in the same compartment with explosives, and it should be well separated from foodstuffs and cargo of an organic nature, especially any yellow label cargo.

Compressed gas cylinders: general requirements. Compressed gas cylinders must not be accepted for shipment unless they have suitable protection for the valves and fittings on the cylinders. The protection generally takes one of three forms. The cylinder may be (1) provided with a valve protection cap that screws on over the valve assembly, (2) of the dished head design with the valve recessed into the cylinder, or (3) completely boxed for shipment so that the valve assembly is well protected.

Compressed gas cylinders must be stowed on their sides unless racks are provided for vertical stowage. The author recommends the stowage of these cylinders on their sides in the bilge and cantline style whenever possible. Building racks and stowing the cylinders standing up may be necessary when the deck space is jammed and there is no room for laying them down, but this should not be the choice if the alternative method is possible. Although there are exceptions, cargo should be stowed in the ship in the position in which it has the most stability. Doing this will avoid problems with cargo in heavy seas.

In general, cylinders of compressed gas should never be stowed over cargoes that are liable to heat, such as coal.

When cylinders of compressed gas are stowed *on deck protected,* simply covering them with tarpaulins is not considered adequate protection. Dunnage should be used over the cylinders, then the tarpaulin, then more dunnage.

Cylinders of flammable compressed gas must not be closer to the ship's side than 8 ft; if they contain nonflammable gas, they should be at least 3 ft from the ship's side. This applies to stowage below or on deck.

Flammable compressed gas must be separated from explosives by the machinery spaces.

Cargoes prohibited from all vessels. Some cargoes must not be transported on ships of any type. A few of these are mentioned here to give the student some idea of the cargoes considered most dangerous by the Coast Guard.

1. Dynamite, picric acid, trinitrotoluene, and other high explosives containing more than 75% liquid explosive ingredient.

2. Dry fulminate of mercury.

3. Liquid nitroglycerin.

4. Certain kinds of fireworks, such as flash cracker or salutes containing more than 12 grains of explosive content, those combining an explosive with detonator or blasting cap, containing yellow or white phosphorous, and others.

5. Wet charcoal or charcoal screenings.

6. Bales of cotton that are actually wet or show signs of having been in contact with oil or grease.

7. Loose or damp hay and straw.

Cargoes prohibited from passenger vessels. A question that appears on the U.S. Coast Guard license examinations from time to time relative to what cargoes are prohibited from passenger vessels prompts the author to offer this as a short but complete answer.

Passenger vessels are prohibited from carrying:

1. All class *A* explosives.
2. All class *A* poisons.
3. Highly corrosive liquids.
4. Highly flammable liquids.
5. Highly flammable solids.
6. In general, any article that is likely to endanger the lives or health of the passengers and crew or safety of the vessel.

Need for precise knowledge of the regulations. The U.S. Coast Guard through its publication, Proceedings of the Merchant Marine Council, has the following to say about the need of personnel in the industry to know the basic classifications and labels of these dangerous articles.

Time after time in the testimony of investigation of fires, it is noted that the officers and the crews will refer to "red label" cargo. The red label is principally applied to containers of flammable liquids and flammable compressed gasses. Another red label that may be seen infrequently is the *fireworks* label.

From the discussion on p. 225, it is seen that cargoes may have red, yellow, green, or white labels. Therefore, the term "red label" is not correct unless the cargo actually is in that category. To illustrate the tendency to misuse the term "red label" we will discuss the testimony of a ship's master during an investigation about 1948.

Question: Do you believe that any of the cargo taken aboard was classified as dangerous cargo?

Answer: Red label cargo is always loaded above decks and any red label cargo that would be loaded below decks would be noticed by the officer in charge who is on deck.

Question: Did you carry any red label cargo on the vessel?
Answer: Red label on deck.
Question: What was the nature of the cargo, that is, this red label cargo?
Answer: Sodium compound and phosphoric acid was another.

As can be seen from these questions and answers, neither the master nor the questioner indicated an exact knowledge of the requirements of the regulations. The statement of the master that, "Red label cargo is always loaded above decks . . ." is entirely incorrect. There are many red label cargoes that can be stowed below decks. When asked about the nature of the red label cargo, the master replied, "sodium compound . . . phosphoric acid." There is no shipping name such as "sodium compound" permitted. There are about 20 different sodium substances that are named in the dangerous cargo regulations, and they are either oxidizing materials, class *B* poisons, or flammable solids, calling for yellow, white, and yellow labels respectively. What the master meant by phosphoric acid is not certain. Perhaps he was referring to phosphoric oxychloride. If so, the container should have carried the white acid label. At any rate, it can be seen readily that the master, in discussing red label cargo, named two substances neither of which is red label cargo.

It should be quite obvious that, for purposes of safety for the ship and the crew, the masters and officers of all ships should study the dangerous cargo regulations. In only this way can they understand the significance of the different colored labels and thus be able to handle and stow this cargo intelligently and in the safest possible manner.

THE STOWAGE FACTOR

Stowage factor defined. The *stowage factor* is defined as the number of cubic feet required to stow 1 ton of a given cargo. It is a value that is used to answer two very important questions. First: When given a certain amount of cargo, what is the amount of space that will be consumed in stowing it? Second: When given a certain volume of space, what is the number of tons, units, or pieces that will go into the space? These two questions or ones related to them are continually coming up during the voyage of every ship, especially when the plans are being made for stowing the ship whether it is a full load or simply a few hundred tons.

These questions cannot be answered precisely, because the actual amount depends upon the broken stowage resulting when the cargo is stowed. This latter value varies greatly as pointed out on p. 130. We will use the following equation when calculating broken stowage:

$$L = \frac{V - v}{V} \times 100$$

where L is the percentage of broken stowage.

V is the volume consumed in stowing the cargo.

v is the volume of· the cargo stowed in V.

Lists of stowage factors should not be used without great care. If the list fully describes the containers and gives other particulars so that there is no doubt that all the factors of the listed item are the same as the item being considered for stowage, there is little danger of a serious mistake. It is recommended, however, that unless the list is one made personally by the officer using it and relates to a particular trade route and commodity type, current data should be taken concerning the commodity in question. Then, a trustworthy stowage factor should be calculated prior to any attempts to estimate space or tons as mentioned in the above two typical questions.

Calculating the stowage factor. The definition of the stowage factor points out that it is simply the specific volume of the commodity expressed in units of cubic feet per ton. The stowage factor is equal to the cubic feet per 2240 lb; hence, if we divide 2240 by the density of the commodity we obtain the stowage factor. Density is defined as the pounds in 1 cu ft for our purposes. We can express these facts as follows:

$$f = \frac{2240}{D}$$

where f = stowage factor.

D = density of the commodity in pounds per cubic foot.

2240 = a constant equal to the number of pounds in 1 ton.

However, data concerning cargo are not often received in terms of its density. More often the measurements of the container and its gross weight are available. Of course, we can calculate the density from these data, but why not express the equation for stowage· factor as one operation instead of two separated operations. The equation would be:

$$f = \frac{2240 \times v}{w}$$

where v = volume of the container.

w = gross weight of the container in pounds.

When handling grain, information concerning the cargo is often given in terms of pounds per U.S. bushel. Since the volume of the U.S. bushel is equal to 1.2445 cu ft, the equation for the stowage factor of grain would be:

$$f = \frac{2240 \times 1.2445}{w}$$

$$f = \frac{2787.6}{w}$$

where w = weight in pounds per U.S. bushel.

When handling other bulk commodities such as ores, sulfur, and sugar, the only way that the stowage factor can be obtained is by weighing a known volume of the substance. A level bucketful can be used or a box built with a volume of exactly 1 cu ft.

Obviously, it is not necessary to have the weight of a single container with its volume. The volume of the entire shipment and its gross weight or any part of the shipment can be used to calculate the stowage factor. Such data are given on the ship's manifest and on the bills of lading. Volume and weight information are readily available during all the phases of the cargo operation. The use of such data obviates the need of looking further for the information.

Using the stowage factor. The stowage factor is used to answer the questions mentioned above and always with some estimated value for broken stowage percentage. The best way to illustrate the use of the stowage factor in conjunction with the broken stowage is to present some general equations and then some numerical examples.

When given a certain volume of space (V), a cargo with a stowage factor (f), and an estimated broken stowage percentage (L) we find the tons (T) that will fit into the space as follows:

$$T = \frac{V \cdot (1 - L)}{f} \tag{18}$$

When given the same data and instead of the tons (T) we want to know the number of pieces (P) that will fit into the given space, we change the denominator of the right hand side of the equation to equal the volume of a single container (v); hence:

$$P = \frac{V \cdot (1 - L)}{v} \tag{19}$$

When a given number of tons of a certain type of cargo is to be stowed, we find the space that it will occupy by the following equation:

$$V = \frac{T \cdot f}{(1 - L)} \tag{20}$$

If the number of pieces are given instead of the tons, the space required would be:

$$V = \frac{P \cdot v}{(1 - L)} \tag{21}$$

There are times when it is convenient to combine the stowage factor with an estimate of broken stowage and to express the result as a known value. We will define such a value as the ratio of f to $(1 - L)$ and express it as F; thus:

$$F = \frac{f}{(1 - L)} \tag{22}$$

Note then that the following statements are true:

$$T = \frac{V}{F} \quad \text{and} \quad V = T \cdot F$$

Numerical examples

EXAMPLE 1

Given: A hold of 60,000 bale cubic. A cargo consisting of cases weighing 400 lb and measuring 2.5 ft by 2 ft by 2 ft to be stowed. Estimated broken stowage 10%.

Required: The number of tons that can be stowed in the hold.

Solution: Solving for the stowage factor of this cargo:

$$f = \frac{2240 \times 10}{400}$$

$$f = 56 \text{ cu ft}$$

After finding the stowage factor we use the eq. 18 for finding the answer to our problem:

$$T = \frac{60,000 \times 0.9}{56}$$

$$T = 964 \text{ tons}$$

EXAMPLE 2

Given: The same data as for example 1.

Required: The number of cases that could be stowed in the hold.

Solution: Using eq. 19:

$$P = \frac{60,000 \times 0.9}{10}$$

$$P = 5400 \text{ cases}$$

EXAMPLE 3

Given: 500 tons of a cargo with a stowage factor of 50. Estimated broken stowage 25%.

Required: The amount of space required to stow this cargo.

Solution: Using eq. 20:

$$V = \frac{500 \times 50}{0.75}$$

$$V = 33,333 \text{ cu ft}$$

Note that the accuracy of the results of such solutions depends entirely upon the officer's guess of the broken stowage that will result from the actual stowage operation. An officer in a given trade route can increase the accuracy of his estimations of broken stowage by maintaining records of the broken stowage that resulted in a number of specific cases. These records should consist of a tabulation of average broken stowage percentages resulting with the most common cargoes carried on the route in question and in particular sections of the ship. Where longshore gangs are maintained as units, this fact should be noted also because longshoremen's operations constitute a variable and some interesting facts may come to light. Without such records, the estimates of a given officer will not increase notably in accuracy. With such records, the estimates are based on facts and as time passes they should be very accurate. If the estimate does prove highly inaccurate, the officer at least knows that there must be some good reason and can start checking into the facts. One observation gives a basis for judgment, but the basis is more trustworthy as the observations increase in number and are averaged out.

Loading full and down. A problem relative to the amounts of two different kinds of cargoes that must be loaded to obtain a full and down condition can be solved after an officer fully understands the above stowage factor ideas. Variations of the basic problem are more practical than the type of problem presented in most books on cargo stowage. The basic problem deals with choosing the exact amount of two cargo types that will place the ship down to her maximum legal draft and at the same time fill up her internal volume. A good example of where this problem is met in the industry is at certain ports of Portugal where cork and pyrites are loaded. One of these is definitely a measurement cargo and the other a weight cargo. A measurement cargo is one that stows at or above a stowage factor of 40. Generally the freight charges for such cargoes will be based on measurement tons equalling 40 cu ft each.

Without using specific values, let us look at the elements of the problem. What would we always know? There are four things that we would know: (1) The total free space available for stowing the cargo.

(2) The cargo deadweight of the ship as she goes on the loading berth. (3) The stowage factor of the heavy cargo. (4) The stowage factor of the light cargo. When solving these problems we will use a stowage factor that has been combined with a broken stowage factor and indicate the resulting value by use of F. What we are trying to determine is: (1) How many tons of the light cargo and heavy cargo must be loaded to put the ship full and down?

For a general solution let us write down the following factors: Let V equal the free space available. Let T equal the cargo deadweight available. Let s equal the stowage factor (broken stowage combined) of the light cargo. Let b equal the stowage factor (broken stowage combined) of the heavy cargo. These are all known factors. Let X equal the tons of light cargo and Y equal the tons of heavy cargo that must be loaded to put the ship full and down. The latter values are unknown.

It is obvious that in order to put the ship down, the total of X and Y cannot be more or less than T. Hence we write:

$$X + Y = T \tag{23}$$

We also note that the product of sX equals the space that will be occupied by X and that bY equals the space occupied by Y. The sum of sX and bY must be equal to V to have the ship full. Hence we write:

$$sX + bY = V \tag{24}$$

Equations 23 and 24 comprise a set of simultaneous equations. That is, we have two equations with two unknowns. We can solve for one of the unknowns and then insert the known value in either equation and solve for the second unknown. There are several ways of going about the first solution. The easiest method follows. Start with eqs. 23 and 24. Multiply eq. 23 by one of the coefficients of eq. 24 and rewrite the set. We have done this using the coefficient s.

$$sX + bY = V \tag{24}$$

$$sX + sY = sT \tag{25}$$

Subtracting eq. 25 from eq. 24 we obtain:

$$bY - sY = V - sT$$

Factor out Y on the left hand side and solve for Y:

$$(b - s)Y = V - sT$$

$$Y = \frac{V - sT}{b - s} \tag{26}$$

After solving for Y the value of X can be found easily.

The general solution of the problem given above is presented for a thorough explanation. It is not recommended that the reader try to memorize the formula derived but rather the *method* used. Any given problem can be reasoned out more easily if the general idea is clear.

Numerical example

Given: A Victory ship is loading pyrites with $F = 14$, and cork with $F = 254$. She has 453,000 bale capacity and 8000 cargo deadweight available.

Required: How many tons of pyrites and how many tons of cork must be loaded to put the ship full and down?

Solution: Always write down the meaning of the symbols used. Let X equal the tons of cork, and Y the tons of pyrites. Then we have:

$$X + \quad Y = 8000$$

$$254X + 14Y = 453,000$$

Multiply the top equation through by 14 and subtract the result from the bottom equation:

$$254X + 14Y = 453,000$$
$$14X + 14Y = 112,000$$

$$\overline{\hphantom{2}240X \hphantom{+ 14Y} = 341,000}$$

$$X = 1421 \text{ tons}$$

$$Y = 8000 - 1421$$

$$Y = 6579 \text{ tons}$$

Loading full and down with required trim.[1]   A problem related to the above deals with the solution of how much of two kinds of cargo must be loaded in the end hatches of a ship during the final stages of loading to get the ship full and down with a required trim. This problem is best illustrated by an example.

Numerical example

Given: A Mariner class ship with free space in No. 1 main deck space equal to 16,000 bale cubic. This space has its center of gravity 60 ft from the forward perpendicular. This is expressed as L.C.G.—F.P. = 60 ft. Free space is also available in No. 7 second deck equal to 29,000 bale cubic. This space has L.C.G.—F.P. = 416 ft. The ship's tipping center is 264 ft from the F.P. The deadweight remaining is equal to 900 tons. The trim is presently 4 in. by the head. The $MT1$ equals 1522.

Two cargoes remain to be loaded: (1) Wolfram concentrates in double cloth bags with $F = 14$.

(2) India tea in packages with $F = 86$.

[1] It is recommended that the reader review the material on pp. 60–70 as he studies this section.

Required: The number of tons of wolfram and tea that must be loaded in No. 1 and No. 7 spaces to put the ship full and down with a trim of 6 in. by the stern.

Solution: The most direct approach is to solve first for the number of tons of the combined cargoes that must go forward and aft. Thus, we write let X = tons aft; let Y = tons forward. Obviously, then:

$$X + Y = 900$$

This is one equation of a set of two needed to solve for one of the unknowns. The second equation is obtained by working with the trimming moments needed to obtain the desired trim. The forward space is $(264 - 60)$ or 204 ft forward of the tipping center. Hence, the forward trimming moment is equal to $204Y$. The after space is $(416 - 264)$ or 152 ft aft of the tipping center. Hence, the after trimming moment is equal to $152X$. Note that the trim in the beginning is 4 in. by the head and that the desired trim is 6 in. by the stern. This means that we must change the trim, through our loading of the cargo, a total of 10 in. Since the ship is now down by the head and we want it to be down by the stern finally, we note that the after trimming moment must be in *excess* of the forward trimming moment. It must be in excess a sufficient amount so that the difference yields a net trimming moment aft that will give the ship a total change of trim of 10 in. This can be expressed mathematically as follows:

$$\frac{\text{Excess of moment aft}}{MT1} = 10 \text{ in.}$$

Or:

$$\text{Moment aft} - \text{Moment fwd.} = MT1 \times 10$$

$$152X - 204Y = 15{,}220$$

This is our second equation with the two unknowns. Multiply the first equation by 204 and then *add* the result to the second equation to eliminate Y. Solve for X, then for Y.

$$152X - 204Y = 15{,}220$$
$$204X + 204Y = 183{,}600$$

$$356X = 198{,}820$$

$$X = 558 \text{ tons aft}$$

$$Y = 900 - 558$$

$$Y = 342 \text{ tons fwd.}$$

With this information we proceed to solve for the exact amount of wolfram and tea forward and aft by using the same technique as that employed in the problem involving the loading of pyrites and cork. This time we know the same elements. Let us work with the forward end first. Note that we know a total of 342 tons will go in the forward space and that the space is equal to 16,000 cu ft. Hence we can write: let A = tons of wolfram fwd.; let B = tons of tea fwd. Obviously, then:

$$A + B = 342 \text{ tons}$$

$$14A + 86B = 16,000 \text{ cu ft}$$

Multiply the first equation through by 14, and subtract the result from the second equation.

$$14A + 86B = 16,000$$
$$14A + 14B = 4,788$$

$$72B = 11,212$$

$$B = 156 \text{ tons of tea fwd.}$$

$$A = 186 \text{ tons of wolfram fwd.}$$

In a similar manner, we solve for the distribution in the after space. Let W equal the tons of wolfram aft. Let T equal the tons of tea aft, then:

$$W + T = 558$$

By multiplying the first equation by 14:
$$14W + 86T = 29,000$$
$$14W + 14T = 7,812$$

$$72T = 21,188$$

$$T = 294 \text{ tons of tea aft}$$

$$W = 264 \text{ tons of wolfram aft}$$

This particular problem may arise during the last day of loading. If the problem does not entail both full and down conditions, only a partial solution with respect to the weight distribution for trim will be required. The holds involved do not necessarily have to be the end holds, but if a specific change in trim is to be obtained, the holds must be on opposite sides of the ship's tipping center.

Stowage factors used with lumber. The stowage factor of general cargo has been defined as the number of cubic feet required to stow a ton of cargo. It was also pointed out that the stowage factor never varied and should always be used in conjunction with an estimated broken stowage value. It must be emphasized that these foregoing remarks had reference to the stowage of ordinary dry cargo. These ideas are changed somewhat when dealing with lumber.

The stowage factor for lumber is defined as the number of cubic feet required to stow 1000 board feet of lumber. The symbol for 1000 board feet is M.

One thousand board feet will occupy $83\frac{1}{3}$ cu ft if there is no broken stowage. But, there is always some broken stowage as the lumber is stowed in the ship. There will be more broken stowage in the end holds than in the midship holds. With shipments that have large lots of uniform lengths, such as those found on the intercoastal run of the United

States, the average broken stowage will be between 20 and 25%. Poor stowage might raise this percentage to 30%, whereas excellent stowage will lower it below 20%. On shipments of varied lengths and many sizes, such as are found in foreign trade, the broken stowage will probably run between 25% and 30%.

When considering stowage factors for lumber, the estimate of broken stowage is included. As a general average figure in the problems discussed in this book, we will assume the stowage factor of lumber to be 110 cu ft per M.

In practice, the ship's officer should keep a record of the stowage of his ship in various compartments. From these data, he will be able to judge the broken stowage with accuracy. With a reliable stowage factor, we can estimate the space that is required to stow any given shipment of lumber. If we are given the size of the compartment, we can calculate the number of pieces of any given type of lumber required to fill the space.

BOARD FEET IN A SHIPMENT. To use the stowage factor for lumber, it is necessary to have the board feet of lumber in a shipment. A board foot is defined as the amount of lumber in a piece 1 in. thick and 1 ft square. The number of board feet in any given piece of lumber may be found by this equation:

$$\text{Board feet} = \frac{T \times W \times L}{12}$$

where T = the thickness in inches.
$\quad$ W = width in inches.
$\quad$ L = length in feet.

To change the answer to the board feet in a shipment all we have to do is multiply by the number of pieces in the shipment.

THE DECIMAL CONVERSION FACTOR. When lumber is surfaced, the thickness and widths are reduced. Therefore, when a 2 by 4 in. piece is received by the ship, it may be only $1\frac{3}{4}$ by $3\frac{3}{4}$ in. This fact introduces an error in stowage calculations unless it is taken into account. The number of board feet in any given shipment is reduced when the rough sizes are reduced. To find the true amount of lumber in such a shipment, multiply the gross amount of the lumber by the ratio of the finished cross-sectional area to the rough cross-sectional area. This ratio is called the *decimal conversion factor* (*dcf*). In the case of a 2×4 finished to $1\frac{5}{8}$ by $3\frac{5}{8}$ in. the decimal conversion factor would be:

$$dcf = \frac{1\frac{5}{8} \times 3\frac{5}{8}}{2 \times 4} = 0.7363 = 0.74$$

To use this factor, always round off the figure to the nearest two decimal places. If it is exactly 50 in the third and fourth places, then raise it to the next highest figure.

With the conversion factor, the calculation of the amount of lumber is based on the rough sizes and the amount thus obtained is called the gross measurement. Multiplying the gross measurement by the conversion factor we obtain the net measurement. We always consider the net measurement when calculating stowage requirements.

TWO GENERAL EQUATIONS, SPACE OR PIECES. Two equations are used continually by the supercargo when checking and planning the stowage of lumber. One equation is for space requirements to stow a given shipment:

$$\text{Space} = \frac{T \times W \times L \times P \times 110 \times dcf}{12,000}$$

where Space = the space required to stow the shipment.
T = thickness in inches.
W = width in inches.
L = length of the lumber in feet.
P = total pieces in the shipment.
dcf = decimal conversion factor if there is a difference between the rough (nominal) and finished (standard) size.
110 = a constant equal to the assumed stowage factor of sawed lumber.
12,000 = a constant equal to the product of 12 and 1000, the 1000 being used to convert board feet into M's.

The second equation is derived from the first and is used to solve for the number of pieces that can be stowed in a given compartment, knowing the type of lumber available:

$$P = \frac{\text{Space} \times 12,000}{T \times W \times L \times 110 \times dcf}$$

It is recommended that the reader learn the reasoning involved in deriving the equation rather than memorizing the equation itself.

STOWAGE OF LOGS. Space for stowage of logs or the inverse problem is approached in the same way as that for sawed lumber except that the number of board feet is found by using a *mean* diameter to find the cross-sectioned area and a different stowage factor is used. If the logs are all the same length, use 135 as the stowage factor; if they are of various lengths, use 150.

CHAPTER 6

The ship's loading and discharging equipment

SHIP'S RIGGING

The purpose of this chapter is to describe the methods and equipment used to load and unload ships today. Included with the presentation of extant practices is a discussion of the limitations of each, precautions, and proposals for the future.

The married fall system. By far the most common rig found on merchant ships for the purpose of loading and discharging cargo is the *married fall* system. This rig is sometimes referred to as the *yard and stay* or *burton* system. The last two names are used most often among seafarers. In this rig, one of the ship's booms is guyed so that its outer or upper end is over the hatch and the other is over the dock. In the days of sail, discharging and loading was performed by using two blocks with runners through them in a manner similar to the system in use today. The block plumbing the hatch was sometimes secured to the mast's stay and the block over the dock was frequently secured to one of the ship's yards. Thus the dock boom is still called the yard boom and the hatch boom is called the stay boom. The falls rove through the

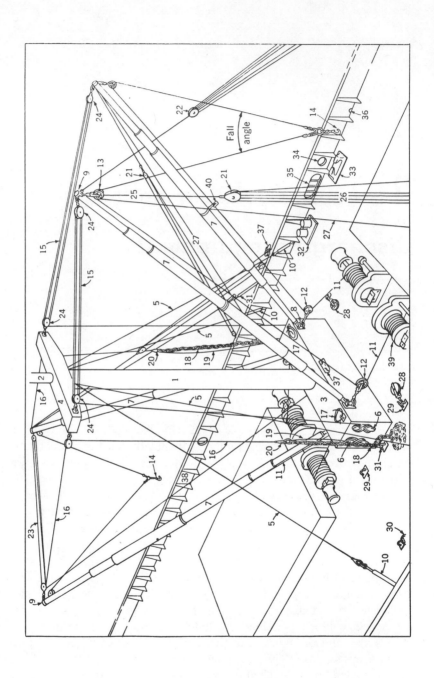

Fig. 6-1. The married fall system. This sketch shows two variations in the rigging of the married fall rig. The rig on the left shows the use of the midship guy (23) in place of the inboard guy (22) which is seen on the boom in the foreground of the set of booms on the right. The inboard guy on the boom to the extreme right is not visible. Another variation is the topping lift rig. The set of gear to the left is rigged with a single part. At the lower end of this part a bale or flounder plate is attached and to it the bull chain (18) and bull line (19) are secured. The gear on the right is shown rigged with a twofold tackle topping lift (15) with the hauling part leading down to a large cleat (6) on the masthouse (3).

The general nomenclature is as follows: (1) Mast. (2) Topmast. (3) Masthouse (resistor house with electric winches). (4) Crosstree. (5) Shrouds. (6) Topping lift cleats. (7) Booms. (8) Boom gooseneck assembly. (9) Link or spider band. (10) Turnbuckle (closed barrel). (11) Cargo runner or fall. (12) Heel block. (13) Head block. (14) Cargo hook. (15) Topping lift, twofold wire tackle. (16) Topping lift, single part (bale). (17) Chain stopper for hauling part of (15). (18) Bull chain. (19) Bull line. (20) Flounder plate. (21) Outboard or working guy or vang. (22) Inboard guy or vang. (23) Midship, schooner, or spanner guy. (24) Topping lift block. (25) Guy or vang pendant. (26) Guy or vang tackle. (27) Preventer guy. (28) Snatch block, used as fair lead. (29) Pad eye. (30) Ring bolt. (31) Shackle securing bull chain to pad eye. (32) Bitts. (33) Open chock. (34) Closed chock. (35) Freeing port. (36) Scupper drain. (37) Cleat. (38) Bulwark. (39) Winch drum. (40) Lizard. Courtesy U.S. Navy.

blocks attached to these booms are given the same names respectively. Hence, the designation of *yard* and *stay* system.

When steam replaced sail and also on many sailing vessels, cargo was handled on swinging booms for many years. The practice of using two booms, as seen in Fig. 6-1 in which both booms are *fixed,* originated on the west coast of the United States during the late nineteenth century. The swinging boom is used today only when handling loads considered to be beyond the capacity of the fixed rig. On most ships it is not safe to burton a load on fixed rigging if it exceeds 3 tons; however, if the guys are carefully positioned, size of parts are large enough, or a *safe* rig such as the Ebel rig (discussed later) is used, then heavier loads may be burtoned.

The stay fall is an up and down fall while the yard fall is the fall that pulls the load across the ship. Actually, both falls carry the load across the ship, and it is only after the athwartship movement is complete that either the yard or stay fall takes the entire load, depending upon which way the load is moving. Moving the load athwartship is known as burtoning the load, and the fall on the dock boom often is referred to as the burton whereas the fall on the hatch boom is known as the hatch or up and down fall. This is so despite the fact that when loading the hatch fall also carries the load across the ship. It is evident, then, that a confusing array of terms exists when speaking about this rig. The fall over the dock may be termed the dock fall, the burton fall, or the yard fall; likewise, the fall over the hatch may be referred to as the hatch fall, the up and down fall, or the stay fall. Inasmuch as the use of the dock and hatch terminology results in the least possible confusion, these are the terms that will be used in this discussion.

The booms (7) of Fig. 6-1 are able to pivot in two planes. The vertical movement of each boom is controlled by the topping lift (15)–(16). The transverse movement of the boom is controlled by the outboard or working guy (21) and the midship or schooner guy (23). The midship guy is also known as the spanner guy.

At the lower end of the boom, a fitting known as the gooseneck (8) allows movement in the two directions mentioned.

The cargo fall (11) leads from the winch drum (39) directly to the heel block (12) which is mounted below the gooseneck fitting. The gooseneck and heel block are generally made up in a single assembly. The fall then leads up the boom through lizards or fairleads (40) to the head block (13) and to the cargo hook (14).

Topping lift rigging. Figure 6-2 illustrates a topping lift with the hauling part led to a small winch mounted on the king post. All modern ships are being fitted with this *topping lift winch;* however, there are many ships that are not so equipped. Without the topping lift winch the hauling part leads down to a large cleat and is made fast with one round turn plus five or six figure-of-eight turns and then seized. This is the method used if the topping lift consists of a wire rope rove off on a twofold or double luff tackle. The wire used in this case would be a ¾-in. wire 6 strands and 19 wires per strand made of improved plow steel or plain plow steel. Improved plow steel wire rope is about 13%

FIG. 6-2. Cargo rigging: electric topping lift winch.

stronger than plow steel wire rope. Some topping lifts consist of a single heavy wire shackled to the *spider band* at the head of the boom. This wire, called a bale, runs through a single block made secure aloft which acts as a fairlead before it runs downward to the deck. On the lower end of such a topping lift a *flounder plate* is attached. The flounder plate is a triangular plate of about ¾-in. thickness with holes punched or drilled at the three corners about 1 in. in from the edge. The topping lift is attached to one of these corners while the *bull rope* and the *bull chain* are attached to the other two corners. The chain has links of about 1-in. diameter and the rope is about 4 in. three strand manila. The topping lift would be made of 1¼ or 1½ in. improved plow steel wire rope, 6 strands and 19 wires per strand (see Fig. 6-3).

When the boom has been topped up with the wire purchase rig, it is simply stopped off and secured to the cleat. When rigged with a bale, the boom is raised or lowered by first taking the weight of the boom on the bull line and then unshackling the bull chain. The bull rope is led to a winch gypsy head for this purpose. When at the desired level, the bull chain's lowest link is shackled to a pad eye on deck and the bull line is slacked off until the chain has all the weight.

Obviously, the use of either the wire purchase and cleat or bull line and chain requires considerable time and entails a number of operations

Fig. 6-3. Single part topping lift. This shows the topping lift lead block secured to the crosstrees, the bale, the bull line, and the bull chain. Courtesy U.S. Maritime Commission.

requiring good judgment and a certain amount of seamanship skill to be executed safely. The use of a topping lift winch obviates the need for any stopping off or shifting from cleat to gypsy head and back again or heaving with the hauling part on the winch, all of which can be disastrous if a mistake is made by the personnel. All that is necessary is to push a control button and the winch either tops up or lowers the boom. Some of these winches are made so that they can lower or top with the boom loaded; others cannot handle a loaded boom. If the topping lift winch is not designed to handle a loaded boom but an attempt to do so is made, the excessive torque requirements of the winch will cause a large rise in current through the armature and this will result in a safety device breaking the circuit and an automatic braking mechanism being applied. This is a safety device that prevents the excessive current from burning out the armature.   If the circuit breakers fail to operate, the armature will be burned out and a great deal of expense will be incurred by repairs and lost time.

Guying systems.   As can be seen from Fig. 6-1, there are two distinct systems of guying the fixed booms of the yard and stay rig.   With the inboard guy, it is necessary to find a place down on deck to secure it.   This brings additional gear to a location already overly crowded, and as a result the safety of the working area is impaired.   The load on the cargo hook is always between the heads of the two booms or directly under one of them; therefore, there is little or no stress on the inboard or midship guys.   Thus the lightweight midship guy is quite sufficient, and it is placed aloft out of the way.

The outboard guys are often referred to as the working guys because they are the guys that are under the greatest stress.   The stress on the guys appears when the load is being transferred athwartships (burtoned) or when it is being supported anywhere between the two boom heads. An analysis of the stresses on the falls and guys is made later.   It is important for all officers to know how to keep these stresses at a minimum.

PREVENTERS.   In addition to the regular outboard guy on the fixed boom, an additional wire is attached to the head of each boom and led to the deck to act as a *preventer guy*.   This preventer guy is made of $\frac{5}{8}$- or $\frac{3}{4}$-in. wire rope.   It may be completely of wire or have a tail spliced onto the lower end so that the part used to secure the preventer will have more flexibility than the wire itself.   These tails are made of manila rope 4 in. three strands, or $\frac{3}{4}$ to 1 in. chain.   If they are made of manila, they are susceptible to being cut by plates or other items being handled; if of chain, they are less vulnerable to damage.   Quite frequently the regular guy and preventer are set up so that the regular guy takes all the load and the preventer is only supposed to take a stress in case the regular guy parts.   *This is not a safe practice.*   The net result in case the regular guy does part is that the preventer parts also.   The ship's officers must make certain that the load is being carried equally by the regular guy and the preventer.   The safest procedure is to make both the regular and preventer guy secure at the same point on deck or as close together as possible and to equalize the stress on all parts.   It follows also that it would be more sensible to use one guy rigged to have the strength of the ordinary guy plus the preventer.

The preventer is a constant source of trouble and in many cases fails when the regular guy fails; however, almost all ships use them today.   In the records of the Accident Prevention Bureau of the Waterfront Employers of San Francisco, there is only one case wherein the preventer held after the regular guy parted. In this particular case, the preventer was not made secure properly and when the boom started to swing the preventer took up the strain gradually until the wire became jammed on the cleat and the boom's swing was checked.

The S.S. Schuyler Otis Bland and three recently converted Mariners operated by Pacific Far East lines are the only ships known to the author that have been equipped with guys strong enough to carry the capacity

TABLE 6-1

ROPE SIZES AND BREAKING STRENGTHS

All Values Are for Three-Stranded Rope with Standard Lay
(The safe working loads (S.W.L.) can be found by dividing the breaking strength by 6.)

Nominal Size			Net Weight of 100 ft, lb	Minimum Length in 1 lb (Net Weight), ft	Approximate Gross Weight Full Coils, lb	Minimum Breaking Strength	
Threads	Circumference, in.	Diameter, in.				Plymouth Ship Brand Manila, lb	Plymouth Sisal, lb
6-Fine	9/16	3/16	1.47	67.9	50	450	360
6	3/4	1/4	1.96	51.0	50	600	480
9	1	5/16	2.84	35.2	50	1,000	800
12	1 1/8	3/8	4.02	24.9	50	1,350	1,080
15	1 1/4	7/16	5.15	19.4	63	1,750	1,400
18	1 3/8	15/32	6.13	16.3	75	2,250	1,800
21	1 1/2	1/2	7.35	13.6	90	2,650	2,120
	1 3/4	9/16	10.2	9.80	125	3,450	2,760
	2	5/8	13.1	7.65	160	4,400	3,520
	2 1/4	3/4	16.3	6.12	200	5,400	4,320
	2 1/2	13/16	19.1	5.23	234	6,500	5,200
	2 3/4	7/8	22.0	4.54	270	7,700	6,160
	3	1	26.5	3.78	324	9,000	7,200
	3 1/4	1 1/16	30.7	3.26	375	10,500	8,400
	3 1/2	1 1/8	35.2	2.84	432	12,000	9,600
	3 3/4	1 1/4	40.8	2.45	502	13,500	10,800
	4	1 5/16	46.9	2.13	576	15,000	12,000
	4 1/2	1 1/2	58.8	1.70	720	18,500	14,800
	5	1 5/8	73.0	1.37	893	22,500	18,000
	5 1/2	1 3/4	87.7	1.14	1,073	26,500	21,200
	6	2	105.	.949	1,290	31,000	24,800
	6 1/2	2 1/8	123.	.816	1,503	36,000	28,800
	7	2 1/4	143.	.699	1,752	41,000	32,800
	7 1/2	2 1/2	163.	.612	2,004	46,500	37,200
	8	2 5/8	187.	.534	2,290	52,000	41,600
	8 1/2	2 7/8	211.	.474	2,580	58,000	46,400
	9	3	237.	.422	2,900	64,000	51,200
	9 1/2	3 1/8	264.	.379	3,225	71,000	56,800
	10	3 1/4	292.	.342	3,590	77,000	61,600
	11	3 1/2	360.	.278	4,400	91,000	72,800
	12	4	426.	.235	5,225	105,000	84,000

Standards: Smaller sizes of ropes are usually ordered by the number of threads, the larger sizes by circumference. Six, nine, and twelve-thread rope is packed in standard 25 and 50 lb coils. All larger sizes are put up in full coils of 200 fathoms—in half coils of 100 fathoms. One fathom equals 6 ft.
Courtesy Plymouth Cordage Co.

load placed on the booms without help from a preventer. Prototype ships built by the Maritime Administration in the future will probably be equipped with adequate guys.

A proposal made by L. A. Harlander had as an objective the elimination of guy failures by the installation of a guy winch with a clutch mechanism that would slip when a predetermined load was exerted on it.[1] In this manner when the stress on the guy became too great, there would be an indication by the slipping of the guy winch drum. If the slipping could be controlled so that it would be gradual and not jumpy, the idea might prove workable. However, if the winch released its tension suddenly, the results might be almost the same as if the guy broke. Perhaps a rig that would ring an alarm bell when the stress became too great would be cheaper and just as effective.

Inasmuch as the primary force that places stress on the guys comes from the winch, it seems that the most logical step would be to place an effective and reliable governing device on the winch to limit its pulling power. This is discussed in greater detail on p. 253.

SPOTTING THE GUYS. When securing the outboard guys to the deck after topping the booms, consideration should be given to the location of the lower end of the guy with respect to the stress that will be placed on it when under a load and with respect to the possibility of jackknifing.

Guy failures account for the great majority of cargo gear breakdowns. Bending of the boom due to too much compression caused by the component of thrust from fall, guy, and topping lift is the second most important cause of breakdowns. A number of very practical points relative to the task of positioning guys for greater safety are presented in the following section. These factors should be common knowledge of all deck officers and longshoremen.

P.M.A. PRACTICAL TESTS

Most of the facts presented below with respect to strains on guys under various conditions were obtained through experimentation carried out on a model closely approximating the C-3 type. The work was carried out by the Pacific Maritime Association's Accident Prevention Bureau, and results were published in *Bulletin* 16, August 1948. Special mention of it is made, because it is a contribution toward safety and good management on all ships.

Conditions of the tests. The model was adjusted to the beam of 70 ft, a hatch 24 ft wide, and the heel of the boom 10 ft aft of the hatch. The

[1] L. A. Harlander, A Proposed Improvement for Cargo-Handling Gear, SNAME, San Francisco, May 1951.

heels of the booms were placed 8 ft off the deck and outboard from the centerline a distance of 16 ft in one test and 6 ft in another test. The booms were made to scale at 55 ft of length. The guys were made fast at the ship's side at various positions fore and aft as discussed below.

Horizontal stress. The greatest *horizontal* stress between the heads of the boom for any given height of load above the deck occurs when the load is in such a position that the falls make equal angles with the horizontal. Therefore, when a fall angle of 120° is referred to it means that each fall makes an angle of 30° with the horizontal and the two falls make an angle of 120° with each other. All tests in this experiment were made with a fall angle of 120°.

As usually rigged, the hatch boom's working guy carries much more strain than that of the dock boom. Because of this, the hatch boom guy has been considered in the discussion that follows.

The load was considered to be 1 ton. This makes it possible to note the strains on the guys in terms of the load being hoisted. For instance, where a strain on a guy is read as 3 tons with our 1-ton load, it would be 15 tons if we had a 5-ton load on the hook.

Position of the heel. The athwartship location of the heel of the boom has an important effect on the strain on the guys. In Fig. 6-4, the heels

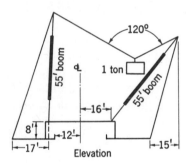

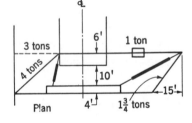

Fig. 6-4.

of the booms are 16 ft outboard from the ship's centerline. With the working guy of the hatch boom secured at a point in line with the two boom heads (indicated by the dashed line), the stress on the guy is three times the load being hoisted when the angle between the falls is 120°. In the experiment the force on the working guy would show up as a 3-ton stress because we are using a 1-ton load. Note what happens, however, when the guy is made secure at a point about 4 ft aft of the heel of the boom. The stress on this guy (as indicated by the solid line) is four times the weight of the load. In this case the load is four tons which is an increase of $33\frac{1}{3}\%$.

Now let us see what happens when we shift the heel of the booms inboard until they are only 6 ft from the centerline. In Fig. 6-5, the heels are arranged as mentioned above; nothing is changed from Fig. 6-4 except the shift in position of the heel. At a fall angle of 120° and with the guy made secure 4 ft aft of the heel, the stress on the working guy of the hatch boom has been reduced from 4 tons to $2\frac{1}{4}$ tons, or $2\frac{1}{4}$ times the load on the hook. This represents a stress reduction of 42% caused by shifting the heels of the booms inboard.

As the heels are moved outboard, greater drift for the load is obtained and this is a definite advantage when handling certain types of cargo, such

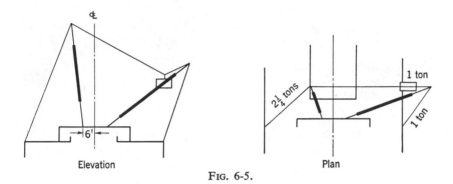

Fɪɢ. 6-5.

as long lengths. However, in Fig. 6-4 the fall angle of 120° was reached at a height of 40 ft above the deck and in Fig. 6-5 it was reached at about 32 ft above the deck. If the load in Fig. 6-4 is lowered to 32 ft above the deck with the falls making equal angles with the horizontal, the stress on the guy will only be reduced to $3\frac{1}{4}$ tons. Hence, in terms of guy stress, the increased drift has not proven an advantage.

It is evident from the above facts that it is not wise to base judgment of the strength of the gear on a ship with widely spaced king posts upon past experience with ships in which the heels were close to the centerline.

Position of the guys. It is generally considered that the best position for the guy is at right angles to the boom when viewed from above. Going back to the conditions illustrated in Fig. 6-4, we will approximate this condition by placing the guy in line with the fall as indicated by the dotted line. As pointed out above, the stress on the guy here is less than when the guy is secured 4 ft aft of the heels of the booms.

If we swing the hatch boom outboard 8 ft from the coaming as shown in Fig. 6-6 with the guy in line with the fall, the guy stress has been increased from 3 tons to $4\frac{1}{2}$ tons. This is indicated by the dashed line. Thus, it is seen that with the guy in line with the falls, a comparatively small movement of the head of the boom makes a difference of 50% in the stress on the guy. With the boom in this outboard position and the guy secured at a point 4 ft aft of the heels of the boom, the guy stress drops from 4½ tons to 3½ tons, a reduction of 22%.

It therefore appears that if a boom is angled outboard from a fore and aft line through its heel, less stress is put on the guy by leading it

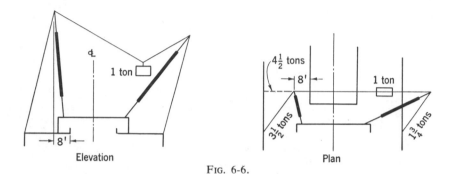

FIG. 6-6.

back to or behind the heel. If the boom angles inboard from a fore and aft line through its heel, the least stress on the guy will occur when it is at right angles to the boom or approximately in line with the fall.

A dangerous condition. A particularly dangerous condition is illustrated in Fig. 6-7. This happens when an effort is made to move the head of the boom aft (or forward depending upon which end of the

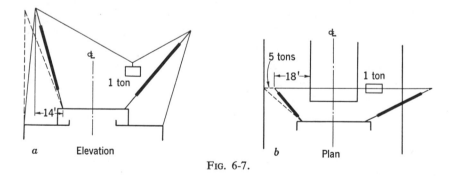

FIG. 6-7.

hatch the gear is located) without topping it. This effort is made frequently when covering the hatch and it is desired to make the hook plumb the beam slots closest to the hatch end beam. It also may result from setting the guys and heaving on the topping lift. Regardless of how it is done, the boom is swung far outboard with the guy secured in line with the fall.   It will be noted in the plan view *b* that the guy makes a very wide angle with the boom and in the elevation *a* that the guy is very nearly vertical.

Under these conditions, tremendous stresses can be built up.   If the heaving on either the guy or the topping lift is continued as far as possible, the boom will approach a position indicated by the dotted lines. The head of the boom will be almost vertically above the point where the guy is secured.   In this position, the guy would be pulling directly against the topping lift.   Theoretically, an infinite stress would be placed on the guy by the horizontal pull of the falls.   *This is a situation that should be watched for and avoided.*   It is particularly likely to occur at the forward end of No. 1 and the after end of No. 5 where the beam is at a minimum.   It may occur also at the after end of No. 3 or the forward end of No. 4 where, on some vessels, the heels of the boom are closer to the rail than they are to the centerline.

Maximum loads function of winch strength.   As an example let us say that the stress on the guy is three times the weight of the load on the

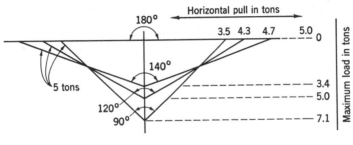

Fig. 6-8.

falls at a fall angle of 120°, as it proved to be by experimentation on the model with the guys secured at a particular point.   With a 5-ton load, then, the stress on the guys will be 15 tons.   Now if any given load is raised to a fall angle of 140°, the stress on the guys may go up to 3.3 times the weight of the load.   If we were hoisting a 1-ton load, the guy stress would be 3.3 tons instead of only 3 tons.   However, the important point here is to note that with 5-ton winches we *cannot lift more than* 3.4 tons to a position with a fall angle of 140°.   Therefore, the guy stress is limited by the winch power to 3.4 times 3.3 or a maximum of 11.2 tons.   As seen in Fig. 6-8, the horizontal pull at a fall angle of 120° is 4.3 tons as compared to 4.7 tons with a fall angle of 140°.   It should be pointed out here that if the booms are rigged with gun tackles in an effort to make the falls capable of handling heavier loads safely, the

winches would then be able to hoist heavier loads to greater fall angles
and the danger of exerting excessive stresses on the guys does exist. The
officer of the ship must be careful of the set of his rigging under such
conditions. Rigged with gun tackles, the stress on the guys could go
up to a maximum of 22.4 tons because theoretically a 6.8-ton lift could
be hoisted to a fall angle of 140°.

From the above it is seen that although the stresses on the guys increase greatly in terms of weight of the load as the fall angle increases,
the weight of the load which can be raised to these higher angles falls
off; therefore, the stresses have a limit based on the capacity of the
winches.

When hoisting long lengths to high fall angles, such as when loading
structural steel or piling, and when the loads are 1 ton, the stress on
the guys may be higher than if hoisting 5-ton loads to their maximum
fall angle. This is because we can lift the lighter loads to higher angles
and increase the horizontal pull between the heads of the booms. At any
given fall angle the stresses on the guy are proportional to the weight of
the load. Maximum stresses, however, are determined by the *strength
of the winches* and not by the weight of the load. If gun tackles are
used, the strength of the winch is increased.

The same situation exists in the case of the stresses on the falls. A
1-ton load at a fall angle of 160° puts a 2.9 ton stress on each fall. The
maximum stress that can be built up is the power of one winch.

The above discussion is correct theoretically, but ship's officers should
be aware of the fact that the usual electric winch does not begin to throw
out the overload trip until a line pull of 8 to 12 tons in high gear is
reached. During the appreciable time lag required to trip the breaker,
the line pull continues to increase. Thus it can be seen that most electrical winches may exceed the 5-ton limit mentioned in the examples and
correspondingly exceed the guy stresses.

It must be emphasized that the maximum stresses mentioned above
are for static loads and do not take into account the increases caused by
jerking winches or temporary overloads that a winch can carry long
enough to act on the parts of the rigging. Stresses from these causes are
large but have not been considered in this study. Following this discussion of static stresses, the elementary principles involved in a study
of the effect of dynamic forces are set forth, see p. 260.

Maximum stresses. It is well known that tight-lining of the falls
causes extremely heavy stresses on the guys. Undoubtedly, a question
may arise in the minds of many officers of the magnitude of the stress
when the falls are tight-lined with an empty hook. Because of the limi-

tation placed on the power of the winch, the stress on the guys depends entirely on the fall angle when the winch is pulling its maximum.

Figure 6-8 indicates the maximum load that a pair of 5-ton winches can lift to various fall angles and the corresponding horizontal pull between the heads of the booms. It is, of course, this *horizontal pull* that puts the stress on the guys. The horizontal pull will be at a maximum when the winches are pulling against each other with an empty hook, and with 5-ton winches this would be equal to precisely 5 tons. Thus, an empty hook is potentially more dangerous than a heavily loaded one.

When 5-ton winches are holding a 5-ton load at a fall angle of 120°, the horizontal pull is 4.3 tons. The stress on each fall under this condition would be 5 tons also; thus, it can be seen that this is as high an angle as these winches can possibly lift such a load.

Topping or jackknifing of booms. Topping or jackknifing of booms can have very serious and costly results. While the extreme conditions

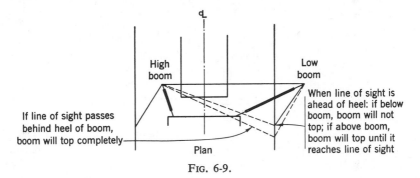

Fig. 6-9.

under which a boom will or will not top are well known, the dividing line, or danger point, is not well known. Experiments with a model such as those carried out with respect to guy stresses have established the line of demarcation between jackknifing and not jackknifing and a means of locating this danger point on board ship.

When the two booms are at different heights, which is usually the case, their respective tendencies to top are different. The fall leading upward from the lower to the higher boom will tend to lift the lower boom. For this reason the working guy of the lower boom must be placed closer to the heel than is necessary in the case of the higher boom. The working guy of the lower boom must be so placed that a line of sight (dotted line in Fig. 6-9) from the pad eye to the head of the higher boom will pass beneath the lower boom somewhere ahead of the gooseneck of the lower boom. If the line of sight is behind the heel of the lower boom, the boom will definitely top. If the line of sight passes above the boom but ahead of the heel, the boom will top until it reaches this line of sight and then it will stop.

Because the higher boom is being somewhat pulled down by the fall, its guy need not be as close to the heel as that of the lower boom and the line of sight from the pad eye to the head of the lower boom may pass behind the heel of the boom. However, the working guy at the height of the gooseneck must be ahead of the line of sight between the gooseneck of the higher boom and the head of the lower boom. If the high boom's working guy is behind this line of sight at the height of the gooseneck, the boom will top. Figure 6-10 is a perspective view along the

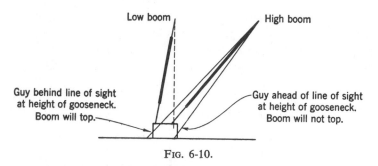

FIG. 6-10.

line of sight from the heel of the high boom to the head of the low boom which illustrates these two conditions. The perspective view shown in Fig. 6-10 is that which would appear to a person observing a set of gear at the after end of a hatch looking toward the port side from the starboard side; in other words, the high boom is the starboard boom (over the hatch) and the low boom is the port boom (over the dock).

As a practical means of adopting this rule it is suggested that a man place himself on the line of sight and in line with the guy. Since the goosenecks on most ships are about 8 ft above the deck, there is danger of topping if the guy is over his head. If the guy is below the top of his head when he is on the line of sight, the boom is safe.

In cases where the booms are at about the same height, the safest procedure would be to secure the guys so that the line of sight crosses the respective booms. The line of sight referred to here is that from the pad eye where the guy is secured to the head of the opposite boom.

Any change in the position of a boom not only affects its own tendency to top but also affects the tendency of the opposite boom to top since the line of sight moves with the head of the boom. It is for this reason that frequently when one boom tops the other will follow it.

The working guy of the yard boom is frequently located in a position that will make topping possible. The tendency to top can be observed by a little slackening of the topping lift. This may not be dangerous; however, it should be checked carefully. At the same time, the working guy of the hatch boom must be checked to make certain it is not located so close to the critical point that moderate topping of the dock boom will cause the hatch boom to jackknife.

Summary of discussion of guy location. Several important facts that all officers should keep in mind when their ship is working cargo have been pointed out in the above discussion. These are summarized below.

1. The closer the heel of the boom is to the rail, the greater the stresses on the guys and booms for the same fall angle.

2. The increased drift obtained by widely spaced heels may not fully compensate for the increased stress on the guys.

3. When a boom is angled outboard from the fore and aft line through its heel, the stress on the guy decreases as it is moved back of the heel. The practical amount of this movement is limited by the critical point for jackknifing.

4. When a boom is on the fore and aft line through its heel or swung inboard from this position, the stresses on the guy and the boom are least when the guy is in line with the fall or at right angles to the boom when viewed from above. Under most conditions, there will be little difference in the amount of stress at these two positions of the guy.

5. Depending upon the spacing of the heels, the stress on the working guy of the hatch boom at a fall angle of $120°$ may be as much as $4\frac{1}{2}$ times the weight of the load. Improper leads of guys can increase these stresses considerably.

6. At any given fall angle the stress on the guys will vary directly with the weight of the load, but the *maximum* stress that can be placed on a guy in any given case is determined by the capacity of the winches not by the weight of the load. In fact, the lighter the load the greater the maximum possible stress.

Additional stresses. As mentioned before, the experiments on the model provided for measuring the stresses on the guys only. There was no provision made for actually measuring the stress on the topping lift or the compression on the boom. These values plus the guy stresses have been calculated by a method described later (see p. 270) and are presented in Table 6-2. The stresses were calculated for the same set of conditions as were described for the experiment, that is, a 1-ton load with a fall angle of $120°$. The figures referred to are those mentioned above. The boom compression shown in the tables includes the compression caused by the stress on the single hauling part of the fall as well

TABLE 6-2

	Guy Stress		Boom Com-pression	Topping Lift Stress
	Calculated	Experimental		
Fig. 6-4				
Hatch boom with guy:				
Behind heel	3.3	4.0	4.8	0.3
In line with fall	2.4	3.0	5.0	1.7
Yard boom guy	1.7	1.75	3.9	0.5
Fig. 6-5				
Hatch boom guy behind heel	1.9	2.25	3.4	0.2
Yard boom	1.0	1.0	3.3	0.7
Fig. 6-6				
Hatch boom with guy:				
Behind heel	2.8	3.5	4.3	0.2
In line with fall	3.6	4.5	6.6	2.1
Fig. 6-7				
Hatch boom guy in line with fall	10.0	8.0	16.2	6.9

as the forces created by the guy, the topping lift, and the cargo fall from the head block to the hook.

Note that, in all cases except Fig. 6-7 where the high stress on the model might have pulled the boom head far enough inboard to lower the guy stress, the calculated stresses on the guys are less than those found by experiment. It is believed that these differences can be attributed to the fact that in the model, as under actual conditions, the various parts are grouped around the boom head some distance from the centerline of the boom used as the reference point in the calculations. It is probable that the boom compression and topping lift stresses actually exceed the calculated values also. The actual stresses on these parts will be further increased by the weight of the boom and fittings at the head.

It is interesting to note that the stresses produced by the arrangement shown in Fig. 6-7 are cut almost in half by placing the guy at right angles to the boom in the plan view. They are cut in half again by leading the guy behind the heel. The values of the stresses involved for Fig. 6-7 with all values calculated considering the hatch boom are as follows:

	Guy Stress	Boom Stress	Topping Lift Stress	
Guy in line with fall	10.0	16.2	6.9	(1)
Guy 90° to boom	5.6	9.7	3.2	(2)
Guy behind heel	2.4	4.2	0.3	

Note that moving the guy from position 1 to position 2 involves a shift of only 4 ft, but the change in the guy's angle with the boom is great and the effect on the stresses is also great. Because the boom is angled outboard, far lower stresses are produced by leading the guy well back.

The stresses on the midship or hatch gear can be drastically reduced by swinging the head of the boom inboard until it plumbs the centerline of the hatch. In this position, the stresses are as follows:

	Guy Stress	Boom Stress	Topping Lift Stress
Guy in line with fall	1.7	3.9	1.3
Guy at right angles to boom	1.0	3.3	1.8

Here again it will be noted that placing the guy at right angles to the boom in the plan view greatly reduces the stress on the gear. In this case the two locations of the guy along the ship's rail are 34 ft apart; this is because we are working so close to the heels of the booms with the hatch boom. Locating the guy behind the heel in this setup would not only produce a stress of 3.7 tons on the guy but also would cause the boom to top before the load reached an angle of 120° between the falls.

All of the above values of stresses have been obtained with the gear rigged with fixed booms as it is normally worked; therefore, they are quite significant when compared with the stresses that would result if the boom was used as a swinging boom. The guy stresses, of course, are negligible, but the boom compression and topping lift stresses fall off too. With a swinging 55-ft boom on a 43-ft mast, the compression on the boom is about 2.3 times the weight of the load, including the pull of a single part fall along the boom, in any position, whereas the *maximum* stress on the topping lift is no more than 1.7 times the weight of the load. This maximum stress is taken when the boom is horizontal.

Additional conclusions

1. Excessive stresses caused by faulty rigging of the gear cannot be safely compensated for merely by the use of preventers or otherwise increasing the strength of the guys. To use this method of compensation may cause the boom to fail.

2. The smallest stresses are produced (because of increased drift and good guy angles) on gear with widely spaced king posts when the head of the hatch boom is well in toward the centerline of the ship, and the working guy is at right angles to the boom in the plan view.

3. Since the pull of the fall along the boom makes up a large percentage of the total compression on the boom, maximum benefits are

obtained by doubling the fall rather than putting the winch in low gear when heavy weights or lack of drift makes either necessary.

DYNAMIC LOADS

In connection with the consideration of stresses on the cargo gear, it is of great importance to take into account the effect of acceleration and deceleration on the total load. We will show in the following discussion that the weight of any given load is virtually increased when the speed of hoisting is increased or the speed of lowering is decreased. The magnitude of this increase can be dangerously high if the winches are not operated carefully.

Newton's second law of motion. Newton's second law of motion states that *if an unbalanced force acts upon a body, the body will be accelerated; the magnitude of the acceleration is proportional to the magnitude of the unbalanced force, and the direction of the acceleration is in the direction of the unbalanced force.* From this fundamental concept we obtain the equation

$$F = {}^{'}Ma \qquad (27)$$

where F = the force acting upon the body.
　　M = the mass of the body.
　　a = the acceleration of the body.

If the weight (W) of a body is the only force acting upon it, it is a freely falling body and has an acceleration equal to 32 ft per sec per sec. This is called the acceleration due to the force of gravity since it is caused by the pull of the earth on the body. It is always denoted by the letter g. Since the force acting on a freely falling body is its weight, eq. 27 becomes

$$W = Mg \qquad (28)$$

from which we may obtain

$$M = \frac{W}{g} \qquad (29)$$

If the mass of the body does not enter explicitly into the problem, it is possible to eliminate it from eq. 27 by substituting its value from eq. 29, obtaining

$$F = \frac{W}{g} a \qquad (30)$$

In eq. 30, F and W are expressed in the same units. In our consideration of loads on the cargo gear we will use pounds or tons force.

Also a and g are expressed in the same units and we will use feet per second per second.

Equations of motion. Now we must also consider some equations of motion for constant acceleration, all of which we derive from the basic definitions of velocity and acceleration.

The speed or velocity of a body is defined as the distance traversed divided by the time elapsed. Hence we have

$$\text{Speed} = \frac{\text{Distance}}{\text{Time}}$$

or in symbols

$$\bar{v} = \frac{d}{t} \tag{31}$$

Note that we have denoted speed or velocity by $\bar{v}$, read vee-bar. This is to prevent confusion when using other symbols for velocity, such as plain v for final velocity of a body after being accelerated from an initial velocity u. Thus $\bar{v}$ is the *average* of v plus u or

$$\bar{v} = \frac{v + u}{2}$$

and

$$\frac{v + u}{2} = \frac{d}{t}$$

$$t = \frac{2d}{v + u}$$

Acceleration is defined as the change in velocity divide by the time during which the change takes place. If the velocity of the body initially is u and it changes so that after a time interval t its velocity is v, then acceleration is, from the definition:

$$\text{Acceleration} = \frac{\text{Change in velocity}}{\text{Time}}$$

or in symbols

$$a = \frac{v - u}{t} \tag{32}$$

Now going back to eq. 30, if the load on a cargo hook is the body and it is traveling up or down at a constant speed without any acceleration except that needed to *balance* the acceleration due to gravity, it should be evident that *a* in

$$F = \frac{W}{g} a$$

is equal to *g*. Therefore, *in this case*

$$F = W$$

However, if the *rate* of hoisting is increased or *rate* of lowering is decreased then *a* becomes greater than *g* and *F* becomes greater than *W*. Thus we see that the load on the hook becomes greater than the actual weight on the hook.

From the equations of motion 31 and 32 we obtain, when *u* equals 0, the equation

$$a = \frac{v^2}{2d} \tag{33}$$

Now we have three equations: 30, 32, and 33.

$$F = \frac{W}{g} a \tag{30}$$

$$a = \frac{v - u}{t} \tag{32}$$

$$a = \frac{v^2}{2d} \tag{33}$$

With these equations we can investigate the change in the load on a cargo hook due to acceleration and deceleration. Using the word deceleration here is merely a matter of convenience. In the problems considered in this type of study, we would most often conceive of the load being lowered at some set velocity and then brought to a velocity of zero by retarding the lowering rate. The increase in *W* would be the same if we were hoisting the load and started from zero and reached the given velocity in the same time or within the same distance. Thus, it becomes unnecessary to apply negative or positive signs to the values but important to keep the concepts clearly within focus. The load is increased above *W* when decelerating only when lowering the load.

The magnitude of the increase in *a* over the value of 32 ft per sec^2 is found by solving for *a* with either eq. 32 or 33. After solving for the increase in *g* [call this value *a'* (*a* prime)] add the calculated value to *g*, substitute the new value for a in eq. 30, and the force on the cargo hook (F) is found.

Numerical examples

EXAMPLE 1

Given: A load of weight W is being hoisted at the velocity of 1 ft per sec. Within the time interval of 0.3 sec its speed is increased to 4 ft per sec.

Required: What is the force acting on the cargo hook during the period of accelerated motion?

Solution: We use eq. 32 to determine a'. Thus

$$a' = \frac{4 - 1}{0.3} = 10 \qquad \text{also} \qquad 10 + 32 = 42 = a$$

Now, using eq. 30 with 42 as the value of a, we obtain

$$F = \frac{W}{32} 42$$

$$= 1.31W$$

EXAMPLE 2

Given: A load of weight W is being lowered into a hold at the rate of 4 ft per sec. The winch driver stops the downward motion within a distance of 1 ft.

Required: What is the force F acting on the cargo hook during the period of deceleration?

Solution: We use eq. 33 to determine a'.

$$a' = \tfrac{16}{2} = 8 \text{ ft per sec}^2$$

Note then that:

$$a = 32 + 8 = 40 \text{ ft per sec}^2$$

which is the value to substitute in eq. 30 for a. Thus

$$F = \frac{W}{32} 40$$

$$= 1.25W$$

CARGO WINCHES

Comments and data regarding three types of cargo winches will be presented in the following sections. The three types of winches found on ships are steam, electric, or hydraulic powered. The steam winch has been replaced by the electric winch on almost all modern vessels. The hydraulic winch has certain advantages which may make it a competitor of the electric winch, but at the present time it is found on only a very few ships.

The steam cargo winch. Before World War II, most ships were equipped with the steam winch, but today they are principally used on tankers.

Before operating a steam winch, all moving parts should be lubricated. Correct lubrication is an essential factor of operation and maintenance. Correct lubrication involves both the selection of the lubricant and the application. In general, the shaft, pinion, crank pin, and eccentric bearings are supplied daily, using a grease gun with Alemite or Zirk fittings. Older models are lubricated by use of grease cups. The faster moving parts of the winch are supplied oil by means of oil wells or hand oiling or swabbing. Although the lubrication of such winches is the responsibility of a member of the engineering department, it is up to the deck officer on cargo watch to make certain the winches are taken care of.

Another preliminary step prior to operating the steam winch is the draining of the cylinders and throttle of all condensation. Drain valves and petcocks are conveniently placed on the cylinders, valve chest, and throttle for draining all condensation. These should all be opened, and after the condensate stops flowing out, the main steam valve should be cracked to allow a small amount of steam to blow through and warm up the winch. After drainage is completed, all valves and cocks should be closed. The winch is then ready for operation.

The winch speed, high or low gear, should be selected before the load is to be handled. Shifting the clutch can be done easily by running the engine very slowly and with a slight pressure against the shifting lever until the clutch is fully engaged. The locking pin or pawl, whichever is provided, should secure the shifting lever in position. Under no circumstances should the winch be shifted from low to high or back again while a load is hanging on the fall.

All hoisting or lowering is done by operating the lever connected to the throttle valve. The winch should have the fall placed on the drum so that when the lever is pulled upward the load is hoisted and when put downward the load is lowered.

RATING AND CAPACITY OF THE STEAM WINCH. A knowledge of the rating and capacity of the winches will enable an officer to understand the limitations of his cargo gear better and should result in more efficient operation. Steam cargo winches generally come in two sizes stated as 7 by 12 in. or 9 by 12 in. These figures refer to the cylinder diameter and the length of the piston stroke. The winches are generally of the double-cylinder, two-speed, single-drum type.

PRECAUTIONS. The principal precaution and disadvantage of the steam cargo winch is the necessity to drain them in freezing weather and

TABLE 6-3

Rating and Capacity

	7 × 12 in.	9 × 12 in.
Line pull in low gear	10,000 lb	20,000 lb
Line pull in high gear	5,000 lb	7,450 lb
Line speed low gear	125 fpm *	110 fpm †
Line speed high gear	250 fpm ‡	250 fpm §

* Based on first layer of ⅞-in. wire rope.
† Based on third layer of 1-in. wire rope.
‡ Based on first layer of ⅝-in. wire rope.
§ Based on first layer of ¾-in. wire rope.

take care that the condensate in the cylinders and valve chests does not become frozen.

Electric cargo winches.   Electric cargo winches are installed in two different ways.   In the first method, quite common for the past fifteen years, the winch itself, its motor, and its motor brake are mounted on the deck or on top of a masthouse whereas the resistors and control panels are mounted inside the masthouse or below deck.   In the second type of installation, which might be referred to as the unit installation, the winch is constructed as a complete unit with the brake, resistors, and control panel in one housing.   The master switch, which is the controller, is located on deck close to the hatch in both installations.

OPERATION.   The operation of electric cargo winches is simple, and maintenance is less exacting than it is on the steam winches.   Before operating electric winches they should be lubricated, but the number of points requiring attention are few.   All gears and jaw clutches are totally enclosed in oil-tight fabricated cases and are splash-lubricated.   Alemite or Zirk pressure grease fittings are provided for the drum shaft bearings, intermediate gear, and pinion bearings.   These points should be serviced at least once for each 4 hr of continuous operation.

To put an electric winch into operation is extremely simple.   On the two-speed winch, the speed change lever should be shifted to the required load position.   In shifting this lever, light pressure should be placed on it and the motor rotated slowly with the master switch on the first point until the clutch jaws are fully engaged.   The locking pin should be placed in the hole in the end of the lever before the winch is operated.   All hoisting or lowering is done by use of the master switch or controller.

RATING AND CAPACITY.   Table 6-4 presents data concerning the line pull and speed of typical electric winches with some other interesting information.

TABLE 6-4

RATING AND CAPACITY

Regular Duty, Two-Speed, Electric Cargo Winch

	High Gear 219 fpm Line Speed	High Gear 279 fpm Line Speed	Low Gear 112 fpm Line Speed
Line pull	7450 lb	3720 lb	14,440 lb

Rope capacity 700 ft of $\frac{7}{8}$-in. wire rope in five layers.   Total weight of winch motor, and brakes: 9050 lb.

Heavy Duty, Two-Speed, Electric Cargo Winch

	High Gear 218 fpm Line Speed	High Gear 305 fpm Line Speed	Low Gear 75 fpm Line Speed
Line pull	7450 lb	3720 lb	20,800 lb

Rope capacity 800 ft of 1-in. wire rope in five layers.   Total weight of winch, motor, and brake: 12,800 lb.
Courtesy American Hoist and Derrick Co.

Electric brakes as well as the conventional band brakes are incorporated in most electric winches.   These magnetic brakes automatically act to hold the load as soon as the current to the motor is shut off, either by power failure or, when the master controller is placed in the off position (vertical position), by the winch operator.

The master switch or controller is usually located on deck close to the hatch so that the operator can properly observe the load.   In normal operations, to lower a load into the hatch the operator pushes the controller toward the hatch or away from himself.   In the vertical position the current is off and the load is held by the magnetic brake.   To hoist a load, the controller is pulled toward the operator or away from the hatch.   Both the hoisting and lowering of the load is done under power.

Hydraulic winches.   At the time of writing this the author knows of no United States flag vessel with hydraulic winches although these winches have been used for some time on Norwegian ships.   One of the principal makers of this equipment is the Norwegian firm of Hydraulik A/S.   The Alfred Conhagen Company, New York, manufactures the Hydro-Lo winch in the United States under license from the Norwegian firm.

The hydraulic winch affords the favorable characteristic of extreme smoothness of operation with precise control.   Greater acceleration is also possible, but this is a questionable advantage because of the possibility of inexperienced or simply careless winch drivers placing shock loads on the cargo gear. With light loads it would be an advantage.

An interesting comparison can be made between the equipment used on the Mariner type ships with their present electric winches and the same equipment that would have been required with hydraulic winches. The Mariner type ship was equipped with AC auxiliary power, but the problem of speed control on AC motors resulted in the installation of DC winches on the ships. This, of course, required the use of motor generators to convert the ship's AC supply. This appears to be a good example of how the cargo handling functions of a cargo ship are given secondary consideration by the planners of the ship in the early stages. The AC auxiliary units were judged desirable, evidently, but in gaining the advantages the AC installations multiplied the electrical equipment needed for cargo handling by almost three times. This, of course, makes the cargo handling activities of the ship three times as vulnerable to breakdown.

TABLE 6-5

AN INSTALLATION OF 24 WINCHES

Mariner Type Ship with Electric Winches	A Ship Equipped with Hydraulic Winches
24 50 hp winches	24 winches with motors attached in single unit
24 control panels	12 simple start-stop switches
24 resistor panels	
12 100 hp AC induction motors	12 50 hp AC constant speed induction motors
24 50 hp DC generators	12 hydraulic pumps with heat exchangers and filters
36 exciters	
Cost: ?	Cost: Approximately $240,000

GENERAL DESCRIPTION OF THE HYDRAULIC INSTALLATION. The cargo winch consists of two fluid motors each driving one end of the winch drum through a semirigid coupling. A control valve is included for handling the winch in operation. All operations of hoisting, lowering, braking, and stopping are accomplished by movements of the control lever in much the same way as the throttle valve is handled on the steam cargo winch.

The use of two fluid motors utilizes a wide range of torque-speed characteristics. For heavy loads, the oil flow is divided between the two fluid motors obtaining full torque at one-half the maximum speed. For lighter loads, the oil flow is directed into one motor only, and the maximum speed at one-half full torque is available.

HOISTING OPERATION. Hoisting is accomplished by pulling the control lever back towards the operator and directing the oil partially or fully (depending upon speed requirements) into both fluid motors simultaneously. A patented check valve feature of the control valve causes the inlet pressure to build up to overcome the load on the winch the *instant* the oil flow starts through the fluid motors. If increased speed is desired, the control lever is pulled farther back to cause all the oil flow to travel through one fluid motor. However, if the load is too great to be handled by one fluid motor, both will remain cut in regardless of the *fast* position of the control lever. The oil pressure automatically adjusts itself to whatever the load on the winch requires. There is no time lag in the pickup of power, and the control valve can be operated *as slowly* or *as quickly* as desired with prompt response at the winch. Rapid acceleration is combined with a smooth elastic start.

LOWERING OPERATION. Lowering is accomplished by pushing the control lever away from the operator. The initial phase of lowering, providing there is a load on the winch, consists of braking by restricting oil circulation through the fluid motors. Further movement of the lever will cause the pressure to be built up and the winch run in reverse. Full speed range at one-half maximum torque is available when lowering.

STOPPING. Stopping locks each motor hydraulically by preventing oil circulation through the fluid motors. In the stop position, oil from the pump by-passes through the control valve back to the suction side of the pump. With heavy loads hanging on the winch, a slight creep can be expected. This is due to internal leakage past the vanes within the fluid motor. In case of accidental stoppage of the pump with the control valve in hoist position, the load will stay suspended as the reverse action of the winch automatically locks the fluid motors hydraulically by closing the check valve feature in the control valve. This prevents reverse circulation. The load can be safely lowered at no power under full control of the winch operator.

PIPING REQUIREMENTS. The pump size and speed are selected to obtain the flow required to attain the maximum desired line speed at the winch. The piping consists of a closed circuit with an expansion tank piped to the suction side of the pump. The expansion tank maintains a head of oil on the system and eliminates any possibility of air being drawn into the oil. The pump delivers a constant flow of oil through the circuit at a pressure in proportion to the load on the winch. Only one pump is required for each pair of winches. The two winches are piped in series and the load at each winch is overcome by a proportion of the total pressure available. Pumps can be driven by a takeoff from a main or auxiliary engine or by a constant speed electric motor.

ADDITIONAL FEATURES. Overload protection is obtained by a builtin relief valve at the pump. Excessive line strains can be prevented by proper adjustment of the relief valve.

As in any hydraulic transmission system, heat is generated through throttling, internal leakage, and other fluid friction losses. Deck equipment operating for short periods of time, such as the anchor windlass or warping winch, normally do not require cooling of the oil to maintain a favorable heat balance. However, the constant operation of cargo winches will require cooling of the oil of approximately 15% of the flow at average sea water temperature. If such a cooling device is employed in the return line, oil temperature can be maintained between 100 and 120°F.

TABLE 6-6

TYPICAL PERFORMANCE RATINGS

Line Pull at Layer of ⅝-in. Diameter Wire

Hoisting	Inlet Pressure, lb per sq in.	Line Pull, lb	Maximum Line Speed, fpm
Using one	250	2580	230
fluid motor	300	3100	230
	400	4100	230
Using two	250	5160	115
fluid motors	300	6190	115
	400	8200	115

Some general precautions. In another section some discussion was made of shock loads due to acceleration and deceleration of loads. Another, and probably more practical, danger arises when operating a cargo winch with an empty hook while the runner is being slacked off. If the slack is run off too rapidly, the runner will not feed off but simply form a number of loops. These loops may become tangled and caught on parts of the winch. When a load is applied to the winch again, the new turns will over-ride the loops. Later when slacking off with a new load, these loops will be released and the runner will slack suddenly. These shock loads can cause considerable stress on the runner and may be the direct cause of gear failure.

Electric winches have an overload safety device that causes a circuit breaker to cut off the current to the winch motor when an attempt is being made to hoist a load that exceeds the capacity of the winch. Unfortunately, these circuit breakers do not act precisely when the line pull reaches the rated capacity of the winch. There is a gradual buildup of the torque until finally the current is automatically cut off. When operating a 5-ton electrical winch, for example, the line pull may reach 8 to 12 tons before the circuit breakers stop the winch action. In the case of tight-lining loads with the yard and stay rig, this can cause serious gear failures.

CALCULATION OF STRESSES

Calculation of stresses by using vectors. It is often convenient to be able to solve for the stress placed on a given part of the ship's rigging by graphic methods. We will discuss the methods used to do this graphically by the use of vector quantities.

The physical quantities of length, time, and mass can be stated quite nicely by using numbers with appropriate units, such as 9 ft, 9 min, 9 lb. These numbers are known as scaler units. However, when dealing with a physical quantity that has a number related to it *plus a direction,* it is more convenient to use vector quantities. Vector quantities are represented by properly *directed* lines the lengths of which represent the *magnitudes* of the vector quantities.

When a number of forces are acting upon a body in various directions, the total force and the direction of that force can be calculated by adding up the various vector quantities. The single force thus calculated is known as the *resultant force*. If the resultant force is zero, then the body will remain at rest. For example, when a cargo hook is suspended between two booms with two falls and a loaded pallet attached to it, we know that the resultant of all these forces is equal to zero because the hook is not moving. It is at rest. Furthermore, it is obvious that the upward forces taken alone must produce a resultant force precisely equal to the downward forces. Therefore, if we have a known weight on the hook, we know that the falls are pulling so that they produce an upward resultant equal to the weight in suspension. With this information we can solve for the stress on each fall. Or, if we are given the stress on each fall, we can calculate the resultant force itself.

One of the most common methods of calculating the resultant force is known as the parallelogram method. In the problems occurring in our study of the stresses on the parts of cargo rigging, we will ordinarily know one force (the load on the cargo hook) and be seeking the value of two forces acting to oppose the given force. These two forces will be the stresses on the two cargo falls. We will also deal with stresses on topping lifts, compression on booms, and approximate stresses on guys. Figure 6-11a shows a weight being suspended by two falls AC and CB with a fall angle of 120°. The weight is suspended at C. We know that the forces acting in the direction of A from C and in the direction of B from C are holding the weight in suspension.

The forces involved may be drawn as shown in Fig. 6-11b. F_1 and F_2 are opposed to the weight W; thus, F_1 and F_2 are creating the resultant R which opposes W. To solve for the stress on F_1 and F_2 by the parallelogram method, R is drawn opposite to W equal to W. In this example let W equal 3 tons. Then R and W would be drawn equal to three units.

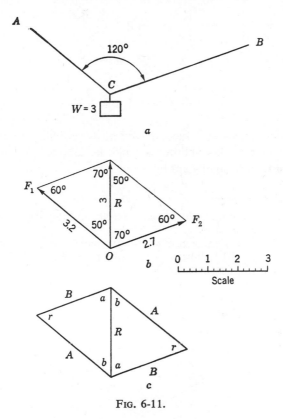

FIG. 6-11.

We start from any convenient point O. From the point O we draw F_1 parallel to CA and F_2 parallel to CB. Next, the end of the vector R is connected to the vectors F_1 and F_2 so as to form a parallelogram. Then the lengths of F_1 and F_2 from O in the chosen units give the stresses acting on the two parts. In this case, F_1 equals 3.2 tons, and F_2 equals 2.7 tons.

If the values of F_1 and F_2 and the direction in which they acted from the point O had been known first, the resultant force R could have been found by reversing the process.

Trigonometrical solution. Note also that the values of the resultant or the forces can be found by using trigonometry when the angles a, b, and r are known (see Fig. 6-11c). These angles would be known because the direction of the forces and the resultant are known. In the above example angle b is 50° and angle a is 70°. Thus, with R equal to 3 we can set down these elements in the diagram shown by Fig. 6-11c. By the law of sines we have

$$\frac{A}{\sin a} = \frac{R}{\sin r} \quad \text{and} \quad \frac{B}{\sin b} = \frac{R}{\sin r}$$

where $A = F_1$, $B = F_2$, $a = 70°$, $b = 50°$, $r = 60°$, and $R = 3$. Hence

$$A = \frac{3 \times 0.94}{0.87} = 3.24 \qquad B = \frac{3 \times 0.77}{0.87} = 2.65$$

The slight differences in values arrived at by graphic and mathematical solutions are due to the inability to read the units on the measuring instrument to the third significant figure.

Numerical example

Given: Two falls are attached to a 1-ton lift and they are both making an angle with the vertical of 60°.

Required: The stress on each fall using the parallelogram method.

Solution: Figure 6-12 illustrates the situation by vector diagram. The answer is obtained graphically as 1 ton.

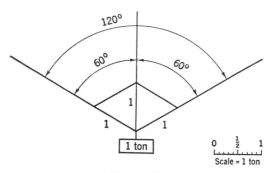

FIG. 6-12.

Effect of fall angle. It is important that the reader note that, with both falls making an angle of 60° with the vertical, the stress on each fall is equal to the load being suspended. By making a diagram as shown in Fig. 6-13a, b, and c, it can be seen that, as the angle between the falls increases above 120°, the stress on each fall goes above the weight being suspended; as the angle between the falls decreases below 120°, the stress on each fall goes below the weight being suspended. This is true when both falls make equal angles with the vertical. The lowest stress possible is equal to one-half the weight being suspended, and this occurs when the angle between the falls is equal to zero. The stress on each fall will be equal only when both falls make the same angle with the vertical.

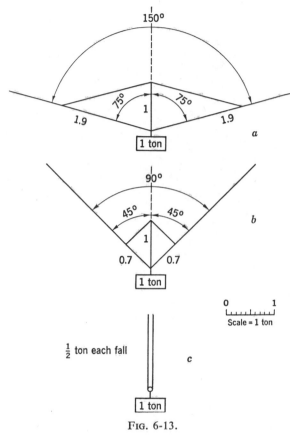

Fɪɢ. 6-13.

From Fig. 6-14a it can be seen that although one fall makes an angle of only 60° with the vertical, it is supporting a stress greater than the weight being suspended. This is because the other fall is making an angle with the vertical that is greater than 60°. Note that the fall with the *least angle* from the vertical carries the *greatest* percentage of the total load. Figure 6-14b shows the result of decreasing the angle on the right side until it is 15° less than 60° rather than 15° greater. Now the load on the fall making an angle of 60° with the vertical is less than the weight being supported; note also that the stress on the other fall which is making an angle with the vertical of less than 60° is greater than the

stress on the first fall.   An analysis of these facts points up the great
importance of limiting the drift between the hook and load while increasing the drift from the head of the boom to the deck of the ship.

Figure 6-14a and b shows the variation of stress on each fall as the
angle between the falls and the angle that each makes with the vertical

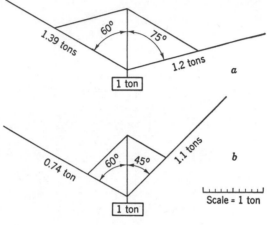

Fig. 6-14.

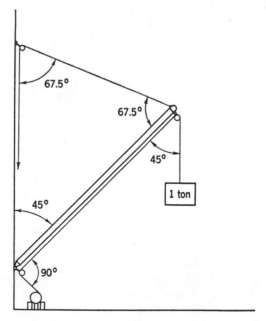

Fig. 6-15.

varies. The conclusions that can be drawn from this brief discussion are: (1) The drifts should be such that the angle that each fall makes with the vertical will never be more than 60°. This is of special importance when the load being hoisted is equal to the safe working load of the fall. (2) The rig and slings used should be set up so that the angle each fall makes with the vertical is as small as possible.

Calculation of stresses on parts of a swinging boom. The parallelogram method can be used to calculate the stress on the topping lift, the fall, and the shackles holding the head, heel block, and topping lift lead block in place, and the compression on the boom when a given weight is being lifted. An example is illustrated by Fig. 6-15 using a 50-ft boom whose topping lift lead block is 50 ft above the boom gooseneck, and the boom is topped at an angle of 45°. We will assume that a load of 1 ton is being supported by the cargo fall. With the angle between mast, boom, topping lift, and parts of the fall being as indicated in the figure, we will start by calculating the stress on the head block shackle and the direction relative to the boom.

First we draw a separate diagram as shown by Fig. 6-16a. In this diagram:

BC equals the load of 1 ton.

BA equals the stress on the hauling part of the cargo fall. Note that it has been given a value of 1.1 tons. The increase of one-tenth over the actual weight is an arbitrary constant used to account for frictional resistance contributed by the sheaves revolving on their pins when the load is actually being hoisted.

BD equals the resultant of the two forces BC and BA. BD gives the stress on the head boom shackle and direction of this stress. The stress equals 1.95 tons.

The problem can also be solved by trigonometry. The trigonometric solution will be more accurate because of errors caused by the measuring instruments. Accuracy by the vector method can be increased by using a large scale for the units involved.

We now solve for the compression on the boom and the stress on the topping lift bale. We draw another diagram as in Fig. 6-16b. BD is equal to the stress on the head block shackle, 1.95 tons, and is in a direction 21° from the boom BE. We know also that the topping lift is 67½° from the boom, and this is also drawn in. Drawing DE parallel to the topping lift direction, we obtain BE equal to the compression on the boom, 2.1 tons. Drawing EF parallel to BD, we obtain the stress on the topping lift bale, 0.75 tons.

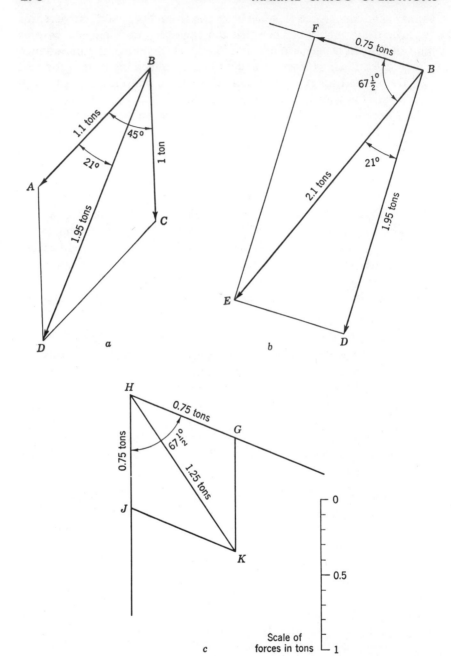

Fig. 6-16.

In the same manner as before, we can solve for the stress on the shackle holding the topping life lead block in place (see Fig. 6-16c). We know the stress on the topping lift is 0.75 tons as solved by Fig. 6-16b; we also know the direction taken by the topping lift parts HG and HJ. The stress on HJ is equal to that on HG because it is a static load. With HG and HJ laid down, we complete the parallelogram and draw HK, the resultant. On our scale, HK has a value of 1.25 tons.

The above examples should illustrate the methods of proceeding when solving for resultant forces with all parts in the same vertical plane, as they are when working with a swinging boom. The problem is considerably more difficult when working with a fixed boom and solving for stresses on guys as the loads are burtoned across the ship.

The height of the topping lift lead block above the deck as compared to the length of the boom has a great effect on the stresses placed on the topping lift, the boom, and the parts of system supporting them. As an exercise, the reader should examine the stress on the topping lift and the thrust on the boom of Fig. 6-16 as the height of the topping lift lead block is reduced at 2-ft intervals and plot the values on a piece of graph paper.

Stresses on fixed gear. A method of solving for the stresses on the parts of a set of fixed cargo gear is described below. Four diagrams are needed to obtain all the data necessary to solve for the stresses. In order to set up the problem, certain important dimensions of the ship and her cargo gear must be known. These required facts are as follows:

1. The beam of the ship.
2. The width of the hatch.
3. The position of the boom goosenecks.
4. The position of the guy pad eyes.
5. The points over which the booms will be spotted.
6. Length of the booms.
7. Distance between heel of boom and topping lift lead block.

It is also necessary to set a desired fall angle or a desired drift over some point between the heads of the booms. If both of these requirements are set, then item 5 above must be picked from the construction of the diagrams and cannot be specified. If only one of these requirements are set, the diagram will give the other. In the following example we will say we want to know the stresses when the fall angle is 120° and the booms are spotted as depicted on Fig. 6-17. We will assume 60-ft booms and the dimensions as shown on the diagram.

The first diagram to make is the plan view as shown in Fig. 6-17. Next we construct the diagram in Fig. 6-18 which is an elevation of the gear on a plane vertical to the ships deck and passing through points AR of Fig. 6-17. The first step is to draw the deck line and erect a perpendicular to represent the mast. Measure off QH equal to RA of Fig. 6-17. At H erect a perpendicular dashed line. Point P on the mast is where the heel of the boom is stepped, in this case 8 ft above the deck. Setting 60 ft on our dividers we measure an arc from P to intersect the dashed

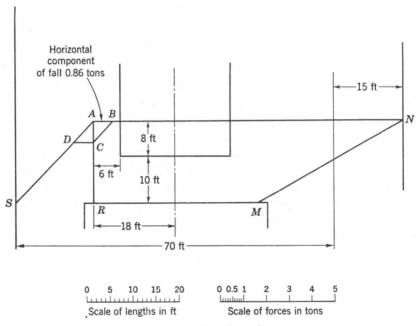

Fig. 6-17. Plan view of gear.

vertical line at H. We mark this intersection E. Now HE is the distance of the hatch boom's head above the ship's deck and PE is the true length of the boom. Next we make PO equal to 43 ft, the distance from the heel of the boom to the topping lift lead block, and draw OE. Now OE is the true length of the topping lift when the boom is topped to this angle. We now have the boom, topping lift, and mast in their actual lengths as they would appear on the vertical plane passing through AR of Fig. 6-17.

We now measure off HG on Fig. 6-18, making this distance equal to AS of Fig. 6-17. Draw in GE to indicate the guy. It is of great importance, to avoid confusion at this point, to note that the guy GE is placed on Fig. 6-18 as it would appear on a vertical plane passed through AS of Fig. 6-17. GE is not a true projection on the plane through AR.

This is done because the projected guy on the plane through AR will not be useful, but the true guy on the plane through AS is needed. Actually we have combined two diagrams to make one and reduced the work required to solve the problem.

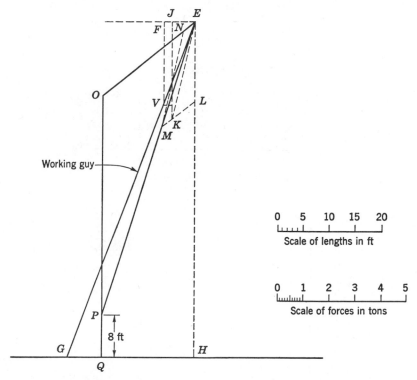

FIG. 6-18. Elevation of hatch boom. PE = boom = 60 ft, true length; OP = heel to topping lift, 43 ft.

Next we construct Fig. 6-19. Figure 6-19 is similar to Fig. 6-18 except that it is for the dock boom. MN on Fig. 6-19 is equal to MN of Fig. 6-17. We will not use Fig. 6-19 except to obtain the height of the dock boom's head above the ship's deck level. Hence, we measure NU, which we will need to construct an elevation of the gear on a plane vertical to the deck of the ship and at right angles to the centerline of the ship. This last elevation is shown in Fig. 6-20.

All the necessary data for drawing the diagram in Fig. 6-20 is available from the three previous diagrams. From the heads of the booms we measure angles 30° down from the horizontal and draw lines to represent the falls. Where these lines intersect is the point at which the cargo hook

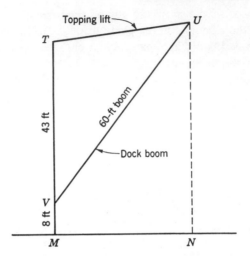

FIG. 6-19.   Elevation of dock boom.

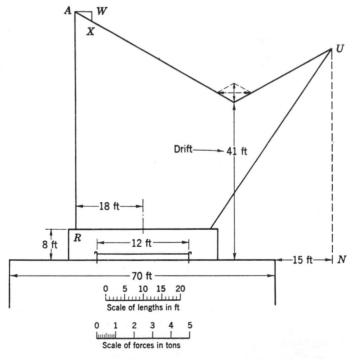

FIG. 6-20.   Elevation of complete gear on plane perpendicular to deck and at right angle to ship's centerline.

would be when the fall angle was 120°. The distance from this point down to the deck is the drift, and we note that it is 41 ft.

We now construct a parallelogram of forces acting on the hook and obtain the stress on each fall and the horizontal and vertical components acting on the head of the boom. Because of the 120° fall angle, we have a stress on each fall equal to the load on the hook. In this case it will be 1 ton, because we will assume a load of 1 ton. Further analysis of the forces involved will show us that the horizontal component is equal to *AW* (0.86 tons) and the vertical component *WX* is equal to 0.5 tons. These forces, *AW* and *WX*, are the forces acting on the boom due to the load on the hook (Fig. 6-20).

We now turn to Fig. 6-17 and analyze the forces acting on the head of the boom in a horizontal plane. First we lay down *AB* along the fall equal to the horizontal component of the force from the fall acting on the head of the boom. Thus, we make *AB* in Fig. 6-17 equal to *AW* in Fig. 6-20. Drawing *BC* parallel to the guy and *CD* parallel to the fall, we complete a parallelogram of forces from which we pick off *AD*. *AD* is equal to the horizontal component of the total tension on the guy as it resists the force *AB*. The resultant of the forces *AD* and *AB* is equal to *AC*. *AC* represents the horizontal component of the forces acting on the boom.

GUY STRESS. Using Fig. 6-18, we proceed to solve for the guy stress which is a tension stress. Draw *EF* equal to *AD* of Fig. 6-17 and parallel to the ship's deck. At *F* drop a line vertically downward to intersect the guy at *V*. Now, *EV* represents the tension on the guy, about 3.4 tons.

BOOM COMPRESSION. To obtain the boom compression, draw *EJ* in Fig. 6-18 equal to *AC* from Fig. 6-17. At *J* drop a vertical line downward, making it equal to the vertical component of the guy tension which in this case is represented by *FV*. Add additional length to the line from *J* equal to the vertical component of the fall tension, which in this case is equal to 0.5 tons and is represented graphically by *WX* of Fig. 6-20. The sum of *FV* plus *WX* is equal to *JK*. Now, draw a line through *K* parallel to the topping lift *OE* until it intersects the boom *EP* at the point *M*. Now *EM* represents the compression on the boom and amounts to 4.2 tons.

This compression figure does not take into account the force applied along the boom by the hauling part of the fall as it runs from the boom head block down to the heel block under a tension stress. This would increase the boom compression approximately equal to the force being applied to the hauling part of the fall, which in this case is equal to 1 ton. Hence, the compression on the boom would be equal to about 5.2 tons.

EQUIVALENT LOAD ON A SWINGING BOOM. Confusion may easily arise when one discusses loads on swinging booms. In practice, such loads are always suspended from the boom on a fall that runs through a head block and down to a heel block and finally to the winch drum. When considering forces on booms theoretically, it sometimes happens that the load is considered as hanging from a line that is secured directly to the boom head as if by a short strap one end of which is shackled to the boom's spider band and the load hanging down from the other end. The reader should satisfy himself that the compression on the boom is different in these two cases, and that the forces acting on the connecting link at the bottom eye of the spider are also different in magnitude and in direction. See Fig. 6-15 and the discussion on p. 275.

To differentiate between these two types of loads, we will call the load on a boom placed there through a fall running through a head block and to a heel block as a *running load*. The theoretical load placed on a boom by a load suspended from a line secured to the head we will call a *standing load*.

To obtain the equivalent *standing* load on the boom in Fig. 6-18, we extend the line *MK* parallel to the guy so that *MK* intersects *HE* at *L*. Now *EL* represents the equivalent standing load on a swinging boom. In other words, the compression on this boom as a swinging boom with a standing load equal to the value of *EL*, which is about 3 tons, would be equal to the compression that the boom is now experiencing. This compression, of course, would be without the additional compression caused by the hauling part of the fall.

To obtain the equivalent *running* load on the boom in Fig. 6-18, it is necessary first to calculate the compression on a swinging boom with the same dimensions and rigged in the same way when it supports a running load of 1 ton. The reader should do this to verify that the compression would be about 3.4 tons including the 1-ton force applied along the boom by the hauling part of the fall. Next we divide the *total* compression we have already calculated to be on the boom (5.2 tons) by this value of 3.4 tons. The quotient is equal to the equivalent running load on this boom we have been investigating. Thus we obtain:

$$\frac{5.2}{3.4} = 1.5$$

Therefore, we see that the 1-ton load on this *fixed* boom is producing a compression on the boom equivalent to a load of 1.5 tons on a *swinging* boom. Since the safe working load (SWL) of the boom is based on a test as a swinging boom and not as a fixed boom, this value of *equivalent running load on a swinging boom* is most significant.

TOPPING LIFT TENSION. Finally, to obtain the tension stress on the topping lift we draw *MN* parallel to *EK* to complete the parallelogram *EKMN*. Now *EN* measured on the topping lift represents the tension on the topping lift. In this case it is equal to 0.6 tons.

Note that if point *K* falls below the boom in a diagram, such as Fig. 6-18, the boom will not jackknife, but as *K* rises, the topping lift tension diminishes. If *K* falls on the boom, *EN* becomes a point and the tension on the topping lift is zero. If *K* falls above the boom, the topping lift tension becomes negative and will actually lift the boom up, or in other words cause the boom to jackknife. The hatch boom will usually go all the way once it starts due to other forces involved. The dock boom may rise part way and then stop with the topping lift hanging in a bight with the forces on the boom, guy, and fall in balance. However, there is no universal pattern, it all depends upon the forces, their direction, and their magnitude. If the winch driver notices the dock boom starting to raise up, he can stop it by stopping the winch and lower the boom by slacking back. If he sees the hatch boom start to raise up, as at the beginning of jackknifing, he should slack back quickly and be alert and ready to jump for safety. With booms rigged properly, of course, there is no danger.

WORKING WITH ABOVE NORMAL LOADS

Limiting factors. The limit to the weight of the load that is safe when working with any cargo handling rig is dependent upon the size and type of wire being used for the fall. The type of tackle is a factor also, but this is discussed separately under the discussion of doubling up. In this section, reference is to the single whip as normally used with the yard and stay system. Although the fall is the limiting factor when initially hoisting the load on the up and down lift, it should be remembered that the guys may be the limiting factor when burtoning the load across the deck. The guys are thrust into the role of a limiting factor whenever they are not positioned properly or the drift between the hook and the bottom of the load is excessive. We will consider the fall as a limiting factor only in this section. Table 6-7 on breaking strengths is presented for reference when considering the rigging of any given gear. Equations for finding breaking strengths should only be used when tabulated data is unavailable.

A single strand of ⅝-in., 6 by 19, plow steel wire rope has a breaking stress of 12.9 tons and ¾-in. wire of 18.5 tons. Many ships now use improved plow steel wire rope for which the breaking strengths are: ⅝-in., 14.9 tons; ¾-in., 21.2 tons. From these figures, it is evident that improved plow steel wire rope is about 1.15 times stronger than plow

TABLE 6-7

WIRE ROPE BREAKING STRENGTH

Breaking Strength,
tons of 2240 lb

Rope Diameter, in.	Improved Plow Steel	Plow Steel	Mild Plow Steel
½	9.5	8.3	7.3
⅝	14.9	12.9	11.2
¾	21.2	18.5	16.0
⅞	29.7	25.0	21.7
1	37.3	32.5	28.2
1⅛	47.0	40.8	35.5
1¼	57.7	50.2	43.6
1⅜	69.3	60.3	52.5
1½	82.1	71.4	62.1
1¾	110.7	96.4	83.6
2	142.8	124.1	108.0
2¼	178.5	155.4	

The data presented in this table applies to 6 by 19 classification ropes with fiber cores either preformed or nonpreformed. For the breaking strengths of galvanized ropes, deduct 10% from the strengths shown. For wire strand cores and independent wire rope cores add 7½% to the listed strengths.

All strengths taken from Wire Rope Institute Catalog, Washington, D. C., 1947.

steel. This is an increase of 15%. Most of the newly built ships, such as the Mariner type ships, are equipped with improved plow steel for all running as well as standing rigging. The fiber core is used almost universally for the running and standing rigging on merchant ships.

Running rigging and safety factors. When determining *safe working loads* for running rigging, a safety factor of at least 5 should be used. This gives a safe working load (S.W.L.) of 3 tons for the ⅝-in. improved plow steel and 4 tons for the ¾-in. improved plow steel wire rope of 6 by 19 construction with fiber core. The safety factor of 5 may seem excessive, but it must be remembered that this is the factor only when the line is new. During normal use with shipboard rigs, the wire rope is subjected to treatment that will reduce its original breaking stress rapidly. The ton referred to in this discussion is the ton of 2240 lb.

Boom ratings. Tests of fully rigged cargo gear are made by the American Bureau of Shipping and equivalent authorities in other countries. These tests have become necessary since various nations began enforcing regulations relative to tests and periodic inspections of cargo handling gear as recommended by the International Labor Convention of 1932.

Without proper gear certification, ships are subject to delays in many ports of the world while they undergo tests and inspections locally.

The rules of the American Bureau of Shipping specify standards to be complied with for certification of the ship's cargo gear and maintenance of that certification.   These standards also apply to the maintenance of chain and wire slings and certain other loose gear used during the longshore operations.   Periodic annealing of wrought iron gear is required, and all blocks, wire, and loose gear should be furnished with certificates of test by the manufacturer.   The American Bureau of Shipping specifies a factor of safety of 4 for all gear.[1]

After the gear is installed, the complete assembled rig is tested by swinging live proof loads of an amount greater than the rated capacity in the presence of a surveyor.   The live loads are required for rating of newly built ships.   Upon satisfactory completion of such test, the heels of the booms are stamped with the safe working load and the date.   It should be remembered that this test is given to the gear as a swinging boom, but the boom almost always is used in a fixed position.   This fact changes the stresses on all part and should be kept in mind and investigated by the ship's officers by various diagrams of the gear and its arrangement on their particular vessel.

Gear certification.   The surveyor issues a certificate covering the proof loads and angle at which each boom is tested.   This certificate together with all manufacturer's certificates regarding loose gear is inserted in the ship's Register of Cargo Gear.   This Register has pages for entering certification data of the original proof loads, the annual surveys, and the surveys every four years when the proof loads have to be applied again.   Pages are also available for recording the annealing of all wrought iron gear.   This simple bookkeeping process provides evidence to any interested party of the condition of the cargo gear and the maintenance given it.

The American Bureau of Shipping rules require that new ships be furnished with a diagram showing the arrangement of the assembled gear and indicating the approved safe working load for each component part of the gear.   With these diagrams, replacement of loose gear may be ordered to suit the safe working loads.

Certification of cargo gear in the case of existing ships permits the use of spring or hydraulic balances to register proof loads required to be applied to the assembled rig.   Figures 6-21 and 6-22 show such a test arrangement.   In the case of an actual 5-ton design, the thrust load in the boom and the tension loads in the topping lift and cargo falls are cal-

[1] L. C. Host, Certification of Ships' Cargo Gear in the United States, *The Log,* November 1953.

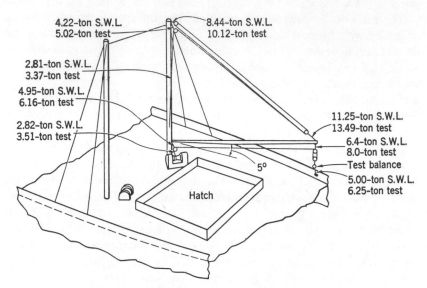

Fig. 6-21.   Test arrangement for 5-ton boom.

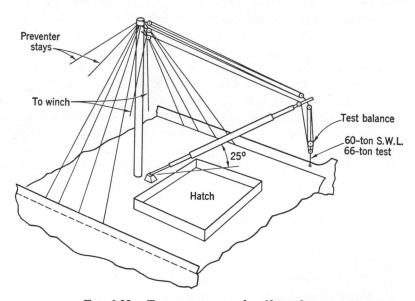

Fig. 6-22.   Test arrangement for 60-ton boom.

culated under the application of the safe working load of 5 tons and the test proof load of 6¼ tons at the cargo hook.

Doubling up. Whenever the load to be hoisted by the yard and stay rig exceeds the safe working load of the rigging, some alternative rig should be employed that will increase the safe working load. The safety factor of 5 is recommended when arriving at safe working loads with running rigging. The alternative rigs discussed in the following sections are known as methods of *doubling up*. If the wire fall has just been renewed and the mate is confident of the skill of the winch drivers, he may not require doubling up for loads close to the limit. For example, if a load of 3¼ tons is to be hoisted by a gear equipped with a ⅝-in. plow steel wire rope, the mate may consider that a safety factor of 4 is sufficient. This would permit hoisting the 3¼-ton load with a ⅝-in. plow steel wire rope. The doubling up process is slow and costly, and freight rates generally reflect the cost of handling heavy items. It is often a great temptation to attempt the loading of items whose weights are just over the limit of the regular gear. Because of the risk involved, the practice of overloading the gear should be discouraged.

YARD AND STAY WITH GUN TACKLES. When forced to double up with a swinging boom, the time required to transfer the load from the dock to the ship or vice versa will be greatly increased. This increase in time can be cut down by using systems that retain the advantages of fixed booms rather than changing to a live boom operation. This is especially important when a large number of loads just over the safe limit are to be handled. One of the easiest methods of augmenting the load limit of the gear is to rig both booms with gun tackles. This requires two additional 14-in. cargo blocks, four shackles, and two cargo falls that are double the length of the regular falls (see Fig. 6-23).

The first step is to run the old fall off the winch drum. Next, the new fall is placed on the winch drum and led up to the head block via the heel block. The fall is then rove through the traveling block and the standing part is secured to the spider band at the head of the boom. This is done with both booms. The added traveling blocks should have beckets on them to permit the attachment of a common ring or separate swivels of a standard cargo hook assembly. The booms have to be lowered to the deck in order to make this conversion. When the booms are topped again, the rig is ready to handle cargo with fixed booms under the standard yard and stay system (see Fig. 6-24). If the booms are 5-ton booms with ⅝-in. improved plow steel wire rope falls, the load limit should be kept at 5 tons. If the booms are 10-ton booms with a ¾-in. wire fall, the load limit should be kept to 8 tons. The greatest danger point with this rig would be the guys. The guys should be checked carefully, all strain equalized between guy and preventer, and the position choosen to give the least strain to the guy. Slings should be applied carefully so that a minimum of drift is allowed between hook and load. In this way the hook will not have to be hoisted an excessive distance

FIG. 6-23. Doubling up with gun tackles of the yard and stay. A closeup of the arrangement of the blocks at the cargo hook. Note the small chain between the tops of the blocks to prevent the slack block from toppling over and fouling itself.
The cargo hook is of the Liverpool pattern. Courtesy Clark Equipment Co.

above the deck and the angle between the falls can be kept to a minimum, thus relieving the strain on the guys. The angle between the falls should be kept below 120° as explained on p. 272.

FOUR FIXED BOOMS. If a hatch is double rigged, that is, with a set of gear at each end, it can be doubled up to work with fixed booms with the same limit to loads as the yard and stay with gun tackles but in a much shorter time and with more safety. The time for rigging is cut down because the booms do not have to be lowered to the deck. Another advantage is that the stresses on the guys and booms are shared by the

two sets of gear.   The gear required is the same as for the yard and stay
with gun tackles.

First, the two hatch booms would be topped over the hatch and the two
dock booms out over the dock in the conventional manner.   The only

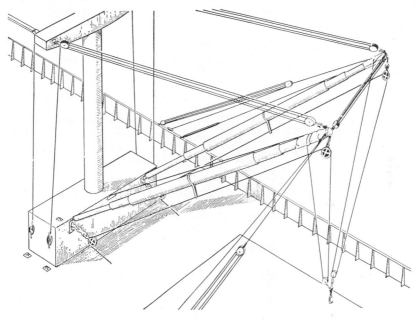

FIG. 6-24.   This sketch shows the typical yard and stay system rigged with gun
tackles on each boom.   If the head block has no becket, the runner should be
secured to the boom itself about 4 ft back from the head with two round turns.
The eye splice at the end of the runner is shackled to the link band at the head
of the boom.   The turns around the boom must be started from the inside to
prevent chafing against the runner leading from the head block to the heel block
in operation.   Note the preventer guy on the far side.   If 5 tons are burtoned with
this rig, every possible precaution to insure minimum guy stresses and equal strain
on all parts must be taken.   Courtesy U.S. Navy.

difference would be that their heads should be in a fore and aft line and
about 2 ft apart.   The long cargo fall is then rove off on one set of the
the gear without being lowered by using the old cargo fall as a messenger.
The lower end of the new and longer fall is rove through the additional
cargo block, and the shackle is used to connect the end of this fall to the
end of the regular fall on the opposing gear.   This connection is hoisted
to within a few feet of the head block on the other gear, and the winches
of that gear are secured.   The additional cargo blocks, now acting as
traveling blocks, are secured to a cargo hook as in the rig of Fig. 6-24

(see Fig. 6-25). The load is hoisted and burtoned by the use of one set of cargo winches. The stress on the guys will not be as great as on the first rig, but the falls will receive the same stress; hence, the load limit is 6 tons with ⅝-in. wire or 8 tons with ¾-in. wire.

The use of a traveling block insures an even strain on all parts. If the traveling blocks are eliminated, the four falls shackled directly to the

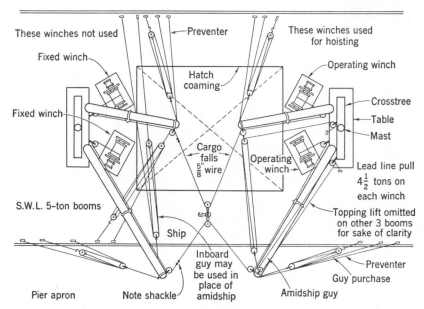

FIG. 6-25. Doubling up with four fixed booms. This is a plan view of a hatch fitted with two sets of gear and doubled up for hoisting heavy lifts. The capacity of this rig with ⅝-in. improved plow steel wire rope would be 6 tons with a safety factor of 5. If ¾-in. wire rope is used, the capacity is 8 tons. Courtesy U.S. Army.

cargo hook, and all four winchs used, there is some possibility of an unequal strain being placed on one of the falls during the operation. However, if the winch drivers are all experienced and the operation is done slowly, it is much faster than rigging with the traveling block. If a number of lifts are to be handled by this means, it is recommended that the traveling block be used. If only one lift is to be handled and all four falls are attached directly, the operation should be done with care.

ONE SWINGING BOOM. If the load is over the limits set above or the circumstances of the operation call for more direct control of the load, it may be necessary to resort to the use of the swinging boom. One good reason for using the swinging boom instead of attempting to rig up with gun tackles on two fixed booms is that it is faster when only one or two loads are to be handled.   Another reason is that the load on the guys and boom is kept at a safe level.

To prepare this rig, it is necessary to drop the dock boom to the deck and reeve off a fall of double length as a gun tackle with the standing part secured to the spider band at the head of the boom.   This is the same procedure as that required by the yard and stay with gun tackles.

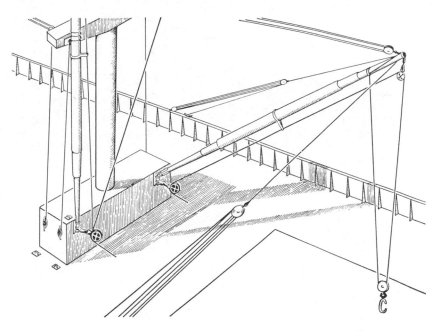

Fig. 6-26.   Doubling up with one swinging boom and gun tackle.   Courtesy U.S. Army.

The topping lift hauling part can be placed on the drum of the outboard winch drum and used as a working topping lift.   The working guy can be left where it is located normally.   If a spanner guy is rigged, it can be used to pull the boom inboard by leaving it in position with the hatch boom winged to the offshore side.   The hauling parts of both guys should be led to the gypsy heads of the winches of the gear immediately forward or aft of the swinging boom by using snatch blocks as fairleads where necessary.   Figure 6-26 illustrates this rig.   There is a very small stress on the guys during this operation because they are used only to guide the swinging boom.

The limit of this system is 5 tons if ⅝-in. improved plow steel wire rope or ¾-in. wire rope is used on a 5-ton boom.   If ⅝-in. wire rope is used on a 10-ton boom, the limit is 6 tons; however, if ¾-in. wire is used

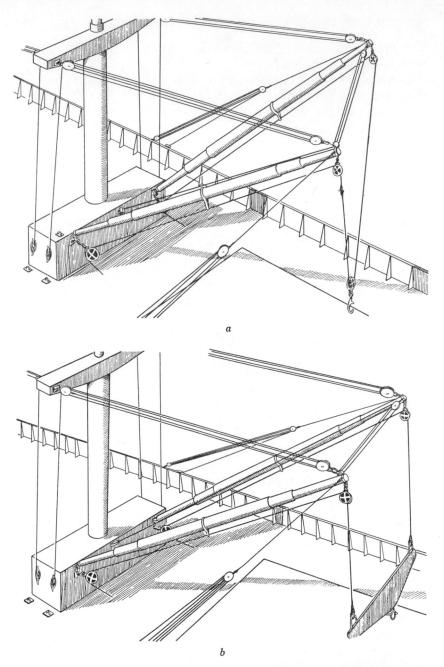

a

b

FIG. 6-27. (*a*) Doubling up with two swinging booms and traveling block. The limit of the load with this rig insofar as the boom is concerned is twice the safe working load of one boom. The limiting load as far as the fall is concerned is twice the safe working load of the fall. If gun tackles are used, the fall limit on a 10-ton boom, the limit is 8 tons. If new wire is used when the 10-ton boom is used, these limits for that boom can be raised slightly. The responsibility rests entirely on the ship's officer in charge of the operation.

TWO SWINGING BOOMS. By using both booms of a set as swinging booms for picking up a single heavy lift item, the load limit can be increased insofar as the boom as a limiting factor is concerned. But the limit as set by the fall size is still the same. In other words, if two 5-ton booms are swung together and rove off with ¾-in. falls, the limit is greater than 5 tons. The limit is double the *safe working load* of the wire fall; in this case, it would be 8 tons.

When one stops to consider the risk entailed when attempting to lift loads slightly over the safe working load, it does not make good sense to make a practice of it. A safety factor of 5 should be set and conscientiously adhered to. If a fall starts to strand or part suddenly without even the warning of a parted strand, there is great possibility of loss of life and certainty of heavy damage to the ship and cargo.

Figure 6-27a and b shows two ways of rigging two booms to operate as swinging booms. Both of these systems make it possible to increase the load insofar as the boom is a limiting factor. Figure 6-27a shows the use of a traveling block. The heads of the booms should be about 3 ft apart horizontally; their vertical distance apart is not of major importance. If the horizontal distance between the boom heads is too great, the angle between the two parts of the traveling whip increases and this reduces the size of the load that can be carried.

Swinging the two booms in an arc is not easy. It must be done slowly and will require the topping and luffing of the booms; therefore, the topping lifts must be powered.

Figure 6-27b shows the use of an equalizing beam. This accomplishes the same thing as the traveling block. Using a beam in this manner makes it possible to keep the heads of the booms farther apart.

The heavy lift boom. Almost all ships are equipped with at least one *heavy lift boom* or *jumbo boom*. As can be seen from the above discussion, when the weight of the unit to be taken aboard goes above 3 tons, one of the doubling up rigs can be used. These will preclude using the jumbo rig which is very slow in operation and may require an hour or

becomes four times the safe working load of one part. Thus, with this rig, using a gun tackle and having only 5-ton booms, the load that can be taken on board is 10 tons. With 10-ton booms and ¾-in. wire rope, the limit to the load is 16 tons. (b) Doubling up with two swinging booms and an equalizing beam.
Courtesy U.S. Navy.

more to prepare for use. However, when the weight of the unit goes above the safe working load of any of the doubling up rigs, there is nothing left to do from the standpoint of safety but rig the jumbo boom. Now and then, for expediency, loads exceeding the safe working load will be taken on board with the conventional gear. Such practices may prove to be very costly instead of economical.

The heavy lift boom is usually shipped in a pedestal mounted along the ship's centerline. There are usually two ratings for its capacity; the lowest is without a preventer stay being rigged. The maximum rating is with the preventer stay rigged. The preventer stay is a large wire rope that is normally carried unrigged on the mast supporting the jumbo rigging. Two stays are generally used. The Mariner type uses a preventer stay of 2¼ in. diameter improved plow steel 6 by 19 wire rope. The jumbo boom has a capacity of 25 tons without using preventer stays. When the stays are rigged, the capacity is raised to 60 tons. The purchase and topping lift are lead to winches with specially built derrick drums capable of handling long lengths of wire. The purchase of this 60-ton boom is 1500 ft long made of 1 in. 6 by 19 improved plow steel wire rove off on an upper quintuplet block and a lower sextuplet block with sheaves of 20-in. diameter. The topping lift is 1190 ft long made of 1⅛-in. improved plow steel 6 by 19 wire rope rove off on sextuplet blocks with sheaves of 20-in. diameter. The hauling parts of the purchase and topping lift pass through two lead blocks and then to the drums of the derrick winches.

The guys of this heavy lift boom are rove off on threefold blocks and are made of ⅝-in., 6 by 19, improved plow steel wire rope 650 ft long. No pendants are used on the lower ends of these guys because during certain stages of the use of the boom, it becomes necessary to almost two block the guy blocks with a short pendant at the upper end. Besides this fact, the hauling part of the guy is led, by the use of fairleads, to the winch drum of the regular cargo winch of this gear.

With this rig, as shown in Fig. 6-28, four men operating the two guy winches, the purchase, and the topping lift can control the boom. The capacity of a given rig on a given ship will be stated on the ship's capacity plan or on a blueprint showing the plan and elevation views of the rigging.

Handling a heavy lift requires careful planning before any attempt is made to hoist it. The method of slinging the load up must be considered carefully. In many cases a sling weighing several tons may be required to lift a load weighing 40 or 50 tons. The weight of the sling must always be considered when calculating the total load on the boom. If a load of 24 tons is to be hoisted and the sling weighs 3 tons, it is necessary to rig the preventer stays even though the load being lifted is less than the rated capacity of the boom without preventers rigged.

The chief officer should be advised of the method being used to hoist, stow, and secure a given heavy lift. This officer should make it his busi-

FIG. 6-28. The heavy lift boom. This is a view of the heavy lift boom on the Mariner type ship. Note the fairleads rigged for guying the boom during the slewing operation. The double guy on the far side of the ship would be on the dock side or lighter side depending upon where the heavy lift was being taken from or where it was being discharged. Using the double guy enables the slewing of the boom out over the dock. Courtesy U.S. Maritime Administration.

ness to be on hand during the rigging and handling of all heavy lifts. If he finds it impossible to be on hand, he should designate another officer to observe the operations. The importance of officer supervision is greatly increased when the ship is not operating in her home port.

When lifting the heavy lift, the load should be taken up only a few inches at first and held steady. All rigging should be checked while the load is held suspended in this position. Then the load can be hoisted very slowly. At no time should there be any attempt to rush the process.

If there is any particular part of the procedure that can be said to be more dangerous than any other, it is when the load is being lowered and it is necessary to stop the lowering process. If this is done with a jerky motion or too suddenly, the stresses on the gear might be raised to a dangerous level and contribute to the failure of some part of the rigging. The stresses can be raised also by hoisting the load too rapidly. Hoisting and lowering heavy lifts should always be slowly and carefully carried out.

At single rigged hatches, where it is necessary to lead the guy hauling parts to winches at the next hatch, care must be taken to assure that drivers of the guy winches can see the signal man clearly. There have been a number of cases where the guys parted because one guy winchman heaved while the other was either heaving or holding fast.

When slewing the jumbo boom, it should be at the lowest position possible for easy operation. The boom should not be slewed when topped so as to reach the hatch area immediately in front of the pedestal. The forces applied to the guys place great strain on the gooseneck, pedestal, and pacific iron when the boom is so high. At lower positions it rotates more easily.

All of the parts of the heavy lift rigging should be carefully stowed away or secured in the rigged condition when not in use. Because of the tremendous weight of the blocks and hooks used, the gear is not generally stripped and secured. The boom is topped as high as it can go, and the purchase and topping lift are secured by lashings after slushing them down with grease. Generally a collar is provided aloft in which the boom is secured. The large blocks are secured by using short wire pendants and turnbuckles. It is also important that the gooseneck and pin of the jumbo (as of all booms) be kept well lubricated.

MODIFICATIONS OF THE MARRIED FALL

Wing and wing. Rigging the hatch boom over the offshore side of the vessel while the dock boom remains over its conventional spot on the pier apron is known as *wing and wing*. It is a simple variation of the regular yard and stay rig used when loading or discharging deck loads and it is necessary to handle loads on both sides of the ship.

The house fall. At some ports, especially on the east coast of the United States, a number of piers are equipped with a cargo block made secure on a steel structure on the face of the dock shed in such a way that a fall rove through it plumbs the dock apron. The structure may be a steel outrigger or a short boom stepped on the side of the building. Such an arrangement is used mostly on piers with very narrow aprons, which are, in some cases, not more than 3 ft wide. They are also very convenient on piers with two decks. The fall used with this rig is furnished by the pier because the regular fall on the ship is too short. The house fall may lead to the ship's winch via proper fairleads or, as in some cases, to a winch on the pier. The hatch boom with its fall will be used as it is normally. Figure 6-29 is a diagram of this type rig.

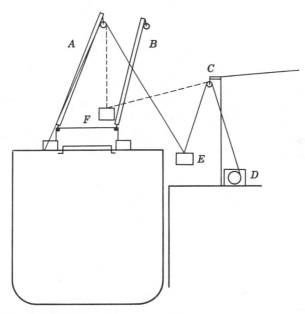

FIG. 6-29. The house fall rig. The house fall may be led from block *C* to a dock winch *D* as shown or to a ship's winch at the foot of boom *B*; both systems are used. When the load is in position *F*, the operator of the winch of boom *A* is in control of the load and has a good view of it. Boom *A* should be used for the ship's fall because its working guy is rigged to handle the stress of burtoning.

The advantages of the house fall are:

1. On piers with very narrow aprons it eliminates the possibility of fouling the head of the dock boom against the face of the dock shed.

2. It provides a steady spotting area under the permanently installed block on the dock.

3. On piers with second docks, it may provide the only means of working the second deck platform because of the limited drift of the ship's booms. When the ship is deeply loaded and the booms are short, the drift over the second deck landing platform may be reduced to only a few feet if the ship's booms are used.

4. If the house fall block can be made fast with sufficient height, it makes it possible to work extremely wide aprons with a spotting point at the dock shed doorway or at any one of as many as three railroad spurs. When working with booms, the dock boom must be lowered to a dangerously small angle from the horizontal in order to work the third track.

Split fall rig. Two variations of this rig will be described. Essentially it consists of unmarrying the yard and stay falls so that they can work independently.

In one rig, the two booms are guyed loosely and we will describe this one first. The dock boom is guyed so that it plumbs a point on the dock and is allowed to swing inboard so that it plumbs another point slightly inboard on the stringer plate. The hatch boom is guyed tightly. Obviously, this type rig is easier to set up if inboard guys are used on both booms rather than the midship guy.

The rig operates as follows, assuming a discharging operation: The single fall of the hatch boom will bring up a load and a man stationed on deck will pull the load outboard just enough to allow it to be landed on the deck of the ship. The hook is removed from the load and it goes below for another load. In the meantime, the dock fall is hooked onto the load on deck. A strain is taken and the load slides outboard. The dock boom being guyed loosely, swings inboard as far as its working guy will allow it. This brings the dock boom over the stringer strake of deck plating. The winch driver hauls away on the fall dragging the load under the boom where he stops it momentarily before hoisting it clear of the deck. The man on deck pushes the load outboard and the load is landed on the dock. When loading, the steps are reversed.

In another arrangement of almost the same type, the two booms are guyed tightly in a fixed pattern. The point plumbed by these booms in both split fall arrangements must be with only a few feet clearance from the ship's side and the hatch coaming.

In this system, again assuming a discharging operation, the hatch boom brings a load up and stops. The winchman holds the load with the hook about level with the top of the hatch coaming. The man on deck takes the hook of the dock fall and puts it on the sling. Now both falls work together and take the load on deck or out over the dock at which point the hatch fall would be released. The load would be landed with the dock fall while the hatch fall went below for another load.

As can be seen, the only difference between the two methods of using the split fall is that in the first system the load is moved across the ship by being pushed or pulled manually or dragged with one fall. In the second system the load is burtoned by temporarily married falls.

With longshoremen trained in the use of the system and with certain types of cargoes, it has proved faster than the married fall system. When handling baggage stowed in deep lower holds on passenger ships, it is quite likely to be more productive than the yard and stay system. Full cooperation of the longshoremen would be mandatory, of course.

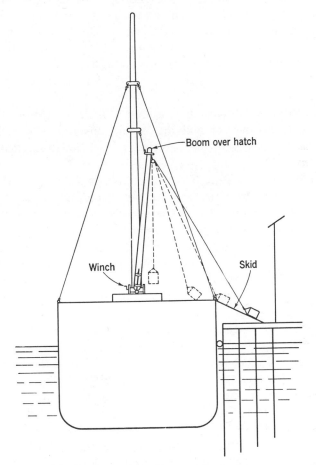

FIG. 6-30. The single whip and skid.

Single whip with skid. This is a system that is extant in some Gulf ports at piers where cotton bales are loaded. However, it is being replaced rapidly by the regular married fall system used with a special type of sling known as a cotton bale hook. The single whip and skid system, illustrated in Fig. 6-30, consists of an inclined plane between the dock and the ship's side and a single cargo fall from a boom spotted over the hatch. As used with cotton bales, the bale is slung up with a rope sling, the cargo hook is secured to the sling, and a strain is taken on the fall. Thus the bale is dragged up the incline from the dock to the deck of the ship, landed momentarily on deck, and then dragged up and over the hatch coaming. As the bale passess over the hatch coaming it swings across the hatchway. The winch driver simply judges the oscillations of the fall and drops the load into the hold to land it on the proper spot.

This system can be used for loading only. On hatches with only one set of gear, both booms can be used to pick up and load bales. On hatches with double gears, three booms could be loading at once. This advantage is completely lost, however, if the longshoremen in the hold cannot keep up with the hook.

The most obvious disadvantage is that it is very hard on the bands holding the bales together and the burlap covering. Such handling often leaves the bale with the covering ragged and torn, making it a definite fire hazard.

Yard and stay jury rig. This rig utilizes two booms with a single winch. The hatch fall is the regular wire rope, but the dock fall is a four stranded 4-in. manila line. The wire fall is made fast to the winch drum as it would be ordinarily. The manila line, however, is worked on the winch gypsy head by a man known as the *burton man* (see Fig. 6-31).

To describe its use, let us assume that we are discharging. First the load is hoisted from the hold as with the regular rig. The manila line A, of course, is married to the cargo hook along with the hatch fall B. To retrieve the slack on this line, the burton man C will take one round turn on the gypsy head and haul away. Thus, when the load is above the hatch coaming, the manila line is quickly removed from the gypsy head and three turns are taken in the opposite direction to the turns on the winch drum. Now, as the winch driver slacks away on the wire fall, the burton man hauls away on his line. This action burtons the load across the deck, and if the load was taken up to the right height the manila line would have all the weight of the load when the wire fall is completely slack. At this point the wire is slacked off a little more by surging the manila line on the gypsy head. When sufficient slack has been obtained, the winch is stopped and the burton man slacks off on his line until the load is landed gently on the dock.

When the load is taken aboard, the burton man lifts the load and then surges his line and slacks off while the wire burtons the load across the deck until the hatch is plumbed. When the wire has all the weight, the burton can be removed from the gypsy head and the load landed in the hold.

A description of this system makes it seem a good deal more difficult than it is in practice. A skillful seaman is needed to handle the manila line, but it is not difficult with a small amount of practice. The author has used this system on tankers to discharge and load drums of lubricating oil at the small dry cargo hatch forward and remembers it as being surprisingly efficient. It is a system that might be placed into use on any ship when a winch breaks down or in a similar emergency.

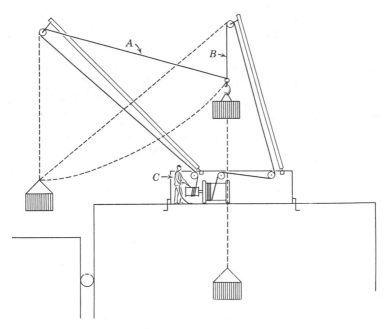

FIG. 6-31. Yard and stay jury rig.

Offcenter block with a swinging boom. An interesting rig utilizing an offcenter lead block on the cargo fall can be set up for working with a swinging boom in case of emergencies or for normal operations if desired. The principal feature of this rig is that the boom can be swung outboard without the use of power, providing the offcenter block is properly located. Power is still required to swing the boom inboard.

OPERATION. On Fig. 6-32 the cargo fall (1) is rove through the offcenter block (2), through the heel block (3), and to the winch. The distance between the offcenter block (2) and the heel block (3) should be approximately 4 ft. Its exact location may be determined with some experimentation; it can be easily shifted provided pad eyes are available. The inboard guy (5) is led at right angles to the boom when plumbed over the hatch. This guy must be long enough to allow the boom to swing out over the dock from position *A* to position *B*. The hauling part of the inboard guy is led to the offshore winch. Now, assuming a discharging operation, when the load has been hoisted high enough to clear the hatch coaming and bulwark, the stress on the fall leading to the off-center block will tend to pull the boom outboard. Hence, as the inboard

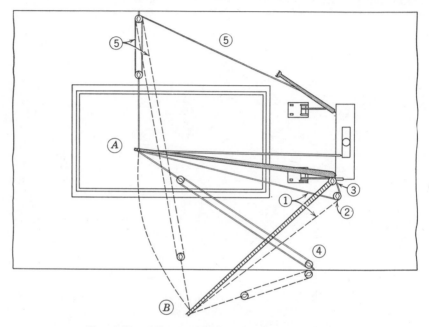

Fig. 6-32. Offcenter block with a swinging boom.

guy is slacked, the boom will slew outboard. The slack of the outboard guy should be taken in by hand. When the load has been landed on the pier, the boom is swung inboard by power on the inboard guy.

The Farrell rig. The first real improvement in many years in the yard and stay system of rigging the ship's gear for burtoning cargo was advanced by Captain V. C. Farrell about 1947.

This improvement over the conventional gear consists of placing the heels of the outboard guys or vangs and the heels of the booms on a common axis or making them coaxial. The greatest degree of usefulness from this rig is obtained by also installing topping lift winches and placing the hauling part of a twofold topping lift through a lead block secured near the ship's centerline. With this setup, all that must be done to top or lower the boom is to press the button controlling the topping lift winch. There is no need to tend the guys. The boom head will move along a straight line parallel to the centerline of the ship.

Once the guys have been secured to the short vang posts, pulled tight, and the fall made clear in the normal manner, one man can hoist all the gear on a ship in less than an hour. If this is done while at sea, the falls must be run up on the winch drums and pulled tight with the cargo hook secured amidships or the falls crossed and shackled into pad eyes to keep the gear from breaking loose as the ship rolls. The latter procedure is necessary regardless of the system used to guy the gear.

With willing and able longshoremen and winch drivers, the full advantage of this rig may be realized. One set of gear may be used to service two spotting points on the ship. With fingertip control of the topping lift winch, the winch driver can alternately top up or lower the boom so as to spot a point first at one end of the hatchway and then at the opposite end. Hence, without having to wait for the spot to be cleared each time, the hook can continue to work.

When opening or closing hatches with beams or pontoons, the process will take much less time because of the ease and speed of positioning the hatch boom over the exact spot necessary to pick up the beam or pontoon. This may be done without having to pull the hook into line with a guide line.

Figures 6-33 and 6-34 show the slight change that is necessary to rig the conventional gear with the Farrell rig. The erection of the vang posts is all that is necessary if the ship already has topping lift winches.

The Isthmian Steamship Company gathered data on a ship that had one hatch rigged with this gear. The comparison should be reliable because it involves two hatches on the same ship working the same cargoes under the same conditions.

Data gathered during a carefully observed voyage showed that the hatch served by the Farrell improved burtoning gear was handling 39% more cargo per hour than one served by a pair of booms rigged in the conventional manner. These gains are based on a comparison between results obtained with No. 5 hatch rigged with the Farrell gear and No. 1 hatch rigged conventionally on the S.S. Steel Fabricator, a C3-S-A2 type vessel. On these ships, No. 1 and No. 5 are single rigged.

The 39% figure was an average for a whole voyage in Isthmian's Indian service. A 46% improvement was experienced for the voyage's loading and discharging operations in American ports. On a full-voyage basis 21% more cargo per hour was handled through No. 5 hatch, with its single pair of Farrell rigged booms, than was handled through No. 2 hatch, which is double rigged conventionally.

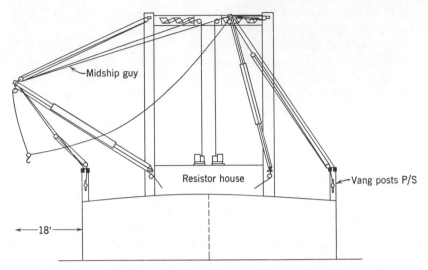

FIG. 6-33. Elevation of the Farrell rig. P/S = port and starboard.

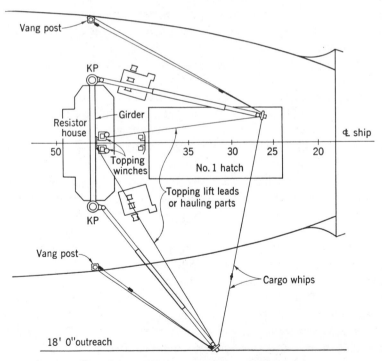

FIG. 6-34. Plan view of the Farrell rig.

The anomalous situation of more cargo per hour passing through the single rigged hatch than the double rigged one came about through a combination of the diminishing returns experienced with double ganging and the fact that cargo handling requirements were sometimes such that it would not have paid to activate both sets of booms on the double rigged hatch.

The advantages experienced with the Farrell gear on the Steel Fabricator include a 70% reduction in the time required to open and close the hatches and an 80% reduction in the time required to place the booms in operation or secure them for sea. The increased spotting ability, it is believed, reduces cargo damage and the gear in general is *safer* than gear that does not employ topping lift winches.

Modification of the pair of booms for burtoning in the Farrell manner, including the installation of two 20-hp topping lift winches, cost about $13,000. To double rig No. 5 hatch in the usual way with king posts and another set of booms and winches would have cost about $39,000.

The Ebel mechanical guy rig. This rig was devised by F. G. Ebel, Senior Naval Architect, Maritime Administration. It was installed on the S.S. Schuyler Otis Bland, a prototype ship designed prior to the Mariner type ships. The cargo handling gear on this ship represents an outstanding improvement over the conventional rig.

Although the married fall system is an efficient system for transferring a great variety of cargo types from shore to ship and back again, there are three outstanding disadvantages to the conventional method of setting this rig up. These are:

1. Maximum load limitations.
2. Lack of spotting ability.
3. Dangers involved.

For reasons that become quite clear after studying the section covering stresses on fixed cargo booms, the load that can be safely burtoned on the regular rig is limited to about 50% of the rated boom capacity. The strength of the working guys usually is the limiting factor. Being designed for hand operation, the working guys are generally made of light equipment and rove off with manila line. If designed to handle larger loads, their size would make them unwieldly. As a result, it has been the custom to expect to rig the fixed boom as a swinging boom when loads become greater than 3 tons. The swinging boom operation is very slow and thus it is very costly to load units over 3 tons from this point of view. Thus, although it would be economical to handle some cargo in units over 3 tons from all other standpoints, this limitation reduces the overall efficiency of the cargo handling gear.

The second disadvantage was partially overcome by the Farrell arrangement. This is the lack of flexibility of the usual burtoning gear because the boom heads are fixed in position over the pier and hatch. This, of course, makes it necessary to bring all cargo directly under the boom head that is going to hoist it and to haul it away from a fixed point of deposit under the boom that lowers it. Changing the position of the boom heads with the unimproved rig entails several men, considerable time, and is dangerous.

The third disadvantage of the old system is the probability of gear failures that exists. Many longshoremen have not the slightest idea of the safest point at which to secure the guy when setting the gear for work. Consequently, if a competent officer is not present to check on the location of guys, excessive stresses may be caused with disastrous results. The guys are usually made just as light as possible, and after a little use they become inherently weak and fail when loads near the limit are hoisted. Because of the time and trouble involved in converting the fixed boom to a swinging boom, there is a temptation on the part of officers to attempt hoisting loads just a little over the safe limit. Careless or inexperienced winch drivers tight-lining a load, spreading the boom heads in the wing and wing position when topped very high, and using excessively long slings are additional possible causes of introducing excessive stresses in the guys and on the booms.

Another dangerous element with the older rig is the amount of slack line lying about the decks and the necessity to shift the topping lift from cleat to gypsy head and back again when positioning the booms.

The Ebel rig adequately meets all three of the above mentioned disadvantages. The gear on the Bland was designed:

1. To handle all loads up to the full capacity of the booms (5 and 10 tons) by the burton system.
2. To provide for complete *power positioning* of the unloaded boom.
3. To eliminate all manual handling of lines.
4. To increase safety.

Figure 6-35 shows schematically the arrangement of the topping lift on the 10- and 5-ton booms. Figure 6-36 shows the arrangement of the mechanical guys on the 10- and 5-ton booms. The topping lift is offset inboard at a point near the centerline of the ship to control the swinging of the boom in the outboard direction. The hauling part is led down the inboard side of the king post through a lead block to the drum of one of the small king post mounted topping lift winches.

The standing part of the guy is secured to the extreme outboard end of the crosstree, run over a sheave at the boom head, down to a sheave at the bulwark, back around the second sheave at the boom head, back to the crosstree through a lead block, and then led down the outboard side of the king post to the drum of the electric guy winch also mounted on the king post.

With this setup, there is complete mechanical control of the boom. The boom can be lifted from its cradle and swung to any desired position

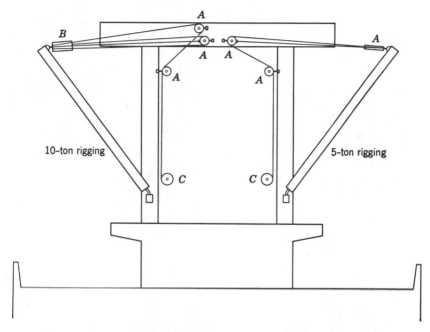

Fig. 6-35. A schematic representation of the topping lifts on the Ebel rig. All blocks are single (*A*) except the boom topping lift block on the 10-ton rig (*B*). The hauling part is led to a topping lift winch (*C*) which is controlled from the position where the winches are operated. All blocks have 14-in. sheaves and are rove off with ¾-in. 6 by 19 improved plow steel wire rope.

over hatch or pier with mechanical power. All hand operations are eliminated, the entire operation being done by one man.

Tests have shown that it takes 1 min 13 sec to raise a pair of 5-ton booms from their cradles to the working position. It takes 56 sec to shift a pair from the working position on one side to the working position on the other side. The 10-ton booms require slightly longer, 2 min 36 sec and 1 min 21 sec respectively. All of these shifts can be performed by the winch driver without moving from his regular operating station. To do the same operation with the conventional gear takes several men 10 to 15 times as long, and the danger of dropping a boom or getting a man injured in handling the lines is ever present.

As mentioned before, with the older system of rigging the married fall system there is always the danger of accidental hoisting of the load to greater heights than the gear was designed for. As a result the guy

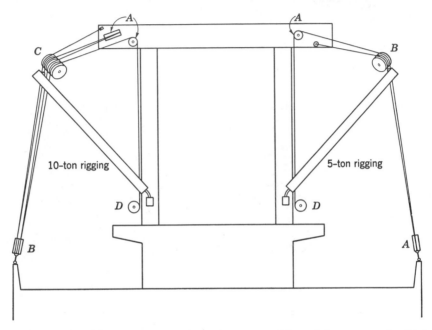

FIG. 6-36. Mechanical guys. A schematic representation of the guys on the Ebel rig. All blocks marked with an *A* are single, *B* indicates a double block, and *C* a quadruple block. *D* marks a guy winch that is controlled from the position where the winches are operated. Note that the standing parts are secured to the crosstrees. All blocks are 14-in. sheave and rove off with ⅝-in. 6 by 19 improved plow steel wire rope.

stresses become very great, especially when a poor guy location is selected by the longshoremen. The consequences may be a parted guy, a collapsed boom, or a jackknifed boom. All of these failures of the gear will result in damaged cargo, damaged gear, and may result in injury or death to personnel.

The Ebel rig is designed so that the effective guy resultant force keeps the stresses moderate even when handling 5- and 10-ton loads. If the load is hoisted to excessive heights, the dock boom head will rise by *riding up* in the bight of the guy tackle until it reaches a position of equilibrium with the load. While the boom head rises, the load remains almost stationary. Thus, the angle between the two falls is limited to a fixed predetermined maximum, and the overloading of any element is precluded.

When the load is lowered by slacking off on the falls, the boom resumes its original position by *riding down* the bight of the guy. The boom is never free from the tensioned guy; therefore, it cannot drop freely. When burtoning 5 tons, the minimum height of the married fall

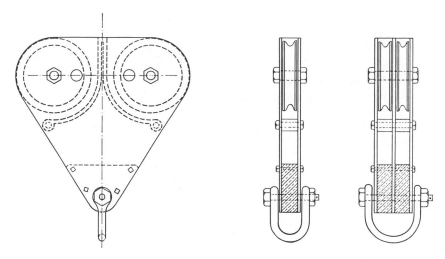

Fig. 6-37. Nontoppling blocks. These blocks are used for doubling up the yard and stay rig to be used with fixed booms. Instead of having to use two separate blocks at the hook, this single, specially built block suffices.

above the deck at which the riding up will occur is about 30 ft, and for lighter loads it is higher. This is ample drift to handle almost any load.

Since only one guy location is provided for, it is impossible to locate the guy improperly. When handling loads with the single fall, the maximum load is determined by the size of the fall; with ⅝-in. 6 by 19 improved plow steel, it would be 3 tons, and with ¾-in. wire rope, it would be 4 tons. When it is desired to hoist 5- or 10-ton loads by the married fall system, it is necessary to use a multiple purchase. This becomes necessary because the winches are generally limited to a single line pull of about 3 tons.

On the Bland, two specially designed burtoning blocks have been provided for burtoning loads up to 5 and 10 tons. They are illustrated in Fig. 6-37. The one with single sheaves is for handling loads up to 5 tons with two part lines. The other, with double sheaves, is for handling 10-ton loads with four part lines. These blocks are self-overhauling and nontoppling and are equipped with roller bearing sheaves. These blocks prevent the twisting and toppling that sometimes takes place when two separate blocks are married for burtoning with a multiple purchase.

ADDITIONAL METHODS OF HANDLING CARGO

The ship crane. The question of which is the most efficient, the yard and stay rig or ship's cranes, would appear to be answered in favor of the yard and stay rig if one were to judge from the number in use at this time. However, when it is remembered that the ship's cranes were introduced many years after the industry had used the other gear, and it is also re-· membered that, in general, the shipping industry has shown itself remarkably unable to make rapid conversions to known better equipment and methods, it seems that perhaps a decision on this question had best wait until more valid and reliable data are available.

The factors involved in deciding the merits of one system as compared to another are: (1) Initial cost. (2) Cost of maintenance. (3) The productivity of the system. (4) The flexibility of the system. (5) Safety. From the foregoing, it is evident that, in order for anyone to be in a position to say anything conclusive about either gear, they would have to have a modern cost accounting system and industrial engineering organization in order to obtain the facts on which a comparison could be made.

TYPES OF INSTALLATIONS. Early installations of cranes on Swedish and German ships were about 3-ton capacity with a 30-ft radius of reach. In 1950 the M.V. C-Trader, owned and operated by the W. R. Chamberlin Company in the packaged lumber trade between Oregon and California, was equipped with two 10-ton capacity cranes with a reach of 38-ft radius. In 1953 two cranes with a capacity of 5 tons and with a 38-ft maximum radius were installed on the FS-790, an Army Transportation Corps self-propelled barge, see Fig. 6-38. A second barge for refrigerated cargoes was being constructed and equipped with these cranes in 1954. Until the original installation on the C-Trader, no United States ship had been equipped with such heavy duty shipboard cranes. Some converted L.S.T.'s, however, had been equipped with small capacity shoreside type cranes.

Cranes have been installed on either side of and on the centerline of the ship. When installed on the centerline, it is with the intention of one crane being able to work both sides of the ship and one end of two adjacent hatches. This is more economical and means less weight. However, if the crane is on the centerline, it must be much larger in order to provide ample reach over the side.

The installations made on the United States ships mentioned above were on relatively small ships. Judging from the experience of the owners on the C-Trader, given below, the cranes have been highly successful. Whether they would be equally successful if given a complete and scientific test period on large general cargo ships, no one can say at this time. It seems, however, that there are many things in their favor. Figure 6-39*a* and *b* shows two possible installations on large ships.

FIG. 6-38. Hydraulically powered ship's crane. This is a view of the type of crane placed on the Army Transportation Corps' Cargo Barge FS-790. These are similar but smaller than the cranes on the lumber schooner C-Trader. Courtesy Colby Steel & Manufacturing, Inc.

OPERATING EXPERIENCE DATA ON C-TRADER. The average rate of loading per hour, per crane, is 80,000 board feet as compared with 20,000 board feet with the yard and stay gear, per hour, per set of gear. The average rate of discharging is 110,000 board feet per hour, per crane as compared with 25,000 board feet per hour, per gear. The C-Trader carries only two cranes to service three hatches; with standard gear at least four sets and possibly five would be installed. The operating company reported that the C-Trader's port time was reduced to one-half of what it would be with the regular gear.

After three years of operating experience during which the C-Trader's owners used able seamen shipped by the Sailor's Union of the Pacific as crane operators, they reported no appreciable loss of time, no excessive repair costs, and no problem in breaking in the sailors as crane operators. Most of the sailors had never operated a crane of any kind before working these shipboard cranes. Because of the simplicity of operation, there was no problem in training new men. This could never be said of the yard and stay system.

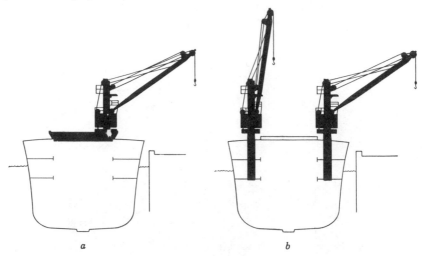

a   *b*

Fig. 6-39. Because of the limited radius of the boom on cranes it is necessary to install them so that ample reach over the side of the ship is obtained. The above sketches illustrate two ideas. (*a*) The diagram illustrates the possible application of a movable crane mount. (*b*) The diagram envisions mounting two cranes on each outboard of the ship's centerline instead of one on the centerline.

Courtesy Colby Steel & Manufacturing, Inc.

ADVANTAGES OF THE SHIP CRANE. *Spotting area.* The crane is able to pick up and drop loads over a greater area, which should, under certain conditions, reduce delay time of the hook. Figure 6-40*a* and *b* indicates the working zone of the crane as compared with the working zone of the conventional burtoning gear.

Safety. Cranes are installed without guys and their supports do not include shrouds and stays. All supports are built into the mounts for the cranes. This fact leaves the decks of the ship clear of numerous lines of running and standing rigging and thereby adds to the safety of operating the ship.

Simplicity of operation. The operator needs only a few minutes of instruction and one man can prepare or secure the gear in a few minutes.

DISADVANTAGES OF THE SHIP CRANE. Although the above advantages leave little room for argument, the disadvantages often listed might not be truly against the crane. One disadvantage that seems to be at least partially valid is that the flexibility of the crane is not as great as the yard and stay. In other words, the crane cannot handle *all* the cargo that the yard and stay can. Economical factors such as initial cost for equal facilities and performance with general cargo will have to await a

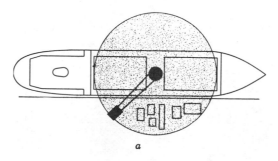

a

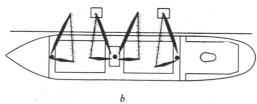

b

Fig. 6-40. The spotting ability of the crane is graphically compared to that of conventional gear in this sketch. (*a*) The spotting area of the crane is that covered by the shaded section. The shaded area of the sketch (*b*) shows the spotting areas of the conventional gear. Note that this indicates the possibility of one crane doing the work of four sets of gear provided the hook could keep up with the men in the hold. Although this would not ordinarily be possible, it is conceivable that two cranes could take the place of four sets of gear. Courtesy Colby Steel & Manufacturing, Inc.

thorough investigation by an unbiased group with valid and reliable data on hand. Perhaps some group sponsored by the industry, such as the International Cargo Handling Coordination Association, will some day set about a search for all the facts about this and many other questions.

The most reliable data for comparison of any two systems are obtained when both systems are placed on the same ship at points that are as nearly the same as possible, as Isthmian did with the Farrell rig on the S.S. Steel Fabricator. Perhaps this will be done on the experimental Liberty type ships that the Maritime Administration is preparing for observation. If cranes are placed on any of these ships throughout, all data will be suspect because, regardless of the facts brought out on any one ship, there will always be the question that will have to remain unanswered of: How would any other given rig have performed on the same ship and under the same conditions?

Fɪɢ. 6-41. The two falls leading to the hook dampen all pendulous swinging created by tangential forces when slewing the crane boom. Courtesy Colby Steel & Manufacturing, Inc.

Two features of the first cranes placed on ships that proved to be detriments to speedy operations were: (1) The pendulous swinging of the load when the crane was slewed between ship and shore. (2) The need to adjust the height of the load as a separate operation when luffing the boom. Luffing the boom means topping or lowering it.

The first objection was overcome by using two falls leading out over sheaves at the end of the jib instead of a single fall to support the load. This arrangement can be seen in Fig. 6-41.

The second problem was overcome by designing into the controlling machinery a device that would allow the boom to be luffed while the load remained at a constant height. This is known as *level luffing*. It prevents the load from swinging when the boom level is adjusted and requires much less power when topping the boom with a load on the hook.

THE OVERHEAD CRANE. As an example of an experimental rig that was tried and found to be inefficient for today's general cargo carrier, we will look briefly at the Harrison overhead crane. This gear was placed on the S.S. Sea Hawk about 1946 at hatches No. 1, 2, and 3. Conventional gear was installed at No. 4 and 5. The Sea Hawk was a C-3 type ship (see Fig. 6-42 and 6-43).

This crane was a type of modified shop crane placed on runways which were mounted on deck athwartships at both ends of the hatch. The crane consisted of a bridge girder supported by the athwartship runway girders. Two trolleys carried the winches on which the cargo falls were rove off. The trolleys were mounted on the bridge girder. The operator's station was placed under the bridge girder clear of the hook. All machinery was contained in the trolley for lowering and hoisting the hook, moving the bridge girder athwartships, and moving the trolleys longitudinally on the bridge girder. Cantilever trusses were hinged to the outboard ends of the runway girders, and when the ship docked, these trusses were swung outboard so that the bridge girder could reach out over the dock when working cargo. When ready for sea, these trusses had to be swung inboard and secured in a fore and aft position.

On the Sea Hawk, one 5-ton trolley was installed over hatch No. 1, two 5-ton trolleys over hatch No. 2, and two trolleys over No. 3 capable of being adjusted to lift either 3 tons or up to 15 tons. Hook selection was made by throwing a single lever on the trolley. This arrangement allowed fast lifts of loads up to 3 tons or slower lifts of loads up to 15 tons. By using an equalizing strong back, a 30-ton lift could be accomplished by using two hooks without any change in the rigging.

Some tests made involving the cycle times of this gear as compared to those of the standard gear showed that when handling loads of 3 tons or less, the burtoning system was about 10% faster. Figure 6-44 is a chart that illustrates the results of all the tests taken on the Sea Hawk. From the curves on this chart it is evident that the overhead crane gear as installed was much faster when handling loads over 4 tons. Perhaps one reason why this gear or some variation of it has never been used is that on almost all ships, under normal operating conditions as practiced today, the average load is well under 3 tons. The majority of the loads are about 1 ton.

Fig. 6-42. Harrison overhead crane as installed on S.S. Sea Hawk.

Fig. 6-43. Overhead crane showing the hinged cantilever jibs rigged for working cargo. The need for wide apron piers with this gear is obvious.

Besides being very fast with heavy lifts, the overhead crane gear gave much better spotting ability over the dock and in the hatch.

The gear's disadvantages were as follows:

1. The overhang of the cantilever jibs was fixed so that very wide camels were required to work the ship at docks with narrow aprons.

2. The drift was limited. This would make it very difficult or impossible to handle certain types of cargo.

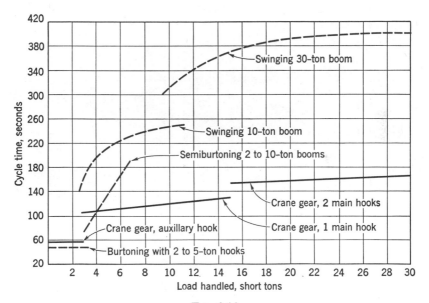

Fig. 6-44.

3. On the large hatches where double gear must work to keep the hatch hours equalized between the large and small holds, both trolleys were carried on the same bridge girder; thus, the top speed of both gangs working in the hold would be governed by the slowest of the two.

4. The transverse movement was relatively slow due to the large mass of the load, bridge, and trolleys.

5. The deck run was almost completely lost for the stowage of big deck loads, which in recent years have grown in importance.

Extensible boom overhead cargo gear. Another type of cargo handling gear that was designed to overcome some of the disadvantages of the overhead crane was proposed but never tested. This gear was called the *extensible boom overhead cargo gear*. In this proposal, the bridge was carried on rollers by a longitudinal fixed runway girder.

Extensible booms were to be hung under the bridge by a system of rollers. These booms, independent of each other at double rigged hatches, could be put out over the side any desired distance either to the port or starboard. Figure 6-45 shows a hatch with only one extensible boom installed.

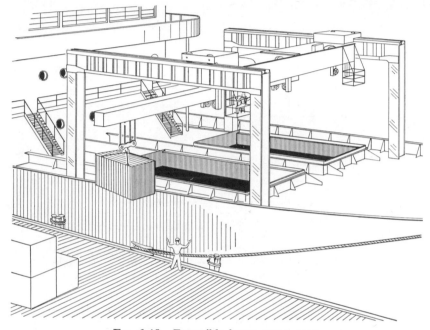

FIG. 6-45. Extensible boom cargo gear.

The dock crane.   The dock crane is used extensively in European ports and many other sections of the world, but it is found at only a few terminals within the United States. Of the many advantages of the dock crane listed by some authorities, the most valid is that the area of deposit is much larger. The crane may pick up a load from any point in the square of the hatch and deposit it on the pier anywhere within the reach of the crane jib. On docks with especially wide aprons that are served with two or three spur tracks of a belt railroad, this is an important advantage. The crane can discharge into or load from railroad cars on any track or from the doors of the warehouse shed. The ship's booms cannot do this because of their limited reach.

Other arguments in favor of the dock crane are not always valid. Situations dependent upon the operating conditions determine whether these arguments truly describe an advantage. For instance, it is said that the crane is better because only one man is needed to operate it;

therefore, it requires less labor. This argument is not valid if the employers must hire a standard sized gang regardless of the operation. It is true that perhaps the extra man could be used to advantage at some other operation, but if there *must* be two winch drivers then it means that each will work only half of the time.

With dock cranes, there is always a means for unloading lighters that come alongside the dock when a ship is not present. This is definitely an advantage in European ports where a large amount of cargo is brought to the dock by lighters while the ship is not there. Lighters may be unloaded with crane trucks and fork lift trucks also, but the dock crane is more flexible.

The strongest objection to the dock crane is that there is a very large initial investment, and this investment is to duplicate equipment that will always be provided by the ships being serviced. The ship must carry gear for handling cargo because she will go to many places in the world where no cranes are available; indeed, there may not even be any dock in some of her ports of call.

On docks that have smooth road beds and where fork lift trucks, tractors, trailers, and similar materials handling equipment is available and used to its fullest efficiency, cargo can be handled just as fast with a small spotting area as with a large one. The only thing that slows up the conventional gear is failure to clear the position under the hook which results in hook delay. Properly used equipment on a modern pier will result in no hook delay from this cause.

Why then, in the face of what has been said above, are there so many dock cranes found throughout the world? The author believes the answer lies in the lack of modern materials handling equipment of an auxiliary nature plus the fact that much lightering work is done and the dock crane finds more frequent use than it would in most ports of the United States. From the standpoint of pure efficiency for discharging ships, the yard and stay system and dock crane are not far apart. Ships must be equipped with the yard and stay or ship cranes; therefore, it appears that the question of dock cranes must be answered in terms of local conditions.

There are three general types of cranes used for aiding ships in discharging and loading at piers handling general cargoes. One of these is a cantilever crane mounted on the roof of the dock shed with a level luffing jib. This makes it possible to pick up cargo from the ship and deposit it on the dock with just two motions: (1) The vertical motion of the hook. (2) The luffing of the boom. More than one crane can be used at a hatch without interfering with each other or with the ship's rigging.

The other types are gantry cranes with jibs that may or may not be level luffing but are always capable of slewing. Slewing is the term used to describe the action of revolving the crane assembly. The word *gantry* simply indicates that the crane is mounted on a structure that spans over something. There is the semigantry crane which has one set of legs sup-

Fig. 6-46. Level luffing dock cranes. These are dock cranes of the full portal or gantry type with a capacity of 3 tons. They are level luffing, but because of the narrow ledge between the outer edge of the crane support and the dock edge, part of the advantage of level luffing is lost. Courtesy Wellman Engineering Co.

ported by a rail along the face of the pier shed wall or on the top edge of the wall. The legs rest on wheels, of course, that run on tracks. The other type of gantry crane is the full arch gantry with all of its legs supported on wheels that run on tracks laid upon the dock apron (see Fig. 6-46). These last two types must slew their loads to get them from the ship to the dock or vice versa unless they are level luffing and set back from the dock's stringer piece.

A special type of crane known as the *transporter* used to discharge bulk products like iron ore and coal consists of a builtup boom that projects out over the ship horizontally. A trolley runs along the length of the boom carrying a winch with a grab bucket on the falls. The operator's cabin may or may not move with trolley. The capacity of these booms may vary considerably but they average somewhere between 5 and 20 tons. The transport crane is used at many terminals in the Great Lakes (see Fig. 6-47).

FIG. 6-47. The transporter type crane. This is an example of the *transporter* crane generally used for discharging at bulk handling docks. This particular crane is rigged with a 9-ton bucket and is located at Western Maryland Port Covington Pier, Baltimore, Md. Note the operator's cage below the boom and to the left of the bucket. Courtesy Wellman Engineering Co.

The Siporter. On passenger ships there are holds for the stowage of cargo many decks below the passenger quarters, and long narrow trunkways must be cut through these decks in order to reach the hold with the conventional yard and stay system or with ship cranes mounted on deck. The *Siporter* was developed to help solve this problem. It consists of an extensible boom on which a trolley is mounted for carrying the cargo fall and hook. The operator rides along in a carriage that contains all the hoisting machinery. The entire assembly is fitted within a sideport opening in the ship's hull (see Figs. 6-48 and 6-49). The sideport, of course, is well below the decks used for passenger accommodations and

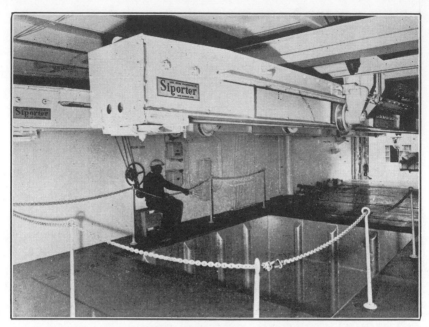

FIG. 6-48. This is a view of the Siporter from within the ship. The man on the left controls the load when it is being lowered into or hoisted out of the hold. Courtesy Lakeshore Engineering Co.

FIG. 6-49. This is a view of the Siporter from out on the dock. The trolleys and hoisting blocks with the short sling pendants and hooks are clearly visible. In other models of the Siporter, there is one operator who rides a carriage back and forth with the load. Here, however, a second operator can be seen to the left. He controls the load when it is extended out over the dock. Courtesy Lakeshore Engineering Co.

working rooms. Loads are picked up and taken inside through the side-port and lowered down into the hold a vertical distance of only one or two deck levels.

The Hulett unloader. The Hulett unloader is a special type of combination crane and grab bucket as shown in Figs. 5-21 and 5-22. The grab buckets are capable of picking up 20 tons of iron ore in a single bite.

FIG. 6-50. A typical floating crane being used on the offshore side of a ship while the ship's gear and a house fall work on the dock side. Courtesy Dravo Corp.

With these rigs a load of 10,000 tons of iron ore can be discharged in 4 hr. When the iron ore is somewhat depleted within the hold and not enough depth remains for the bucket to get a full bite, the Hulett unloader is used to pick up a large bulldozer and place it in the hold to push the remaining iron ore into a pile under the hatch. In this way the Hulett unloader can continue working at a high rate of productivity for a longer time.

Floating cranes. For handling heavy lifts some high capacity cranes are mounted on the decks of barges so that they can be brought alongside a ship on the offshore side while the ship is working cargo from the dock. The barge carrying the crane may have a large deck space for transporting the heavy lift; others may not have this space. The decision as to whether to use the ship's heavy lift boom or to go to the expense of chartering a heavy lift crane is entirely a matter of economics. The cost of chartering the crane and its crew must be compared to the cost of

FIG. 6-51. The floating crane *Monarch* has a 250-ton lifting capacity. Here it is shown lifting 130 tons. The lift is another crane's cabin, engine-room, and turret as a builtup unit. As would be expected, the *Monarch* is listing about 10°. Courtesy Todd Shipyards Corp.

using the longshoremen to break out the ship's heavy lift boom and the accompanying delays on the ship. Of course, if the heavy lift exceeds the capacity of the ship's gear, then a suitably large floating crane must be used. The capacities of these cranes range from 50 to 100 tons with a few in the major ports of the world being capable of lifting as much as 250 tons (see Figs. 6-50 and 6-51).

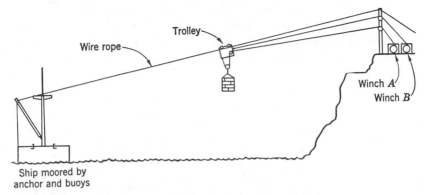

Fig. 6-52. The trolley position was controlled by the operation of winch B. When the trolley is directly over the landing position on the beach or over the ship's hatch, winch A is operated to lower or hoist the load.

Fig. 6-53. Rigging on the ship for the unloading ropeway. Courtesy British Ropeway Engineering Co.

Conveyors. Many types of conveyors are used for assisting in the loading and discharging of cargo. Two types are used to accomplish the loading and discharging completely. These are the endless pocket type and the air conveyor. Full loads of bananas are discharged and

Fig. 6-54. View of the patented trolley to which the load is transferred from the ship's cargo fall. After the transfer is made, the trolley runs down the inclined wire rope to the beach. Courtesy British Ropeway Engineering Co.

loaded by the use of canvas belt conveyors. Figure 7-21 shows the type of conveyor used with bananas. Copra and grain in bulk are discharged by the use of air conveyors. Auxiliary conveyors for bringing cargo from or taking cargo to the wings of the hold and for similar uses on the pier are discussed in Chap. 7.

Aerial ropeways. Aerial ropeways have been used in many places for loading and discharging ships. Figure 6-52 is a diagram of a ropeway

FIG. 6-55. A view of the shoreside end of the wire rope along which the trolley rolled. Courtesy British Ropeway Engineering Co.

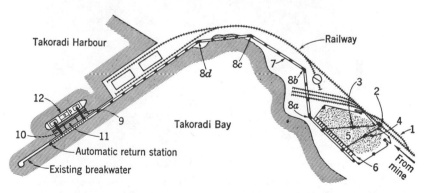

FIG. 6-56. Bauxite loading station at Takoradi Harbour, Gold Coast, West Africa, using an aerial ropeway with an endless belt transporter. (1) Railway supply line. (2) Wagon tippler, 200 tons per hr. (3) No. 1 drag scraper, 200 tons per hr. (4) No. 2 drag scraper, 200 tons per hr. (5) Storage pile, 40,000 tons. (6) Bunker front and ropeway loading chutes. (7) Bicable ropeway, 300 tons per hr. (8a, b, c, d) Automatic angle stations. (9) No. 1 traveling belt transporter, 200 tons per hr. (10) No. 2 traveling belt transporter, 200 tons per hr. (11) Steel wharf structure. (12) 10,000-ton vessel. Courtesy British Ropeway Engineering Co.

that has been used successfully to load and discharge ships at an open roadstead. This idea was used at the port of Kukuihaele, T. H., for loading bagged sugar and discharging general cargo from a ship moored

FIG. 6-57. View of the aerial ropeway and dock at Takoradi Harbour. The buckets on the left are going down full; those on the right are returning to the storage pile to be refilled. Courtesy British Ropeway Engineering Co.

about 200 yd off the beach onto a rocky cliff rising 200 or 300 ft up from the beach edge.

During World War II the British Ropeway Engineering Company developed a very simple system for unloading from a distance of 200 ft from a harbor quay after the quay itself had been destroyed by enemy action. A wire rope was attached to the mast of the ship at the crosstree level (see Fig. 6-53). The other end was anchored ashore after it had been pulled taut. Patented equipment was used to hoist the load out of the ship's hold and deposit it on an independent trolley (see Fig.

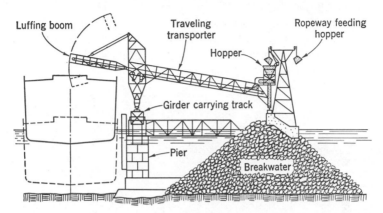

FIG. 6-58. A diagram of the transporter with its endless belt at the dock end of the Takoradi Harbour bauxite loading station. Courtesy British Ropeway Engineering Co.

6-54). Owing to the inclination toward the beach, when the trolley was released with its load it rolled to the beach end where it was deposited (see Fig. 6-55).

FIG. 6-59. View of a ship alongside the dock at Takoradi Harbour being loaded with bauxite. Courtesy British Ropeway Engineering Co.

On the beach, the trolley was removed from the wire rope and returned to the ship on a separate line. On the actual installation, loads of 1500 lb were handled, but greater loads could easily be accommodated.

An installation for loading bauxite at Takoradi Harbour, Gold Coast, West Africa, consists of a ropeway carrying buckets which feed a hopper which in turn feeds a traveling belt transporter. The belt on the transporter deposits the bauxite into the ship's hold. The ropeway buckets discharge into two transporters alternately so that fore and aft holds are loaded at the same time. This system averages about 330 tons per hour.

Figures 6-56 through 6-59 show the elements of this bauxite loading station.

FIG. 6-60. Aerial ropeway at Cyprus erected 1930. Courtesy British Ropeway Engineering Co.

An interesting bicable plant for loading ships with pyrites was erected on the south coast of Cyprus in the middle 1930's. This ropeway has a capacity of 200 tons per hr. Its length is 1800 ft. The full buckets travel on wire rope 2 in. in diameter; the empty buckets return on $1\frac{1}{4}$ in. wire. A 30 hp motor drives the Lang lay hauling rope at a speed of 274 fpm. Figure 6-60 illustrates this installation.

At Avonmouth, England, an aerial ropeway is used in conjunction with cranes and hoppers to discharge bulk coal, ore, zinc concentrate, phosphate, and superphosphate. This ropeway is 5070 ft long and designed for a maximum capacity of 250 tons per hr when handling zinc concentrates. The capacity is less when handling the other products.

Figure 6-61 shows the ropeway-transporter built at Al-Fatha, Iraq. This is a transporter spanning the Tigris River and can accommodate vehicles up to 42 ft in length and handle a gross weight of 53,000 lb.

The total weight of the carriage and load car is 38,000 lb, so that the maximum total rolling load on the main cables is 91,000 lb. The total length of the cable is 2278 ft from the engine and winch house on one side to the anchorage on the other.

FIG. 6-61. The Tigris ropeway-transporter. Courtesy British Ropeway Engineering Co.

PROPOSALS FOR THE FUTURE

Much has been written and said about the need for improved ways and means of loading and discharging cargo, but the actual increase in efficiency has not been very encouraging. It is true, however, that great increases in productivity have been realized in some specialized trades.

Most of the progress over the years has been in the carriage of bulk commodities. In fact, in some ports the productivity of longshore labor in 1928 was higher in general cargo than it was in 1953. In one United States port the rate of productivity in handling *general* cargo dropped from 1.54 tons per man-hour in 1928 to 0.5 tons per man-hour in 1953. This retrograde came about despite the improvements made in materials handling equipment and methods during these years. The reason for this alarming fact is at least partly due to the failure of labor and management to work out their relations in a healthy and progressive manner.

In 1928 at one terminal on the west coast of the United States it required 2300 man-hours to discharge 8000 tons of raw sugar, which was all carried in bags. In 1953, after converting to the carriage of sugar in bulk, the 8000 tons of sugar could be discharged in 1010 man-hours. This is in direct contrast to the general cargo picture.

Just what the future will bring is, of course, not known. There has been much conjecture but little positive change. Going up and over the gunwale of the ship and then down into her depths as a way of getting the cargo from the dock into the ship is deplored by the materials handling theorist. The system violates the fundamental principles of efficiency in handling. As it is done today, the cargo is brought to the pier apron to a point only a few feet from where it will be stowed on the ship. Then we send it to its resting place not in a straight line but along a circular route. The movement should be *straight,* direct from the pier to the ship. This idea definitely favors the sideport which has been neglected in the past years rather than used more extensively.

Some men who have thought seriously about what should be done to improve productivity in the field have proposed radical changes, such as changing not only the cargo handling gear but also the piers to accommodate a specially designed ship. The greatest obstacle to a radical change is the tremendous initial cost. When and if a great change will come about and the probable nature of that change is a matter of endless discussion among interested groups.

The Ellis ship to shore system. One proposal that has been made entails a redesigned terminal as well as a redesigned ship. This is the Ellis ship to shore system. The idea was proposed by Charles Ellis Engineering Company and although as yet it has not been attempted, it is well worth serious consideration. Perhaps some modified version of the system might someday be used to put a ship on a paying basis in some particular trade.

The system consists of a series of small rail carriages each having one-third to one-half the capacity of a normal railroad car. The carriage weighs 600 lb and will support 15 tons of cargo. These carriages are loaded with pallets or containers on the dock before the ship arrives. Each carriage can handle three pallets about 6 ft by 7½ ft by 6½ ft high. A loaded carriage has about 900 cu ft of storage space, or a floor space of 18 ft by 7½ ft. Thus, one carriage will handle passenger automobiles, small trucks, and large crates.

The carriages are moved about the marine terminal or ship's hold and 'tweendecks by standard tractors. Travel from terminal to ship, via a brow or elevator, is effected by chain conveyor. The average freighter or combination ship would have one set of sideports and one elevator forward and one set aft.

The pier would have a system of carriage trackage installed for its full length. Across the pier, at two loading points, chain conveyors with brow or elevators leading into the ship will be installed. The terminal to ship transfer gear is slow and rugged. It takes a carriage about a minute to pass through the sideport. Thus, the total cargo moving between the ship and terminal per hour is from 1500 to 1800 tons.

The carriages upon arrival on the ship at the upper deck stop on a platform that has four small turntables for the purpose of changing the direction of the wheels of the carriage. After stopping and having the wheel direction changed electrically, the carriage moves fore or aft to an elevator that will take it down to its stowage deck. At the correct level it moves fore or aft again and finally into its stowage position either along the centerline of the ship or in the wings. Change of direction is always accomplished by the use of the small turntables.

One of the first objections that will be raised against the idea is that there are some cargoes that could not be accommodated, such as heavy lifts over 15 tons and pieces that are too large to fit through the sideports and within the decks with their limited heights. This objection might be met with the proposal that the ship be fitted with a heavy lift boom forward and aft. Large and heavy pieces could be stowed on the deck of the ship without slowing up the regular discharging or loading procedure.

Another and more serious difficulty is that the pier where the ship is loaded as well as the discharging pier must be redesigned in order to accommodate the system. Thus, a company wanting to use the system would have to remodel every terminal at which the ship was to call on her itinerary. The ship could not be diverted to any other port or dock except those especially fitted out to work with the system. This might preclude the use of the system in normal foreign trade where a ship must have extreme flexibility or sacrifice many cargo offerings. However, it does not completely remove the possibility of the system being worked into a specialized coastwise route with ships of a limited size.

An objection to the idea that will also be raised is that there is much lost space; the broken stowage would be excessive. While it is true that there would be much lost cubic in such a system, perhaps it is worthwhile to examine the cost of trying to pack cargo into every nook and corner of the ship against the savings of a fast turn around. To the average ship operator, the idea that space should not be utilized at all costs is somewhat difficult to accept. However, there are many examples where space has been completely ignored in favor of reduction in handlings and a rapid turn around. One of the most successful of these is the Seatrain type of operation.

PRIMARY CAUSE OF DELAY

As cargo is worked into and out of ships today, there is one very important cause of delay which raises the cost of the operation tremendously. This is the *lack of spotting ability* in the hatch. The lack of spotting ability means the inability to pick up or land a load from any point in the hold of the ship. When discharging, the load has to be brought from the wings, by one method or another, before it is picked up and taken from the hold. Some of the methods used to get the cargo from the wings to the hatch square are rough on the cargo and the cargo handling equipment and result in much damage to both. Other methods are slow, and this time costs much money during the life of the ship. Still other methods combine both of these disadvantages. When loading, the problem is simply reversed in direction. The loads must be landed in the hatch square and taken to the wings.

Moving heavy loads between square and wings. To move loads that are too big for men to pick up and carry or otherwise handle by hand into the wings, the following equipment is needed: six hardwood rollers about 6 in. in diameter; a wire rope messenger of ¾-in., 6 by 19, improved plow steel wire about 60 to 75 feet long with an eye splice in each end; some dunnage boards to provide a road bed; several crowbars; and a snatch block for wire rope with at least a 12-in. sheave. The load should be already mounted on a pair of skids made of heavy timbers. The load is landed on the rollers pointing in the direction that it is desired to move it. After landing, the messenger is attached to the end of the load pointing in the correct direction. The messenger then is led through the snatch block, which has been secured to a frame clamp or pad eye in the direction of the stowage position, and back to the square and placed on the cargo hook. A strain is now taken on the cargo fall and the load moves out to the chosen position. The crow bars are used to lift the load up by leverage and remove the rollers when the load is finally stowed. A reversal of the procedure is required to get the load out to the square again. The messenger is desirable because it saves wear and tear on the cargo fall. The cargo fall itself could be used, connecting it directly to the load and leading it through the snatch block. It is evident, however, that the nips and chafing of the fall would result in heavy wear and quick breakdown on the fall. It is better to use a messenger.

The danger of bulling cargo. Although rollers have been mentioned above, cargo is often dragged out of the wings or into the wings over an improvised surface of dunnage. Sometimes this dunnage surface is greased to reduce friction. Many men have been killed or seriously injured during this process of bulling cargo. With the idea of alerting ship's officers to the dangers of this operation that is carried out aboard ships every day, we will discuss it briefly.

It takes less force to skid an object over a smooth surface than it does to lift it, but once the object fetches up against a piece of dunnage, other stowed cargo, or any fixed object, the only limit to the force applied is the strength of the winch. As pointed out previously (see p. 270), some electric winches can pull up to 12 tons before stalling although they may be rated as 3- or 5-ton winches. It is obvious then, that great responsibility rests upon the signalman and winch driver to be alert and to stop heaving immediately under such circumstances. Failure to do so will result in carrying away a beam clamp, snatch block, or other part of the assembled rig.

It is poor practice to bull cargo with the fall led through the head block of the boom. The lead should be directly from the heel block.

Snatch blocks are often booby traps. Many snatch blocks cannot withstand the loads that the wire used in them can handle. The flanges on beams may bend if the clamp itself does not carry away or slip off first. There are seldom enough pad eyes in the hold to meet all the requirements. Because of these weak points and others, it is practically impossible to rig up a bull line which will not carry something away if the signalman and winch driver are not wide awake all the time unless there is someway of limiting the available line pull of the winches.

A safety device suggested by R. W. Netterstrom, Safety Consultant, consists of a "fuse" inserted in the rig between the fall and the drag line or messenger. This could consist of one 3-ft and one 6-ft length of ⅜-in. wire rope, each with eyes at both ends. Both wires would be shackled in to join the fall to the messenger, but obviously only the 3-ft length would be taking any strain. The excess of the 6-ft wire would be stopped to the short wire neatly with a few turns of seizing wire.

With a breaking strength of about 5 tons (not safe working load), the ⅜-in. "fuse" would limit the line pull to that amount. In case the short wire parted, the winch driver could immediately stop the winch. Meanwhile the longer wire would prevent the fall and messenger from whipping about in the hatch. With such a "fuse," bulling from the head of the boom would be permissible and the probability of injury to personnel and damage to equipment would be reduced.

Moving light units between square and wings. There are at least four other methods of moving cargo from the square to the wings when dealing with lightweight items, depending upon the nature of the cargo and the space being worked.

1. *Using powered or hand trucks.* Cargo may be landed in the hatch square on the platform of a hand or powered four wheel truck and maneuvered into the wings. A roadway may be laid of light steel plates to prevent the truck from rocking and spilling its load. Such loads may be made up of endless rope slings or loads on a pallet sling.

2. *Using roller conveyors.* Cargo may be landed in the square and moved to the stowage position in single units over a system of roller gravity conveyors.

3. *Manually.* Cargo may be picked up unit by unit and carried out to the wing and stowed. If the cargo is not too fragile, the sling load may be pushed back and forth until it is swinging in a pendulous manner and then dropped into the wing as close to the stowage position as possible.

4. *Using platforms and chutes.* With certain types of bagged cargo, platforms may be built in the hatch square and then by use of wooden chutes, which are lighter and much easier to handle than the heavy metal conveyors, the cargo may be allowed to slide into the wings. When discharging, the same technique is used by working the square of the hatch down lower than the wings. In this latter case, chutes may be dispensed with and the bags in the upper tiers slid down the funnel shaped cargo block into the hatch square.

From the above, it should be evident that a good deal of work requiring a lot of extra time is involved in overcoming the disadvantages of having to work cargo from the wings and ends of the hold of the ship.

Statistical study of delay values. By observing the loading and discharging activities of any ship using the yard and stay system, ship crane, or dock crane, it becomes quite clear that the hook is usually much faster than the men on the dock or those working on the ship. The hook will be delayed nearly always at both ends of its travel. This clearly points up the fact that the present gear we have on the ship is fast enough as far as actual travel time for the hook, in and out, loaded or light, is concerned. The loading and discharging systems now employed on ships can best be improved by taking action against the methods used to get the cargo up to the hook, away from the hook, and actually hooking on or unhooking the load. This is true if we speak of the primary cause of delay and we assume the use of a rig that carries the load up over the ship's rail from the dock to the ship and back again when we discharge.

An example of the type of observations that may be made by any officer in any operation are given below. The data so obtained may be used to discover the exact extent of the delay on the ship and/or dock. Besides illustrating the truth of the statement regarding the fact that the hook is delayed by activities of the longshoremen, such observations may lead to a greater understanding of the fundamental faults of any particular system. Thus, valuable suggestions may be made to the operations department regarding changes designed to improve the productivity of the longshoremen as a result of greater understanding on the part of the officer afloat who works with the gear in many ports and under varied conditions.

The cycle referred to on the forms is the period of time from hooking on one load until the hook has traveled in or out and back again and the hook is again attached to a load. The delay time should be counted as all the time that passes after the hook has arrived in the opposite position after the athwartship travel period. The delay time will include the time required for swinging the load into the wings, preparation for unhooking and hooking on, waiting for the landing spot to be cleared, dragging the cargo out of the wings, and any similar activity. In other words, we are assuming that an ideal system would be for the load to be landed, unhooked, the empty hook to return, and the load to be hooked on with no delay except for the actual hooking on or unhooking of the sling. The value of the delay can be stated in terms of time units, tons, or cost. The form as set up would result in obtaining the value of the total delay. Knowing the number of cycles per hour and the weight of each sling load, this delay can be stated in terms of tons per man-hour or gang-hour of lost productivity. Also, knowing the number of men in each gang and the rate of pay for each man, the cost of the delay time can be calculated. The equations necessary for making such calculations are given in Table 6-8.

Cost of delay per ton equation. Table 6-8 gives the data and symbols that can be obtained by making the type of observations indicated:

TABLE 6-8

COST OF DELAY FACTORS

Description of Factor		Factor Symbols and Use
Total cycle time in seconds	C_d	Obtained by taking average of all cycles observed
Delay time in seconds	d	Average of all delays
Cycle time without delay	C	$C_d - d = C$
Pounds per sling load	L	By observation
Number of men per gang	N	By observation
Hourly rate of pay per man	S	By inquiry
Proportion of delay time in total cycle time	$P, \%$	$d/C_d \times 100 = P, \%$
Tons per gang hour with delay	R_d	$1.6L/C_d = R_d$
Tons per gang hour without delay	R	$1.6L/C = R$ *
Tons per man hour with delay	r_d	$R_d/N = r_d = 1.6L/C_dN$
Tons per man hour without delay	r	$R/N = r = 1.6L/CN$
Cost per ton with delay	K_d	$S/r_d = K_d = C_dNS/1.6L$
Cost per ton without delay	K	$S/r = K = CNS/1.6L$

* The constant 1.6 is simply the value of the ratio 3600/2400 which appears in the tons per gang hour formula.

But:

$$K_d - K = C_dNS/1.6L - CNS/1.6L = dNS/1.6L$$

Thus, we have an expression for finding the *cost of delay* for every ton handled. This expression is the right hand term in the last equation above.

$$\text{Cost of delay per weight ton} = dNS/1.6L$$

The officer interested in making such observations may prepare forms to suit his own operations, but the data he obtains should be similar to that shown in the example presented in Table 6-9. After obtaining such information as the weight of the load, number of men in each gang, and the rate of pay, he merely stations himself by the hatch with a stop watch and takes a number of observations. The greater the number of observations and the more explicit the remarks explaining the causes of delay and other facts about the operation, the more valid and reliable will be the data obtained.

Measurement ton costs. The cost of delay per measurement ton may be obtained from the cost per weight ton by multiplying the latter value by the ratio of 40 to the stowage factor of the commodity. By equation this would give:

$$\text{Cost of delay per measurement ton} = \text{Cost of delay per weight ton } \frac{40}{f}$$

Where f = stowage factor of the commodity.

TABLE 6-9

OPERATIONAL DATA ON CARGO GEAR

Vessel: S.S. Pioneer Bay

Commodity: Cotton waste

Location: #3 T.D. Fwd. across

Packaging: Bales

Loading

Weight of each load: 1500 lb

Ob-serva-tions	In Lift	Delay on Ship	Out No Lift	Delay on Pier	Remarks and Summary
1	25 s.	15	20	20	Sling was wire snotter with sliding hook.
2	20	15	25	12	Distance from weather deck to pier averaged 22 ft. Electric winches, longshoremen were average.
3	37	55	15	20	Most delay was caused by inability of longshoremen in ship to stow bales quickly.
4	30	107	23	11	Average cycle with delay: 114 sec.
5	48	20	25	7	Average delay (total): 69 sec. Average cycle less delay: 45 sec.
6	38	14	18	12	20 men per gang. Total cost in salary and benefits:
7	35	31	21	15	$4.50 hourly per man. Cost of delay per weight ton
8	23	77	20	19	
9	40	115	13	25	$$= \frac{69 \times 20 \times 4.5}{1.6 \times 1500}$$
10	31	155	24	13	
11	49	79	20	16	$$= \$2.70$$
12	29	16	19	39	
13	18	83	14	22	
14	39	33	17	19	
15	45	22	14	27	
16	19	21	12	53	
17	15	6	11	20	
18	22	30	12	19	
19	19	21	13	20	
20	24	43	16	18	
21	29	52	10	39	
22	23	112	15	25	
23	17	8	13	12	
24	21	95	15	10	
25	18	6	12	11	

This value may be calculated directly by the equation:

$$\text{Cost of delay per measurement ton} = \frac{dSN}{90v}$$

Where v = the volume of each load.

Keeping records of this type will help the ship's officer build a store of factual knowledge about the cargo operations on his ship.

Improving the spotting ability. Some ways and means of improving the spotting ability of conventional gear are presented below. Some of these are merely proposals, others are actually in use on today's ships.

FARRELL'S RIG. When the yard and stay is equipped with vang posts and topping lift winches that can handle the boom with a load on the hook, the load can be landed or picked up from any place in the square of the hatch.

EBEL'S MECHANICAL GUY RIG. With the guy and topping lift winches readily operated from the winch driver's operating station, the load may be landed or picked up from any point within the hatch square.

FARRELL'S COORDINATED ROLLING WING DECK. This is a device that consists essentially of a movable deck arranged so that it rolls from the wings into the square and back out again with a full load of cargo. The rolling wing decks are large enough to cover the wings on both sides of the hatch square. They are mounted on 4 in. diameter wheels which roll athwartship on flat bar tracks welded on top of the deck and hatch beams. The height of the rolling deck, including the tracks, is $5\frac{7}{8}$ in. A system of wire rigging coordinates the movement of the rolling decks so that when the deck on one side is rolling outboard or inboard the one on the opposite side also rolls outboard or inboard automatically. This makes it impossible for both decks to roll to the low side in case the ship takes a sudden list.

When the ship is ready to load, the rolling wing decks are moved out of the recesses by heaving on a wire messenger with the cargo hook. The decks will meet at the centerline directly under the hatch opening. In this position, the cargo is loaded. When the rolling wing decks have been loaded, they are rolled back into the wing recesses using the cargo hook and runner again. It takes about 18 sec to move the loaded decks out into the wings. When this has been done, the square is left clear and it can be loaded up; thus, all the work is done under the cargo fall and movement to the wings has been eliminated. In discharging, the process is reversed.

These decks definitely increase the spotting ability because they bring the wings of the hatch under the hatch square and in effect enlarge the hatch opening.

ENLARGING THE HATCH OPENING. From the standpoint of improving spotting ability and increasing the efficiency of work in the hold of the ship, it would be ideal to have a hatch with covers almost as large as the entire hold. It would be desirable, of course, to have a 4- or 5-ft border around the hold to assist in working the ship when the hatches were all open. Evidently the increase of the hatch opening size has gone about as far as it can because of the limitations placed upon the size by longitudinal strength requirements. Although the lengths of hatch openings

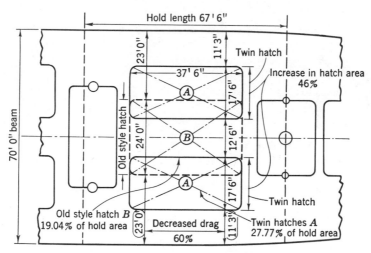

FIG. 6-62. Plan of twin hatches for C3-S-DB3 cargo vessels. *A*, twin hatches, solid line. *B*, old style hatch, dotted line.

have reached a very large percentage of the total length of the hold, the widths have been limited in order to retain continuous longitudinal strength members.

TWIN HATCHES. One answer to this increase in hatch opening area is the use of *twin hatches*. Instead of having one hatch opening, provide two smaller openings, but with a total area that is greater than the single opening. Spreading these athwartships reduces the distance from the hatch opening to the wings. The twin hatches shown in Fig. 6-62 were proposed for use on the C-3 type ship built by the Maritime Commission. Some of the statistics regarding this suggested change are: (1) The drag distance to the wings would be decreased 60%. (2) The twin hatch area would amount to 27.77% of the total hold area. (3) The single large hatch area amounts to 19.04% of the total hold area. (4) Thus, the hold hatch area would be increased 46% over the old arrangement.

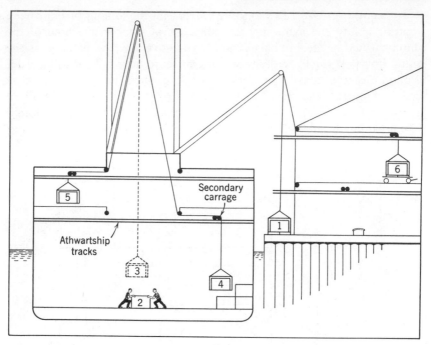

Secondary carriage

Athwartship tracks

a

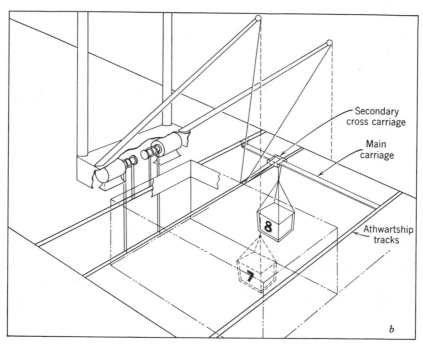

Secondary cross carriage

Main carriage

Athwartship tracks

b

From the above information, it certainly appears that the twin hatch system would improve the spotting ability. There is a reduction of the size of the opening into the hold from the single large opening to just one of the twin hatches amounting to 27%. This means that there would be a smaller limit on the largest piece that could be lowered into the hold. This seems like an insignificant disadvantage, and certainly cannot explain why the idea has never received a thorough test. Again, the only valid way of comparing this idea with present systems is to place it on a ship with conventional design, and gather data with as many variables as possible eliminated.

FETCHKO'S UNDERDEK WING LOADER. Before a class of Cadet-Midshipmen of the United States Merchant Marine Academy in 1952, the author discussed the idea of increasing the spotting ability as a means of increasing the efficiency of the cargo operations so long as loads were handled over the deck of the ship by the yard or stay or crane method. A few weeks later, Cadet-Midshipman Joseph A. Fetchko came to the author's office and presented a set of preliminary drawings of an idea for a device that would improve the spotting ability of the cargo gear. The device seemed practical, so Mr. Oliver D. Colvin was asked to consider it with his staff of engineers. Eventually patents were taken out and more detailed engineering design features were thought out. As this is being written, the device has not yet been placed on any ship. However, it represents an idea that was born within healthy educational environment, and this is good. Whether it will operate as conceived on certain types of commodities cannot be determined until it is tried out. To give this idea or any other similar idea a fair trial it must be placed on one hatch of at least one active ship and tested under all types of conditions. Then and only then, can anyone say that it will or it will not work.

It is the author's opinion that the shipping industry should maintain some means of testing all such ideas thoroughly. There is a desperate need for authentic data on all questions that arise concerning the entire topic of cargo operations. There are too many people in the field who,

---

FIG. 6-63. The Underdek Wing Loader. Showing a section of a freighter alongside a double decked pier with a narrow apron (a), and a perspective view of an upper 'tweendeck (b). Ordinarily, when a load is picked up at position 1, it is landed at 2 or nearby within the hatch square. The hook returns to the pier for another load. At times the hook must hang back on the dock or on deck while position 2 is cleared, this is the delay time. The Wing Loader makes it possible to take the load directly to position 4 or 5. As indicated in (a), it can be adapted to use in the dock shed also. Courtesy Colvin and Fetchko.

when they first hear of a new device, tend to condemn the idea, sometimes, so it seems, simply because it is *new*.

Fetchko's wing loader (see Fig. 6-63*a* and *b*) consists of a set of athwartship tracks welded to the overhead in the hold to the under side of the two hatch end beams. A main carriage runs longitudinally between these two tracks. By use of a system of lines running to special hydraulic winches, the main carriage would move athwartship across the entire breadth of the ship. The main carriage would provide tracks and support for a lighter secondary cross carriage which would engage the cargo runner. The load is conceived as being lowered into the hold but not landed. While the load hangs suspended in the hatch way, the secondary carriage is moved into transverse alignment with the fall. The main carriage would then be moved athwartship. As this was done, a flanged roller, mounted on the secondary carriage, would come into contact with the fall. As the main carriage moves outboard, the load would be moved into the wings. It would also rise unless the cargo fall was slacked out steadily. After a few operations the exact height at which to hold the load when lowering it into the ship would be discovered and adjustment of the fall could be minimized. One man in the hold with operating controls strapped to his chest would operate the carriages. He would also signal to the winch driver controlling the hatch fall if it became necessary to slack off or heave away. In this manner the load would be moved to the wings and could be landed without being touched by any longshoremen. The loads could be tiered until the drift was too small for safety in handling them. Discharging would be done simply by reversing the procedure. The loads could be built up in the wings and picked up from there and moved to the square from where they would be discharged as normally done now.

There is no doubt that the rig would improve the spotting ability of the cargo gear.

UNDER DECK BULL LINE. A device consisting of a small winch mounted in the wing with a fall that could be hooked and unhooked easily on the regular cargo hook has also been proposed. This would be a married fall system for moving the cargo from the wings and out again, each time hooking and unhooking the bull line. The winch is mounted on a track and travels fore and aft along the port and starboard wings on the extreme outboard edge of the hold. This is another device that has never been tested thoroughly, but it appears to have merit insofar as its objective of increasing the spotting ability of the ship's gear.

THE SNATCH ROLLER. This is a device that can be quickly attached or detached from the flanges of an I beam and which provides a portable position from which to secure a chain fall, or any suitable device, for lifting loads around the edge of the hatch square and placing them in the wings or ends of the hold. The snatch roller is envisioned as being secured to the lower flange of an I beam while the I beam is secured, in turn, to the ship's beams in such a way that it can roll athwartship. The I beam would run longitudinally as shown in Fig. 6-64. This is still another device, simple in design and not costly, which has been

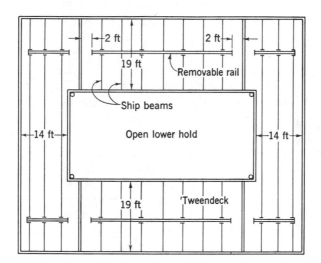

Fig. 6-64. Diagram of the 'tweendeck showing how the overhead removable rail (the I beam) is attached to the ship's beams. This rail is cut in three parts on each side and provided with a stop at each end to prevent the snatch roller from rolling off. Courtesy J. Guadagna.

proposed but has not been given a thorough test to determine its merits or demerits. The snatch roller is the invention of J. Guadagna, a practical longshoreman, who conceived the idea as he witnessed the slow and dangerous methods presently being used to move cargo into the wings of ship's holds after landing in the hatch square.

SECONDARY CAUSE OF DELAY

Another cause for reduced productivity of longshoremen is the time spent in preparation of and securing the apparatus used to actually load or discharge the cargo. Although this cause of delay in cargo operations has been rated as a secondary factor here, there are ports where the aggregate of all the hook delay times will be equal to or even less than the time used to prepare and set up the gear. On the average, the hook delay time should be more than the preparation time.

Some of the activities included in the preparation and securing of the gear are the positioning of the booms, opening and closing of hatches, laying dunnage or metal plate runways, hoisting materials handling trucks on and off the ship, rigging save alls, and setting up safety lines and lights.

Reducing the secondary cause of delay. There have been two important improvements made in this area with many more proposed.

THE TOPPING LIFT WINCH. The topping lift winch is one of the most important improvements because it not only reduces the time required to position booms but also makes the process much safer. One of the most dangerous activities connected with the cargo operations is the topping and lowering of booms with a rig that requires taking a hauling part of the topping lift to the winch gypsy head. Dropped booms and the accompanying rapidly overhauling lines on deck have taken their toll of seamen and longshoremen for years. With the topping lift winch this has been eliminated.

The old system, still used on many ships, consists of a single bale wire with a bull rope on the end to pull the boom up with power from the winch, or a twofold tackle rove off with wire with the hauling part leading to a large cleat at the foot of the mast or king post. In either case, the hauling part has to be transferred to the winch gypsy head and back to a cleat while the boom is kept aloft by the use of a stopper. One type of rig uses a chain to hold the boom aloft instead of transferring the hauling part back to a cleat. This reduces the danger by eliminating the transfer from drum to cleat, but it retains the man at the gypsy head with a hauling part and leaves the possibility of trouble open from that direction.

Either system that is used requires a considerable amount of time. It is necessary to stop off the hauling part, remove from cleat to gypsy head, heave away slowly, stop off, transfer to the cleat, and finally make secure. All this activity requires at least four skillful and *sober* seamen and results in topping *only one boom*.

The topping lift winch is a small 20 hp electric winch generally secured to the mast or king post so that it is out of the way. The topping lift hauling part leads directly to the winch drum and the winch may be operated by pressing a button or operating a small lever arm. Such controls are constructed so that the winch operates only while the switch is held in or down and will stop when pressure is taken off the control. This is an important safety feature.

Some of these winches require that the boom be unloaded when topping or lowering; other winches may be operated with a loaded boom. Some are held from backing off by rachet mechanisms, others by brakes after the boom has been positioned. Some topping lift winches are drums on an extended shaft of the regular winch. To be operated, a lever is used to engage the topping lift winch drum with the powered shaft and disengage the cargo fall winch. After the boom has been positioned, the topping lift winch is disengaged and the cargo fall winch is engaged.

FOLDING METAL HATCH COVERS. This is the second important improvement in reducing the time needed to prepare hold and gear for working or to secure it. There are now about 1000 ships throughout the world equipped with folding metal hatch covers; 35 of these ships are United States flag ships.

There are two types: the *single pull* and the *Mege* type. The single pull type is pulled forward or aft by the cargo fall and the leaves or sections tilt up into a vertical stowage position on deck at either end of the hatch (see Fig. 6-65a, b, c). The Mege type, a variation of which was placed on the Mariner type ship, consists of two or three large sections per hatch. These sections are raised from the sealed or closed position by pressing upward against wheels located at the corners of the section. The cover is then opened up by using the cargo fall attached to a permanently installed messenger somewhat similar to a book that has been laid down split into two parts. The sections are hinged at each end of the hatch and along a transverse seam joining two adjacent sections. When the hatch is open, these sections stand upright at the end of the hatch. Figure 6-66a and b shows an example of this type. Watertight integrity is provided by a gasket around the perimeter of the cover which sets against a knife edge and is held tight by the use of a number of dogs around the edge of the cover.

These covers may be used on the 'tweendeck spaces as well as the weather deck. They save many hours of work each time the ship is readied for cargo work. Under the old system, I beams that had to be carefully slipped into beam slots along the hatch carlings were used to provide transverse strength. Over these beams the hatch boards had to be replaced, and over the boards at least three tarpaulins had to be carefully stretched, folded, and tucked under a batten. After being tucked behind a steel batten, they were secured by driving wooden wedges against a cleat set at an angle to the batten. All this required much time; the activity was always accompanied with the lusty curses of the longshoremen and amidst the general confusion, all too often, bones were broken. Whether or not any bones were broken, *time* in large amounts was always consumed.

The folding metal hatch cover can be opened by the longshoremen in about 5 min, after the dogs have been removed. The older system re-

(a)

(b)

(c)

FIG. 6-65. (a) The messenger is attached to one section of the cover. When a strain is taken on the messenger, all sections roll toward the end of the hatch. (b) As they reach the end of the hatch they tilt upright, as seen in this view. (c) When the last section reaches the end, all sections are stowed in this fashion. This is the way the single pull MacGregor-Comarain hatch opens up. Courtesy (a) and (b) Port of New York Authority; (c) MacGregor-Comarain, Inc.

quired from 30 min to 1 hr to open after the wedges had all been removed.

Aside from the time saving element found with these metal hatch covers, there is the important advantage of having the decks clear of the parts used to cover the hatch. There are no beams, boards, or covers lying about the deck to bark shins or act as dangerous obstacles to men passing along the decks at night or in foul weather. The elimination of cluttered decks is a very great advantage from the standpoint of safety.

FOLDING METAL HATCH COVERS FLUSH WITH THE DECK. The folding metal hatch cover that requires a raised coaming with dogs for making it watertight is the type that was discussed above. In general, for use in the 'tweendeck spaces, it is desirable to have a cover that fits flush with the deck. A metal cover that fits flush with the deck but is not watertight was used on the third deck of the Mariner type ships; however, on the second deck a folding metal hatch cover was installed with

(a)

(b)

FIG. 6-66. (a) This is a view of the Mege type folding metal hatch cover and the system of closing the cover using the ship's gear. (b) This is a view of the Mege type cover as installed on the second deck of the Mariner type ships. Note the a coaming raised $4\frac{1}{2}$ in.   Even the $4\frac{1}{2}$ in. was less than the standard of 9 in.; this allowance was made because of the construction of the cover.   On the so-called open shelter deck ship, a 9 in. coaming is included in compliance with the load line convention of 1929 as interpreted by the American Bureau of Shipping and the U.S. Coast Guard. Other construction characteristics are also necessary to gain the classification of open shelter deck ship.

OPEN SHELTER DECK CLASSIFICATION, AN ADVANTAGE?   The advantage of having a ship designated as an open shelter deck ship is the declaration of all the shelter deck space as exempted space and thereby reducing the gross and net tonnage of the vessel.   The disadvantage is that the draft to which the vessel can load is thereby limited also.   The draft limitation is not a disadvantage, however, if the shipowner's trade is in cargo that runs to a stowage factor in the order of 70 or above. The reduction in the gross and net registered tonnage, however, is a permanent advantage because many of the fixed costs of operating a ship are based on the vessel's gross or net tonnage.

It is not certain, by any means, that under every type of operating condition the savings obtained by having the shelter deck space exempted is equal to the additional costs in cargo handling due to having to work around a raised platform in the square of the shelter deck space for the life of the ship.

One study made on this question revealed that on a ship about the same size as the Mariner type ship, the gross tonnage would be reduced from 12,500 to 9700 tons, a reduction of 2800 tons.   The net tonnage would be reduced from 7500 to 5600 tons, a reduction of 1900 tons. Table 6-10 shows the estimated savings that would result from having a full scantling ship of the Mariner type classified as an open shelter deck ship.[1]   Note that the savings per year vary with the trade route.

Whether or not these savings are more or less than the costs of delay time and lost space accrued as a result of the 9-in. hatch coaming cannot be demonstrated precisely.   An analysis of some of the fundamental principles of cargo stowage gives some evidence that seems to support the view that any savings are equaled by the raised handling costs.

One fundamental principle of cargo stowage that we have noted is

[1] Russo and Sullivan, *Design of the Mariner Type Ship,* Paper presented at spring meeting of SNAME, Boston, 1953.

---

fairleads and messenger with the link spliced into the end.   After the dogs are released and the watertight seal is broken, all that must be done to open this hatch is to hook the blacksmith into the link and heave away.   In the lower decks, the covers fit flush with the deck. Courtesy U.S. Maritime Administration.

TABLE 6-10

SHELTER DECK COST COMPARISON

Trade Route	Number of Entries United States and Foreign Ports	Savings	
		Dollars per Year	Dollars per Trip
U.S. Atlantic ports to west coast of Italy	9–11	5,740	975
Mediterranean and India	9–23	8,586	2605
United Kingdom	3–4	21,159	3023
Far East		3,165	1055
Scandinavia	8–4	3,154	631
South America	8–9	3,294	659

the need to maintain a level surface over the stowed cargo block. Admittedly, this is more important in the lower holds of a ship than in the upper 'tweendeck areas where the 9- or 4½-inch coaming appears. Nevertheless, the desirability of a level surface still exists. With the raised coaming and accompanying brow extending into the stowage areas around the square of the hatch, the longshoremen are given an initial problem that is not easily solved. Regardless of the solution, time is consumed in getting around this difference of levels in the stowage compartment. The delay time caused by having to move cargo from the square of the hatch is increased by having to traverse the broken surface of the deck. This delay time takes on great significance in face of the high wages paid to longshoremen.

It is obvious from the above discussion that it is desirable to have *flush watertight* folding metal hatch covers for use in open shelter deck ships on the second deck. If such a cover is approved by the American Bureau of Shipping, the U.S. Coast Guard, and the Ministry of Transport of Great Britain, the advantage of shelter deck classification *plus* a flush hatch cover in the shelter deck spaces will be enjoyed by the ships of these nations. Since the Bureau of Veritas, the French Classification Society, has approved such a cover, French ships already have this advantage. It seems quite likely that all nations will soon approve such covers and in the future there will be more open shelter deck vessels with flush watertight hatch covers on the second deck.

AUTOMATIC OPENING AND CLOSING DEVICES. The first folding watertight hatch covers were opened by using cargo runners or messengers with power from the regular ship's winches. Some recent installations, however, have been equipped with electric or hydraulic opening and closing devices. To open the covers it is necessary to take off the dogs and raise the cover off its gasket. Then, by turning on a switch, the cover is opened by a builtin power unit. Hydraulic opening devices make it possible to open or close the hatch in a few minutes even when the ship is without power. This is possible because the electric pumps used with the hydraulic apparatus maintain a high pressure at all times. Therefore, even though the ship's power plant becomes inoperative, there is always sufficient pressure to operate the closing or opening mechanism.

ROLLING BEAMS. A number of ships have been fitted with beams that can be rolled to one end of the hatchway when the hatch is being worked. This device makes it unnecessary to hook onto the beams, hoist them out of their stowed positions, and land them on deck. The beams can be taken out, if desired, by maneuvering them to a spot where they can be lifted clear. Some of the difficulties that developed with this idea were the jamming of the beam along the track by uneven pulling when moving it forward or aft and allowing the track to become clogged with debris during the normal course of working the cargo making it difficult or impossible to roll the beam along the track. These two objections can be overcome by constant care and attention, but they do present a continuing problem to the ship's personnel and under practical operating conditions can cause a great deal of trouble.

The rolling beam is supported by its flanges resting on the track ledge and locked into position when the hatch is closed and covered. When the hatch is opened, a lever is used to turn a cam which lowers a small wheel to the track and the weight of the beam is then on the wheel and not on the flange. With both ends of the beam on wheels, the beam can be rolled clear at one end or the other or, if desired, to the center of the hatchway. When everything works well, this is faster than hooking onto each beam, removing it from its sockets, and landing it on deck or in the wings of the space below decks. It also makes things safer on deck by eliminating some of the congestion there. There should always be an effort to keep the working spaces *safe*.

PONTOON HATCH COVERS. The pontoon hatch cover was an idea that eliminated the hatch beams and the boards. Canvas tarpaulins were still required to cover the hatch on the weather deck to make the covering watertight. Ordinarily, such coverings consist of three number four canvas duck tarpaulins. The first tarpaulin placed on the hatch is usually folded to just cover the hatch. The second and last cover is tucked under a batten bar which is in turn secured by driving wooden wedges against the batten bar cleat. The covers should always be placed on the hatch with the seam facing aft. The corners of the hatch cover must be carefully folded in a mitered fold to prevent green seas from tearing them loose. The wedges should have the straight grain placed against the cleat and the sawed diagonal edge against the batten. This makes the wedge less likely to split when driven home with a topping maul. The topping maul is a large hammer with a heavy head used for work about the ship.

The pontoon hatch covers made it more difficult to find space on deck to stow the parts used to cover the hatch. Removing the pontoons, however, was quicker than removing all the beams and the individual hatch boards. In order to eliminate some of the congestion on deck, it is sometimes wise to land the pontoons on small trailers on the dock and leave them there while working the ship.

FARRELL'S AND EBEL'S GUYING SYSTEMS. When removing hatch beams or pontoons, it is necessary to have the hook pass directly over the place where the liftup is to take place. This is usually accomplished, with the older systems, by topping, lowering, or winging the hatch boom well outboard. This maneuver takes time and when winged far outboard, as sometimes is done when lifting out the beam nearest the boom heels, the strain on the working guy of that boom can be 10 times the load on the falls or even greater. In the case of a jammed beam, a guy might easily be parted with disastrous results. *Safety* becomes a factor here also.

With booms that can be easily lowered or topped, these troubles are eliminated and the operation becomes easier, faster, and safer. The Farrell and Ebel systems of guying, with topping lift and/or guy winches, definitely accomplish this.

CRANES. Deck cranes and dock cranes also speed up the opening and closing operations and make for greater safety for the same reasons that were mentioned in the sections on the Farrell and Ebel rigs.

CHAPTER 7

Materials handling

principles and equipment

MATERIALS HANDLING AS A SUBJECT OF STUDY

When we consider the materials handling problems of the marine terminal and the ship, we are considering a special handling operation. Nevertheless, basic materials handling principles apply, and a brief survey of some of these should be helpful to the ship's officer, terminal manager, operations manager, and the stevedore. Two noteworthy benefits are obtained from a knowledge of these principles: (1) The most elementary yet worthwhile accomplishment is to make all personnel conscious of the fact that they are dealing with a problem for which basic principles do exist. Hence, the word is spread that there is a source of factual data concerning such problems. This is good for it tends to reduce reliance on pure opinion and to emphasize facts. (2) Knowledge of the principles helps to explain *why* one way of doing a job really is better than another and *why* one piece of equipment is better for a given job than another. This knowledge of *why* gives the man, operations manager down to longshoreman, a feeling of self-confidence that encourages thinking and will, *in the long run,* result in better utilization of machines and manpower.

There are several excellent books written on the subject of materials handling and they discuss the guiding principles for the materials handling engineer in great detail and give numerous examples of their application. The reader desiring a more detailed coverage of the field of materials handling is advised to read one of the several books devoted exclusively to the subject. In the following pages, we will survey the most important basic principles and discuss some of their applications with reference to machines and techniques used in the maritime field.

Professor Immer has classified the various principles under four categories. He calls them *planning, operating, equipment,* or *costing* principles.[1] The author has listed them here in what he considers the order of their relative importance as they have been applied on the waterfront in the past 25 years. After the first few, it becomes difficult to judge their relative importance; in fact, the last eight or nine as discussed may be considered as equal in importance.

After reading the comments under each principle listed, the reader may reflect that the ideas set forth are seemingly quite obvious and fundamental. This is true. But it is also true that adherence to the principles is the only effective way to produce an efficient materials handling operation. For example, the first principle is simplicity itself, yet compliance with the idea is one of the most promising aspects of cargo operations.

The operating principle of unitization. *Materials handling becomes more efficient as the size of the unit handled increases.*

Some of the most radical changes in ship operation are based on this principle. The Seatrain operation has carried this idea further than any other segment of the shipping industry. The *unit* here is a railroad car. Compliance with the unitization principle has produced a profitable operation despite the fact that other principles of ship stowage and materials handling have been disregarded, for example, the principle of stowing the cargo so as to use the greatest amount of her cubic as possible. The amount of lost space is probably over 50% but the reduced cost of loading the ship and the speed with which she is loaded and sent on her way with a paying load more than makes up for the lost space (see Fig. 7-1).

Although the Seatrain is an exaggerated example, it serves very effectively to emphasize the importance of this principle. The Trailer-Ship is another development that will give further proof of the validity of the idea, if more proof is needed.

[1] J. Immer, *Materials Handling,* McGraw-Hill Book Co., New York, 1953, p. 23.

The pallet load, the unit container, and unitized loads using steel strapping with outer supports are developments that are slowly being exploited more and more by foresighted operators the world over. They are all based on the principle of unitization.

With present day ships, rigged as they are for handling the loads of yesteryear, there is a limit on the economical size of the units that can

Fig. 7-1. The Seatrain terminal, Edgewater, New Jersey. This type of operation is an example of a type of carrier that operates successfully in spite of the violation of many old ship-operating principles. These carriers have no flexibility and do not use their cubic capacity at all efficiently, yet they are successful. The reason can be attributed to their high satisfaction of the principle of unitization and the reduction of terminal time to the minimum. Courtesy Port of New York Authority.

be handled on general cargo ships. This important basic principle may produce radical changes in the future ship as the cost of labor and specialized routes make themselves more evident. The author refers to the possibility of the development of a ship capable of handling loads in units of 25 or 50 tons in containers much larger than those presently accepted as standard. Assuming a stowage factor of about 80 for general cargo, a container that would weigh on the *average* of 50 tons would have to have an inside volume of 4000 cu ft. If a ship was built and rigged to handle such loads with speed and safety and all such containers were loaded and waiting when the ship docked, the materials handling costs would drop tremendously. If the overall operation could be coordinated to such a degree that many of these containers were loaded by the shipper and delivered to the terminal ready for loading, the efficiency would be even greater.

At any rate, the small single carton or single bag must be eliminated in the future and combined, somehow, into a larger unit. Those operators who become conscious of this fact and bend their efforts toward this end first will be the first to realize the great potential savings. It is encouraging to hear of the development of this trend here and there within the industry over the world.

The equipment principle of terminal time. *The shorter the terminal time the greater the efficiency of the materials handling equipment.*

The only time that a piece of materials handling equipment is making money for its owner is when it is actually moving cargo. This principle can be used by the operating manager as a guide in deciding upon the merits of one type of materials handling equipment as compared to another. Other factors being somewhat parallel, the system that reduces the terminal time to the smallest value is obviously the best. This idea applies to all materials handling equipment large or small. It is the principle that makes the fork lift truck and pallet combination superior to other systems.

Before the elevating platform truck and skid, the mechanically powered load carrying truck was used on marine terminals. The latter was simply a four wheeled truck with a motor power attachment. This piece of equipment is very inefficient from the standpoint of terminal time. It carries the load between the pickup point and the discharge point with ease, but the truck and driver are tied up, accomplishing nothing, while the load is laboriously placed on board or taken off the truck. The simple, yet highly effective, improvement of an elevating platform used in conjunction with skids immediately rendered the fixed platform powered truck obsolete except for specialized uses. The elevating platform and skid, however, are slower than the tapered forks used with a pallet and so the former quickly gave way to the latter mainly because of the validity of the terminal time principle although there are other advantages. The pallet load may be tiered without using dunnage between tiers because the pallet provides its own base. The pallet offers other advantages of its own. The pallet's overall height is less than the skid and this becomes important when considering the maximum height of a tier of unitized cargo. The pallet is lighter than the skid for equal strength.

Let us consider the world's largest piece of materials handling equipment, the *ship*. With proper cost accounting methods, the cost per unit of time while a fork lift truck is standing idle can be obtained; however, the author has been unable to obtain an average figure for use as an example.   There are some figures available for the cost per day of a ship, which is really just an oversized materials handling machine through which the cargo must pass in its journey from shipper to consignee.   A ship standing at a dock costs between $2000 and $3000 per day.[1]   Now the meaning, in dollars and cents, of terminal time becomes quite clear.

It appears that there will be a large increase in the profits awaiting the first group who finds a successful answer to reducing the terminal time of the general cargo carrier.   The ideal arrangement would be to have a single container that is loaded and waiting for the ship when it arrives in port.   It is inconceivable that a container holding several thousand tons could be lifted and placed on a ship.   The alternative is to reduce the size of the container to a practicable magnitude or perhaps adopt the idea of a floating unit that would be comparable to the trailer unit of the modern truck and semitrailer.   Still another idea, which has been patented, visualizes finger piers supporting the seagoing cargo carrying spaces of a ship above the tide level so that a well ballasted ship with the power unit could be maneuvered into the dock underneath it.   Then, by pumping out the ballast, the powered unit with its buoyant body would rise up, engage the cargo container, and lift it off of the narrow finger piers.   The finger piers would be only a few feet in width.   With sufficiently strong connections between the cargo containers and the powered buoyant part, the load is taken to sea.   In effect, this highly revolutionary idea is a seagoing elevating platform truck.   Can such an idea be made to work?   Although we cannot answer that question here, we can say, emphatically, that *if it could* there would be tremendous savings in the cost of ship operation.   Water transportation would enter a great new era of enlightened efficiency.

The operating principle of gravity utilization.   *Move materials by the use of gravity where possible.*

At the marine terminals of the world, this has long been an exploited principle when the cargo can be carried on the ship in bulk form.   The best example of the use of gravity for loading ships is the ore carrier of the Great Lakes.   Grain docks and some oil docks utilize gravity to a large degree also.   Here we have a force provided by nature that will move cargo with a minimum cost if a suitable pipe or chute to direct the flow is provided.   In some operations gravity has been used successfully to load bagged and cased products also.   Case oil, which is the term applied to refined oil loaded in 5-gal containers and packed into uniform boxes, two containers per box, was at one time loaded by means of specially built spiral conveyors.   This conveyor was actually a chute

[1] J. Immer, *Design Criteria for Cargo Handling,* Paper presented at Second Cargo Symposium of the U.S. National Committee, ICHCA, New York, 1954.

and the boxes slid down into the hold. The base of the spiral conveyor was equipped with a ring of gravity rollers and the individual cases upon leaving the spiral conveyor were diverted along several short lines of gravity roller conveyors scattered through the hold of the ship. The length of the spiral conveyor could be adjusted by adding or removing

FIG. 7-2. Great Lakes iron ore loading terminal. This is a view of the chutes leading into the ship. Iron ore is running into the ship down the foremost chute. This operation is an excellent example of the full utilization of the principle of gravity. Courtesy Pittsburgh Steamship Co.

sections. This system was used at refineries in Port Arthur, Texas and New Orleans, La. Productivity of the longshoremen was almost doubled by using this system as compared with the conventional yard and stay rig.[1]

Figure 7-2 shows the chutes at a Great Lakes terminal where iron ore is stored in large bins and then released in runs of 60 to 80 tons. When released, the ore simply pours into the ship's hold. In one test case made

[1] B. Stern, Cargo Handling and Longshore Labor Conditions, Bureau of Labor Statistics, GPO, Washington, 1932.

at one of these terminals, 12,500 tons of iron ore was loaded in 16 min. On the average, these terminals load the ore at the rate of 5000 tons per hr. The number of men required for the operation are less than found in a single gang of longshoremen handling general cargo.

The planning principle of improved flow or the straight line. *Efficiency in materials handling is increased by the elimination of switchbacks and vertical movement.*

This principle recognizes the simple fact that the shortest distance between two points is a straight line and inasmuch as *motion is money,* the most economical flow for materials is in a straight line. This principle is badly violated on almost every general cargo terminal in the world. The cargo may flow almost in a straight line up to the ship's side on the pier apron due to a well organized and carefully planned receiving operation, but what happens at the pier apron? The cargo's ultimate position in the ship is only a few feet away in a horizontal or almost horizontal direction, but as ships load today, the cargo travels in a circle to get there. To eliminate some of this inefficiency, it seems that a greater utilization of sideports should be made.

The author was an officer at one time on a ship that was years ahead of today's ships in this respect although she was built in 1922. This ship had six hatches with an upper and lower 'tweendeck. All six of the upper 'tweendecks and the last five of the lower 'tweendecks were equipped with sideports on both sides of the ship. This ship and a sister ship, the Manulani and Manukai, were operated by the Matson Navigation Company. When they arrived at Honolulu to load bagged sugar and canned pineapples for the homeward bound voyage, better than twenty gangs of longshoremen would swarm aboard, and with a well organized plan the ship virtually sank at the dock. Every sideport on the dockside was opened and with platforms built with idle pallets, fork lift trucks and gravity roller conveyors were utilized to load the 'tweendecks while the ship's gear and gantries with chutes were used to load the lower holds. Incidently, the sugar is now mostly handled in bulk which is far more efficient; but the sideport operation proved itself on these ships before bulk sugar handling was accomplished. There is no argument with the physical fact that it requires only a comparatively small amount of energy to move a ton of material along a smooth horizontal surface, whereas it takes a tremendous amount of energy to raise that ton only a few feet.

It is unlikely that a perfect satisfaction of this principle will ever be approached on today's existing docks and ships, but all future development should be directed toward that end. The loading terminal of

Isthmian Steamship Company, located at the outer end of Erie Basin in Brooklyn, New York, comes close to making it possible to run cargo in a straight line at least from the receiving point on the dock to the ship. But when alongside the ship, the cargo must go on its circular path to the hold of the ship.

The planning principle of air rights. *Dock area is increased by utilizing the third dimension.*

Fɪɢ. 7-3.   Utilization of air rights increases effective dock area.

This principle may be considered too high on the list, but with the limited dock space found on many existing terminals it is quite obvious and fortunate that the idea is being exploited fairly well on today's piers. Satisfaction of this principle is possible now with high stacking fork lift trucks and pallets, whereas it was impossible before such equipment was used. Even with the cargo stacked as shown in Fig. 7-3, some piers are heavily congested. Imagine the effect of having to spread all the cargo out; the inefficiencies would all be compounded and many present operations might even be rendered completely uneconomical. Hence, although it is almost taken for granted on today's terminals, the principle exists and its importance, as well as its simplicity, cannot be denied.

The costing principle of determining handling costs. *For an intelligent analysis of any handling system, the costs of the handling operation must be known.*

This is a difficult problem, but every effort should be made by management to determine the costs of every step in the terminal's operation. How else can one system be compared to another to determine which is truly the best from an economical standpoint? One system may be higher in productivity than another yet be more costly. This cost analysis must be done by experts in the field of industrial engineering and cost accounting. The facts obtained may reveal astonishing weaknesses in any given system and allow for better planning in the future or perhaps point the way to immediate desirable changes.

The operating principle of safety. *High productivity with economy is impossible without safety.*

Everybody agrees that safety is a necessity, but too many people fail to remain safety conscious when planning and executing plans and this includes materials handling plans. Cargo operations on the marine terminal and especially on the ship have a high potential of unsafe conditions. Management and labor must be constantly reminded to enforce safety regulations.

One of the worst violations of a common safety factor at the marine terminal is the lack of proper lighting, especially in the hold of a ship. The author cannot remember ever having seen a really well designed lighting system for cargo hold interiors with one possible exception. The large 100-ft holds on the U.S.N.S. Pvt. Leonard C. Brostrom and Marine Fiddler, two C-4 type ships converted to heavy lift ships, have about 30 lights scattered about the overhead of the hold. This arrangement is at least a long step in the right direction. A well designed system would be one that provides light in all parts of the hold interior even when cargo is stowed in various bays. The light provided should be *bright* not a yellow glimmer. This is not all; the well designed system must be reliable and rugged so that it cannot be made inoperative by working cargo into and out of the spaces. Finally, it must be made accessible to the ship's officer and inaccessible to unauthorized persons. The use of a number of cluster lights in a hatch is inefficient, vulnerable to sudden breakage, and dangerous as a fire hazard. Besides all these defects, their use normally results in leaving some spots that are not being actually worked in darkness, and this, of course, makes an ideal place for the sneak thief to go to work on the cargo. There is nothing so frustrating, and sometimes so futile, as the efforts expended by a ship's officer to keep all holds rigged with the minimum of three cluster lights on a busy cargo ship working all hatches on a rainy or foul weather night. The cords become broken and the lights become smashed and eventually the supply of lights becomes inadequate. Can it be that with all the modern materials and design talent in the industry of lighting engineering that ships must continue to go their way shrouded in darkness? Any additional cost for a ship with a really well designed lighting system is warranted.

The costing principle of equipment amortization. *New handling equipment is warranted if the expense of the new equipment is exceeded by savings sufficient to amortize the cost in a reasonable time.*

The economies realized by abandoning old methods and equipment in certain cases have paid off the costs of new equipment in 3 months.[1] This, of course, is an extreme case but it serves to point up how costly the old methods must have been. Just what the amortization period should be when making a decision regarding new equipment is something that must be decided after considering many things, including such items as legal allowances for depreciation rates and period of expected use. Some management has adopted the policy of approving the equipment that gives the lowest handling costs regardless of the time required to pay for itself; this policy guarantees that long term savings will not be overlooked. The life expectancy of equipment may be as high as 20 years with the majority down to 10 years. It seems sensible to set the amortization period somewhere near but below the life expectancy. Approximately 5 to 6 years on the average should be a reasonable time.

Note, however, that it is going to be difficult, if not impossible, to determine the potential savings by changing the methods of operation unless the handling costs are known. This places emphasis on the importance of the principle of determining handling costs. The fact that handling costs may not be known is probably one reason why mechanization was slow to come to the marine terminal and why, in general, new methods and equipment are not readily adopted.

The equipment principle of flexibility. *Materials handling equipment is more useful and therefore more economical as its flexibility increases.*

This particular principle cannot be followed blindly but should be used with caution in the face of all other facts about a given operation. Obviously, the fork lift truck and pallet system is far superior to the elevating platform and skid with respect to flexibility. Fork lifts may be used to handle skids as well as pallets if necessary, but elevating platform trucks can handle skids only. Besides this, the fork lift truck can be fitted with attachments to make it possible to handle bars, pipe, rolls

---

[1] J. Immer, *Materials Handling,* McGraw-Hill Book Co., New York, 1953, p. 30.

of paper, drums, bales, and many other items without pallet or skid. Thus, it becomes quite clear which is the better handling equipment. The general cargo carrier that can really handle general cargo of types and sizes without delay for refitting is the best such carrier. For instance, for flexibility she should be able to carry general packaged merchandise, a limited quantity of bulk liquid cargoes, 50,000 to 100,000 cu ft of refrigerated cargo, heavy lifts up to 50 or 75 tons, bulk grain with a minimum of expense for fittings, long lengths, and dangerous cargoes. Now, the ship is a piece of materials handling equipment whether a general cargo carrier or a Seatrain. But the Seatrain type ship has proved to be a successful operation in spite of being far from a flexible carrier. This ship represents the antithesis of flexibility; she can call at only one type of specially built dock and can carry only one type of cargo. The same thing can be said of the Trailer-Ship concept. In spite of their merits in reality, they would be condemned if judged solely within the framework of the principle of flexibility.

The operating principle of mechanical equipment. *Heavy units are moved most economically through the use of mechanized equipment when gravity cannot be used instead.*

Practically all units on the marine terminal may be classed as heavy; therefore, mechanization should have great advantages. Mechanical equipment reduces fatigue which is a safety consideration and also may affect productivity. Mechanization speeds the handling process and, excluding labor problems, the number of men can be reduced. The reduction of men has a twofold advantage; the possibility of injury and the cost of labor are reduced. It is important to point out that the men remaining on the job would not be required to do as much heavy labor, and if mechanization is allowed to take effect it will produce jobs for the others. Without mechanized equipment, it becomes impossible to utilize overhead clearances economically by stacking cargoes high on the dock.

One of the biggest obstacles to more and better mechanization of materials handling methods on the terminals and on the ships, especially the ships, is the attitude of labor. This problem may be solved by education and training over a long period of time, but it will not be easy. The fact that labor seems unable to accept is that more mechanization and better use of present mechanization makes industry more stable, gives it a healthy financial foundation, and eventually will use more men. At the same time, the men will be relieved of back breaking manual labor. With labor and management cooperating fully on a completely mechanized coastwise operation, this branch of water transportation would probably be able to flourish once again. This would involve the full use of the unitized load, sideport operation, the latest industrial trucks, and an abandonment of the standard sized longshoreman gang. Under these conditions, the longshoremen and the seamen would have more jobs, and as for the longshoremen the job would be easier and safer.

Equipment principle of standardization. *After thorough experimentation, it is economical to standardize the equipment and methods of materials handling.*

The advantages of following this principle are a reduction in the number and makes of parts for making repairs and an increase in the efficiency of the personnel making the repairs. It is even desirable to standardize such simple pieces of materials handling equipment as pallets; the objective here would not be to economize on the cost of the pallets but to economize on the maintenance, handling, and storage costs.

It should be obvious that the maintenance and repair of a heterogeneous mixture of handling equipment is not as economical as that of standard equipment. The important thing is to make certain that the standard equipment chosen is the best, based on all the other principles mentioned in this section.

Operating principle of maintenance and repair. *It is economical to avoid breakdown through correct maintenance and to anticipate repairs and replacements.*

It should be obvious that it is not good business to run any equipment until it breaks down. It should be equally clear that some regular inspection and check off system for lubrication and replacement is necessary to prevent unexpected breakdowns. Even the simple pallet needs attention. Having a standardized set of pallets, a supply of boards cut to fit the pallets can be maintained. When an end board or any other part of the pallet is found cracked or damaged, this part should be replaced immediately. In this way, the total number of actively used pallets is kept high and greater damage is prevented.

Planning principle of coordination of handling and movement. *Greatest economy is realized when the handling and movement of materials is coordinated.*

This is merely another way of stating the fact that the greatest materials handling economies will be obtained through complete overall planning so that all functions dovetail together in a smooth flowing organization. What the receiving clerk does with the cargo when it is delivered to the pier should not be done without consideration of the stevedore's activities when he picks it up for loading on board the ship. Full coordination is impossible without a well prepared tentative cargo plan and with delivery to the pier scheduled as much as possible. Companies that neglect to organize the flow of cargo to their dock and work with an incomplete or without any tentative plan are violating this basic principle and their activities are certain to be inefficient.

Planning principle of making the organization handling conscious. *For full cooperation, create full understanding of the philosophy that motion is money, extra handlings are evil, and reduced handlings are good.*

This is an educational program and includes management as well as labor. It may take on the form of voluntary participation in a time and motion study, attendance at the showing of a materials handling film with discussions, suggestions relative to materials handling, or a series of lectures concerning the need for increased productivity through mechanization as a means of maintaining a high living standard.

MATERIALS HANDLING EQUIPMENT

In the following paragraphs we will describe the various types of materials handling equipment and comment briefly on those items used most frequently. The changeover from hand powered equipment to mechanically powered equipment took place over a period between about 1932 to 1941. These years were the average years for the first purchase of dock tractors and lift trucks respectively. The first purchases of powered conveyors and crane trucks were also between these years. The earliest recorded purchase of dock tractors is 1918 and of lift trucks it is 1928. These facts give some idea of the speed of mechanization along the waterfront. It can hardly be called rapid.

Hauling and handling materials. To reduce the uneconomical use of man power and thereby bring some degree of efficiency to the marine terminal, there must be a continued effort to reduce the number of handlings of all products carried by the ship and to develop machines to handle a given job with the least inefficiency. Efforts along these lines have produced a variety of materials handling equipment. Each has a number of uses for which it is better fitted than any other type of equipment. The two broadest classifications that can be drawn between types of equipment are equipment which is best for *hauling* and that which is best for *handling*.

We will define hauling as the horizontal movement of cargo for a distance of over 300 ft. Handling is defined as the vertical movement or relatively short horizontal movement of cargo, that is, under 300 ft.

TRACTOR-TRAILER COMBINATION COMPARED TO FORK LIFT TRUCK AND PALLET. The best contrast between equipment best suited for hauling and that best suited for handling is made between the *tractor-trailer combination* and the *fork lift truck and pallet*. The former is essentially a hauling combination, whereas the latter is a handling combination. In many simple operations, the costs can be made much higher than they should be merely by an improper decision regarding the type of equipment that should be used. Here are some figures on the use of fork trucks for hauls between 300 and 1000 feet for similar commodities. Note the productivity in tons per man-hour obtained on the different lengths of haul.

USING FORK LIFT TRUCK

Commodity	Length of Haul, ft	Tons per Man-Hour
Glass bottles in cartons	900	0.47
Flour in bags	300	3.58
Firebricks on skids	1000	1.05

The productivity when working with shorter hauls would be expected to be greater, and, as seen from the following table, the productivity is greater. The point is that the productivity values should not be so divergent. It should be obvious that it is not economical for a fork truck to make a run of 1000 ft with one pallet load when a tractor could be hauling four to six such loads while a man and fork truck were loading other tractors.

USING FORK LIFT TRUCKS

Commodity	Length of Haul, ft	Tons per Man-Hour
Glass bottles in cartons	65	1.27
Flour in bags	60	8.06
Firebrick on skids	160	6.79

THE TWO WHEELED HAND TRUCK. The common hand truck will remain a useful tool in the handling of cargo in spite of how mechanized the total operation may be made. Where labor is very cheap, the purchase of mechanized units may not be warranted according to the principle of amortization. The hand truck can be used for the movement of packages too heavy to be moved by hand or to increase the unit load of small packages on occasional short trips. The hand truck can be used also as a pry or lever in much the same way as a crow bar. With two or more men working with hand trucks, a large crate or case may be raised several inches and transported a few feet very slowly. The nose is wedged under the case, the wheels are chocked, and the operator bears downward on the handles. This action raises the case on the nose of the truck and with two or more trucks at opposite ends the entire case may be raised off the deck and moved slowly in a straight line (see Fig. 7-4).

Two or three men make the best combinations for working with the hand truck. With three men, two will remain at the loading terminal to load the truck while the third man acts as the prime mover. With two men, the operator of the truck also helps to load.

The load must be placed on the truck in just the right way to make it easy to transport. If the load is too low on the bed of the truck, the handles are difficult to keep down while pushing the truck. On the other hand, if the load is too high on the bed of the truck, the operator has a difficult time supporting the load while maneuvering the truck. If the load is placed on the bed so that it is well balanced when the truck

FIG. 7-4. Here is an example of how two 2-wheel trucks can be used to move large crates and cases under special requirements. Courtesy U.S. Navy.

is tipped backward about 60° from the vertical, surprisingly heavy loads can be handled easily by an experienced man.

The working loads may run anywhere from 200 up to 600 lb depending upon the size and type of truck. The trucks are able to support more than it is normally possible to transport on them. Models weighing about 45 lb have a capacity of 900 lb, while heavy duty models weighing 155 lb have a capacity of 2000 lb.

The two wheeled hand truck is only economical for very short occasional movement of materials and then only if the cost of labor is extremely low or some special circumstances exist, such as a low volume of movement or limited working room. Two types of hand trucks are shown in Fig. 7-5a and b. Figure 7-6 shows a method of loading light bulky cases. The operator must experiment a few times to discover the best way in which to load any given container Care must be taken not to place a fragile case or bag over the nose so that the upper containers will damage it.

THE FOUR WHEELED PLATFORM HAND TRUCK. This type truck is also useful today in cases where labor is very cheap or the volume of movement is too low to warrant the purchase of powered equipment. It is much faster and easier to use this truck than the two wheeled type when working cargo to and from the pier apron on marine terminals. The loads can be made up on the platform of the truck within the pier shed and transported directly to the hook on the apron where the load is hoisted aboard. If the load is too heavy for one man, two may be used.

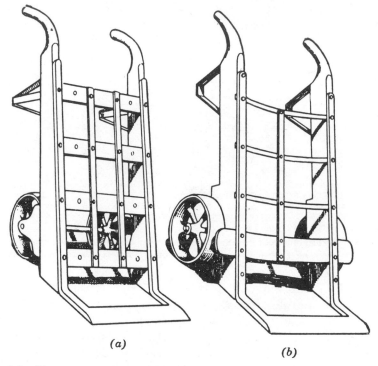

(a)   (b)

FIG. 7-5. Here are two types of hand trucks. Type *a* is known as the Western style and *b* as the Eastern style. Courtesy U.S. Navy.

The same method applies to discharging. The load can be landed on the bed of the truck and immediately moved away to clear the spot for the next load. If the two wheeled hand truck is used, the spot is blocked until the hand truck is loaded after the load is landed on the pier. The use of the platform truck thus eliminates an additional handling and reduces the costs and the damage to the cargo.

Four wheeled platform hand trucks find use in ship's holds to move loads between the hatch square and the wings. The load is landed on the bed of the truck and pushed to the wing or built on the bed in the wing and pushed out to the square. It is necessary to lay down a roadway of light steel plates or dunnage boards over which the truck can pass easily.

THE TRACTOR-TRAILER COMBINATION. For hauling purposes the tractor and trailer combination is excellent. One important requisite necessary for the efficient use of this combination is a smooth surface on the pier apron and in the dock shed.

FIG. 7-6. With experience an operator of a two-wheel truck can load surprisingly large loads on the bed. Here we see a load of 15 cases of light weight loaded on the bed of an Eastern style two-wheel truck. Without trying to experiment to discover the best way to load such containers, only six cases would have been loaded. Courtesy U.S. Navy.

The tractor is a short highly maneuverable vehicle powered by gasoline with a sheet steel bumper face in front and a trailer coupling device on the rear. Its primary purpose is to pull a number of trailers on a train. It may also be used to push railroad cars along spur tracks and similar work. Most tractors used on marine terminals are equipped with four wheels and although they may be capable of greater speeds, they should not be driven over 5 mph, especially when hauling a trailer train.

The trailer is actually a special type of four wheeled platform truck. It is able to take heavier loads than the platform truck. Trailers are constructed in many ways: some are fitted with four wheels that turn, others with only the two front wheels turning, caster wheels are fitted on still others. The bed of the trailer averages about 3 by 7 ft and is about

14 in. high. The bed is usually made of hard wood and bound with steel. Sometimes the bed is covered completely with a light steel plate for heavy duty work (see Fig. 7-27).

When pulled as a train by the tractor, the trailers follow in the tracks of the tractor. One tractor can be used to keep the hook supplied with trailers, either loaded or empty depending upon the operation. For example, in loading, the tractor will arrive at the hook on the pier apron with four to six trailers in tow. Dropping these trailers, the tractor removes the empties and travels to the point on the dock where the cargo is originating. The empties are dropped and a loaded set is picked up. The loaded set is then taken to the pier apron again and should arrive before the last of the previously loaded set has been emptied. Depending upon the length of the haul and the coordination of the entire job, one tractor may be able to keep two or three hooks supplied. With the tractor-trailer combination, a fork lift truck should be employed to load the trailers or empty them on the dock. No fork lift is needed under the hook because the loads are hoisted from or landed directly on the trailer bed.

Assuming an ideal operation, then, the following would be needed: three trailer trains, one tractor, and one fork lift truck. Only four men would be required, assuming all pallets were loaded and stacked on the dock awaiting this operation. As the distance from the loaded pallets to the pickup point on the pier apron decreased, there would eventually be some point where it would be more economical to do away with the tractor-trailer combination and bring in another fork lift. Any given operation must be analyzed carefully on its own merits.

Fig. 7-7. Attachments for the fork lift truck. (*a*) Load backrest. (*b*) Bartel device for rolls of newsprint. (*c*) Car wheel handling device. (*d*) Gooseneck boom. (*e*) Detachable cab. (*f*) Gripping forks for bricks and cinder blocks. (*g*) Pallet unloader used with pallet plate eliminates need for pallets. (*h*) Hydraulic crate clamp device. (*i*) Revolving roll clamping device. (*j*) Side shifter attachment for positioning loads to left or right. (*k*) Clamp and fork attachment for handling tin plate safely. (*l*) Bottom dumping hopper. (*m*) Shovel scoop for handling loose free flowing materials. (*n*) Fork extensions for handling materials of increased depth. (*o*) Canopy guard. (*p*) Vertical drum handling attachment. (*q*) Revolving forks for dumping skid bins. (*r*) Horizontal drum handling device. (*s*) End dump hopper for safe handling of steel scrap, forgings, etc. (*t*) Triple lift attachment increases the telescopic fork lift to 16½ ft. (*u*) Carton clamping device for handling large fragile cartons. (*v*) Hydraulic clamping device for bales, boxes, drums, and fragile containers. (*w*) Multiple barrel handling attachment. (*x*) Multiple drum handling attachment. (*y*) Hydraulically operated pusher attachment equipped with ram for pushing off coils of steel, wire, and similar materials. Courtesy Yale and Towne Manufacturing Co.

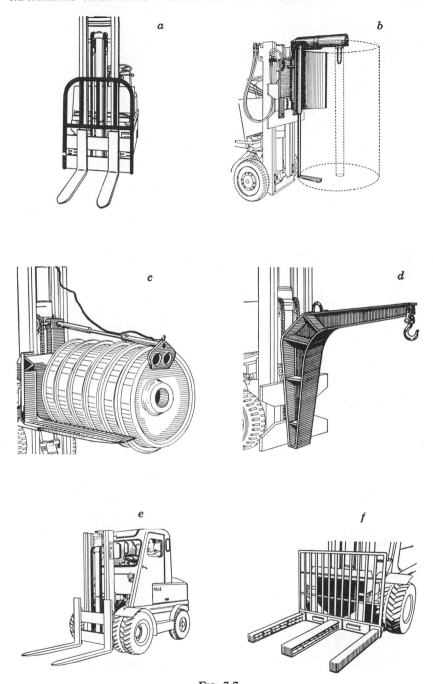

FIG. 7-7.

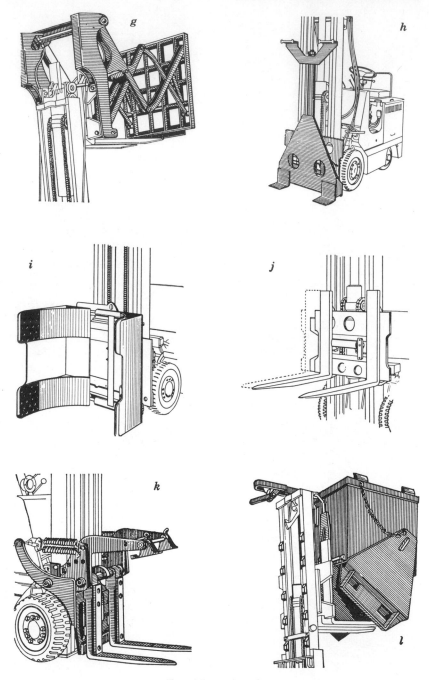

Fig. 7-7 continued.

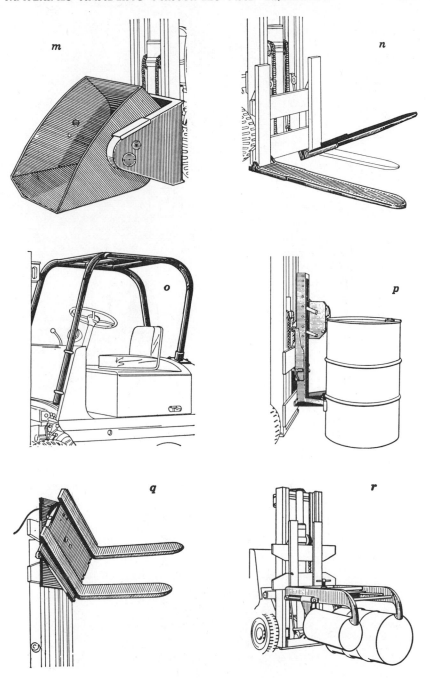

FIG. 7-7 continued.

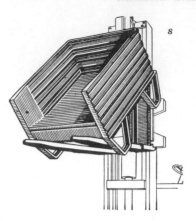

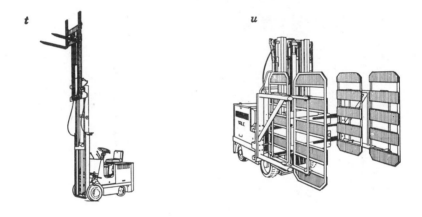

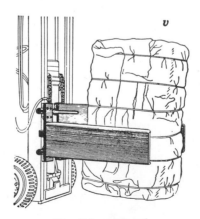

FIG. 7-7 continued.

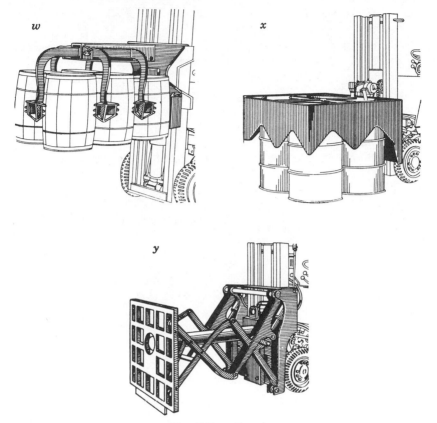

FIG. 7-7 continued.

THE FORK LIFT TRUCK.   The fork lift truck is the most widely used piece of handling equipment.   The load is supported on a pallet that is carried on a pair of parallel bars that protrude in front of the truck body itself.   These bars or forks are thin and slightly beveled and attached to the truck by a sturdy frame.   Almost all of these trucks used on marine terminals are equipped with a hydraulic lifting device that is capable of raising the load for high level tiering.

The fork truck may be driven by electricity, gasoline, gas-electric, diesel, or engines using liquefied petroleum gas as a fuel.   It is extremely flexible.   It handles loads on either the skid or the pallet.   It handles some commodities without the use of a pallet, such as rolls of paper, bales, and lumber.   Some models are able to stack loads with a 48-in. depth as high as 15 ft.   There are many attachments for the fork truck that enable it to handle a number of special commodities without pallets. Figure 7-7 shows some of the many different types of attachments.

The capacity of the fork lift truck. The capacity that a fork lift truck will carry may be stated as a given weight with the center of gravity a given distance from the face of the forks. For example, it may be given as 4000 lb at 15 in. This means that the truck will carry a maximum load of 4000 lb with the center of gravity no more than 15 in. forward from the heel of the forks. If the center of gravity is closer than 15 in. the maximum load is still 4000 lb. If the distance is greater than 15 in., the maximum load is less than 4000 lb. This is explained below.

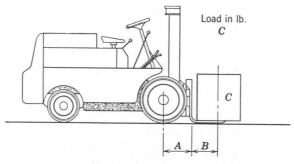

Fig. 7-8.

Inasmuch as the load is always carried ahead of the front driving wheels, the centerline of the driving axle is the pivotal fulcrum point for the load. The truck is usually designed so there is a safety factor of 25% additional weight carried in the back of the fulcrum point when the maximum load is carried with its center of gravity 15 in. forward of the heel of the fork. If the load has a depth that is greater than 30 in., the center of gravity will be farther than 15 in. from the heel of the forks. The maximum load under these conditions will be equal to the quotient when the sum of the distance from the axis of the drive wheels plus the distance from the fork heel to the load's center of gravity is divided into the inch-pound capacity of the truck. The inch-pound capacity of the truck is found by multiplying the maximum load by the sum of the distance from the axis of the drive wheels to the fork heel plus the distance stated in the manufacturers rated capacity for the truck. This can be made clearer by referring to the diagram in Fig. 7-8. Let

A = inches from the center of the drive axle to the heel of the forks.

B = inches from the center of the maximum specified load to heel of forks.

C = maximum specified load in pounds.

D = the inch-pound capacity.

Then $$(A + B)C = D$$

Now, if the depth of the load changes B to a greater value, E, the maximum possible safe load is reduced and may be determined by the following equation:

$$\frac{D}{(A + E)} = X$$

Where X is equal to the new maximum safe load in pounds.

If the depth of the load changes B to a smaller value, the maximum load is still equal to C.

Aisle widths. When space is at a premium, it is desirable to know the minimum aisle width allowable for working the fork truck when handling loaded pallets at right angles to the aisle. If this is known, it may be approached when planning the layout of incoming cargo on the dock for maximum use of the dock area.

The following aisle widths are normally required for the efficient operation of fork trucks of the capacities listed:

Truck Capacity, lb	Aisle Width, ft
2000	10
4000	12
6000	14

These figures are based on a 48-in. load depth. For shorter loads, these requirements are slightly smaller. These are not the minimum possible aisle widths in which the fork truck can turn and place or remove a load, but allow clearance for smooth and rapid operation and for two way traffic.

For the minimum aisle width with a set clearance to be determined by the terminal superintendent or other responsible officer, an equation such as that given in Fig. 7-9 may be used.

Floor loads imposed by fork trucks. The following table gives estimated average loads, in pounds per square foot, exerted on a floor by fully loaded fork trucks of the various capacities indicated:

Truck Capacity, lb	Floor Load Exerted, lb per sq ft
2000	260
3000	280
4000	320
5000	340
6000	380
8000	440

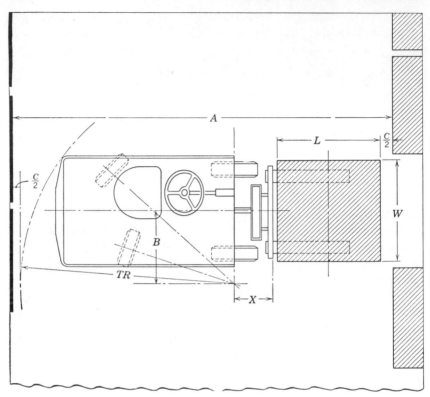

Fig. 7-9. Layout for aisle width equation. A = aisle width. B = distance from centerline of truck to centerline of point about which truck turns when steering wheels are in extreme cramped position. TR = turning radius. L = length of load. W = width of load. C = clearance set at 6 in. X = distance from centerline of drive axle to face of fork.

Aisle widths. The following equation is sufficiently accurate for obtaining required aisle width for finger fork truck operation when stacking loaded pallets of various sizes at right angles.

Examples: For loads having width (W) less than $2B$

$$A = TR + X + L + C$$

Let $B = 25$ in., $X = 14$ in., $L = 48$ in., $C = 6$ in., and $TR = 61$ in. Then

$$A = 61 + 14 + 48 + 6 = 129 \text{ in., aisle width}$$

For loads having width (W) more than $2B$

$$A = TR + \sqrt{(X + L)^2 + [(W/2) - B]^2} + C$$

Let $B = 25$ in., $X = 14$ in., $L = 48$ in., $W = 60$ in., $C = 6$ in., and $TR = 61$ in. Then

$$A = 61 + \sqrt{(14 + 48)^2 + [(60/2) - 25]^2} + 6$$
$$A = 129.3 \text{ in., aisle width}$$

It must be remembered that the weight exerted by a four wheeled vehicle and its load is not subject to exact calculation because, although the weight is exerted only at four small points of contact between the wheels and the floor, the effect on the floor is as if the same weight were spread over a larger area, the size of which can only be assumed.

Furthermore, the percentage of the total weight exerted at the front wheels of a fork truck increases as the weight of the load increases so that, when the truck is loaded to the tipping point, there is no weight on the rear wheels at all. Accuracy of estimate is complicated by the fact that, although two floors have the same rated capacity, they may be affected differently by concentrated moving loads. The above figures, therefore, can be considered only as approximate averages to be used as a guide in determining the required floor capacities for the operation of fork trucks of various capacities.

It may be necessary to calculate the load imposed on a floor by a fork lift truck with a given load less than the maximum limit. In doing so, it may be considered that each of the four wheels is supported by a rectangular area of which the wheel is the center. Each of these four rectangles would have an area equal to the wheel base times the tread. The wheel base is equal to the longitudinal distance from the center of one axle to the center of the other. The tread is the transverse or athwartship distance between the centers of the contacting points of the treads on the tires. From this fact comes the following equation for calculating the floor load imposed in pounds per square foot (X):

$$X = \frac{36 \times (\text{Weight of truck} + \text{Weight of load})}{(\text{Tread} \times \text{Wheel base})}$$

where the weight of truck and load are in pounds and the tread and wheel base are in inches.

LOAD CARRYING POWERED TRUCK. For specialized work a four wheeled nonelevating platform truck may be used. This type truck was one of the first mechanized trucks used on marine terminals. Its great disadvantage for general cargo work on the marine terminal is quite apparent. The operator must rely on a second device for loading and discharging, and it transports only one unit at a time. Exactly the same function can be accomplished by one trailer with a tractor. Adding two additional trailers, you remove the necessity of the tractor being tied up at either end of its run; this is a great increase in efficiency. However, on certain types of jobs use may be found for this type of equipment. The types of jobs would be those that are occasional in nature, require careful control of the load, and include very heavy loads.

Some models are capable of carrying 10 tons. The platform of these trucks may be at variable heights off the deck. Some models have platform heights running between 20 and 24 in. Lower platform models have heights of only 11 in.

The greater the weights that are carried the more concern there should be about the height of the platform. Packages weighing between 150 and 200 lb should not be lifted above the knee and then only when the man is trained to lift properly. Packages of 75 to 100 lb should only be lifted waist high, although they can be transported at shoulder level if loaded onto the man from shoulder height by helpers. Packages of 25 to 35 lb may be lifted shoulder high.

HIGH AND LOW LIFT ELEVATING PLATFORM TRUCKS. These trucks are designed to pick up loads on skids, transport them, and deposit them without the aid of an assisting device. In other words they are self-loading and discharging. The skid is a platform built over side runners or stringers so that there is about 6 to 8 in. clearance under the skid bed. The skid also may be constructed of angle iron with stilts at the four corners.

This type of truck was first introduced in industrial plants about 1915, 4 years before the first fork lift truck was built. The load on this type truck is carried over the wheels and does not extend out in front of the body. This fact makes it possible to construct the trucks to handle very heavy loads without having to put equally heavy counter balancing weights at the rear. Some models are capable of handling loads up to 30 tons, but these are obviously not the type of equipment to be found working on the average marine terminal.

The high and low lift elevating platform truck represents the first improvement beyond the nonelevating platform truck. They are many times more efficient than the simple load carrying truck because they are self-loaders and unloaders when used in conjunction with the skid. The terminal time is reduced to a minimum.

CLAMP TRUCKS. The clamp truck is a type of fork lift truck. The forks are replaced by an attachment capable of gripping a container between two arms and raising it off the deck. The truck then transports the item and sets it down where desired. In other words, this device accomplishes all that the fork lift truck does but without the use of a pallet. Figure 7-10 shows a clamp truck picking up a roll of paper. The load may be a single item or in units. If in units, these should be strapped together or carefully stacked and handled with a broad faced gripping device (see Fig. 7-7u). The containers must be capable of withstanding the pressure of the gripping plates without damage.

A recent development of flexible gripping arms made of spring steel has made it possible to lift palletless loads of such items as compressed gas cylinders nine at a time, a stack of automobile tires, and other units. The gripping arms can be placed on any lift truck clamp. Each pressure plate is loosely mounted on three spring-steel fingers. This allows the pressure plate to tilt in the direction or directions dictated by the load

FIG. 7-10. Clamp truck. Hydraulically operated clamps pick up vertical rolls of newsprint, rotate them 90°, and lay them down horizontally for easy discharge. Note crisscross two layer dunnage floor to provide a firm and level surface for stowage of rolls. Courtesy Clark Equipment Co.

shape and provides for proper load distribution among the fingers. Further accommodation is permitted by the individual flexing of the fingers. The design of the arm structure is such that, from the front view, each pressure plate toes in at the bottom. From the top view the pressure plates toe in at the front. These features make it possible to accommodate variations in the size of objects in the load and also apply pressure tending to hold the load together. Pressure can be set to suit the load by a dial at the operator's position. A high friction plastic coating bonded to the pressure plate reduces necessary grab pressure. Capacities run between 1500 and 2700 lb.

CRANE TRUCKS. The crane truck has found considerable use on narrow apron piers in ports of the Eastern seaboard of the United States.

These trucks are able to pick up net slings or pallet sling loads and transfer them with ease. They are popular where the pier structure makes it impossible or inconvenient to utilize the much faster methods of tractor-trailer combinations and/or fork lift trucks with pallets. Their terminal time is lengthened because they are not self-loaders or unloaders, and for the same reason extra labor is required at the terminal within the pier shed.

Fig. 7-11. The crane truck. Courtesy Port of New York Authority.

When handling certain extremely bulky and awkwardly shaped materials that are best accommodated in a net sling, these trucks find their greatest usefulness. Figure 7-11 shows a typical crane truck handling a load. The boom on the truck shown in this illustration cannot be slewed; however, some models incorporate this feature into their design. Because of the limited drift under the boom head and the length of the sling, the boom is fitted with a wide flanged roller on its tip so that the sling with all its parts can be hove up short for transporting the load.

UNIT CARRIERS. The unit carrier, also referred to as the straddle truck or ross carrier (probably because the Ross Company was the first to make the machine), was developed originally for the rapid handling of lumber. It is now used for lengths of all kinds such as pipe, steel rails, structural steel shapes, and steel plates. With specially constructed pallets and lifting arms it has been used to handle multiple pallet loads. A truck of this type with sufficient vertical clearance and width to pass over the bed of a semitruck trailer is in use in Honolulu to unload or load a full truck load of pineapples in boxes in a single operation (see Fig. 7-12).

Its operation is simple. The load is built up on *bolsters,* as shown in Fig. 5-13, and the truck runs over the load. The operator engages the flanges of the hoisting arms under the bolster and hoists the load off the deck. The truck is then ready to move away. The load is released by reversing this process at the other end of the run. The load can be picked up and released in less than 30 sec. The load can be gripped to

Fɪɢ. 7-12. The unit carrier. It takes only 30 sec to load this truck or discharge it with this piece of materials handling equipment. Courtesy Clark Equipment Co.

the undercarriage to prevent the load from being displaced when traveling over rough surfaces, and the truck can attain speeds up to 35 mph.

The unit carrier can be classed as a piece of hauling equipment as well as handling. The tractor-trailer combination and the unit carrier are the only two efficient hauling devices found on the marine terminal today, although the traveloader, a new piece of equipment, may develop some similar uses.

THE TRAVELOADER. The traveloader is a combination fork lift truck and unit carrier. It is a self-loading device like the fork lift truck and unit carrier. It is able to carry long lengths and very large loads like the unit carrier but has the advantage of being able to work with its own forks to make up a complete load. At either terminal it can select any part of a master load to discharge. It is able to stack its loads and work into or from railroad cars and trucks with platforms. Furthermore, because of the size of the loads it can handle, it becomes feasible to use it for hauling. A fork lift truck or the traveloader itself can assemble

FIG. 7-13.   The traveloader.   Courtesy Baker-Raulang Co.

FIG. 7-14.   The traveloader handling length of pipe.   Courtesy Baker-Raulang Co.

master loads consisting of five pallets that can be picked up by the traveloader in one operation (see Figs. 7-13 and 7-14).

OVERHEAD MONORAILS.   This is a system of moving materials about a dock shed of a marine terminal that keeps the deck clear of moving vehicles and utilizes the overhead for roadways.   Overhead monorail

FIG. 7-15. This is a view of the pier apron at the American Sugar Refinery dock in New Orleans where the overhead monorail system is used to transport the sling loads of sugar into the refinery. The man to the extreme left has his hands on the controls. One load can be seen just disappearing into the pier shed through the doorway. Note that the *split fall* system is being used here with a house fall arrangement replacing the dock boom. These house falls can be moved up and down the pier apron to spot a point directly abreast of the ship's hatch boom, and they carry their own power unit with them. Courtesy Port of New Orleans.

systems have been used successfully at several piers for over 20 years. On all of these installations, one commodity was continually handled over a fixed route, usually relatively short.

Probably one of the best examples of the overhead monorail type installation is at the American Sugar Refinery dock at New Orleans (see Fig. 7-15). At this terminal, the overhead monorail passes outside of the dock shed and over the pier apron. The sling loads are landed on the pier and the hook of a house fall is disengaged. Next, the hook of the trolley is engaged and a button on the control is pressed in by an operator on the dock. The trolley begins to lift up the load of seven bags of sugar and after hoisting it about 4 ft off the deck, it begins to move along the monorail. Eventually the load reaches a height of about 8 ft. It continues to travel by electrical power until it passes over a platform where another operator reaches up and presses a stop button. The controls travel with the trolley; instead of push button control there may be switches operated by pull cords. At this particular terminal the load of bags is landed on a platform where workers rip open the bags and the sugar falls out on a conveyor belt that takes it into the refinery.

The lack of flexibility of this system is evident. It may be, however, that with additional trackage and with suitable methods for switching the trolleys from one track to another from a single control point, as well as locally, that sufficient flexibility will be incorporated into the overhead monorail system to make its operation not only feasible but highly economical.

AUTOMATIC MATERIALS HANDLING SYSTEM RADIO CONTROLLED. A system based on the use of electrically operated traveling carriers on monorails with all movements of the carriers to be controlled by radio impulses has actually been designed, but it has not yet been installed on any terminal.

The designers of this system have provided means of controlling the carriers or trolleys by a local loading or unloading crew as well as by a central control dispatcher. A loading crew at any position on the dock would have temporary local control of an empty carrier. After loading the carrier, the central dispatcher is signaled by mechanical means and he takes control.

The major problem in adapting this idea to a marine terminal already built is the low dock shed doors. Other problems would be the fluctuation of the level of the ship's deck at various stages of loading and of the tides. These problems, however, relate only to running the monorail out over the ship so that the trolley could pick up its load directly from or discharge it into the ship's hold. Once the ship's gear has placed the load on the apron, the system could be used to transport materials about the dock shed. With sufficient clearance over the ship's deck a rig such as that shown in Fig. 7-16 would connect the hold directly with the dock shed. Figure 7-17 shows a factory installation of this same type system, and one can easily see its possibilities for use on the marine terminal.

Such a system would certainly provide continuous flow of cargo with an elimination of delay time on the pier apron. A more efficient distribution of the standard longshore gang could be effected with the probable result of greater tonnage being handled without an increase in personnel.

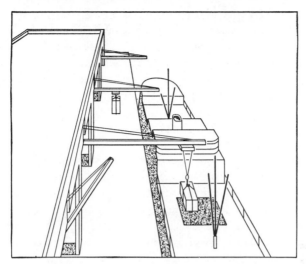

FIG. 7-16. Radio controlled monorail system. Arrangement that would provide connection between the ship's hold and the dock shed direct without having to use the ship's gear. Courtesy Trenton Marine Service Corp.

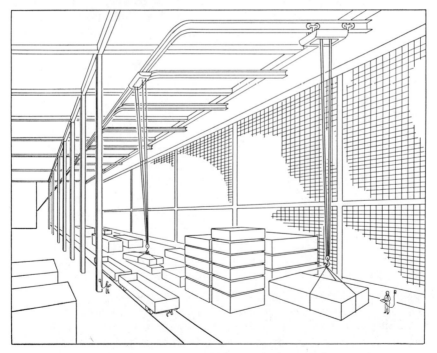

FIG. 7-17. Typical factory installation of a radio controlled monorail system.

Conveyors. On the marine terminal, conveyors are used for loading and unloading trucks, railroad cars, and lighters; for loading and discharging the ship through sideports and through the hatches; and finally for moving cargo to and from the wings in the holds of the ship.

GRAVITY CONVEYORS. These are either simple wooden chutes or made of metal and fitted with steel rollers or wheels. The roller or wheel type conveyor comes in sections usually about 5 or 10 ft long and in widths of 18 to 24 in. They may be either steel or aluminum and are built to withstand rugged usage. The roller rotates on free rolling steel ball bearings. The sections are fitted with bars at one end and hook connectors at the other, which enables quick setting up and taking down as needed. They are not made for really heavy loads, the weights transported over them should be limited to about $\frac{1}{2}$ ton.

Wooden conveyors, or chutes, as they are called, are somewhat lighter than the steel roller or wheel conveyors. They must be used on some cargoes in place of the steel type, such as explosives of the class *A* or *B* type. They are built of surfaced hardwood and sometimes provided with guard rails. In fact, chutes used to handle explosives must have a 4-in. guard rail by law.

Metal chutes built in a spiral have been used successfully to lower case oil and bagged sugar and coffee into a ship's hold taking advantage of gravity. See p. 359 wherein the principle of gravity is discussed.

POWER CONVEYORS. Powered conveyors of many types have been used with great success on marine terminals. These may be classified under four broad headings: (1) Endless belt. (2) Endless pocket or bucket. (3) Screw. (4) Pneumatic elevators or air conveyors. No attempt will be made here to lay down rules or guiding principles to point out where conveyors should be or should not be used. It is believed that it is evident that every operation should be analyzed with conveyors being used as a possibility. The advisability of using them must be determined upon the facts obtained and considered within the framework of the principles of materials handling already discussed. This is, of course, a logical method of approach when considering all available equipment.

Endless belt conveyors. The endless belt conveyor consists of a canvas, leather, or rubber belt that runs over a drive pulley from which it derives its power. The belt is mounted on a bed in such a manner that a series of wheels take the burden of the load as the load is placed on top of the bed. The underneath side of the bed is fitted with one or two idler rollers over which the belt passes as it cycles around the bed. Most goods can be sent up inclines as much as 32° if the belting is made of some good nonslip material. The use of cleats on the belt enables lifting goods up a greater incline. These conveyors may be obtained in portable models as well as permanently installed in a fixed position. Figure 7-18 is an illustration of a portable type endless belt conveyor showing some of the names of the parts and the mechanism that allows it to be adjusted for working at various elevations down to horizontal movement. These portable models are extremely versatile materials handling tools. They can be used to mechanize the loading of trucks, loading ships through sideports, raising cargo from one deck to another

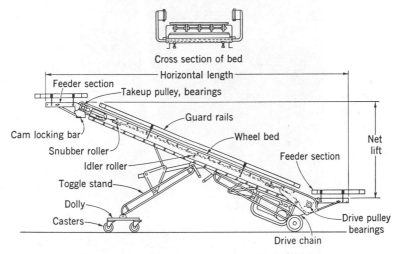

FIG. 7-18. Endless belt conveyor. Courtesy The Rapids-Standard Co.

where it might be discharged through a sideport, and for many similar tasks (Fig. 7-19). When loading ships through the hatches or discharging from sideports where conveyors might be used, gravity types would be most desirable. Gravity should always be used, if possible. Figure 7-20 is another portable model for heavier work.

Endless pocket conveyors. Probably the most intensive users of the endless pocket type conveyor in the marine field are the banana carrying ships. They load and discharge entire loads using conveyors of this type. They are large, heavy, specially built, and very costly pieces of equipment. But, the speed and economy obtained in the handling of this very special type of cargo, where speed is important, more than warrants the financial outlay. These ships utilize conveyors that bring the cargo from the lower 'tweendeck levels to upper 'tweendeck levels where sideport connections with the pier are available. The conveyors used for this work are the endless belt type, described above. The endless pocket type of conveyor is used to take the stems from or to the lower holds to or from the pier apron. They consist of heavy canvas pockets that rotate around a bed that is constructed with a joint in the

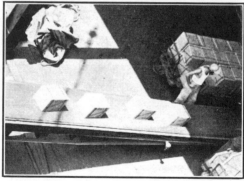

FIG. 7-19. The endless belt conveyor. View of the ship end (upper) and dock end (lower) of an endless belt conveyor being used to load cartons through the ship's sideport. The ship's gear, of course, can continue to work in the lower holds of the same hatch. Courtesy Cadet-Midshipmen U.S. Merchant Marine Academy.

middle of its length so that the conveyor consists of two legs. Making a huge A, the conveyor is set in place after the ship docks with one leg of the A resting in the ship's hold and the other out on the dock. The

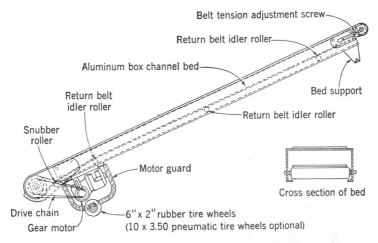

FIG. 7-20. Endless belt conveyor. Courtesy The Rapids-Standard Co.

FIG. 7-21. The endless pocket conveyor. This is the type used to load and discharge banana stems. The dock end is supported on a gantry capable of moving up and down the pier. Courtesy Port of New York Authority.

banana stems are placed in these pockets by longshoremen and taken from the ship to the pier or vice versa, depending upon whether the ship is discharging or loading (see Fig. 7-21).

A special type of pocket conveyor made of steel has been permanently installed on board the S.S. Independence and Constitution. The cargo is brought to the ship through a sideport at a level above the cargo hold but where sufficient space has been allotted to form a small working area. The cargo comes to this working platform by portable belt conveyors, fork lift trucks, or cargo fall. From here the cargo is sent to the hold on the conveyor in packaged units. The units are placed in a receiving space made of metal bars spaced a few inches apart. The conveyor pocket consists of a row of similar metal arms and these slide by the spaces between the fixed bars of the receiving space. As the pocket comes upward in its rotating movement, its arms engage the unit. The pocket, which resembles a metal cage, remains in a horizontal position as it rotates around the bed of the conveyor. The pocket eventually passes through a similar grating at the lower end and deposits the container in another space where it must be picked up and stowed before the next unit arrives. The cagelike pocket travels around the bed or framework of the conveyor in a manner somewhat similar to a carriage on a ferris wheel. The conveyor can be stopped by an operator at either end in case of an emergency. The size of the unit that can be handled is controlled by the size of the pocket on the conveyor, in the above case the unit is about 4 by 4 ft on each side.

Air conveyors. Machines utilizing air suction methods of picking up and carrying materials through a flexible noncollapsible tube of large diameter are called *air conveyors* for the purpose of conveniently classifying them in this section. They are used to discharge a number of commodities and there may be wider use of them in the future. Pneumatic elevators for discharging grain fall into this category. They are a conveyor type in the sense that they utilize an air stream as the conveyor belt. Among the commodities that are discharged by air conveyors are bulk copra, grain, and bulk cement. They may be large permanently installed units or portable units capable of being moved from pier to pier. Floating grain air conveyors (pneumatic elevators) brought alongside of the offshore side of the ship are used to discharge full cargoes of grain into waiting barges or coastal steamers at the rate of 250 tons per hr.

Pallets. The pallet as used in conjunction with fork lift trucks and in some operations with straddle trucks has become a very important piece of materials handling equipment. The pallet was developed after the platform skid for use with the fork lift truck especially. It is far superior to the skid for marine terminal work for a number of reasons.

It is lighter, has less vertical height, and is capable of being quickly and easily tiered without the use of dunnage between each load.

PALLET DEFINITIONS.   Before discussing pallets in general it will be best to define some of the terms that will be used later.

SINGLE FACED: A pallet that has only one deck.

DOUBLE FACED: A pallet that has a top and bottom deck.

REVERSIBLE: A double faced pallet with both decks being capable of supporting a load.

TWO WAY: The fork truck may enter from two directions.

SINGLE WING: A pallet on which the outside stringers are set inboard 4 to 6 in. from the ends of the deck boards of the upper deck but flush with the lower deck boards. This gives a nonreversible double deck pallet adaptable for use with straddle trucks.

DOUBLE WING: A pallet on which the outside stringers are set inboard an equal distance, about 4 to 6 in., from the ends of the deck boards of both decks. This is the construction of most stevedoring pallets and allows for the accommodation of the bar of the bar and spreader type sling.

FLUSH: A pallet on which the outside stringers are flush with the ends of the boards of both decks.

DECK: The top and bottom surfaces of the pallet.

STRINGER: The separations and supports for the decks, sometimes called "runners."

CHAMFERS: Beveled edges to permit easy entrance of forks without catching or chipping the end boards.

END BOARDS: Deck boards on the extreme outside edges of the pallet. These are the most vulnerable parts of the pallet. They should be of the best wood, at least 6 in. in width, and renewed as soon as split.

DRIVE SCREWS: Fastening device for assembling top and bottom deck boards to the stringers. They are either spirally twisted or have annular rings.

SOME PALLET TYPES.   There are four basic types of pallets with reference to the type of work for which they are intended. They are: (1) The stevedoring. (2) Shipping. (3) Warehouse. (4) Factory or manufacturing plant pallet. Although this book is mostly concerned with the stevedoring pallet, some comments will be made regarding all four types.

The stevedoring pallet. The stevedoring pallet is used to handle cargo on marine terminals and as such it receives a good deal of rough treatment. Because of their heavy duty, the stevedoring pallets are made of heavier materials than any of the other types. The stringers are made of 3 by 4 in. or 4 by 4 in. lumber and the deck boards are made of 2 in. thick deals nominal size. The end boards should be not less than 6 in. in width and made of No. 1 or 2 stock board grade. The other deck boards may be of random widths but should not be less than 4 in. The stringers should be 4 by 4 in. material if the length of the pallet is over

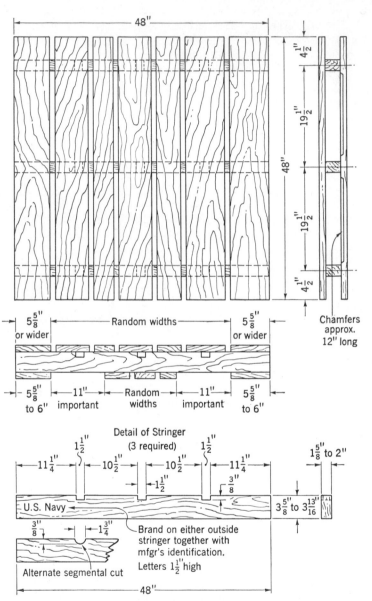

FIG. 7-22.   Courtesy U.S. Naval Supply Research and Development Facility, N.S.D., Bayonne, N. J.

48″ × 48″ NAVY STANDARD
HARDWOOD PALLET

●

NAILING

a.   Use #6 screw gauge x 2½″ cement coated or chemically etched drive screw nails or #10 wire gauge x 2½″ cement coated or chemically etched annular ring (fetter ring) nails.

b.   Boards 3⅝″   to 4½″ require 2 nails at each bearing point.

4¾″	to 6¾″	"	3	"	"	"	"	" .
7″	to 9″	"	4	"	"	"	"	" .
9⅛″	to 11″	"	5	"	"	"	"	" .
11⅛″	to 12″	"	6	"	"	"	"	" .

c.   Drill deck boards if necessary to prevent splitting.

d.   Stagger nails to prevent splitting.

e.   Nailing thru notches not acceptable.

f.   When a board exceeding 5″ nominal width covers a notch, one less nail can be used.

LUMBER

a.   Use sound square edge lumber free of decay and free of knots with an average diameter greater than ⅓ of the width of the board.   No piece shall contain any defect which would materially weaken the strength of the piece.

b.   Use the following woods: white ash, beech, birch, rock elm, hackberry, hickory, hard maple, oak, pecan.

c.   Use random width boards 3⅝″ or wider, surfaced one side ⅞″, hit or miss.   Surfaced faces to be exposed faces.   All boards on any one face to be of uniform thickness.

d.   Space between top deck boards to be 1″ min. and 1½″ max.   Space between bottom deck boards not to exceed 1½″ except 11″ spaces as noted.

e.   Boards must be placed so that each notch is completely covered by a single board of not less than 4″ nominal width.

f.   Length tolerance plus or minus ¼″.

g.   Minimum moisture content shall be not less than 12% and the maximum moisture content not to exceed 25% at time of shipment.

●

DEPARTMENT OF THE NAVY
Bureau of Supplies and Accounts

SW RELEASE NO. 52C (Superseding RSX Release No. 52B)
31 October 1948

6 ft. The fastenings used on stevedoring pallets may be either stove bolts or drive screws 4 in. long with large heads.

The stevedoring pallet must be capable of accommodating a large number of commodity types and sizes and as a result a number of sizes have been used. For large, bulky packages such as furniture and general household goods, the 4 by 7 ft size has proven convenient. For smaller packages, the 4 by 5 ft size is commonly used. The Navy standard 48 by 48 in. hardwood pallet shown in Fig. 7-22 is designed with a view for sending pallet loads from the shipper to the consignee. It is not generally used on marine terminals as a stevedoring pallet.

The shipping pallet. The shipping pallet must conserve space and weight as much as possible. It is not loaded, unloaded, and handled as much as the stevedoring pallet and can be made with smaller scantlings throughout. Consideration of the accommodation of the shipping pallet in connecting carriers and stowage in the ship has led to the use of a few standard sizes that are smaller than the stevedoring pallet. The Navy has indicated that either the 48 by 48 in. or 40 by 48 in. size is the most economical size for palletized loads. The latter are the best if the closed truck body is utilized, because the truck requires a 40-in. dimension for greatest use of available cubic. If rail transport or truck transport with open platform bed is used, the 48 by 48 in. pallet is suitable. The average box car width is 110 in. whereasa the average truck closed body type has a width of 88½ in. If the shipping pallet's smallest dimension is 48 in., the two pallet loads cannot be stowed side by side in the closed body truck and this means a great deal of lost cubic during transport. These figures apply to closed body trucks and box cars of the United States. When considering transport in other countries, the dimensions of the connecting carriers at the foreign port must be determined for full coordination of the cargo movement. If open flat bed trucks are used, the 48 by 48 in. pallet can be accommodated. The stringers on the shipping pallet should be of 2 by 4 in. material whereas the decking should be of only 1 in. boards (see Fig. 7-23).

The warehouse pallet. The warehouse pallet is used to receive commodities in a warehouse for storage purposes for periods that may extend to many months or even years. The materials are palletized as economically as possible, and the pallets are tiered and left in storage. Careful planning of aisle widths and pallet sizes is necessary to obtain efficient use of available area.

The factory pallet. The factory pallet is used to handle special materials in large volume as the material is worked during the manufacturing process of some product. Factory pallets must be specially designed in size and strength. It is obvious that in every case a study must be made of the entire procedure and the best pallet determined in the light of the data obtained.

Pallet patterns. Operations on the commercial marine terminal utilizing the stevedoring pallet do not permit extreme care in building pallet loads. It is sufficient to make certain that the tiers are built up in such

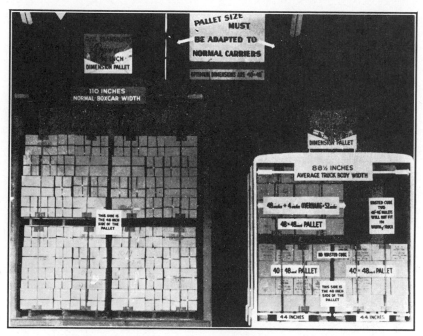

Fig. 7-23. Land carrier dimensions affect shipping pallet sizes. Courtesy U.S. Navy.

a way that one tier ties together with another so that sufficient stability for the load is obtained to keep it together while being transported on the pier.

In the building of loads on pallets for shipment on the pallet, or when the operation makes it possible to exercise care in this matter, greater utilization of the pallet area available can be obtained by building the load in accordance with some definite pattern. When building the pallet load, some items may be allowed to extend beyond the deck of the pallet an inch or so. This may be done with steel drums and cases made of wood. It should be avoided with bagged commodities or cargo in cardboard cartons. Figure 7-24 shows some standard Navy pallet patterns. All possible arrangements on the 48 by 48 in. pallet can be reduced to four basic patterns, which, for the sake of common nomenclature, may be identified as *block, row, pinwheel,* and *brick.*

BLOCK: A square or round container will always utilize this pattern on a 48 by 48 in. pallet. This is the least desirable of all the patterns in that there can be no cross tiering to tie the load together for stability.

Block   Row

Pinwheel   Brick

FIG. 7-24. Basic pallet patterns.

ROW: The row pattern is one of the most common and is used with oblong materials where a multiple of the widths and a multiple of the lengths approximate 48 in. An excellent cross tie is provided by placing alternate layers at 90° angles.

PINWHEEL: The pinwheel pattern is another widely used pattern for material of an oblong nature which does not readily conform to the row pattern. Cross stacking is easily accomplished by reversing alternate layers. The major objection to this pattern is the fact that there is usually a chimney in the center of the load. This pattern is extremely flexible and can be varied.

BRICK: The brick pattern can only be used in a few well defined instances: namely, with a box whose width is one-half or one-quarter of its length, and whose length is one-half, one-quarter, or one-third of 48 in. Frequently a box will fit both the pinwheel and the brick patterns. However, when the pinwheel pattern is used, four or eight columns are formed and this gives less stability to the load:

It must be remembered that these patterns cannot be followed under practical operating conditions on most marine terminals. In the first place, the containers are placed on the pallet at the pier in most cases for transport to the pier apron only. In the second place, union labor agreements prevent the full utilization of a pallet by limiting the load to a set number of containers or a set height with the last tier used frequently to tie the load together. These pallet patterns are for use on shipping pallets where space utilization is of importance.

PALLETIZED LOADS VERSUS LOOSE CARGO. Although there is probably no doubt in the reader's mind about the fact that palletizing loads reduces the labor involved in transporting cargo, it will help to emphasize the fact if we present a quantitative comparison of palletization and single unit operations. Figure 7-25 is a chart showing the net savings in man-hours in shipping 100 tons of general cargo on pallets as compared to shipping the same cargo as loose packages.

All of the operations indicated in this chart would not be performed in a commercial venture; however, we can use the applicable data and obtain an approximation of the differences in man-hours between the two systems in question. Using the complete chart let us use appropriate information and prepare Table 7-1.

TABLE 7-1

| | Man-Hours Required | |
Operation	Palletized	Loose Cargo
Load and strapping pallets at contractor's (shipper's) warehouse	50	0
Loading car at contractor's (shipper's) warehouse	8	50
Unloading car at pier	9	24
Loading and stowing on ship	37	47
Unloading ship at discharge port	24	164
Loading truck at dock	8	54
Unloading truck at consignee's	9	57
Total man-hours	145	396

From Table 7-1 we see that loose cargo, in this case, took about $2\frac{3}{4}$ times more man-hours than the palletized cargo. If we knew the hourly

Operation	Palletized	Loose cargo
Loading pallet at contractor's	15 man-hours	No man-hours
Strapping pallet at contractor's	35 man-hours	No man-hours
Loading car at contractor's	8 man-hours	50 man-hours
Unloading car at supply depot	9 man-hours	24 man-hours
Stowing at supply depot	9 man-hours	30 man-hours
Issuing at supply depot	6 man-hours	30 man-hours
Loading car at supply depot	8 man-hours	50 man-hours

FIG. 7-25. Palletized unit loads vs. loose cargo. This chart compares two cargo handling methods at each operation in a typical shipment of supplies from Navy contractor to point of use. The number of man-hours required to handle 100 tons of palletized cargo (77 pallet loads) is compared with the number of hours required to handle the same amount of loose cargo (4080 separate packages). The figures used are based on the studies conducted by materials handling officers in the United States, Guam, Pearl Harbor, and Trinidad. Ideal working conditions are assumed.

Operation	Palletized	Loose cargo
Unloading car at shipside	9 man-hours	24 man-hours
Loading and stowing on ship	37 man-hours	47 man-hours
Unloading ship to dock	24 man-hours	164 man-hours
Loading truck at dock	8 man-hours	54 man-hours
Unloading truck at supply dump	9 man-hours	57 man-hours
Stowing at supply dump	9 man-hours	39 man-hours
Unloading at supply dump	8 man-hours	55 man-hours
Unloading at point of use	9 man-hours	58 man-hours

Total number of man-hours required for materials handling at all operations:

Palletized cargo....203 man-hours

Loose cargo...... 682 man-hours

Net saving effected by palletized unit loads..................682 – 203 = 479 man-hours

A plus value .... palletization greatly reduces pilferage potential and damage to individual packages wages paid the longshoremen and other labor in a given case, we could easily arrive at an estimate of the cost difference. Commercial utilization of the palletized load offers some problems that reduce the gross savings indicated by the above figures.

SOME OF THE PROBLEMS OF PALLETIZATION COMMERCIALLY. In the above movement of 100 tons, 77 pallets were used. These 77 pallets represent about 3 tons of weight and 554 cu ft of space. They must be shipped back to the shipper empty unless some form of pallet exchange or pooling is devised. All of the savings in man-hours are not to the credit of any one of the three parties directly affected by palletizing the cargo. In fact, according to the above figures, the shipper used 8 man-hours more than he would if the cargo had been left loose. Therefore, out of a total saving of 251 man-hours, 8 hr is actually lost at the shipper's warehouse, 211 man-hours are saved at the loading and discharging marine terminals, and finally 48 man-hours are saved at the consignee's warehouse. Thus, in practice it becomes a problem of coordinating the entire operation and arriving at an equitable distribution of the costs involved in initiating the program. Although problems exist, there is evidence that they are capable of solution and as time goes on more and more palletized loads will be shipped.

There are others in the field besides the shipper, shipowner, and consignee who benefit by palletization of cargo and who should be expected to share some of the costs, namely, the underwriter and the contracting stevedore. They might share the cost by reducing their charges to the shipowner and shipper. The underwriter would certainly be a beneficiary of the reduced pilferage and individual container damage that accompany palletization.

PALLETIZED OPERATIONS TODAY. It should be obvious from the above data, that palletization is more economical on short runs where labor costs are high on both ends of the run. This is, in fact, the type of operation where it is proving itself highly satisfactory today.

As an example, the Canada Steamship Lines Ltd., running between Great Lakes ports, palletizes all types of commodities except pipe, reels of cable, and other bulky or odd shaped items. These latter types are made up into some type of unit load capable of being handled by mechanical materials handling equipment.

All of the cargo arrives at their docks either by rail or truck. Some shippers ship on their own pallets and the operation has been coordinated to the extent that the steamship company does not charge for the weight or cubic consumed by the pallet in return for the use of the shipper's pallets on the return voyage. A second arrangement is the establishment of a pallet pool with a group of shippers. This requires an accounting

FIG. 7-26. Eight palletized loads of cartons of ketchup arrive on the pier on an open platform bed truck. The two fork lift trucks can unload the truck in less than 10 min. Courtesy Canada Steamship Co.

FIG. 7-27. This is an excellent view of the tractor-trailer combination being used to unload railroad box cars. Five trailers are being pulled by a three wheeled tractor. Note the smooth roadway surface. Courtesy Canada Steamship Co.

system for the pallets exchanging hands between the shippers and the steamship company. A third arrangement, designed to encourage the use of palletization, is for the steamship company to rent pallets to a shipper but not charge for shipments made on the company's ships.

The Canada Steamship Company utilizes ships with sideports, elevators on the ship, and 'tweendecks with limited clearances. As can be seen from Figs. 7-26 to 7-31 the operation utilizes the fork lift truck and

FIG. 7-28. The palletized cargo is stacked on the pier to await the loading operation. When the ship is ready to receive, a fork lift truck loads the trailers of a tractor-trailer combination as seen here. The train proceeds to the ship entering over a brow and through a sideport. Courtesy Canada Steamship Co.

tractor-trailer combination to its fullest degree. They handle 1 million tons of palletized cargo a year and have attained the productivity rate of 7 tons per man-hour. In this operation about 60,000 pallets are used. The sizes used in this operation are 46 by 66 in. mainly with some use of 48 by 48 in. and also some use of 38 by 66 in.

Alaska Steamship Company operations. The greatest utilization of the unit container and palletized load on oceangoing ships is found on the ships of the Alaska Steamship Company. The company has developed an operation in which practically all cargo is carried in one of three systems all of which use the unit load idea. The cargo crib consists of a pallet 6 by 4 ft upon which the cargo is placed and then secured by the use of removable sides and top which are in turn secured with metal banding. Figure 7-32 shows this popular and efficient shipping device being stowed in a hold fitted to receive such cargo without wasting time with dunnage.

In addition to handling cargo on these pallets, the cargo is also transported in the cargo gard which is a unit container and also in larger

FIG. 7-29. Here a fork lift truck is taking a load on board over a brow and through a sideport. Using fork lift trucks instead of the tractor-trailer combination for hauling may be more economical if the distance that the loads are moved is under 300 ft. A study of costs involved should be made to be certain which is the cheapest method in any given operation. Note that a rope yarn has been used to tie the top tier and offer some added security to the load. Oceanborne palletized loads require strapping for greater security and stability of the loads.
Courtesy Canada Steamship Co.

units consisting of truck trailer units. The operations of this company point in the direction that all cargo operations are going to move in the future.

EXPENDABLE PALLETS. Obviously, some of the problems of palletization would be solved if a pallet could be devised that was strong enough to withstand the rigors of ocean shipping and yet was cheap enough to discard at the consignee's terminal and not returned. In other words, if the pallet could be made economically expendable.

Actually, there are pallets on the market now that have been used as expendable. One type consists of double face or double wall corrugated decks securely glued to convolutely wound, single face corrugated posts. The posts range from 4 to 16 in number and from 5 to 7 in. in diameter. The pallet produced is seen being used in Fig. 7-33 where the weight on the individual unit is 2100 lb whereas the weight on the bottom pallet is, of course, 6300 lb.

FIG. 7-30. Tractor and trailers proceed to the correct deck level on an elevator on the ship. Obviously, small three wheel tractors with a high maneuvering ability are required. Courtesy Canada Steamship Co.

BINDING THE PALLET AND LOAD TOGETHER. The pallet load may be made into a single unit by either strapping the containers to the pallet or using a palletizing adhesive.

1. In the palletizing adhesive system, cartons are stripped on the bottom with two strips of adhesive and laid up brick layer fashion if possible so that the cartons are interleaved together. This results in a unit load that is all glued together and in turn glued to the pallet. The ultimate consumer merely has to give the boxes a sharp upward push to break the adhesive bond in order to remove any boxes from the load.

2. In the metal strapping system, thin metal straps tie the material to the pallet. The usual method is to put at least two metal straps all the way around the pallet and load in both directions.

For ocean shipping the metal strapping system would be preferable.

AN EXPERIMENTAL EXPENDABLE PALLETIZED SHIPMENT. The practicality of using expendable pallets was demonstrated in 1948 when Bristol-Meyers Company in cooperation with the Isthmian Steamship Company shipped 110 cartons of Trushay Lotion made up into 24 pallet loads. The shipment was on expendable pallets and went from the Hill-

FIG. 7-31. When the trailer loads arrive at the proper deck level, a fork lift truck stows the palletized cargo. As can be seen here, the deck clearances are sufficient to allow for the convenient stowage of two average pallet loads. Courtesy Canada Steamship Co.

side, N. J., plant of Bristol-Meyers to their warehouse in San Francisco, California. Each pallet load weighed slightly less than 2000 lb.

The shipment was closely observed, and from data taken it was estimated that one-fifth of the time was required for handling the palletized goods at the plant as compared to the unpalletized cartons. One man with one fork truck did the job with 80% savings in man-hours of handling. This does not correlate with the data given by the palletized study made by the Navy and given above. From this it is obvious that each operation must be judged upon data obtained from an individual study in each case.

Fig. 7-32. The stowage of cargo cribs in a ship's hold. The turn of the bilge has been boxed in to provide for rapid and easy stowage of the cribs without the use of additional dunnage. Courtesy Alaska S.S. Co.

Fig. 7-33. Expendable pallets. Courtesy Addison-Semmes Corp.

410

About 20% was saved in direct charges for the transportation of the palletized merchandise by truck, since the trucking company had speedier release of its equipment.

Bristol-Meyers also reported savings in the maximum utilization of their warehouse space through palletized storage. Worker safety was increased and fatigue was reduced. The important advantages of less damage to individual cartons and less pilferage was noted.

The steamship company reported a saving of 80% in the number of man-hours needed for truck unloading, storage, and transfer of merchandise to shipside for loading. There was also a saving of 50% in man-hours required for ship loading operations. Unloading, storing, and transfer of the shipment on the west coast paralleled the savings made in New York.

The pallet used was a patented model registered under the name of "The Chuckaway." It was 40 by 48 in. and weighed only 6 lb. Its price at the time of the experimental shipment was less than $1. It was treated to make it moisture proof.

SUMMARY OF ADVANTAGES OF PALLETIZED LOADS

1. Less labor required in handling the materials at all terminals.

2. Less possibility of pilferage and damage to individual containers.

3. Packaging may be eliminated on some products that are palletized properly, resulting in a saving.

4. On some palletized loads, only one or two labels or stencils are required for identification. Without pallets, labeling costs are considerably higher. This is sometimes overlooked as a shipping cost, because labels are applied by a shipping clerk but the costs of preparation of the labels by office help may not be counted into the cost of shipping of which it is really a part.

5. Less personnel problems are experienced because fewer men are necessary when working with pallet loads. The operation is safer. Fewer men have fewer accidents and thus insurance premiums should be reduced.

Unit containers. The principle of unitization tells us that economy is realized in materials handling when the unit is increased in size. Thus, the palletized load proves itself economical when the operation is coordinated through the various handlers and handling equipment. In the same way and for the same reason, the *unit container* has proved itself economical in certain trades with certain types of commodities. There are hundreds of these metal containers being used on shipping routes today. One company that sells these containers reports over 2000 units in use. One of the largest users of unit containers is A. H. Bull and

Company running between United States east coast ports and the West Indies. They have between 500 and 600 units in use. The unit container aids in safe and economical transportation of cargo in three ways: (1) Pilferage is cut to a minimum. (2) Damage is greatly reduced. (3) Cost of handling is reduced in the same way as for palletized cargoes.

The unit container is especially good for commodities that are considered highly pilferable, such as shoes, watches, drugs, cigarettes, cloth-

Fig. 7-34. The dimensions of a unit container. Courtesy Dravo Corp.

ing, and jewelry. Figure 7-34 shows the Dravo Transportainer's dimensions, which can be taken as typical. The inside cubic capacity of this unit is 275 cu ft. The weight capacity is about 6 tons.

These containers are of welded steel construction and afford considerable protection for the cargo carried in them. They can be dragged by tractors, lifted by fork lift trucks, or hoisted by ship's gear (see Figs. 7-35 and 7-36). The life expectancy of these containers is at least 10 years.

One of the first problems that confronted the users of these unit containers was a customs charge when entering the foreign country of delivery as if it were merchandise. These problems have since been worked out and today there is one shipper sending merchandise from London to a southern European port overland, passing several national borders with a minimum of paper work but with a maximum of protection for his products.

One of the hidden advantages of these containers is customer good will. The purchaser of merchandise is not interested in a monetary

FIG. 7-35. The unit container being handled with a fork lift truck. From the dimensions of the container given in Fig. 7-34, it is evident that the capacity of the fork truck would have to be calculated on the basis of the load's center of gravity being a distance of 46½ in. from the face of the forks (see p. 378). Courtesy Dravo Corp.

settlement for items ordered several weeks in advance in anticipation of today's market. Such short and damaged goods must be reordered and an additional waiting period is enforced. These unit containers have a good record of affording maximum protection for cargo shipped in them so that all of the merchandise arrives in good condition and at the time of expected arrival.

There must be a two way flow of cargo to make these unit containers economical. The shippers and carriers must cooperate in coordinating the movement to achieve this. One company ships cigarettes, beer, candy, clothing, film, firearms, hosiery, and similar products to the West Indies and brings the containers back filled with rum, mail, notions, tobacco, and similar items.

Sling types. An important part of the materials handling equipment on the marine terminal is the *sling*. As used in this section, a sling is any device attached to the cargo or its container for the purpose of hoisting it on board the ship. There are many sling types, some might be classified as general slings because they can be used on a large number of container types, and others might be classified as special slings because

Fig. 7-36. A unit container being landed in its stowage position in the hold of a ship. Courtesy Dravo Corp.

they are used on only a particular type of container or type of cargo. The choice of sling for any given operation should be made with the objective of getting the maximum safety, minimum delay on the ship and on the dock, and minimum damage to the cargo. Safety is obtained by using slings that give small angles between the parts at the hook and afford an easy and effortless method of attaching and releasing.

ENDLESS FIBER ROPE. (See Fig. 7-37.) This is one of the most common slings used. Many ships carry their own supply of these slings when operating in trades where bagged goods such as coffee or raw sugar are carried in large amounts. For a full loading operation, about 25 slings for every set of gear on the ship should be available. Not all of these will be needed at any one time.   In fact, the mate who doesn't carefully control the slings given out will, on some runs, find that many more than 25 per gear will be used.   About 8 to 10 slings will keep one gear going, more or less may be required depending upon the cycle of the total operation.

These slings average about 18 ft in length when made, that is the rope should be cut in lengths of 36 ft when making them.   They should be

FIG. 7-37.   The endless rope sling.   Courtesy Moore McCormack S.S. Co.

made out of 3½-in. three stranded manila or sisal.   When the short splice is completed, there should be no twists in the sling, otherwise they are difficult to work with.   To prevent turns from being worked into the sling as the splice is made, one turn should be thrown out of the sling just before marrying the two ends preparatory to making the splice.   This is a seemingly trivial point but quite important.

The endless fiber rope sling is well adapted to use with bagged goods if the bags are rough gunnies, bales, tires, single large lightweight but strongly constructed cases, reels of wire, and similar cargoes.   This sling should not be used on bags of refined commodities, such as refined sugar or flour nor on bags of cement. Cement bags are unable to withstand the sling pressures; the bottom bags invariably split and spill the contents causing considerable damage to the cargo through loss of contents plus making a mess of the ship and contaminating other cargo. These slings should not be used for hoisting several small cases or cartons or for steel products.

Fig. 7-38.   The web sling.   Courtesy Moore McCormack S.S. Co.

THE FIBER ROPE SNOTTER.   This is simply a length of rope with an eye splice at each end and generally fitted with a sliding hook as described under the section on the handling of lumber.   Two of these slings are used on the cargo hook and ride the hook in and out because they are released instantaneously at the end where the load is landed.   They are used mainly when handling lumber of the finer grades.

THE WIRE ROPE SNOTTER.   This sling is constructed in the same manner as the fiber rope snotter, but it has a wider number of uses.

Besides being used on lumber of the rougher grades, it is also used on steel products, such as pipe, steel rails, and structural steel shapes. Long wire rope snotters without sliding hooks are used to handle some large bulky cases. When used for this purpose, both eyes are placed on the cargo hook and the case rests in the bites thus formed.

FIG. 7-39. The airplane or platform sling. This shows the use of spreaders and safety nets to prevent packages from falling off. Courtesy Port of New York Authority.

THE WEB SLING. (See Fig. 7-38.) This is simply an endless rope sling with a canvas web sewn between the two parts. It is one of the best slings for handling refined bagged products or bagged cement.

THE PLATFORM, TRAY, AIRPLANE, OR PALLET SLING. (See Fig. 7-39.) All of these terms are used to describe the wooden platform type sling. Before pallets were used so widely, this was a simple platform made of

FIG. 7-40. Chime or cant hooks. Courtesy Port of New York Authority.

2-in. lumber and fitted with rings at the four corners where four hooks hanging down from a suitable spreader would be engaged. The rings on the platform have been removed, in the case of the pallet, and bars are now used to fit between the upper and lower decks outside of the runner or stringer on the double type pallet. The bars hang from a spreader which is required to keep sling pressures from bearing against the containers piled on the platform. This is the most widely used sling in ports where fork lift trucks are used to handle the pallet. It has always been a popular sling, however. These slings may be used with safety for almost all types of cargo, such as cartons, crates, cases, bagged goods, cylinders, barrels, drums, carboys, furniture, and short lengths of lumber or pipe. There may be some situations where the platform sling is used where the web or endless rope sling would actually be better. One operation that might be mentioned would be the handling of some bagged commodities and also baled goods.   The principal reason for the rope sling being superior is that with them there is less delay because of

Fig. 7-41.   Fiber rope net sling with a pie plate.   Courtesy U.S. Maritime Service.

having to return a number of slings after the landing spot is clogged with empties.

CHAIN SLING.   Chain slings are used when handling heavy concentrated cargoes such as pigs of iron, lead, tin plate, or copper bars.   They are safer because they stand up better than wire rope with such heavy loads.

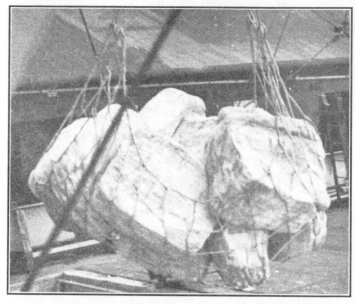

FIG. 7-42. Wire rope net sling. Rubber bales are handled in this type sling.

FIG. 7-43. Side dogs used on steel plate.

CANT OR CHIME HOOKS. (See Fig. 7-40.) These are used exclusively for hoisting a number of drums or cask type containers at the same time. They are also used for hoisting hogsheads of tobacco, but the hook is very broad and offers several inches of bearing surface.

FIG. 7-44. Bale hooks. This view shows bale hooks rigged two to an eye with four sets comprising the entire sling. This is not the same as the type described in the text which has only one hook to a snorter. Courtesy Boston Port Authority.

FIBER ROPE NET. (See Fig. 7-41.) The fiber rope net is made of interwoven 2-in. fiber rope in sizes of about 12 by 12 ft square. For some products they may be lined with canvas. They are used for bagged goods, mail, single cases, or heavy duty drums. When lined they are used for bulk products such as brazil nuts or fertilizer. They should not be used for crates and cases in general because excessive sling pressures are exerted, and damage to the cargo will result. They are also poor slings for lightweight drums for the reason just mentioned, and if used, some leakers are almost certain to develop.

WIRE ROPE NET. (See Fig. 7-42.) The wire rope net has some special uses, one of the most common is for handling rubber bales.

CRATE CLAMPS.   The crate clamp is used not only for crates as the name implies but also on reels or wire cable and rolls of heavy paper.   It is an excellent sling for crated automobiles and similar containers because it can be applied and released quickly plus the fact that there is no accumulation of slings at either end of the hook's travel.

FIG. 7-45.   Bale tongs.   Hoisting three cotton bales at one time.   Courtesy New Orleans Board of Harbor Commissioners.

SIDE DOGS.   (See Fig. 7-43.)   Side dogs are used exclusively for handling steel plates.   When plates are extremely long and limber, more than one pair should be used.   Even as many as three pair may be required to prevent the bending of the plates.

DOG HOOKS.   Dog hooks are similar to crate clamps.   The difference is that the dog hook is attached to the bottom of the crate or case and, because of the dog leg shape of the hook's shank, they set in place securely.   When a strain is taken on the cargo fall, they tend to grip the bottom and will not slip off.   They have the advantage over crate clamps in that they are a little less likely to be accidently released, but they are more difficult to set in place than the crate clamp.

BALE HOOKS. (See Fig. 7-44.) Bale hooks consist of about 8 to 10 snotters of 2- or 2½-in. fiber rope spliced into a steel ring. At the lower end of each snotter which is about 6 to 8 ft long, a hook is attached having a shank of about 8 in. in length. The ring is placed on the cargo hook after the smaller hooks on the several snotters have been engaged on the steel bands of the bales. At least two bands should be engaged

FIG. 7-46. One type of newsprint sling. Courtesy Port of New York Authority.

on each bale to prevent one band from taking the entire weight and perhaps breaking. These cannot be used on bales that are extremely heavy. They are commonly used on wool bales of 200 or 300 lb each.

BALE TONGS. (See Fig. 7-45.) Bale tongs are levered tongs similar to ice tongs. They are used to handle cotton bales. They make an excellent sling because they can be applied and removed with great speed.

NEWSPRINT SLING. (See Fig. 7-46.) Newsprint is easily damaged by cutting the outer surface or denting the edges of the ends, and the slings designed for use with this commodity generally have the objective of reducing this possibility, which is high with the endless rope sling. These types of slings are good examples of a specialized sling developed because no general sling could be called really well adapted to handling the commodity.   As said before, the endless rope sling is often used for hoisting newsprint, but it is not a good sling for the purpose.

THE PIE PLATE.   (See Fig. 7-47.)   The pie plate is a circular platform placed in a rope net sling to prevent sling pressures from damaging cargo

FIG. 7-47. The pie plate used with fiber rope net.

hoisted in the net. It is an awkward sling and should be replaced if at all possible wherever it is used.

TRUCK AND AUTO SLINGS.   (See Fig. 7-48.)   There are a number of designs of these slings for handling automobiles that are not crated. Improvised slings generally result in damage of some type to any car hoisted by them. A specially constructed sling with ample spread between the vertical parts should always be used.

SPECIAL SLINGS.   On many pieces of machinery and certain odd shaped units of considerable bulkiness and/or weight, slings will be found attached as the cargo arrives at the pier. Great care must be taken not to allow such a sling to become lost or damaged during the voyage. If it is removed, note carefully how it was attached.

Fig. 7-48. One type of automobile sling. Courtesy Moore McCormack S.S. Co.

EQUALIZING BEAMS. When using more than one fall to hoist a heavy lift, the load can be distributed between the two falls without the use of a traveling block by attaching the falls to a heavy steel beam and slinging the load midway along the length of the beam. A beam used for this purpose is an *equalizing beam* (see Fig. 6-27).

CHAPTER 8

The ventilation

of cargo holds

ELEMENTS OF THE PROBLEM

The body of knowledge covered by this chapter would probably be more accurately described by air conditioning of cargo holds; however, through common usage on ships through the years, the term of *ventilation* is now used to indicate the steps taken to prevent damage to cargoes from condensed moisture within the cargo holds. One good reason for this is because until about 1938 the only technique used was ventilation. The technique was *ventilating,* but *air conditioning* was being accomplished. The control offered by the choice of either ventilating or not ventilating often is not sufficient to prevent condensation under conditions encountered at sea. It was left for a shipper of products suffering from improper air conditioning at sea to recognize this need on ships first. Thus, Mr. Oliver D. Colvin, president of Cargocaire Engineering Corporation, was the first to take positive action toward giving to ship's officers full control of the phenomena that causes condensation to appear on the ship's hull or cargo. His investigations into the reasons why his canned milk shipments suffered damage by rusting ultimately resulted in the use of a dehumidifier coupled with a forced air ventilation system.

The simple psychrometric principles involved and the exact methods used to minimize condensation are the topics of this chapter.

Before proceeding with a discussion of these principles, the author wishes to comment upon some interesting factors bearing upon the subject matter of this chapter. It has been observed that in the past a number of ship's officers have failed to recognize the need for correct ventilating procedures. Part of the cause of this is the failure to make themselves cognizant of the simple physical principles that would enable them to fully understand the problem with which they are dealing. As a result, the general opinion among many officers with years of experience is that the best thing to do always is to see that the cargo holds are given the maximum amount of air possible. As will be seen later, under some conditions this is the exact opposite of what should be done. With cowl ventilators only, the ventilation at times is woefully inadequate. Note however, that if an officer is of the opinion that fresh air is always needed, and the actual conditions call for restricting the ventilation, then the inadequacy of the cowl vents is actually preventing the officer from causing damage. Note also, that with the installation of powerful forced air ventilating systems, this same un-informed officer now can do even more damage to his cargo than before the *improved* means of ventilation was provided. A group of underwriters actually obtained statistical data which substantially proves that this latter possibility actually took place in a segment of the U.S. Merchant Marine. Before World War II, the damage to cargo on the intercoastal run from condensation was determined on a percentage basis. These data were obtained on ships equipped with cowl ventilators only. Following World War II, data were taken on ships with forced ventilation systems. These data showed that the incidence of damage due to condensation actually had increased, notwithstanding the improved ventilation system. The improved ventilation system, if used correctly, would have reduced the damage but to the amazement of all concerned the damage had increased.

The only answer to the question of how such a thing could happen is that the users of the improved means, because of their lack of knowledge, were now able to do more damage than previously.

Fundamental objective of ventilation. Ventilation has the single objective of preventing moisture damage to cargo that originates from condensation within the cargo holds. Since the condensation comes from the air, it seems logical that before discussing the matter further we should learn something about the composition of air and what other types of airborne damage there are besides moisture damage. Because air is everywhere and because of our intimate association with it from infancy, we all accept it as a highly commonplace substance and take for granted that we know all there is to know about it. As implied above, damage caused by condensation is only one of several forms of airborne damage. Components of air other than water vapor also may cause damage to cargo. These will also be dealt with briefly in this chapter; however, it must be emphasized that the only effective and practicable method of combatting moisture damage is through air conditioning by whatever means is at our disposal. Other airborne damage types must be eliminated by other techniques, not because air conditioning would not be effective, but because it would not be practicable.

Composition of air. The principal components of air and the amounts involved are: nitrogen, 78.03%; oxygen, 20.99%; argon, 0.93%; carbon dioxide, 0.03%; neon, helium, krypton, hydrogen, xenon, ozone, radon, 0.02%. These components and their amounts are the technical division for the total air of the earth's atmosphere. It must be pointed out that air near the earth's surface contains some additional substances and all of these amounts will vary to some degree. The additional substances are dust, water vapor, and under certain conditions accidental components. In a ship's hold, these accidental components are in the form of vapors from commodities stowed in the closed space.

Sources of airborne damage to cargo. Nitrogen acts simply as a diluter. It is a very stable gas and does not readily react with other substances so as to produce any problem in the protection of the ship or cargo. Argon, carbon dioxide, and the remaining gases either do not appear in the air at the surface of the earth or appear only as traces and consequently offer no problem.

Oxygen is a powerful chemical agent and readily combines with other substances. It is well known that oxygen is necessary for combustion; however, within cargo holds it causes more subtle damage through the process of corrosion. It is important to note that moisture must be present also in order for corrosion to take place. A highly practical corrosion preventative measure would be to remove the moisture from the air in areas where it is possible to do so.

Dust exists in all air to some extent. Dust particles are so small that they float through the air for some time before falling to rest. Dust particles average about 0.5 microns in diameter (2×10^{-5} in.). Excessive dust can cause considerable damage to cargo. This is an obvious fact and one of the first recognized by students of cargo stowage. It should also be recognized that protection from this airborne damage by ventilation is not possible. Protection from dust damage is obtained primarily by careful planning of the stowage so that dusty cargoes are loaded first, discharged last, or segregated from cargoes that may be damaged by dust. The classical example of a dusty cargo is portland cement, but there are many others, such as sulfur, bauxite, coal, copper concentrates, guano, nitrates, and ores of all kinds. Protection from dust for cargoes stowed in the same compartment and same level can be obtained by erecting a dust-tight bulkhead. This is ordinarily only necessary when a dusty cargo must be handled while delicate goods are stowed in the vessel. The damage caused by dust is known as *contamination*.

Accidental components of air in the hold are the fumes or vapors from liquids, gases, or solids stowed therein. The damage caused by this means is known as *tainting* damage. The vapors of turpentine can cause tea to taste of turpentine. Rubber can give a heavy, pungent, and characteristic odor to silk goods stowed in the same hold. Tainting of this sort will result in damage claims. Protection against tainting damage can only be obtained by segregation, and usually the segregation should provide for the space of at least one cargo hold between a highly odorous and a very delicate cargo. Temporary vapor-tight bulkheads are not practicable as are temporary dust-tight bulkheads.

Of all the components of air, water vapor is the most variable in amount. It may vary from only a trace in the air over a desert far from any large body of water to as much as 4% by volume under extremely humid conditions. It is contributed to the air by evaporation from water surfaces, soil, and living tissues. Water vapor may also be contributed to air by transfer from hygroscopic substances, and in fact this is the source of the water vapor that causes most of the trouble in a closed hatch. This transfer differs from transfer by evaporation; the controlling factors will be discussed later. The amount of water vapor that a given air sample can hold varies directly with the temperature of the air. We commonly speak of moist and dry air with the implied meaning that the atmosphere takes up vapor much as a sponge takes up water, but the fact is that the vapor occupies space without regard to the other gases. At any given temperature the same amount of vapor can be diffused through a vacuum as through an equal space occupied by air. In other words, the amount of vapor that can occupy a given space depends *entirely* on the temperature. The amount can be approximately doubled with each increase of 20°F within the ordinary ranges experienced in the free air. Thus by raising the temperature from zero to 80°F, the capacity of a given space for moisture is increased almost 16 times.[1]

[1] *Weather Forecasting*, U.S. Dept. of Commerce, Weather Bureau, U.S. Government Printing Office, Washington, D. C., 1952, p. 10.

TERMS OF PSYCHROMETRY

Relative humidity. When air contains all the water it can hold at a given temperature, it is said to be *saturated*. When the dry bulb temperature of saturated air is decreased, the air will reject some moisture in the form of what is known as condensation. When the dry bulb temperature of saturated air is increased, the air will cease being saturated and will immediately have the ability of holding more water vapor. The ratio of the amount of water vapor actually in the air to the amount that would be in the air if the air were saturated is known as the *relative humidity*.

Absolute humidity. The amount of water in air may be expressed as a unit of weight of water vapor per unit of volume of dry air. *Absolute humidity* is the term used to describe this unit. In engineering work, absolute humidity is expressed as pounds of water vapor per cubic foot of dry air or grains of water vapor per cubic foot of dry air. The psychrometric chart (Fig. 8-1) may be used to determine absolute humidity by first obtaining the specific humidity and then dividing by the volume per pound of dry air. This latter value is also found on the psychrometric chart.

Specific humidity. Specific humidity is defined as the weight of water vapor per unit of weight of dry air. In engineering work it is generally given as grains of water per pound of dry air or pounds of water vapor per pound of dry air.

Dew point. Dew point is defined as that temperature below which the air will be unable to retain the moisture it presently contains. The dew point of any given air sample is entirely dependent upon the absolute humidity. The reader should note that under a constant barometric condition of pressure, the dew point also varies directly with the specific humidity. This last relationship is reflected in the way that you read the dew point and specific humidity from the psychrometric chart which is constructed assuming a standard barometric pressure of 29.92 in. of mercury.

Wet bulb temperature. Heat causes water to acquire the properties of a gas. When applied to a water surface, heating results in a part of the water turning into a vapor. The heat that is expended in this process, which is called evaporation, is rendered latent or imperceptible so far as temperature effects are concerned until the vapor is again condensed into visible water particles. When this happens, the heat reappears. This explains why evaporation from a moist surface has a cooling effect, and it logically follows that the more rapid the rate of evaporation the faster will the heat become latent and the greater will be the cooling of the surface from which the heat is drawn. The wet and dry bulb hygrometer indicates the relative humidity based on the principle that the rate of evaporation is directly proportional to the relative humidity of the surrounding air.

To most seamen the wet and dry bulb hygrometer is a common instrument; however, a few comments concerning it are in order. It consists of two thermometers mounted close together. The bulb of one is covered with a wick that is dampened just before reading it or kept constantly dampened if mounted on a bulkhead in a permanent location. The temperature of the wet bulb thermometer will register the dry bulb temperature reduced by the cooling effect of the rate of evaporation. The rate of evaporation, of course, depends upon the relative humidity. This is the most accurate method in use for arriving at the relative humidity and the dew point of the air, providing the wick is clean, there are no artificial heat sources affecting the thermometers, and the wet bulb has a light flow of air over the wick to wipe away the high humidity air film that will develop around the bulb in dead air. If any one of these requisites is violated, the resulting relative humidity and dew point will be in error. In case of the lack of all air flow, the wet bulb reading would be too high; the reader should be able to see quite readily the direction of the error in the resulting relative humidity in such a case.

Wet bulb depression. The wet bulb will always be either equal to or less than the dry bulb reading. The difference in the wet bulb and dry bulb reading is called the *wet bulb depression*. The wet bulb depression obviously will vary directly with the relative humidity. It will be zero when the air is saturated. The relative humidity may be read from Table 8-1 if data from a wet and dry bulb hygrometer are employed.

Vapor pressure and saturated vapor pressure. When water enters the air by evaporation, it acts as another gas in the mixture of gases which compose the air. This water vapor exerts a pressure in all directions that is independent of the pressure of all the other gases in the mixture. This is known as the *vapor pressure* of the air. The water vapor in the air exerts a pressure that varies directly with the amount of vapor per unit of volume of dry air, i.e., the absolute humidity. This pressure is commonly expressed in inches of mercury and its value, whatever it may be, is contributing to the total length of the barometric column. The maximum value this vapor pressure can reach under conditions of constant temperature and pressure occurs when the air sample being considered is saturated. Every change in air temperature or pressure gives a change in *saturated vapor pressure*.

The table in the upper left hand corner of the psychrometric chart (Fig. 8-1) gives the saturated vapor pressures for temperatures between

TABLE 8-1

RELATIVE HUMIDITY TABLES

Difference in Dry and Wet Bulb Readings

		0	1	2	3	4	5	6	7	8	9	10	11	12
	30	100	89	78	67	57	47	36	26	17	7			
	35	100	91	82	73	65	54	45	37	28	19	12	3	
	40	100	92	84	76	68	60	53	45	38	30	22	16	8
	45	100	92	85	78	71	64	58	51	44	38	32	25	19
	50	100	93	87	80	74	67	61	55	50	44	38	33	27
	55	100	94	88	82	76	70	65	59	54	49	43	39	34
	60	100	94	89	84	78	73	68	63	58	53	48	44	39
	65	100	95	90	85	80	75	70	65	61	56	52	48	44
	70	100	95	90	86	81	77	72	68	64	60	55	52	48
	75	100	95	91	87	82	78	74	70	66	62	58	55	51
	80	100	96	92	87	83	79	75	72	68	64	61	57	54
	85	100	96	92	88	84	80	77	73	70	66	63	60	56
	90	100	96	92	88	85	81	78	75	71	68	65	62	59
	95	100	96	93	89	86	82	79	76	72	69	66	63	60
	100	100	97	93	90	86	83	80	77	74	71	68	65	62

Difference in Dry and Wet Bulb Readings

		13	14	15	16	17	18	19	20	21	22	23	24
Dry Bulb Reading	30												
	35												
	40	1											
	45	13	7	1									
	50	22	16	11	6	1							
	55	29	24	19	16	10	6	1					
	60	34	30	26	22	18	14	10	6	2			
	65	39	35	31	28	24	20	17	13	10	6	3	
	70	44	40	36	33	29	26	23	19	16	13	10	7
	75	47	44	40	37	34	31	27	24	21	19	16	13
	80	51	47	44	41	38	35	32	29	26	23	20	18
	85	53	50	47	44	41	38	36	33	30	28	25	22
	90	56	53	50	47	44	41	39	36	34	32	29	26
	95	58	55	52	49	47	44	42	39	37	35	32	30
	100	59	57	54	51	49	47	44	42	39	37	35	33

Relative humidity readings taken as percentage.

Example: What is the relative humidity of air with a dry bulb temperature of 70 and a wet bulb temperature of 60?   Answer: 55%.

20 and 84°F, with a barometric pressure of 29.92. Note that the temperature column headed Wet Bulb can be entered with the dew point or dry bulb if the air is saturated, because they are all equal.

The vapor pressure of air depends upon the concentration of water vapor per unit of volume of air but so does the absolute humidity of air and the dew point. It is important to note and remember that the vapor pressure is an indirect measure of the absolute humidity, specific humidity, and dew point. This fact is of importance when studying the basis of the moisture equilibrium charts, p. 439.

Equations for calculation of relative, specific, and absolute humidity. Relative humidity can be expressed as a ratio of two masses or two pressures

$$RH = \frac{A}{A_s} = \frac{e}{e_s}$$

where A = existing absolute humidity.

A_s = absolute humidity if saturated.

e = vapor pressure.

e_s = saturated vapor pressure.

Specific humidity is obviously a ratio of the weight of water vapor in the air to the total weight of the air expressed in the appropriate units. It is also the ratio of the vapor pressure to the total barometric pressure multiplied by a constant. The value of the constant depends upon the units used for expressing the specific humidity. The constant is equal to 4500 if the specific humidity is expressed in units of grains per pound.

$$W = \frac{\text{Weight of vapor}}{\text{Weight of air}} \qquad W = K\frac{e}{p}$$

where W = specific humidity.

e = vapor pressure.

p = total air pressure.

K = constant (value depends upon units of W).

Absolute humidity is equal to the ratio of the weight of water vapor in the air to the volume of the air sample being considered. Inasmuch as we always obtain the specific humidity from a psychrometric chart based on a pound of dry air, we can find the absolute humidity by dividing by the volume of one pound of dry air.

$$A = \frac{\text{Weight of vapor}}{\text{Volume of air}} \qquad A = \frac{Ke}{pv}$$

where v = volume of one pound of dry air and the other symbols are the same as those in the equation for specific humidity.

The weight of dry air is more than the weight of air mixed with water vapor per unit of volume. This fact sometimes comes as a mild surprise to the reader who is accustomed to considering moisture as always adding weight to the dry form of the substance. But water vapor, which is acting as just another gas in the total mixture of gases in the air, is actually lighter than the mixture in its dry state; hence, any addition of moisture makes the total mixture have less mass per unit of volume.

HOW TO USE THE PSYCHROMETRIC CHART

The psychrometric chart, Fig. 8-1, is a development of the Carrier Corporation. Whereas tables may be used to solve problems involving psychrometric data, the use of a chart makes the process easier and faster. Inasmuch as it is necessary to have a thorough understanding of the amounts of moisture involved in changing the various psychrometric values of air, it is desirable for the reader to become familiar with the use of this psychrometric chart and the notations that appear on it.

Definitions, abbreviations, symbols

DRY BULB TEMPERATURE: DB. Temperature of air as registered by an ordinary thermometer.

WET BULB TEMPERATURE: WB. Temperature registered by a thermometer whose bulb is covered by a wetted wick and exposed to a current of rapidly moving air.

DEW POINT TEMPERATURE: DP. Temperature at which condensation of moisture begins when the air is cooled.

RELATIVE HUMIDITY: $\%RH$. Ratio of actual water vapor pressure in air to the pressure of saturated water vapor in air at the same temperature.

SPECIFIC HUMIDITY: W. Moisture content of air. Weight of water vapor in grains or pounds per pound of dry air.

ABSOLUTE HUMIDITY: A. Moisture content of air. Weight of water vapor in grains or pounds per cubic foot of air.

ENTHALPY: h. Total heat. A thermal property indicating the quantity of heat in air above an arbitrary datum, in Btu per pound of dry air.

VAPOR PRESSURE: e. The pressure exerted by the water vapor contained in the air in inches of mercury.

VOLUME (as used in psychrometrics): v. Cubic feet of the mixture per pound of dry air.

POUNDS OF DRY AIR: The basis for calculations so this value remains constant during all psychrometric processes.

d = enthalpy deviation, Btu per pound of dry air.

h_s' = enthalpy of air saturated at the wet bulb temperature.

q = heat added in process, Btu per pound of dry air. (Heat removed = $-q$.)

m = weight of moisture added to air, grains or pounds per pound of dry air. (Moisture rejected = $-m$.)

Subscripts 1, 2, and etc. indicate the entering and progressive states in the process.

The dry bulb, wet bulb, and dew point temperatures, and the relative humidity are so related that, if two properties are known, all other prop-

erties shown in Fig. 8-2 may be read from the chart. When air is saturated, dry bulb, wet bulb, and dew point temperatures are identical.
Enthalpy of air for any given condition is the enthalpy at saturation
corrected by the enthalpy deviation due to the air not being in a saturated state. Our only interest in the enthalpy value as found on the chart
is to investigate the approximate heat load involved when renewing the
air in a refrigeration system requiring the addition of fresh air from time
to time. Not being burdened with the necessity of making precise calcu-

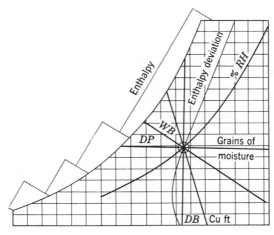

Fig. 8-2.

lations along these lines, we will not concern ourselves with the enthalpy
of added or rejected moisture which is given on the chart. The sensible
heat factor also appearing on the chart will not be used in any of our
calculations and therefore an explanation of this value will be omitted.

Numerical examples

EXAMPLE 1. Reading the properties of air.

Given: DB = 70°F. *WB* = 60°F.

Required: %*RH, DP*, volume (*v*), specific humidity (*W*), absolute humidity (*A*), and enthalpy (*h*).

Solution: Locate point of intersection on the chart of the vertical line representing 70° *DB* and the oblique line representing 60° *WB*. All values are
read from this point of intersection.

Interpolate between relative humidity lines on 70°F *DB* line, read
RH = 56%.

Follow horizontal line left to saturation curve, read *DP* = 53.6°F.

Interpolate between lines representing cubic feet per pound of dry air,
read *v* = 13.53 cu ft.

Follow horizontal line to right, read the specific humidity, $W = 61.4$ grains per lb.

Divide 61.4 by 13.53 to obtain absolute humidity of 4.54 grains per cu ft.

Follow wet bulb line to "Enthalpy at saturation" scale and read $h_s' = 26.46$ Btu. Read enthalpy deviation for point of intersection $d = -0.07$ Btu. Then the enthalpy of air at given condition $h = h_s' + d = 26.46 - 0.07 = 26.39$ Btu per lb of dry air.

EXAMPLE 2. Reading the properties of air.

Given: $W = 100$ grains per lb. $RH = 60\%$.

Required: Volume (v), absolute humidity (A), DP, DB, WB, and enthalpy (h).

Solution: Locate point of intersection on the chart of horizontal line representing 100 grains per lb and 60% RH line. All values are read from this point.

Interpolate between lines representing cubic feet per pound of dry air, read $v = 13.98$ cu ft.

Divide 100 by 13.98 to obtain absolute humidity (A) of 7.15 grains per cu ft.

Follow vertical line downward to dry bulb temperature scale, read 82.4°F.

Follow horizontal line to left to saturation curve, read $DP = 67.1$°F.

Follow wet bulb line to the saturation curve, read $WB = 71.8$°F.

Continue out on wet bulb line to "Enthalpy at saturation" scale and read $h_s' = 35.6$ Btu. Read enthalpy deviation for point of intersection $d = -0.10$ Btu. Enthalpy of air at given condition $h = h_s' + d = 35.60 + (-0.1) = 35.5$ Btu.

EXAMPLE 3. (*a*) Calculating the cooling load based on a pound of dry air entering.

Given: Initial air $DB = 85$°F, $WB = 77$°F. Final air $DB = 50$°F, $WB = 50$°F.

REQUIRED: Number of Btu removed from the incoming air.

Solution: Read $h_{s1} = 40.58$, $h_{s'2} = 20.30$; $d = -0.09$ Btu, $d = 0$; $h_1 = 40.58 - 0.09 = 40.49$, $h_2 = 20.30$.

$$q = h_2 - h_1 = 20.30 - 40.49 = -20.19 \text{ Btu per lb}$$

(*b*) Calculating the amount of moisture rejected from the incoming air based on a pound of dry air entering.

Read $W_1 = 127.9$ grains per lb; $W_2 = 53.5$ grains per lb.

$$m = W_2 - W_1 = 53.5 - 127.9 = -74.4 \text{ grains per lb}$$

(*c*) Calculating the cooling load based on the total amount of air entering a recirculated air stream.

Given: Initial and final air as given under (*a*). Outside air added at the rate of 1000 cfm.

Solution: Divide 1000 by the volume of 1 lb of entering air, $v = 14.12$ cu ft per lb. 1000/14.12 = 70.9 lb of dry air. Cooling load,

$$H = 70.9 \times 20.19 = 1431.47 \text{ Btu}$$

EXAMPLE 4. Calculating total amount of moisture involved in changing DP of a given amount of air.[1]

Given: $DB_1 = 90°F$, $DB_2 = 90°F$; $DP_1 = 80°F$, $DP_2 = 35°F$. 100,000 cu ft of air involved.

Required: The number of pounds of moisture that was removed from the air to cause the change in DP.

Solution: Read $W_1 = 156$ grains per lb of dry air. $W_2 = 30$ grains per lb of dry air. $m = W_2 - W_1 = 30 - 156 = -126$ grains per lb of dry air. $v_1 = 14.3$ cu ft per lb.

Divide 100,000 by 14.3 to find number of pounds of dry air in state $1 = 7000$ lb.

Hence the number of grains rejected amounts to 7000×126 or 882,000 grains. But, since 7000 grains equals 1 lb the amount in pounds is equal to $882,000/7000 = 126$ lb.

EXAMPLE 5. Calculating the effect on the DP of air when water vapor is removed from the air. *Note:* In solving this particular problem, we will assume a constant DB. When water vapor is absorbed or released by a substance there is a transfer of heat also, hence our assumption of a constant DB will produce some error in our final results. The amount of error will be negligible for our purposes. In this problem we will also assume a constant volume of dry air which will be the volume for state 1. To eliminate these assumptions would complicate the problem and serve no useful purpose in our study of the subject involved.

Given: 100,000 cu ft of air with a $DP = 75°F$, $DB = 80°F$.

Required: The new dew point if 100 lb (700,000 grains) of water vapor is absorbed from this body of air.

Solution: Read $W_1 = 132$ grains per lb of dry air. $v_1 = 14.0$ cu ft per lb of dry air.

Hence: $100,000/14.0 = 7092$ lb of dry air are being considered. $7092 \times 132 = 936,144$ grains of moisture in the air before absorption commenced. 936,144 less 700,000 equals 236,144 grains of moisture remaining after absorption ended. 236,144 grains in 7092 lb of dry air is equal to $236,144/7092$ grains per lb or 33.3 grains per lb.

Therefore the new DP is read on the horizontal line representing a specific humidity of 33.3 grains per lb $= 37.5°F$.

HYGROSCOPIC MOISTURE TRANSFER

Hygroscopic defined. The word *hygroscopic* is an adjective implying the ability to absorb moisture in the form of a gas. Hence, hygroscopic moisture is that moisture which is absorbed by a substance capable of absorbing water vapor in the gaseous form. Not all substances are capable of this phenomenon. If a substance is capable of absorbing hygroscopic moisture then it is known as a hygroscopic substance.

---

[1] Problems of this type must be solved later to understand thoroughly why it can be stated that the condition of a commodity in a nonventilated hatch controls the storage atmosphere's DP.

Examples of hygroscopic substances are all substances of an organic nature, such as all grains, wood and wood products, cotton, wool, sisal, jute, paper, sugar, and other products of animal or vegetable origin. Examples of nonhygroscopic substances are all metals and glass products.

Factors controlling hygroscopic moisture transfer. Hygroscopic moisture will leave the hygroscopic substance and enter the ambient air in a manner that is similar but not identical to the transfer of free moisture to the air. Moisture in the liquid state will leave the parent body and enter the air as a gas so long as the ambient air is not saturated. The speed of evaporation depends upon the relative humidity of the ambient air and the temperature of the water. Evaporation will continue even if the water is lowered in temperature to the freezing point or below. When water vapor enters the air from ice without passing through the liquid state, the process is known as sublimation instead of evaporation. The important point is that this process, evaporation or sublimation, will continue if the ambient air has a *RH* of less than 100%.

Hygroscopic moisture will leave its parent body if the vapor pressure within the substance exceeds that of the ambient air. This warrants some discussion. The hygroscopic moisture within a hygroscopic substance will possess a vapor pressure somewhat similar to the vapor pressure at the surface of liquid water or on the surface of a block of ice. For any given substance this vapor pressure varies as the *moisture content* of the substance and the *temperature* of the substance. A given combination of moisture content and temperature will produce variable vapor pressures between different commodities. It has already been pointed out that the water vapor in the air also has a vapor pressure which is dependent upon one thing only, namely, the moisture content of the air. Recall that the dew point is also dependent upon one thing only, namely, the moisture content of the air.

It has been said that the hygroscopic moisture will leave the substance if the vapor pressure of the ambient air is less than the vapor pressure of the substance. It follows then that if the two vapor pressures are equal there will be no transfer of water vapor. Under these conditions the air and substance are said to be in moisture equilibrium. Although it may not seem as logical, nevertheless it is true that if the vapor pressure of the air is greater than that of the substance, the water vapor will "flow" back into the substance.

Significance within the ship's hold. If a hygroscopic commodity in a ship's hold has a moisture content and temperature such that the resulting vapor pressure is greater than the air in the hold, water vapor will leave the commodity and enter the air until either the vapor pressure of the air builds up to meet the vapor pressure of the commodity or the vapor pressure of the commodity falls to that of the air. If we constantly ventilate with this low vapor pressure air, we rule out the first possibility. The air passing through the hold will continue to remove water vapor from the commodity. The student is apt to jump to the conclusion that the latter procedure will, in fact, lower the vapor pressure of the commodity to that of the air. While it is true that the commodity's vapor pressure will be lowered, it will not be lowered an appreciable amount unless the process is continued much longer than the longest passage made by any modern ship or air is used with a much lower vapor pressure than that found at sea.

On the other hand, if the hatch is not ventilated for any reason, the possibility of building up the vapor pressure of the air to that of the commodity does exist; in fact, that is what will happen under such conditions. It must be pointed out that under no circumstances will the vapor pressure of the commodity fall to meet that of the air. This can be demonstrated clearly by a numerical example which will be given later.

THE MOISTURE EQUILIBRIUM CHART

Use of moisture equilibrium charts. The moisture equilibrium chart illustrated by Figs. 8-3 and 8-4 can be used to determine the dew point temperature that the air surrounding a hygroscopic commodity will have when in moisture equilibrium with that commodity.

Recall that for any given moisture content of the air the water vapor in the air will have a certain vapor pressure; also recall that for every vapor pressure value there is a corresponding dew point value. Inasmuch as there is a one to one correspondence, the value of which never varies because they are functions of each other and depend upon no other factor, it is obvious that if we choose any vapor pressure x_1, there will be a corresponding dew point value y_1, and a corresponding specific humidity z_1. Hence, if we know any one of these values, either x, y, or z, we always can find the other two, providing, of course, that we have suitable tables or a suitable psychrometric chart.

It has been noted that all hygroscopic commodities have vapor pressures depending upon the commodity's *moisture content* and *temperature*. (Moisture content of a commodity is expressed as a percentage by weight. If the moisture content of lumber is given as 25%, it means that for every 100 lb of lumber there are 75 lb of dry wood fiber and 25 lb of water in the form of hygroscopic moisture.) The vapor pressure comparison is the criterion used to tell whether hygroscopic moisture is being absorbed by the commodity, by the air, or if the air and the commodity are in moisture equilibrium. But, vapor pressure can be stated in terms of dew

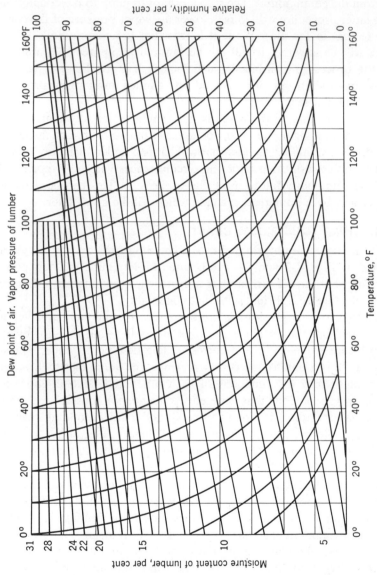

FIG. 8-3. Moisture equilibrium diagram of lumber for determining the vapor pressure of lumber from its moisture content and temperature. Courtesy Cargocaire Engineering Corp.

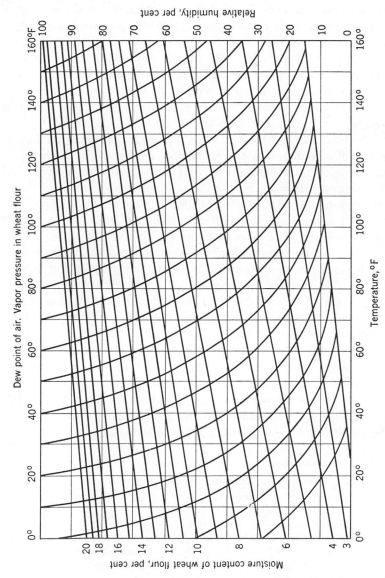

FIG. 8-4. Moisture equilibrium diagram of wheat flour (approximate). Courtesy Cargocaire Engineering Corp.

point temperatures. The moisture equilibrium charts give the vapor pressure of the commodity in terms of the dew point temperature that air with an equal vapor pressure would possess. This is done because we are interested in knowing final dew points rather than vapor pressures; that is to say, the resulting dew point has more meaning than the resulting vapor pressure.

The charts can be entered with the air's relative humidity and dry bulb temperature to obtain the dew point of the air. Now, if the *dew point corresponding to the vapor pressure in the commodity* is equal to the air's actual dew point, moisture equilibrium will exist. Note the expression, "dew point corresponding to the vapor pressure in the commodity." Hereafter, in this book, this long and somewhat awkward expression will be replaced by the expression, *commodity's dew point*. It should be clear, however, that the commodity itself cannot have a dew point as defined earlier.

If the commodity's dew point is greater than the air's dew point, moisture will leave the commodity and enter the air. If the dew point relationship is reversed, the flow of moisture will be reversed.

It should now be apparent that if a commodity with a high moisture content is stowed in a nonventilated hold, the dew point in that hold will be high. If the exact moisture content and temperature of the commodity are known, the exact level that the dew point will reach within the hold can be obtained from a moisture equilibrium chart. Before this can be demonstrated by means of a numerical example, the method of reading a moisture equilibrium chart must be explained.

The moisture equilibrium chart has the following data recorded upon it: The commodity's moisture content, dry bulb temperature, and vapor pressure (given in terms of dew point); the air's *RH*, *DB*, and *DP*. Entering with any two known factors for the commodity, the third can be read from the chart; the same is true in the case of the air.

Numerical examples

EXAMPLE 1. Reading the moisture equilibrium chart.

Given: Lumber with a moisture content of 20% and a temperature of 70°F.

Required: The commodity's dew point.

Solution: Locate the point of intersection between the curved dry bulb temperature line for 70°F and the vertical moisture content line for 20%. Follow a horizontal line to the left to the dew point scale. Read 66°F as the commodity's dew point.

EXAMPLE 2. Reading the moisture equilibrium chart.

Given: Air with an *RH* of 70% and a *DB* of 70°F.

Required: The *DP* of the air.

Solution: Locate the point of intersection between the curved *DB* temperature line for 70°F and the slanting dashed line for a *RH* of 70%. Follow a horizontal line to the left to the dew point scale. Read 60°F as the air's *DP*.

EXAMPLE 3. Estimating the reaction between cargo and air.

Given: The data from examples 1 and 2.

Required: What will be the dew point in an unventilated hold loaded with the lumber of example 1 if when secured, the air's dew point was as given in example 2?

Solution: From the discussion about hygroscopic moisture transfer, it should be clear that the hatch will eventually have a dew point of 66°F. In other words, the hatch would have a dew point precisely as dictated by the commodity.

The proof of the truth of the last statement is demonstrated in the following section.

CONTROL OF STORAGE ATMOSPHERE BY THE COMMODITY

Closed container hypothesis. In view of the laws controlling the transfer of hygroscopic moisture and the factors controlling vapor pressures in air in hygroscopic materials, this hypothesis can be made: The characteristics of the air in a closed container are controlled by the temperature and moisture content of a hygroscopic material within the container if the weight of the material is *much greater* than the weight of the air. It is the author's desire to show that the hypothesis stated above is true, using a hypothetical example, and to comment upon the significance of such facts in their application to the proper care and custody of cargo on a ship.

The *closed container* we will have in mind is a nonventilated, well secured, ship's hold. That the weight of the material is very much greater than the weight of the air involved will be quite obvious upon comparing them in our hypothetical case or under practical conditions as they exist on board ship.

Assume: A hold of 80,000 grain cubic. Sixty thousand (60,000) cubic feet is consumed in stowing 600 tons of jute. The jute has a temperature of 80°F and a moisture content of 10%. When the hold is secured, the air has a *DB* of 80°F and *RH* of 90%.

In order to illustrate the reaction between the air and the jute and arrive at a proof, we must accept certain basic laws of psychrometry. These laws are as follows:

I. Water vapor will always flow from an area of high vapor pressure to an area of low vapor pressure.

II. Water vapor pressure in air depends upon the moisture content.

III. Vapor pressure in a hygroscopic commodity depends on two factors, namely, (1) the moisture content and (2) the temperature of the commodity.

IV. Vapor pressure, dew point temperature, and specific humidity all vary directly and have corresponding values.

To prove the hypothesis we must resort to a quantitative analysis of a given problem. We will use the assumed data given above to illustrate the reaction between the jute and the air and, as a result, establish a proof. Note that the assumed data is a typical arrangement on a ship.

Proof: On the moisture equilibrium chart, locate the point of intersection between the temperature line for 80°F and the vertical moisture content line for 10%. Moving horizontally to the left, read the commodity's dew point as 62°F.

On the psychrometric chart locate the point of intersection between the 90% relative humidity line and the vertical *DB* temperature line for 80°F. Read the following data from this point of intersection: $DP_1 = 76.8°F$; $W_1 = 140$ grains per lb; $v_1 = 14.05$ cu ft per lb of dry air.

Laws I and IV above tell us that under the initial conditions, water vapor will flow from the air into the jute. This initial reaction will continue until one of three possible things occurs:

1. The vapor pressure of the air falls until it meets the present vapor pressure of the commodity.

2. The vapor pressure of the commodity will rise to meet the present vapor pressure of the air.

3. The vapor pressure of the commodity will rise and that of the air will fall so that they come to equilibrium at some intermediate level between their initial conditions.

In effect, the hypothesis says that possibility number one (above) will take place. If a quantitative study of the reaction proves that this is true, then we will have proved the hypothesis.

Our quantitative study amounts to a comparison of the quantities of moisture involved. Initially the jute contains $(600 \times 0.1) = 60$ tons of hygroscopic moisture. Sixty tons is equal to 94.08×10^7 grains. The air contains 140 grains per lb of dry air, and there are $(20,000/14.05) = 1423$ lb of dry air in the hold. The total moisture in the air of the hold amounts to $(1423 \times 140) = 199,220$ grains.

We have already noted that initially some of the water vapor will leave the air and enter the commodity. The question we must now answer is how much? The only thing that can stop the flow of moisture is the attainment of equal vapor pressures by the air and the commodity. Since the only change taking place is the transfer of water vapor from the air to the commodity, the question of how long this will continue arises. It is obvious, due to the enormous differences between moisture contents, that even if all the water in the air left it and entered the commodity, the latter's moisture content would be practically unaffected on a percentage basis. This means that its vapor pressure would also be practically unaffected. It is evident then that possibility number one, of the three mentioned above, will take place.

To make this more evident, let us examine the final conditions of the air and the commodity assuming the air is brought to a dew point of 62°F.

At a DP of 62°F and DB of 80°F we read the following: $W_2 = 83$ grains per lb of dry air. Assuming the same amount of dry air we find that moisture equilibrium will be reached when the total amount of moisture in the air is $(83 \times 1423) = 118,109$ grains. Thus it is seen that the amount of moisture that would have to leave the air to make the dew point fall from 76.8 to 62°F is $(199,220 - 118,109) = 81,111$ grains.

This 81,111 grains would, of course, be absorbed by the jute. The factors affecting the jute's vapor pressure would not be appreciably changed by the absorption of 81,111 grains. The jute already contains 940,800,000 grains at 10% moisture content. Adding 81,111 grains would change the percentage only slightly, to 10.0007%.

The final condition in the hold will be with a commodity whose vapor pressure is the same as that at the beginning of the reaction, but with air whose DP has been lowered from 76.8°F to 62°F.

SIGNIFICANCE OF THE HYPOTHESIS. The significance of the above fact, as related to the proper care and custody of cargo, is that it offers a complete explanation of the following items to the ship's officers:

1. Why it is possible to restrict all ventilation if hygroscopic commodities are shipped sufficiently dry, without danger of moisture damage.

2. Why it is desirable to have hygroscopic commodities with low moisture contents.

3. Why hygroscopic commodities stowed adjacent to a warm bulkhead can cause high dew point storage conditions.

4. Why the upper 'tweendecks is the most likely place for heavy condensation.

5. Why *continuous* proper ventilation is necessary for dew point control.

The hypothesis is also significant because it offers an explanation of the causes of continuous heavy condensation and certain other types of moisture damage problems. Finally, it illustrates the extent of the control that the ship's officer has in meeting practical ventilation needs on a ship under operating conditions.

Determining moisture content. Much has been said about the importance of the moisture content of hygroscopic commodities with reference to the problem of moisture damage in a ship's hold. It seems logical that we should discuss briefly the methods used to ascertain moisture contents.

WEIGHT DIFFERENCES. One method consists of weighing a known volume of the commodity. This sample of the commodity is then placed in an oven and heated to 212°F for about 3 hr. This should remove all the moisture from the sample of the commodity. The sample is again weighed. The difference between the two weights is equal to the weight of the moisture in the original sample. To obtain the percentage of moisture content, divide the weight of the moisture removed from the sample by the original weight of the sample and multiply the quotient by 100. Stating this by use of a mathematical equation, we have:

$$\frac{W_1 - W_2}{W_1} \times 100 = \%\text{M.C.}$$

where W_1 = original weight of commodity sample.
W_2 = dry weight of commodity sample.

If dry densities of the commodities to be so checked are available, there is no need for the oven to dry the sample out. In this case, after carefully weighing the sample, the density of the sample could be calculated and the moisture content calculated from these data similarly to the method outlined above.

THE MOISTURE METER. Another system involves the use of a device that measures the resistance to an electric current as it passes through a sample of the material to be tested. A galvanometer registers the resistance, but instead of indicating voltage or amperage, the dial is calibrated to read percentage of moisture by weight. Since the scales have to be calibrated from empirical data for every commodity type, a different instrument is needed for every commodity. The principal difference between such instruments would be the calibration of the scales and the method used to insert into the commodity the electric terminals over which the electric current is to pass. Figure 8-5 shows the electric moisture meter for the instantaneous determination of moisture contents of lumber within a range of 7 to 24%.

MEASURING HYGROSCOPIC TRANSFER. A third method is based on the premise that the condition of the air in an inclosed space is controlled by the condition of any hygroscopic material contained in the space. We have already proven that this premise is reasonable; see pp. 443–445.

This method requires a container of several cubic feet capacity capable of being hermetically sealed and fitted with a psychrometer. The psychrometer must be so fitted that measurements of the inside air can be taken after the air and commodity have reached moisture equilibrium

Fig. 8-5. Electric moisture meter for instantaneous determination of moisture content within a limited range. In use the needles in the handle are driven into the board as shown. The rheostat (selector) in the upper left hand corner of the instrument is then adjusted until the needle on the milliammeter (upper right hand corner) is vertical. The moisture content of the board is then read direct from the dial on the rheostat. A modification of this instrument is used for determining the moisture content of grain. Courtesy Association of Marine Underwriters of British Columbia.

without allowing any admixture with outside air. The important data obtained from this experiment are (1) the dew point of the inside air and (2) the dry bulb temperature of the commodity (same as the air). Since we know that the air's dew point results from the commodity's temperature and moisture content, we can use a moisture equilibrium chart to obtain the moisture content of the commodity.

Numerical example

Obtaining moisture content by allowing moisture equilibrium to be reached. *Given:* Some wheat grains are spread thinly on a screen within a hermetically sealed container. After 6 hr, a wet bulb on the inside of the container reads 65°F and a dry bulb reads 70°F. It is assumed that the wheat and air are in thermal equilibrium.

Required: Moisture content of the wheat.

Solution: On a psychrometric chart locate the point of intersection between the vertical dry bulb line and slanting wet bulb line. Follow horizontally to the left and read the dew point which equals 62.3°F.

On the moisture equilibrium chart, locate the intersection point of the horizontal dew point line and the curved dry bulb line. Follow vertically downward and read the grain moisture content, 15%.

Of the three methods mentioned, the electrical moisture meter is the most practical for use by ship or dock personnel interested in making spot checks on moisture contents. The principal advantage of this method is the speed with which a check can be made. The disadvantage is the reliance that must be placed on the correct operation of a delicate instrument. It would be necessary to check and calibrate such an instrument frequently to be certain it is giving true readings.

Moisture contents in practice. Although it is evident that more moisture content information, in some instances, would contribute to better outturns of shipments, there are wide areas wherein the shipowner receives no information concerning the moisture contents of hygroscopic cargoes as they are shipped. In cases where the moisture content may be known, the information is not passed on to the officers of the ship nor to any dock force personnel. In some cases, even if the information were passed on, its significance would not be understood.

Moisture content of grain, seeds, nuts, and pulses is of considerable importance, and sometimes shippers of these products are required to certify to the moisture content of such items. When the moisture content of grain [1] is sufficiently low, this item is almost completely dormant. It may be kept in sealed containers for years even if heated to abnormally high temperatures. For example, barley may be heated to approximately 200°F without losing its germinating power or causing any decomposition of its substance. This is a valuable property to have in grain, especially when loaded in a ship's hold, but it is lost when the grain is damp. As the moisture content rises in grain, it ceases being dormant and commences to respire, or in other words, to live. This respiration process is a complicated series of biological and chemical changes which are influenced by existing conditions within and without the substance. These changes or processes are frequently referred to as germination, fermentation, turning rancid, sprouting, and so on. The end products of these processes are water vapor, carbon dioxide, and heat.

---

[1] As used here and in the rest of this discussion grain will include all types of grain, pulses, and seeds.

There is no clear and definite moisture content level below which grain may be considered dormant and above which it respires; however, all grain may be considered practically dormant below 10% moisture content. Under normal conditions of storage on land, where ambient temperatures change slowly, the following moisture contents are generally considered safe for several months' storage: soy beans, 16%; maize, 14.5%; wheat, 14%; rice, 12%; flax seed, 11%.[1]

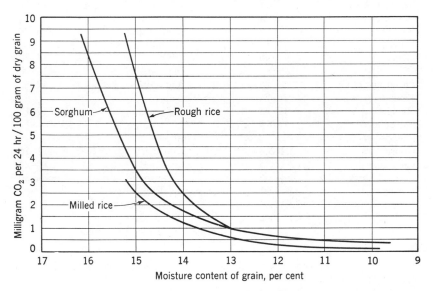

FIG. 8-6. Respiration of grain as a function of its moisture content. Temperature of grain, 100°F; length of test, 96 hr. Courtesy Coleman *et al., U.S. Dept. of Agriculture Technical Bulletin* 100.

With higher moisture contents than those stated, the rate of respiration increases rapidly. See Fig. 8-6 for the respiration rate of rice and sorghum grains at 100 degrees temperature. This diagram is based on the amount of carbon dioxide produced in 24 hours as an indication of the respiration rate. It also illustrates the difference between the respiration rate of white rice (also known as milled or polished rice) and rough rice (also known as brown rice), which explains the great difference between the stowage techniques used with the two types of rice.

Table 8-2 gives the moisture contents of a number of commodities as they are shipped in practice as determined by S. J. Duly of London. It should be interesting to the ship's officer to note that in most cases he

[1] Colvin, Hahne, Colby, Care of Cargo at Sea, *Transactions of the Society of Naval Architects and Marine Engineers,* 1938, p. 122.

TABLE 8-2

AVERAGE MOISTURE CONTENTS OF COMMON HYGROSCOPIC MATERIALS *

Material	Moisture Content, per cent	Material	Moisture Content, per cent
Cacao	8–10	Textile fibres	
Cereals		Cotton	8–11.5
Maize (plate)	11–14.4	Jute	12–17
Maize (Danubian)	17–19.5	Silk	11
Rye (Polish)	17.19	Wool, raw	9.5–20
Wheat	10–14	Hides and skins	
Coffee	8.5–10.6	Dry	14–20
Dried fruits		Dry salted	14–20
Dried apricots	.28	Wet salted	40–50
Prunes	24–28	Tobacco	
Raisins	17–28	Leaf, usually	12–13
Sultanas	18–19	range	9.5–17
Oil Seeds		Timber	
Copra	3.4–5.6	Kiln dried	11–16
Cottonseed	7.1–9.5	Air dried	16–24
Ground nuts	4.4–5.6	Unseasoned	over 30
Linseed	5.9–12.1	Wood Pulp	
Soya	7.9–12.1	Kraft (sulfate)	10–20
Tea	6–8	Bleached chemical	10–20
		Unbleached chemical	10
		Mechanical	50–55

* S. J. Duly, Condensation on Board Ship, *Journal of the Royal Society of Arts*, February 1938.

receives these commodities with moisture contents that are at the limit of the safety level, or, as in the cases of Danubian maize, well above it. Hence, it is evident that anything that may cause an increase in moisture content during the voyage is likely to cause some damage to grain cargoes. A discussion of the effects of extreme heat or cold when carrying grain is presented later.

THE DETERIORATION OF A MAIZE CARGO.[1] During the 1936–1937 maritime strike on the west coast of the United States, a ship loaded with about 10,000 tons of River Plate maize was tied up in San Pedro, Calif. Because of the moisture content of the corn that is carried on this particular route, the cargo will heat up rather slowly. If not unloaded within about six weeks, cleaned, and cooled, it will depreciate in value. In this case, the corn could not be unloaded and the temperature in the holds

[1] Colvin, Hahne, and Colby, Care of Cargo at Sea, *Transactions of the Society of Naval Architects and Marine Engineers,* 1938, p. 129.

filled with grain continued to go up slowly. The owners of the cargo made tests in all hatches, and when the temperature approached 100°F they decided to take some action to prevent further rise in temperature.

The method decided upon included the cooling of the bulk corn by use of dry ice. Two tons of dry ice (solid carbon dioxide) were spread over the surface of each of these hot hatches. The carbon dioxide gas, which evaporated from the numerous 50-lb blocks, was cool and heavy. It sank into the mass of corn where it displaced some of the trapped air. The respiration of grain and the metabolism of mold germs require oxygen. Because the oxygen was removed these processes undoubtedly were slowed down, and the heating slowed down accordingly. Heat is produced by this respiration and metabolism process. However, this desirable result was only of minor benefit in the long run.

The dry ice did lower the temperature of a layer of grain on the surface for several feet. This cooling was noted during the first 2 or 3 days. The amount of cooling that the dry ice can perform can be calculated from the following data:

1. Specific heat of dried corn: 0.28 Btu per lb per °F.
2. Latent heat of dry ice: 235 Btu per lb.
3. Final temperature of carbon dioxide gas: 80°F.
4. Temperature of dry ice: −110°F.
5. Specific heat of carbon dioxide: 0.21 Btu per lb.

From the above data it can be seen that 2 tons of dry ice is capable of absorbing about 1,200,000 Btu. With this information and the remaining data (item 1 above) it can be seen that approximately 80 tons of corn could be cooled 26°F or a less amount could be cooled even more. Just how much corn was cooled or the exact degree cannot be stated. But, it can be determined easily that in a hold of about 60 ft by 60 ft area, the 80 tons of corn would make a layer about 1 ft in depth. This gives us some idea of the effectiveness of the method chosen to cool the cargo. It should be remembered that the corn is continually developing additional heat by its respiration.

It was later observed that the cooling action of the dry ice was sufficient to chill only the surface of the grain cargo. The interior remained between 90 and 116°F. This means that the vapor pressure of the corn below the top layer was very much higher than that of the corn in the very cold top layer. From what has been said about hygroscopic moisture transfer, it can be seen that a good deal of moisture would diffuse toward the cold surface. However, the surface was so cold that no moisture could escape from the hot cargo.

When the grain was finally unloaded, the following situation was discovered: The surface layer of the grain was dripping wet and it was estimated that as much as 100 tons of water was collected there. This layer was entirely destroyed because it had been spoiled through germination, molding, and discoloration. The cooling effect of the dry ice vanished rapidly below this surface layer, but the entire mass of grain was hot and moist and was materially depreciated in value.

From all evidence, it seems that if carbon dioxide were to be used, it should have been applied in the form of a warm gas not as dry ice. The gas should have been injected near the bottom of the cargo, so that it could have displaced the air contained in the grain. The surface layer of the grain should have been ventilated with dry air, or relatively dry air, which would have removed any moisture that might have come from the interior.

An experiment similar to the one just suggested was made in another Pacific Coast port at the same time. A powerful portable fan was placed in the open cargo hold and the surface of the grain was ventilated vigorously during the entire strike period of over 3 months. This particular corn cargo did not suffer the heavy damage of the one mentioned above.

During the early part of the first case, the question came up whether or not the damp and warm corn cargo should be dried. This would probably have been the logical thing to do. A simple system for drying the corn was worked out, but the Argentine cargo owner declined because drying the grain would mean a loss of weight in the grain. Of course, he did not anticipate the heavy damage that occurred later. This is undoubtedly true to some degree in other cases; grain shippers should realize that a small loss in weight will often mean a much better outturn and may be more profitable. It is quite probable that in many cases of heavily depreciated grain cargoes the cause could be traced to a high moisture content when loaded.

The effects of hot and cold bulkheads. The effect of a heated bulkhead, deck, or overhead on a hygroscopic commodity is to raise the vapor pressure of the commodity and thereby do one of two things: (1) Drive moisture out of the commodity into the ambient air, or (2) diffuse moisture from the heated zone of the cargo to the cooler zone.

If the moisture is driven into the ambient air, it must be removed by powerful air currents or the dew point will climb until heavy condensation appears on the overhead. When this condensation is heavy enough to drip back down on top of the cargo, heavy damage may be caused. This is a description of the daily cycle in the upper 'tweendecks of a ship in tropical or summer climes when the ship's ventilation system cannot remove the moisture laden air before the evening drop in temperature.

Sudden drops of temperature brought about by squalls can also cause condensation.

It is quite obvious by now that if the initial moisture content is low enough, there will be no effect from heat sources. Unfortunately, cargoes are not usually shipped with extremely low moisture contents; we must rely on reliable ventilation equipment properly operated.

If bulk grain is loaded in a space where one of the bulkheads is considerably warmer than the others, the hygroscopic moisture will diffuse from the heated area toward the cool area. This can cause no trouble if

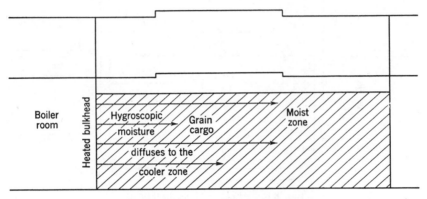

FIG. 8-7. Effect of heated bulkhead.

the moisture content is low; however, if it is bordering on the critical level of about 14%, the cool grain will receive moisture which will drive its percentage above 14%. At the higher level, the grain may heat and deteriorate. This could be an indirect cause of damage to grain (see Fig. 8-7).

If grain is loaded in a hold so that it comes against an extremely cold steel plate, such as the ship's side in the winter or a poorly insulated reefer bulkhead, the vapor pressure is lowered. Moisture will then diffuse from the warmer zones to the cold zones; thus, the percentage of moisture content in the cold zone goes up. This would cause a localized damage area, probably only a few inches thick against the steel plate. The higher moisture content may cause the grain to heat, sprout, and spoil. When discharging, the spoiled grain will tend to adhere to the metal (see Fig. 8-8).

LIMITING DAMAGE DUE TO HOT OR COLD BULKHEAD. The extent of damage caused by hot or cold bulkheads will vary as: (1) The temperature difference between the bulkhead and the cargo. (2) The nature and condition of the grain cargo. If the cargo is prone to heat spontaneously, such as soy beans, the sudden increase in moisture content will cause an increase in the respiration process of the cargo. This latter change will augment the effect of the hot bulkhead. It is obvious that this entire chain of events and the resulting damage can be reduced by conditioning the cargo (drying it out) before shipment. Some protection may be obtained by insulating boiler room bulkheads and similar places. A slow increase in temperature would not produce damaging effects as severe as sudden heating.

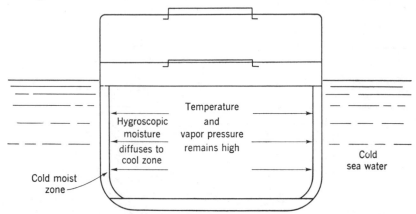

Fig. 8-8.   Effect of cold bulkhead.

Ventilation by natural means.   Most ships as they are being built today are equipped with supply fans, or supply and exhaust fans, for ventilating purposes. The change from the old cowl vent to some method that would guarantee a continuous supply of air, when needed, was long past due when it arrived. In order to have some idea of how much air a cowl ventilating system can deliver to a hold under ideal conditions, let us make some reasonable assumptions.

The capacity of a duct in the amount of cubic feet of air per minute it will handle can be calculated by a simple equation

$$Q = A \times V$$

where Q = capacity in cubic feet.
  A = cross-sectional area in square feet of the distributing duct.
  V = velocity, in feet per minute, of the air flowing through the duct.

If we know the wind velocity and the size of a cowl vent, we can calculate the volume of air delivered to the hold. It must be pointed out, however, that turbulence and eddying of the air as the cowl vent changes the air's direction ninety degrees and confines it within its interior will reduce the effective velocity. We will assume that the reduction is 25%.

Making the above assumptions, calculate the cubic feet per minute (cfm) of air delivered to a hold fitted with four cowl vents, each having diameters of 18 in. at the deck level. The wind velocity is 15 mph (1320 fpm). Two of the vents are trimmed into the wind and two out of the wind.

$$Q = \frac{3.14 \times 81 \times 1320}{144}$$

$$= 2331 \text{ cfm}$$

Reducing 2331 by 25% we obtain 1749 cfm as the capacity of one ventilator. Thus we find that the two vents trimmed into the wind will deliver 3498 cfm of air to the hold. This is under ideal conditions; many things could cause a drastic reduction in this amount.

A reduction of the actual wind velocity, a change in the wind direction, a change in the ship's course, heavy spray, fog, or rain may stop all ventilation of the cargo holds. If this happens when conditions are such that some means of air conditioning is needed to prevent condensation, damage will certainly result. It is evident that natural ventilation means cannot be relied upon unless the ship is carrying cargo for which ventilation is of no importance. However, if ventilation is not required, it would be more economical and sensible to remove all cowl vents and secure the vent coamings by use of wooden plugs and three tightly secured canvas covers.

In contrast to the uncertain capacity of the system just described above, a forced system will consistently deliver 4000 to 10,000 cfm of air depending upon the capacity of the fans and ducts in the design of the system. Used intelligently, such a system can eliminate as much as 80% of all condensation. The remaining 20% can be eliminated if the ship is equipped with a dehumidifier and connecting ducts which are used correctly.

Damage to cargoes caused by moisture. Damage to grain, seeds, nuts, and pulses from moisture has been discussed earlier. The moisture causes a deterioration of the commodity through accelerated respiration which eventually results in partial or complete loss of such cargoes. The moisture that causes such damage may be either free moisture dripping onto the cargo from the deckhead, the hygroscopic moisture contained when shipped, or hygroscopic moisture acquired during the voyage.

Other hygroscopic commodities and nonhygroscopic commodities in packages may be damaged by heavy stains from dripping condensation.

This type of damage may not materially affect the product itself, but damages are claimed on the basis of some reduction in saleability of the product.

Cargoes of metal products may be heavily damaged by moisture condensing directly on the commodity and causing stains or corrosion.

Some special damage types exist as in the case of refined sugar. If refined sugar is allowed to absorb hygroscopic moisture and it subsequently releases this moisture, it will become caked. If excessive caking occurs damages may be claimed; under correct conditions, caking need not occur.

Eliminating moisture damage. Ways and means of reducing the detrimental effects of condensation are outlined below. Some of the systems or techniques in use are not very effective, others are very expensive; the ship operator should investigate all methods with great care. The ship's officer should be aware of all methods and attempt to make them as effective as possible.

AIR CONDITIONING HOLDS. Proper air conditioning of the ship's holds can eliminate all of the moisture damage due to condensation on the ship or cargo and some of the damage caused by hygroscopic moisture. It should be noted that in the case of refined sugar *proper air conditioning* means the closing off of all circulation in the hold.

Stevedores and other practical cargo handlers have for many years practiced certain basic precautions against moisture damage which do not include ventilation. They have found from experience that they cannot rely on ventilation methods. Whether this condition continues to exist depends entirely upon the equipment placed on ships of the future and the knowledge of the officers who use the equipment.

DUNNAGING. The most common technique used is the thorough dunnaging of cargo so that it cannot touch any metal, drainage is provided beneath the cargo, and ventilation air channels through it are provided. This protective measure is necessary with or without suitable air conditioning systems.

COVERING TOP TIERS. The top tiers of cargo are sometimes covered with a moisture repellent material, such as a tarpaulin, to prevent dripping condensation from striking the cargo. The idea here is to catch such moisture and direct it into the frame spaces where it falls and eventually finds its way into the bilges.

One bad feature of this last mentioned technique is that the air may become so moist below the tarpaulin or top covering, whatever it may be, that heavy condensation will occur there, especially if ventilating with low temperature air over the top of the covering. If this happens, the corrective measures could actually be the cause of more damage than if nothing had been done.

HERMETICALLY SEALING CONTAINERS. In some cases, shippers of products of a nonhygroscopic nature but which may be easily damaged by condensation are packing their products in hermetically sealed containers with small bags of a desiccant sealed within the package. The reaction of the trapped air and the desiccant is such that the dew point of the air is reduced to a level where no condensation can possibly occur on the metal parts; furthermore, the moisture content of the trapped air is so low that the contents can remain for years in the package without rusting or other forms of corrosion. The material used to wrap the contents must be capable of shedding free moisture from the outside also. Such a material is on the market under the trade name of *Pliofilm*. It is a transparent plastic sheet. Its disadvantage is that it does not have great tensile strength and may be easily pierced by nails or other sharp objects. Any hole, however small, makes the drying properties of the silica gel ineffective because eventually moisture equilibrium between the inside and outside air will be attained.

COATING EXTERIORS. Some products with a highly polished finish are coated with a thin protective covering applied like paint. This covering prevents corrosion and may be removed by wiping the surface with a rag soaked in a paint thinner or specially designed product.

DEW POINT CONTROL

Importance of dew point control. All of the means used to protect cargo from moisture damage resulting from condensation on cargo or hull are unnecessary if the dew point of the air in the ship's hold is kept below the temperature of the cargo and the hull or deckhead. Control of the dew point should be the basis of all our thinking and efforts relative to minimizing moisture damage in the hold.

It has been pointed out that successful dew point control with natural ventilation systems is obviously quite impossible. Forced ventilation systems will give some measure of protection. They will fail when the outside air has moisture content that is higher than that of the air in the ship's hold. When this occurs, the outside air should not be brought in for ventilating purposes. If ventilation is stopped, the dew point inside the hold may climb up to the level of the outside air. In other words, control is lost. In periods of heavy fog, rain, or mist ventilation with outside air should be stopped. This action also brings about a loss of dew point control.

Control of the dew point is only complete when the ship is equipped with a device capable of manufacturing an adequate supply of low dew point air which is mixed with *recirculated air* in the closed holds; this to be done only when it becomes technically impossible to keep the holds opened to the outside air.

Such a device is called a *dehumidifier*. How a dehumidifier is integrated with a forced ventilation system to afford complete mechanical control of the dew point is the topic of a later section.

Basic rules for ventilating. If there is a single guiding rule that may be used for ventilation, it is as follows: *When the dew point of the outside air is lower than or equal to the dew point of the air in the hold,* **ventilate.** *When the dew point of the outside air is greater than the dew point of the air in the hold,* **do not ventilate.**

Hard and fast rules can sometimes lead us into difficulties because of particular changes that may take place in outside atmospheric conditions; also the rule stated above assumes that the operator has sufficient and trustworthy instruments for obtaining the data needed for making a decision. Because of these considerations, four general rules for four specific situations are given below. It is important to understand that these rules should be used only as guides.

WITH HYGROSCOPIC CARGOES GOING FROM A COLD TO A WARM CLIMATE. This is not a critical situation. There is little danger of ship's sweat although there may be the possibility of cargo sweat. Without instruments to check the condition of the air in the holds, a ship's officer could never be certain that he was doing the correct thing. After battening down, it would be advisable to keep a close check on the condition of the air in the holds and the outside air. In all probability, it would not be necessary to ventilate initially. At first, the inside air would probably have a dew point that was lower than the outside air after the ship sailed and proceeded on a course into warmer climes. The dew point would probably climb upward gradually, but until the inside dew point was higher than the outside dew point there would be no purpose in ventilating.

WITH HYGROSCOPIC CARGOES GOING FROM A WARM TO A COLD CLIMATE. As a ship proceeds from a warm climate to a cold climate, it will be experiencing a gradual drop in atmospheric dew point as well as a drop in dry bulb temperature. Under these conditions, danger of heavy condensation on the ship's hull and top decks exists. The air in the below deck spaces will be receiving large quantities of moisture from the hygroscopic commodities, and unless constant and vigorous ventilation is maintained heavy condensation is certain.

WITH A NONHYGROSCOPIC CARGO GOING FROM A COLD TO A WARM CLIMATE. Under these conditions, the temperature of the cargo being loaded is usually much lower than the dew point of the air through which the ship will pass as it proceeds into the warmer climes. It is necessary to keep the outside air out of the hold; hence, ventilation should be stopped. If ventilation is maintained during the voyage, cargo condensation will occur.

No ventilation will protect the cargo during the voyage, but unless the cargo temperature rises above the dew point of the air at the port of discharge, there will be condensation on the products when they are discharged. However, some damage has been prevented. If the non-hygroscopic cargoes are steel products, they might be badly rusted if soaked with condensation all during the voyage.

The possibility of large masses of steel rising in temperature during a voyage of only a few weeks is small. Few data concerning heat transfer through cargoes in a ship's hold have been gathered. However, the heat transfer is known to be slow. There will be a rise of about 1°F per day per 25° temperature differential between the cargo and the outside or sea temperature. A cargo of steel products 40° colder than the sea temperature will warm up to the sea temperature in about 20 days according to Colvin, Hahne, and Colby.[1]

WITH NONHYGROSCOPIC CARGO GOING FROM A WARM TO A COLD CLIMATE. The possibility of trouble in this situation is remote. There is no possibility of cargo sweat because the cargo is warm and will remain warm during the voyage. Hull sweat can occur but the slightest ventilation will prevent this too.

Mechanical control of the dew point. All mechanical dew point control systems (as differentiated from simple forced ventilation systems) require three distinct *divisions* of equipment. For maximum control under all conditions, all three divisions are necessary. These divisions are:

1. The hold fan and duct system: This acts primarily as a forced ventilation system. It may be designed with a forced supply and natural exhaust or vice versa. The most efficient systems have a forced supply and a forced exhaust.

2. The instrumentation: This is the means of gathering data from which the operator is able to make intelligent decisions concerning what to do with the system. This division will be explained later in greater detail, but it should be mentioned here that these instruments measure the moisture content of the air in the holds and the outside air. With reliable information, the operator can judge accurately how to set up the system. With incorrect information or no information, the system may

[1] Colvin, Hahne, and Colby, Care of Cargo at Sea, *Transactions of the Society of Naval Architects and Marine Engineers,* 1938, p. 121.

be used to cause more condensation than would result without the use of the system at all.

3. The dehumidifier: A machine for removing moisture from the air by adsorption or absorption. Air thus dried is injected into the recirculated air stream within the hold.

The axial flow fans used with the Cargocaire installation at each hatch have a rated capacity of 6000 cfm. The outlets in the holds are fitted with volume controls which are adjusted when the system is installed. These volume controls must not be tampered with otherwise the correct volumes will not be sent to the individual spaces. The duct system is designed to split off portions of the total 6000 cfm being delivered and route it to all the spaces proportionately. In other words, a hold of three divisions vertically, Fig. 8-9, would have the 6000 cfm delivered in units of 2000 cfm to each of the spaces. In each space there are three outlets in a fore and aft direction. Each of these outlets would deliver an equal amount of air, in this case $666\frac{2}{3}$ cfm.

A hythergraph recorder is sometimes mounted at the exhaust side for keeping a record of the condition of the air inside the hold. The operator must compare the data from this instrument with the data from an instrument testing the condition of the outside air located on the bridge of the ship. If the dew point of the outside air is lower than or equal to the dew point of the inside air, the system should be set up to ventilate. If the outside dew point is greater than the inside dew point, the system should be set up to recirculate and add dry air (see Figs. 8-9 and 8-10).

The above description of the hold fan and duct system is the arrangement as installed by Cargocaire on about 160 ships. It is an efficient system and insures ample circulation of air through the holds. With appropriate flexible canvas covered ducts, the air can be made to permeate the cargo instead of simply passing over the top surface. To obtain maximum penetration of the cargo by the air stream, the cargo must be stowed with great care and with particular provision for air channels through the stowed block vertically and horizontally.

Surprisingly enough, the hold fan and duct system as described above was not used on the recently constructed Mariner type Maritime Administration designed ships. These ships were equipped with a force supply system but without a force exhaust system. The exhaust system, in this case, is called a *natural exhaust*. Actually, the exhaust relies upon a slight pressure being built up in the hold for the air to be exhausted through a covered opening into the atmosphere. The hold then becomes what is termed a *plenum chamber,* or a space under a very small pressure. The pressure would be only a fraction of a pound per square inch

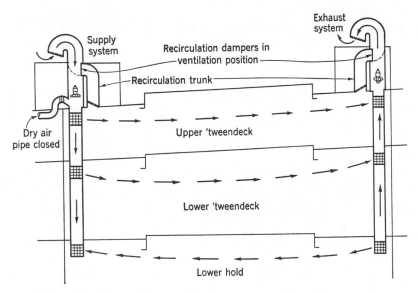

Fig. 8-9. Cargocaire hold fan and duct system showing air flow when set on ventilation. Courtesy Cargocaire Engineering Corp.

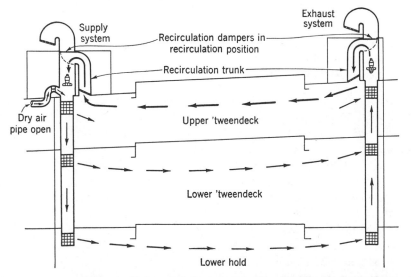

Fig. 8-10. Cargocaire hold fan and duct system showing the air flow when set on recirculation and adding dry air. Courtesy Cargocaire Engineering Corp.

gauge. This system is not as efficient as one having a forced exhaust as well as a forced supply.

MARINER TYPE SHIP HOLD FAN AND DUCT SYSTEM. The levers on all the recirculation dampers on these ships are shifted by power. This is accomplished by the use of *diverting switches* on a control panel which is located on the bridge.

The diverting switches start and stop pneumatic motors which are located at the fan and damper housings at each hold. These pneumatic motors change the position of the levers. The operator can set the system up or change its setting from the bridge without having to visit each individual hatch.

Each hold is equipped with a forced supply system which includes ducts that run longitudinally and discharge the air in an athwartship direction at three points along the length of the hold. The natural exhaust outlet is located at the same end of the hold as the supply trunk. The supply fan has a rated capacity of 6000 cfm except at the smaller end holds where their rating is 4000 cfm.

The flow of dry air, weather (outside air), and recirculated air in the supply section of the damper house is controlled by the diverting switches on the control panel in the chart room. This panel consists of 7 four-way diverting switches (one for each hold), the Brown recorder, indicating lights, and air gages. These switches may be set in four positions:

1. Ventilation.
2. Ventilation with dry air.
3. Recirculation with dry air.
4. Recirculation without dry air.

When on the *ventilation* setting, the weather damper is open, and the recirculation damper and dry air damper are closed. Turning the switch to *ventilation with dry air* simply opens the dry air damper, but all other dampers remain in the same position. When on the *recirculation with dry air* setting, the weather damper is closed while the recirculation damper and dry air damper are open. In the *recirculation without dry air* position, only the recirculation damper is open; the weather and dry air dampers are closed.

All weather openings in the hold ventilating system are equipped with a watertight cover which can be closed manually in case of emergency, such as heavy seas on deck or fire.

NEED FOR ADDING DRY AIR WHILE VENTILATING. When the outside dry bulb temperature is falling rapidly and the system is already on ventilation, the dehumidifier should be set in operation and the dry air used to increase the differential between the hold air dew point and the temperature of the ship's hull. This is a special case, but should be understood so that condensation may be prevented under such conditions.

On runs from South America to the United States during the winter on the east coast, there is an excellent example of the conditions described above. When ships leave the Gulf Stream and pass by Cape Hatteras northbound, the dry bulb temperature may fall 40° within 12 to 24 hr. If precipitation does not occur, the system may remain on

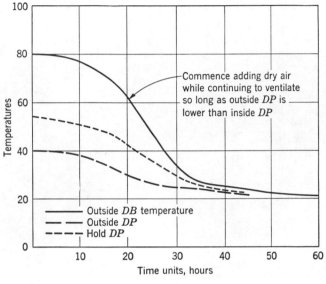

FIG. 8-11.

ventilation. The differential between hull temperature and inside dew point temperature will be decreased until there may be less than a degree difference. The addition of dry air to the ventilation air stream may increase the differential so that in the event of further drops or complications, condensation will not occur. See Fig. 8-11 for a graphic illustration of the above discussion.

NEED FOR RECIRCULATION WITHOUT ADDITION OF DRY AIR. The only time that recirculation of the air in the holds should be maintained without the addition of dry air is when it is desired to raise the temperature of cold nonhygroscopic cargoes stowed below the upper 'tweendeck level. Here is the situation envisioned: The lower hold contains steel products that have been loaded at a very low temperature. Unless the temperature of these products is raised to a level above the dew point of the air at the port where they are to be discharged, they will become wet with condensation when the hatches are opened.

During the voyage, the upper 'tweendecks may reach a temperature above 100°F, while below the waterline the steel will remain cold. The steel's temperature will rise but very slowly and it may not rise enough to prevent condensation from the cause mentioned above. To obtain some heat transfer to the cargo of steel, the air within the hold may be recirculated without the addition of dry air. Adding dry air will do no

FIG. 8-12. Hythergraph cabinet.

harm, but it will accomplish nothing. There is no object in operating the dehumidifier without necessity. To make this arrangement more effective, the upper 'tweendeck outlets and intakes on the ducts only should be covered. Do *not* cover the recirculation trunk openings.

CARGOCAIRE INSTRUMENTATION. The older installations made by Cargocaire Engineering Corporation use a *hythergraph* for measuring the condition of hold air, weather, and dry air made by the dehumidifier. This is an aerological instrument that measures two atmospheric elements: (1) Relative humidity. (2) Dry bulb temperature. These data are used in conjunction with a psychrometric chart or suitable tables to determine the dew point. The dew point is the important element in determining what to do with the total system. One hythergraph is located at each hold exhaust side, one on the bridge, and one near the dehumidifier. On a five hatch ship there would be seven hythergraphs.

These hythergraph recorders are housed in cabinets. One type of cabinet is fitted with a small fan which draws a sample of air into the cabinet through a filter and over the elements of the instrument and eventually discharges the air outside; this type is located on the bridge (see Fig. 8-12).

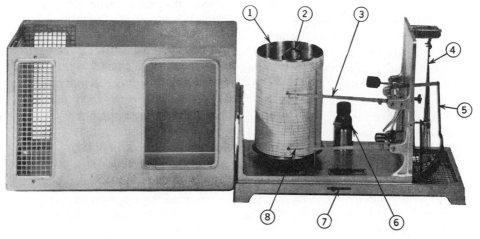

Fig. 8-13. The hythergraph. (1) Chart drum. (2) Clock winding key. (3) Temperature pen. (4) Hair element. (5) Bourdon tube. (6) Ink bottle. (7) Pen lift rod lever. (8) Relative humidity pen.

Another cabinet, similar to the above but without a fan, is located at the exhaust side. The air is forced over the elements of the recorder in the cabinet by virtue of the velocity possessed by the air as it passes through the exhaust trunk. A third type of cabinet is located at the dehumidifier, and the recorder measures the condition of the air made by the dehumidifier. The graphs plotted by this recorder provide a check on the proper functioning of the unit.

Figure 8-13 shows the details of the recorder with the cover off. The chart drum 1 is driven by an internal clockwork, which is wound by the key 2. When the clockwork is fully wound, the chart drum makes one revolution in 8 days.

The recorder has two pens. The upper pen 3 plots the temperature and the lower pen 8 plots the relative humidity. Ink for the pens is kept in the small bottle 6.

The temperature pen is actuated through a linkage by an element called a Bourdon tube 5. This curved hollow tube is filled with alcohol. When the temperature of the air flowing past the Bourdon tube rises, the alcohol in the tube expands tending to straighten out the tube. This motion is transmitted to the pen, causing the pen to rise on the chart.

The relative humidity pen is actuated by a human hair element 4 which expands and contracts with changes in humidity. This change in humidity is transmitted to the lower pen which plots the relative humidity on the chart. Care must be taken not to touch the hair element, as the presence of moisture, oil, or any foreign substance on the hair will introduce errors in the readings.

Two types of charts are used in the recorders. Aside from the different temperature ranges, the two types are identical. The lower part of each chart covers a relative humidity range of 0 to 100% in 2% increments. The chart for the hold and outside air has a temperature scale ranging from 25 to 120°F. The chart for the dry air recorder has a temperature scale ranging from 45 to 140°F. Both temperature scales are in 1° increments.

There is an identification panel on the reverse side of both charts that should be filled in before the charts are filed. The time lines on the charts are at 2 hr intervals, and each day of the week is marked. There are two Mondays on each chart. This enables the operator to obtain a full 7 day record without the necessity of the pens crossing the chart clip. The new week's record should be started on the Monday to the right of the chart clip.

CHECKING THE RECORDER READINGS. These hythergraphs are subject to errors from handling during servicing or from dirt on the hair elements of the relative humidity element. It is of great importance that these errors be measured and recorded. This is somewhat comparable to the necessity of keeping a record of the error in the chronometer. Thus, when a reading is taken and the error applied, correct data are obtained. Otherwise the data will be in error and the operator of the total system may make a mistake that will cause condensation rather than prevent it.

HAND ASPIRATED PSYCHROMETER. The *hand aspirated psychrometer* is used to determine these errors. The instrument consists of a plastic case housing a wet and dry bulb thermometer. The rubber bulb assembly, which is attached to the plastic case, is used to induce a flow of air over the thermometer bulbs.

When taking a reading with the psychrometer, the wick of the wet bulb is wet thoroughly with distilled water using an eye dropper. Do not allow excessive water to remain over the wick. The instrument should be held at arm's length when taking readings and the hand should not be near the metal cover which should be closed over the bulbs. This prevents the readings from being affected by the operator's breath and body heat. Pump the rubber bulb until the wet bulb stops falling. This should take about one minute. The thermometer part of the case should be in the air sample that is being measured. The wet and dry bulb readings are used with a psychrometric chart or suitable tables to determine the dew point. When checking the readings of a hythergraph, pick off the *relative humidity* and compare it with the reading given by the instrument whose error is being determined.

If at any time the operator has reason to believe the hythergraph readings are not dependable, the psychrometer can be used to determine the dew point. Do not attempt to reset or adjust the recorders in order to correct the errors. Keep a record of them and apply them to all readings taken from the instrument. If they become too large, the instrument should be serviced by an expert serviceman.

In checking the chart room, hold, and dry air recorders, hold the psychrometer in the exhaust stream from the recorder cabinet and pump the rubber bulb until the wet bulb thermometer stops falling. Take the appropriate data from the psychrometric chart and compare with the readings from the recorder. Post a record of the errors noted where they can be applied to all readings taken from the instrument in question.

Probably the greatest weakness in the total system for mechanically controlling the dew point in the hold of a ship lies in the instrumentation. On some ships the above system has been maintained in good order and the results are good. However, the system requires a considerable amount of attention to keep in good operating order. It takes time also to obtain the psychrometric information necessary for the operator to make correct decisions as to the proper setting. For these reasons, the instrumentation, as described above, has been neglected. As a result, many ships equipped with an excellent and expensive mechanical dew point control system have failed to use it correctly. If these systems fail to check condensation from any cause, it is probably due to improper operation by the ship's personnel. These machines are constructed according to the facts of the science of physics, and if operated intelligently, they will prevent condensation.

MARINER TYPE SHIP INSTRUMENTATION. On all of the installations made on the Mariner type ships, a system of instruments has been installed that removes almost all excuse for incorrect operation of the total system because of a lack of psychrometric data. The basis of this system is a direct dew point registering instrument known as the *Foxboro Dewcel Unit*. This is a unit that consists of a temperature measuring resistance bulb impregnated with lithium chloride. A small electrical current continually flows through a resistance circuit in the *dewcel bulb*. The lithium chloride salt solution absorbs moisture in direct proportion to the moisture content of the air being tested. The more moisture absorbed the less the resistance and the lower the temperature of the dewcel bulb and vice versa. In this way the temperature of the dewcel bulb becomes a function of the air's moisture content or, what is the same thing, a function of the air's dew point. The temperature of the dew point is read on an instrument known as a *Dynalog Recorder*.

Instead of reading each hold's dew point individually, an automatic recording instrument known as the *Brown Electronik Recorder* prints the dew point readings of all the holds on a continually moving recording chart. Each hold's dew point is indicated with its corresponding number in a green color on the chart. The outside air dew point temperature is shown on the chart by a small printed *w* in purple, and the dew point of the air from the dehumidifier (when operating) is shown by a small *c* in brown. The outside dry bulb temperature is shown by a small *t* in red. This entire assembly is contained within the control panel mounted on the bridge.

With this instrumentation, the operator can check the dew points of all holds with the dew point of the outside air from a single station. If a change in the setting of the recirculation dampers or weather dampers is required, the change can be made from the bridge by simply twisting the diverting switches also mounted on the control panel, as explained above.

THE DEHUMIDIFIER

It should be clear that the dehumidifier is used only when the operator deems it necessary to add dry air to the air in any or all of the ship's holds. The Cargocaire and Kathabar dehumidification units are installed in a centrally located point somewhere amidships on one of the engine room flats. The air that is to be dried is taken into the machine from the compartment where the machine is installed. The air is *not* taken from the hold for drying and then sent back to the hold. The control of the dew point is maintained by making dry air from the atmosphere and inserting this dry air in sufficient amounts to keep the dew point in the hold low enough to prevent condensation on the ship's structural parts or on the cargo. To make room for the dry air, an equal amount of vitiated air is exhausted from the hold.

The Drihold dehumidification unit operates on the principle of taking a small amount of air from the hold that is being controlled, drying this air, and discharging it into the hold again. The difference between the two systems should be clear. The Drihold system calls for a dehumidification unit at each hold instead of having one centrally located dehumidifier. The first two systems are receiving and exhausting air from and to the outside; the latter system is a closed system.

Cargocaire's first unit was the Model H. The desiccant used in this unit is silica gel. Silica gel is a form of silicon dioxide that looks like quartz crystals or rock salt. This mineral has the physical property of being able to *adsorb* water vapor from the air in large amounts. Note that silica gel *ad*sorbs; it does not *ab*sorb. The water vapor leaves the air and clings to the surface of the silica gel. The silica gel is extremely porous and the diameter of the pores are so small that within a single cubic inch of silica gel there is presented a surface area of 50,000 sq ft. This is a physical transfer of water vapor; it is not a chemical process. Since the moisture simply clings to the surface of the silica gel until it is driven off by heat and no chemical change takes place as in absorption, the silica gel never has to be replaced, providing that it is kept clean. It is highly important that the silica gel be kept clean; hence, all air going into the dehumidifier is filtered. The filters should be replaced regularly. After the water vapor is removed from the silica gel by passing heated air over the crystals, the silica gel can be used over again for drying purposes. The Model H design made use of these properties of silica gel.

The Model S Cargocaire dehumidifier is a later design. It is a streamlined model, smaller and lighter than the Model H. The differences between the two machines can be seen by studying the diagram of each. The large and cumbersome inlet air dampers were replaced by a relatively light and small *four-way valve*. Cylindrical silica gel beds replaced the flat beds. Axial flow fans replaced air pumps and heavy conventional fan units. The precooler on the adsorption side was removed. The damper control motor was replaced by the piston that is actuated by compressed air.

The Kathabar dehumidifier uses a liquid desiccant consisting of a solution of lithium chloride. The latest Cargocaire dehumidifier, which replaces the Model S, uses a liquid desiccant consisting of triethylene glycol.

Drihold uses refrigeration to accomplish the dehumidification process. The air is passed over coils of a refrigeration system kept at a temperature of 35°F; thus, the air's dew point is reduced to 35°F in passing through the unit.

An explanation of the operation of these various dehumidifiers is given in the following paragraphs.

Cargocaire Model H. Figure 8-14 is a diagram of the Model H dehumidifier showing all the parts and the air flow through the unit. The machine consists of two distinct sides: *the adsorption side* and *the reactivation side*. There is a change in the function of the silica gel beds each time the position of the inlet and outlet air dampers is changed. As illustrated, the upper bed (11) is acting as the *reactivation bed* and

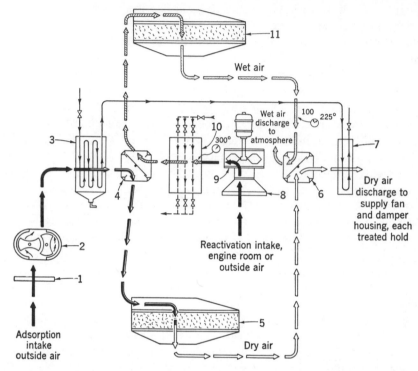

Fig. 8-14. Air flow diagram of Cargocaire unit Model H. (1) Blower filters; (2) blower; (3) precooler coil; (4) intake damper; (5) adsorber bed (drying); (6) outlet damper; (7) aftercooler coil; (8) activating air filters; (9) activating air fan; (10) heating coil; (11) adsorber bed (reactivating). Courtesy Cargocaire Engineering Corp.

the lower bed (5) is acting as the *adsorption bed*. The inlet and outlet dampers are connected together by a linkage system so that when one changes position so does the other; hence, the air flow is reversed in direction simultaneously.

Let us trace the air flow through the machine on both sides. Starting on the adsorption side, the air enters through the *adsorption air filter* (1). These filters are of the viscous type and should be renewed at least every 6 months or more often if they become exceptionally dirty as a result of a dusty cargo, such as copper concentrates or bauxite. The air next passes through the *air pump* (2) which is a positive displacement blower. This blower delivers 3000 cfm of air through the adsorption side and on from the dehumidifier to all the holds where the dry air pipe is open on the supply side of the hold fan and duct system. If one dry air pipe is open, then all 3000 cfm will go to that one hatch; if five dry air pipes are open, 600 cfm will go to each and so on. Next the air passes through the precooler (3). This cooling coil uses the sea water as a cooling agent. The precooler insures that all air entering the adsorption bed has a dew point no higher than the sea temperature. In practice this was not found to offer any advantage and was not included when the system was redesigned, as can be seen by studying the Model S. Leaving the precooler, the air enters the inlet damper (4) which merely turns it into the duct leading to the adsorption silica gel bed. As the air passes through the adsorption bed (5), it gives up its water vapor content and its dew point is lowered to 15 or 20°F, providing the silica gel beds are clean and were sufficiently dried out before the system started to operate.

On the adsorption side as the air leaves the adsorption bed, it passes on to the outlet damper (6) which turns it into the duct leading into the aftercooler (7). The aftercooler reduces the temperature level of the dry air leaving the dehumidifier to about 80°F. Without the aftercooler, the temperature of the dry air leaving the dehumidifier would be extremely high at the beginning of each cycle. The temperature would be close to 200° and gradually fall off to perhaps 100°. The heat would be the residual heat left in the silica gel bed from the reactivation process which is accomplished by passing air at 300°F through the bed. From the aftercooler the air leaves the dehumidifier and goes on to whatever holds have their dry air pipes open. Just beyond the aftercooler there is a sampling pipe open into the passing air stream which picks up the dry air and passes a sample over the elements of the hythergraph located here for the purpose of testing the air made by the unit. If the machine does not make air with a low dew point as measured by this hythergraph, the operator knows that it is not working properly.

Some of the reasons why the machine might not make dry air are: (1) Not cycling properly. (2) Not being reactivated completely due to reactivation air not being heated to 300°F. (3) Beds of silica gel dirty. This last reason is the result of not changing the viscous type filters when dirty. The only remedy is to have the dirty silica gel replaced by clean material.

Starting on the reactivation side, the air passes through a bank of viscous type filters at the reactivation air intake (8). It passes through the reactivation fan unit (9) which keeps the air stream moving on this side. This fan has a rated capacity of about 1500 cfm. Great capacity is not needed, this air only passes through the dehumidifier's reactivation side and then out to the atmosphere.

From the reactivation fan, the air passes through the reactivation air heater (10) where it is heated to a temperature of 300°F. The heater consists of three coils which normally operate with steam at 100 lb per sq in. Leaving the heater, the reactivation air enters the inlet air damper (4). From the inlet air damper the air goes to the reactivation bed. The 300°F temperature of the reactivation air removes the water vapor clinging to the surfaces of the silica gel particles in a process that is similar to boiling or rapid vaporization. This process requires heat in the same way that the process of boiling requires latent heat to change the state of liquid water to gaseous water. Consequently, there is a considerable drop in the sensible heat level of the reactivation air as it passes through the reactivation silica gel bed.

The more water vapor there is in the silica gel the greater the amount of heat used in driving the water vapor from the substance and, consequently, the greater the drop in the sensible heat level of the reactivation air. This fact can be used to determine the approximate stage of the reactivation process when reactivating the beds *out of cycle,* a procedure that will be explained later. When the reactivation air leaves the reactivation bed, it is extremely moist. From this bed, it enters the outlet damper (6) and is turned into a duct that leads to the atmosphere where it is discharged.

The inlet and outlet damper shafts are connected through a linkage system to a common motor. This motor is known as the *damper control motor.* It is set in motion every 2 hr by an automatic electric clock timer. When it is started, it shifts the position of both dampers. When the positions have been changed, a cam on the damper control motor breaks the electric circuit and stops the motor. For 2 more hours the dampers remain in position until the electric timer sets the damper control motor in operation and they are shifted again. Thus the entire system operates on a 4-hr cycle.

Reactivating the silica gel beds. The above completes the explanation of the air flow and cycling process when the unit is operating normally to produce dry air. The unit will not function properly, however, unless *both* silica gel beds are properly reactivated (dried out) before setting the unit into full operation. This out of cycle reactivation process is accomplished by setting only the reactivation side of the dehumidifier into operation and letting it run until each bed has been thoroughly dried out. The electric timer is not used; hence, the heated air will pass through whatever bed it is originally started on until the operator changes the setting of the dampers. This is accomplished by first throwing the knife switch into the closed position. This starts the electric timer. Next a small button on the right hand side of the housing for the timer is pushed. This closes the damper control motor circuit and changes the setting of the dampers in the same way that the timer would if allowed to run the full 2 hr. After changing the dampers in this manner, the knife switch is opened. The dampers will now remain in their present position until changed again in the same way or until the knife switch on the timer is closed.

JUDGING WHEN REACTIVATION HAS BEEN COMPLETED. When reactivating the silica gel beds in this way, the reactivation air should be sent through a single bed until the temperature of the air leaving the reactivation bed is up to 250°F or better. When the reactivation is first started, the bed will be very moist. This means that a large amount of latent heat will be used in the process, and the temperature of the air leaving the reactivation bed will be much lower than the entering air. The entering air is always 300°F; when starting the reactivation process, the exhaust air will be about 125°F. As the moisture is driven off and less and less moisture remains, the temperature of the exhaust reactivation air will rise. When this exhaust air temperature is up to 250°F or better, the bed can be considered dry. At this time the operator will change the setting of the dampers as mentioned above and reactivate the second bed. When both beds have been so treated, the dehumidifier is ready for use. Until both beds have been dried out, the machine will not operate correctly. Once both beds have been dried out as described above, the operator should repeat the process weekly. In this way, the machine will always be ready for use.

Joining a ship with Model H or S dehumidifier. When joining a ship with this type of dehumidifier for the first time, removing a ship from layup, or when, for any reason, you know or suspect the system has not been used for several weeks, it is *imperative* that both beds be reactivated as described above. Once prepared, the weekly reactivation process will not require much time; perhaps 2 or 4 hr will be sufficient. When a bed has been neglected for many weeks or months, it may take several hours to dry out the beds properly. It is important to note that a set time limit cannot be stated. The criterion is the temperature differential of the air being used to reactivate the bed from the entering air to the exhaust air. The temperature differential at the beginning of the process will be 150°F or better. The temperature differential when the bed is dried out will be 50°F or less.

Starting the Model H unit. To start the Model H unit, the operator performs the following simple operations:

1. Push the *start* button on the duplex controller circuit of the *dry air blower* and the *reactivation fan.*
2. Close the knife switch on the electric timer.
3. Open the two valves controlling the flow of cooling water through the precooler and aftercooler coils.
4. Open the steam valves, live steam and condensate, on the reactivation air heating coils.

The unit is now in full operation. The hythergraph recorder should be in operation so that the dry air being produced can be checked. The record kept by this recorder is the principal check that the operator has on the performance of the machine.

Reverse the steps mentioned for starting the Model H unit.

Cargocaire Model S. As mentioned above, the Model S unit is a streamlined version of the Model H. Figure 8-15 is a cutaway drawing of the Model S unit. The four silica gel beds (1) are in the form of vertical cylinders held in place by screens (2) and housed in the four steel cylinders (3). The beds are used in pairs, so that while one pair is drying air (adsorption phase) the other pair of beds is being dried out (reactivation phase).

The unit includes 2 *four-way* valves for controlling the flow of air through it. These valves are called four-way because each of them has four connections to it. The upper four-way valve (5) is connected at each side to the pair of cylinders, at the back to the reactivation air heater (6), and at the front to the dry air cooler (7). The lower four-way valve (12) is also connected at the sides to the pair of cylinders, at the back to the wet air duct (9), and at the front to the adsorption fan housing (10).

The position of the 2 four-way valves determines which pair of beds is adsorbing and which is being reactivated. The valves are shifted by a pneumatically operated piston (4). The piston rod is connected at the top and bottom to a chain which passes over sprockets at the back of each four-way valve.

The flow of compressed air to the cylinder is controlled by an electrically operated (solenoid) valve. This solenoid valve in turn is controlled by an electric timer of the same design as the one used with the Model H. The timer is designed to shift the four-way valves every hour. The total cycle time is 2 hr instead of 4 hr as on the Model H.

Air to be dried is drawn into the unit through a filter by the motor driven adsorption fan (11).

Dry air from the unit is circulated through a cooler and thence to the holds through the dry air pipe connected to the cooler (7). This cooler has the same function as the aftercooler on the Model H.

The reactivation air is drawn into the unit, through a filter by the reactivation fan (8). The reactivation air heater (6) raises the tem-

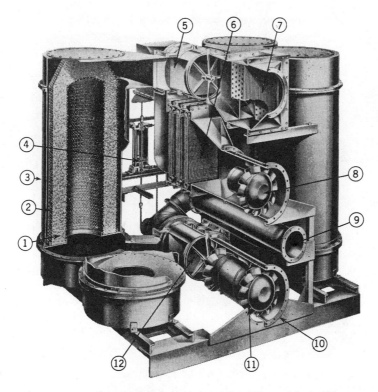

FIG. 8-15. Cargocaire Model S unit cutaway. (1) Silica gel bed; (2) screen; (3) steel cylinder; (4) valve operating piston; (5) upper four-way valve; (6) reactivation air heater; (7) cooler; (8) reactivation fan; (9) wet air duct; (10) adsorption fan housing; (11) adsorption fan; (12) lower four-way valve. Courtesy Cargocaire Engineering Corp.

perature of the air to 300°F. Heating is done by steam. After the reactivation air has picked up moisture from the silica gel beds, it is discharged to the atmosphere through the wet air duct (9).

The operation of the Model S unit is as simple as the Model H. Figure 8-16 shows most of the operating points and their approximate locations with the exception of the switch and controller for starting and stopping the fan motors. The controller is usually located near the unit and controls the electric power supply to the absorption and reactivation fan motors, as on the Model H.

The salt water valves control the flow of sea water to the cooler and usually are located as shown (1).

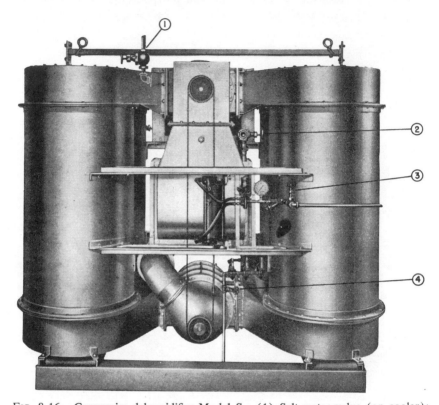

FIG. 8-16. Cargocaire dehumidifier Model S. (1) Salt water valve (on cooler); (2) steam supply valve (on reactivation air heater); (3) compressed air valve; (4) condensate valve (on reactivation air heater). Courtesy Cargocaire Engineering Corp.

There are two connections to the reactivation air heater. Each of these is controlled by a valve. The steam supply to the heater is turned on or off at the steam valve located approximately as shown by (2). The condensate from the heater passes through the valve (4).

The only other operating connection to the unit is the compressed air valve (3). This valve controls the flow of compressed air to the piston and cylinder for automatically shifting the 2 four-way valves and reversing the cycling of the unit.

As on the Model H, there is a hythergraph recorder connected to the unit to sample the dry air made by it. The Model S unit is capable of making 2000 cfm of dry air.

STARTING THE MODEL S

1. Close line switches at controller.
2. Turn controller switch to "Start" and check to see that both fans run properly.
3. Open condensate valve on the reactivation air heater.
4. Open steam valve to reactivation air heater.
5. Open the salt water supply and return valves to the cooler.
6. Open compressed air valve in line to valve control cylinder on the unit. Air pressure should be 35 lb per sq in.
7. Close knife switch in electric timer housing.

STOPPING THE MODEL S

1. Close steam and condensate valves.
2. Close salt water supply and return valves.
3. Turn controller switch to stop.
4. Open line switches in controller and electric timer.
5. Close compressed air valve.

The Cargocaire triethylene glycol (TEG) unit. The triethylene glycol used as a desiccant in this unit is a green liquid that is soluble in water. Hereafter, this desiccant will be referred to as Caire-col, the name given to the solution by the Cargocaire Engineering Corporation. Caire-col is odorless and has an initial boiling point of 540°F. It has a specific gravity of 1.125 and weighs 9.3 lb per gal. In its pure state, it has the ability of absorbing large quantities of water vapor. Within the unit, the air stream is brought into contact with the Caire-col solution by passing the air through a chamber which is continually sprayed with finely divided particles of the desiccant. The difference in the vapor pressure of the water in the air and the vapor pressure of the concentrated Caire-col causes the water vapor to leave the air and enter the solution.

The water vapor is condensed during this absorption process and its addition to the Caire-col solution results in a decrease in the solution's concentration. In other words, the specific gravity is reduced by addition of the water. This also reduces the boiling point of the Caire-col. The machine is designed to operate with a solution of water and Caire-col such that the boiling point of the solution is 305°F. As will be seen, the unit has a concentration side which is designed to keep the solution in the main sump concentrated with the exact amount of Caire-col and water to produce this boiling temperature of 305°F. To keep the solution at the right concentration, a portion of the absorbent is continuously drawn off, concentrated into pure triethylene glycol, and pumped back to the main sump. The original charge of Caire-col is 1400 lb. The sump is provided with a system of baffles to keep the operation of the unit from being affected by the rolling and pitching of the ship.

Figure 8-17 is a diagram on which can be traced the flow of the air, Caire-col solution, and the sea water used for cooling purposes. The air to be dried is drawn from the engine space through washable viscous filters (1) into the absorber (2). It contacts the Caire-col spray and both pass down over the finned absorber cooling coils (3).

The moisture in the air is given up to the solution during this process. After passing over the cooling coils, the Caire-col drops to the sump while the air is drawn around a baffle and up into the eliminator section.

The eliminator (4) is a three pass hook type and is inclined in the air stream at an angle of 30°. Any absorbent that may be entrained in the air is removed by the eliminator, and falls back into the sump. The low dew point air passes to the dry air fan (5) and is discharged through suitable ducts to the holds. The dry air fan has a capacity of 7000 cfm.

The solution pump (6) takes suction from the inboard side of the main sump (7), passes through a strainer to the pump, and discharges directly to the 24 spray nozzles (8) in the absorber. The fine spray mixes with the air and drops down over the cooling coils to the sump, where the cycle starts again.

The above description covers the operation of the absorbing side of the unit. As can be seen, it is very simple. The second part of the unit to be described has the function of removing from the Caire-col the water that was absorbed during the first phase.

The concentration pump (9) takes its suction from the main sump. The concentration pump discharges to a tee where the flow is divided. The greater portion flows through the run of the tee to a thermostatically controlled regulating valve (10). From the valve it passes through the economizer (11) and on to the concentrator (12).

A smaller amount of Caire-col passes through the branch of the tee, referred to before, through a normally open valve and strainer and a fixed orifice and to the concentration sampling chamber (13). This chamber checks on the concentration of the Caire-col by checking on the boiling point temperature of the Caire-col. Recall that the boiling point is affected by the water content of the Caire-col solution; hence, a measure of boiling point is a measure of concentration.

The concentration sampling chamber consists of two parts, namely the heater section and the liquid container section. The heater (14) consists of a tube into which a spiral finned copper heating coil is tightly inserted. The heater is raised to a temperature of approximately 320°F by steam taken from the main steam line leading to the steam chest in the concentrator. A small amount of the Caire-col solution is continually entering the heater where it is vaporized by the high temperature. The vapor from the solution will have a temperature equal to the boiling point of the Caire-col solution in the sump. The control bulb connected to the regulating valve (10) by a capillary tube reacts to the temperature of the vapor. If the temperature of the vapor measured by the bulb is above 305°F, the valve will shut automatically. If the boiling point of the Caire-col is above 305°F, it means that it is of a higher concentration than that for which the machine is designed. When the valve shuts down, no more Caire-col solution goes to the concentrator.

Eventually, as the Caire-col absorbs water during the first phase, without being replenished with concentrated Caire-col, the boiling point of the Caire-col in the sump will fall. The concentration pump continues to operate, however, and the concentration sampling chamber continues to function. The control bulb will eventually note the reduction in temperature of the vapor and open the thermostatically operated regulating valve. Obviously, this valve must be preset to operate over a desirable range. Summarizing, the regulating valve will be opened and closed dependent upon the temperature of the boiling point of the Caire-col as measured by the bulb in the concentration sampling chamber. Thus the flow of Caire-col back to the concentrator is controlled.

Assuming the regulating valve is opened, the main flow of Caire-col to the concentrator passes through the economizer. The economizer consists of a multipass, contraflow, extended fin tube heat exchanger. Caire-col from the absorber sump enters the *cold leg* to the economizer, passes through, and out to the concentrator. Hot Caire-col from the concentrator enters the *hot leg* to the economizer, passes through, and out to the absorber sump. In this way, the relatively cool solution from the sump, by way of the concentration pump, is preheated before entering the concentrator, whereas the return from the concentrator is cooled before returning to the absorber sump.

The concentrator section consists of a shell (12), steam chest (15), reflux coils (16), and main condenser (17). The shell has two sections; the main section contains the steam chest and a small overflow compartment. This is concentric to the main shell and about 1 in. in from the edge. This section extends down to about the middle of the tank. Reconcentrated Caire-col overflows from the main section into the outer section draining by gravity through the economizer and back to the absorber sump. The steam chest is submerged at all times. Sight glasses are provided in the shell to observe the liquid level and boiling action. The vapor rises in the shell until it strikes the reflux coils.

The reflux coils are designed to be always at a temperature of 215°F. Thus any Caire-col vapor which has a boiling point of 540°F will be condensed at this point and fall back into the concentrator. The steam mixed with the Caire-col vapor will not be condensed here but will pass on to the main condenser. After the steam is condensed, it drains off to a fresh water collecting tank.

A high temperature cutout switch is located above the reflux coils. This switch acts to shut down the entire unit when the temperature of the vapor exceeds 217°F as this would indicate a condition of Caire-col carry over.

The heat liberated in the reflux coils and the main condenser is carried away by sea water passing through these units.

GENERAL OPERATION.   After the initial startup, normal operation should be completely automatic. Figure 8-18 shows most of the operating points and their locations.

The unit can be controlled from two different locations. Start-stop buttons and indicator lights are located adjacent to the master control cabinet in the chart room and adjacent to the auxiliary controller on the dehumidifier. The dehumidifier may be placed in operation or secured from either of these stations. The lights (1) indicate that the fan and pump circuits are energized.

The auxiliary controller (2) is mounted on the unit. Its purpose is to house the electropneumatic relay and the terminals of the thermo-switch (3), located on the concentrator above the reflux coils. The relay controls the flow of air to the air operated steam and salt water valves and bleeds the air from the valves when the relay is de-energized. The thermoswitch contact is used to de-energize the main electric controller when high temperature occurs.

A gage board is mounted on the unit showing steam supply, concentration pump, solution pump, salt water supply, and salt water discharge pressures. There is also a static pressure gage that indicates the pressure drop across the air filters. When the gage shows a pressure drop of 0.5 in. of water, the filters need cleaning.

The air filters, provided for filtering the air entering the absorber, require frequent cleaning so that the air volume will not be reduced by the accumulation of dirt.

A filter cleaning station and instructions for servicing are provided near the unit with all equipment. When the filters are cleaned, they are re-oiled. If the operator does not allow all excess oil to drain off, there is danger of getting oil into the system. This will contaminate the solution and reduce the efficiency of the heat transfer surfaces.

A dewcel unit is mounted outboard at the suction of the dry air fan. This dewcel generates an electric signal which is relayed to the Brown recorder in the chart room. The recorder automatically plots the dew point of the dry air produced by the unit. This serves as a check on the operation of the unit.

Although thorough maintenance instructions need not be covered here, a few points will be mentioned. Some of the bearings on the fans and pumps are of a prelubricated sealed type and need no lubrication for the normal life of the bearings. Those that require care should be greased annually and a record of such action kept. Caution should always be exercised when greasing motor bearings. Most motor failures are due to excessive greasing. The only other lubrication required on the unit is the application of valve stem lubricant on the stems of the motorized steam and cooling water valves. This is important as these valves may be operated remotely from the bridge.

All strainers should be checked monthly and cleaned as necessary. Absorber cooling coils may become fouled due to dirty water; these may be cleaned by a suitable brushing and blowing with compressed air. The economizer may require flushing with hot water periodically. The steam chest should be cleaned by using a brush and flushing with a detergent or caustic solution and then rinsing with fresh water. The main condenser and reflux coils may be cleaned by brushing and flushing thoroughly. The spray nozzles can be inspected by removing the air filter. If the spray pattern of any nozzle is uneven, it should be cleaned. The heater element in the sampling chamber will also need flushing out periodically. When isolating any of the above parts for servicing, it is done by closing normally open valves on either side of the part. If the part has Caire-col in it, the Caire-col should be carefully drained off into a clean container and returned to the main sump.

STARTING THE TEG UNIT. When starting for the first time or after an extended shutdown:

1. Check the liquid level in the sump ($\frac{1}{4}$ to $\frac{2}{3}$ glass).
2. Open main condensate valve on the concentrator.
3. Open steam stop ahead of pneumatic controlled steam valve.
4. Open salt water supply valve ahead of pneumatic control valve and salt water overboard valve.
5. Close all line switches.
6. Open stop valve in air line.
7. Set air switch to automatic position.

With the above preparations, the unit may now be started from the engine room or chart room by depressing the start button. The pneumatically controlled steam and water valves should be checked to see if they have opened properly.

After a time delay of 2 to 2½ min for conditioning the unit for the flow of dry air, the time delay device energizes the motor circuits. The dry air fan, solution pump, and concentration pump start, in that order. By looking through the sight window of the concentrator, the operator can see the flow of Caire-col over the overflow compartment and the flow of Caire-col from the discharge pipe coming from the concentration sampling chamber. The flow from the discharge pipe should be in a small stream.

STOPPING AND SECURING THE TEG UNIT. When the unit is to be temporarily secured, depressing the stop button in the chart room or at the dehumidifier is all that is necessary. This operates the electropneumatic valve which in turn closes the steam and cooling water supply to the unit. This also stops the dry air fan, solution pump, and concentration pump. In this condition, the unit may be started at any time by simply pressing either push button.

If the dehumidifier is to be secured for an extended period, it should be completely secured in the following manner:

1. Press stop button.

2. Close steam stop ahead of automatic valve and close condensate return valve.

3. Close cooling water supply stop ahead of automatic valve. Close cooling water outlet valve.

4. Open knife switches on the dry air fan and the solution and concentration pumps.

When secured for longer than 3 weeks, the unit should be set into operation for a short time at least once a week to insure continued free operation of all parts.

Thermotank Drihold indicator. The Drihold system has all three of the divisions of the mechanical dew point control systems located at each hatch. The instrumentation consists of a Drihold indicator. This instrument is designed to mechanically compare the dew point of the inside air to that of the outside air and show on its dial how the system should be operated as a result of such comparison.

The instrument consists of two dew point sensitive elements each housed in a separate chamber. One of these chambers is connected to the outside atmosphere and the other to the cargo space by means of pipes. A sample of the respective atmospheres is drawn through these pipes and over the dew point sensitive elements of the instrument. One element controls a movable dial in the instrument and the other a movable pointer. The position of the pointer on the dial indicates directly whether the system should be set up to ventilate or to recirculate and add dry air.

Figure 8-19 is an illustration of the Drihold indicator. The appearance of the dial and pointer when recirculation and dry air are required is shown in the insert to the left. The same relationship when ventilation is required is shown to the right.

The Drihold dehumidifier and hold fan and duct system. When describing this system, it is natural to view the dehumidifier and the fold fan and duct system as one integrated unit. The air drying unit and the fan and duct housing are all located at each individual hatch. Figure 8-20 is a sketch of the Drihold unit at the deck level. It shows the parts of the unit in detail. When ventilating, the fan is normally operated as an exhaust fan. The damper (1) leading to the drying unit is closed, the upper damper (2) is positioned so as to close off the vertical trunk (3), and the lower damper (4) is opened so as to draw part of the fan's capacity from the lower hold through the duct to the right. The duct to the left leads to the 'tweendeck areas from where the remaining air comes.

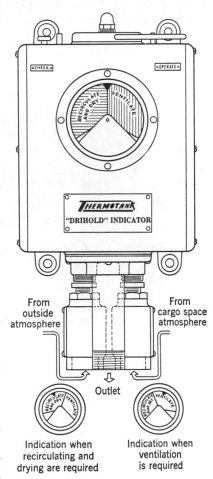

FIG. 8-19. Drihold indicator. Courtesy Thermotank Ltd.

When recirculating, damper (2) is positioned so as to shut off the outside air and damper (4) is set to close the opening between the right hand duct and the fan housing. Damper (1) is opened and about 500 cfm of air is drawn into the air drying unit. The air is forced, by a pressure difference, across the main fan to circulate down through the heat exchanger (5), over the condensing surfaces (6), and back through the heat exchanger into the main air stream. Cold brine having a temperature not less than 30°F should be supplied to the condensing unit.

The fan is of a reversible type and it may be an advantage when operating, at times, to change the direction of flow with a view to maintaining uniform conditions in the cargo space. The fans should nor-

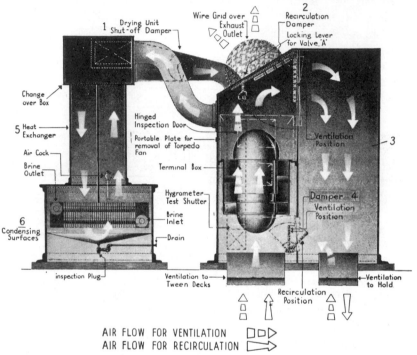

AIR FLOW FOR VENTILATION
AIR FLOW FOR RECIRCULATION

FIG. 8-20.   Arrangement of a Drihold unit.   Courtesy Thermotank Ltd.

mally be operated as exhaust fans, since the pressure created in the cargo hold when operating as supply fans will tend to balloon the tarpaulin covering the hatch.

GENERAL LAYOUT.   The air drying unit, fan, and housing are located at one end of the hold.   When ventilating, this end is normally the exhaust side.   At the other end of the hatch, an opening to the atmosphere through suitable ducts is installed.   This side may be fitted with a fan or may rely on natural circulation.   This side is normally the supply side.

Figure 8-21a is a diagram of the entire system set up to ventilate at a hold and shows the air flow under these conditions.   When ventilating, the upper damper (1) is set to shut off the vertical trunk (2) next to the fan (3), and the lower damper (4) is opened so that the fan will draw

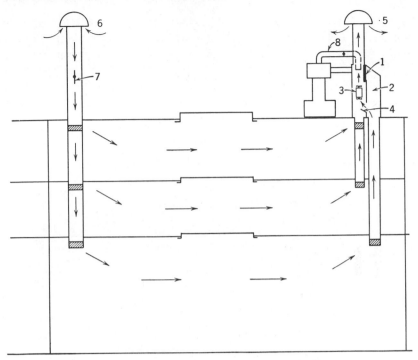

FIG. 8-21(*a*). Drihold system set up to ventilate.

about $\frac{1}{3}$ of its capacity from the lower compartment. The fan discharges the air through the exhaust vent (5) directly to the atmosphere.

The fan capacity may vary from 4500 to 9000 cfm depending upon the speed at which it is operated. All the air exhausted by the fan is replaced through the supply side intake vent (6).

Figure 8-21*b* is a diagram of the Drihold system set up to recirculate and add dry air. The upper damper (1) is set to close off the outside air. The air forced upward by the fan passes to the right and down to the lower compartment through the vertical trunk (2). The entire capacity of the fan passes along this route with the exception of about 500 cfm which is taken into the drying unit through the intake pipe (8). The damper on this pipe must be open.

As the air passes over the refrigeration coils of the condensing unit, the moisture in it is condensed out. Its dew point will be lowered to 32° or 33°F. Inasmuch as this air is continually being drawn from the closed hold and continually dried to some extent, the dew point of the air in the hold will be kept low enough to prevent condensation on the ship or cargo.

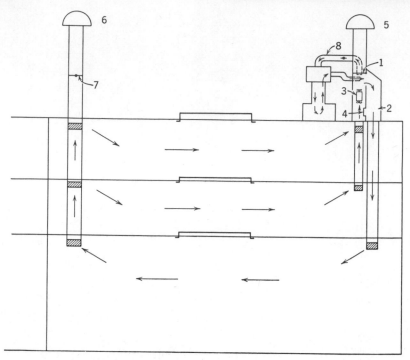

FIG. 8-21(b).   Drihold system set up to recirculate and add dry air.

During the recirculation process, the fan takes air from the 'tweendeck area.   The supply vent damper (7) is closed to the outside atmosphere; hence, the air taken from the 'tweendeck spaces is replaced by air from the lower hold through the connecting ducts seen on the diagram.   This completes the cycle of the recirculated air.

The Kathabar dehumidifier.   The Kathabar unit uses a lithium chloride solution as a desiccant, hereafter referred to as Kathene.   The operation of the unit is explained best by a discussion of the flow diagram as shown by Fig. 8-22.   The Kathene passes through two sides in the operation of the unit: (1) The absorbing side and (2) the regenerating side.

On the absorbing side, the fan (1), with a rated capacity of 5000 to 7000 cfm, draws the air to be dried through the filter (2) into the absorbing chamber (3).   Inside the absorbing chamber, Kathene is being sprayed from a bank of nozzles (4).   The incoming air comes in contact with the finely divided Kathene, and, because of the differential existing between the vapor pressures, moisture leaves the air and enters the Kathene.   During this chemical process, the water is condensed and dilutes the Kathene to some extent.   The air and Kathene drop down and pass over the cooling coils (5) which are cooled by circulating sea water. Below the cooling coils the Kathene drops into the common sump (6) while the dried air passes up the right hand chamber. The air passes through a bank of eliminator blades (7) which pick up any entrained droplets of Kathene. From the absorbing side, the dried air is discharged to the holds. All dry air may be discharged to any one hold or the capacity may be divided up between a number of holds.

The fan on the regenerating side (8) draws air past the filter (9) into a chamber where Kathene is being sprayed over steam heating coils

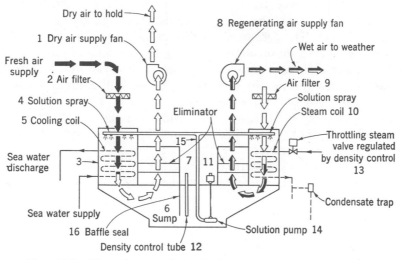

FIG. 8-22. Flow diagram of the Kathabar cargo conditioning unit.

(10). The heat from the steam coils drives the water vapor from the Kathene into the air passing through the regenerating chamber. The moisture that leaves the Kathene in this compartment is the same moisture that was previously picked up by the Kathene on the absorbing side.

The regenerated Kathene drops to the sump and the moisture laden air passes over the eliminator blades (11) and out to the atmosphere. The sump is a common sump for both sides. The Kathene is diluted on one side and regenerated on the other. Obviously the rate of regeneration must be no faster or slower than the rate of absorption. If faster, the solution will become such a concentrated salt solution that the lithium chloride will solidify by crystalizing. If slower, the solution will become dilute and lose its absorption qualities.

To prevent this overconcentration or overdilution, the system is provided with an automatic balancing control. This control is in the form of a density control mechanism. If the solution becomes too concentrated, its density will be above some optimum level. If too dilute, the density will be below this optimum level. The optimum density, of course, is that which allows the Kathene to readily absorb moisture from the air on the absorbing side under operating temperatures.

The operation of this density control device starts with the density control towers (12). Kathene bubbles through these towers where its density is continually measured. There is a connection between the density control towers and the steam regulating valve (13) which controls the flow of steam to the heating coils. When the solution is at optimum level of concentration, the steam valve will be partially open. If the rate of absorption becomes faster than the regeneration rate, the density will fall. The density control towers will relay this information to the automatic steam regulating valve and it will open to cause a rise in the regeneration rate. If the absorption rate becomes slower than the regeneration rate, the density will rise. This fact will result in the automatic closing down of the steam regulating valve.

The sump pump (14) delivers the Kathene up the riser (15) and to the two branch lines. One of these branch lines leads to the absorber, the other to the regenerator.

The two sides are sealed from each other by the baffle (16) which has its lower edge submerged below the surface of the Kathene in the sump.

CHAPTER 9

Research and development

in the industry

Generally speaking, it is true that industrial progress has passed the waterfront by during the first half of this century. The causes seem to be complex and many. But as long as the problem is recognized and men are encouraged to think about how to change things for the better, there is hope that the waterfront activities will make up some of the lost ground in the next 50 years. It is the purpose of this chapter to list some of the institutions or groups that are responsible for making this progress a reality and to indicate broadly what their sphere of influence is. A secondary purpose of this chapter is to outline a few additional ideas that seem to offer the possibility of relief from the inefficient methods seen on nearly all general cargo piers of the world today.

BASIC PROBLEM AND GROUPS RESPONSIBLE FOR SOLUTION

Port speed and sea speed. The most economical marine operation is that which makes the sum of all economical factors affecting port speed and sea speed equal to a minimum value. In the past, the industry has concentrated on the problems of attaining an economical sea speed and much progress has been made. Ships built during World War I burned approximately 0.8 barrel of oil per mile at a speed of 10 knots. Ships of World War II were capable of 0.7 barrel of oil per mile at a speed of 16 knots. These economies have been possible because of better power plant and hull designs.

While the time at sea has been steadily decreasing, the time in port has been increasing. The only time that a ship is earning money for her owners, however, is when she is under way between ports with a paying cargo in her bottoms. Therefore, it is evident that effort must now be expended by labor, management, and the government to increase port speed. Port speed is entirely dependent upon cargo operations.

The correct steps and the correct direction of these steps is the concern of many groups. In the past decade, there has been a steady increase of interest in this matter. At the present time, there is promise of much progress in the next decade. Research and development are the responsibility of labor, management, governmental, and certain private groups. Every group or individual connected with the transportation of goods by water should be concerned with the success of the combined thinking on this matter. Certain groups have greater responsibility than others for some are charged with initiating corrective action as well as investigation of the problem.

It is the author's poinion that immediate relief from the slowdown in port can be attained to some degree by two positive steps: First, there must be an increase in cooperation between labor and management. Labor must be willing to give all ideas for mechanization a fair trial. Management must be willing to give labor a fair share of increased compensation in the form of increased salaries and better working conditions. The greatest problem here is to work out a practicable measuring device for ascertaining the increase in compensation and to define what is meant by a *fair share*.

Second, management, government, and labor must work out a system of encouraging *thought* on ways and means of increasing productivity and, what is of equal importance, a system of giving *all ideas* a full and complete test to determine their worth. A survey of what has happened to several apparently worthy ideas in the last 8 to 10 years is sufficient to discourage anyone from spending time on other ideas. At the present time there is no effective method sponsored by any of the responsible groups to pick up these ideas and to try them out. This is, perhaps, the first step that must be taken to mitigate the problems of the waterfront. Without *ideas* there can be no progress; therefore, it is imperative that a climate that encourages ideas be created by the responsible powers.

A long range plan for increasing the productivity of the waterfront, perhaps beyond the imagination of many contemporary leaders in the field, seems to lie in a gradual abandonment of many basic ideas of design and operation of the ship and pier of the past. In other words, it may be that the only way to make really noteworthy progress is to change the design of the ships and the piers so that they may work more closely together and make greater efficiency possible. This, of course, is no more than an hypothesis. The truth must be determined by research and development by the interested groups mentioned below. Any change must be gradual, but once the need for change is determined, it should be initiated.

Federal Maritime Board—Maritime Administration. The governmental agency having the greatest control over the commercial maritime affairs of the United States is a three member group known as the Federal Maritime Board (FMB) consisting of the chairman and two members. The chairman of the FMB serves as the Maritime Administrator and holds both positions jointly.

The FMB was preceded by the Maritime Commission which was organized pursuant to the Merchant Marine Act of 1936 to replace the older U.S. Shipping Board which was established during World War I. The FMB was set up in 1950.

The FMB is a judicial and policy making group. They act on requests for operational and constructional subsidies and make decisions relative to the various trade routes that the United States shall maintain.

The Maritime Administration, directed by the Maritime Administrator, carries out the policies of the FMB and manages the details of running the maritime affairs of the government.

One of the responsibilities of the Maritime Administration is that of developing plans for research and development leading to more efficient ships. Prototype ships are built and tested and plans are made and kept current for the quick construction in large numbers of these advanced design types. Since World War II two such prototype vessels have been placed in active service. The first was named the Schuyler Otis Bland and designated the C3-S-DX1 of which only one was built. The second type is most commonly known as the Mariner type of which 35 were built and originally named after the nicknames of states, such as the Keystone Mariner. These ships have the classification of C4-S-1a. The work relative to research and development in the field of cargo operations is centered in the Division of Preliminary Design and Division of Technical Development under the Office of Ship Construction and Repair.

At the present time the Maritime Administration has developed seven additional prototype designs besides the Mariner type.   These include 4 cargo ships, a bulk carrier, a tanker, and a trailership.

The *Seafarer* type has the classification of C4-S-RM19a.   This design is comparable to the World War II C3's and C4's and the principal characteristics are as follows:

Dimensions	
Length, overall	529 ft
Length, between perpendiculars	494 ft
Beam, molded	74½ ft
Depth	44½ ft
Loaded Draft	29¾ ft
Displacements and tonnages	
Load displacement	20,330 tons
Light displacement	6,850 tons
Deadweight	13,480 tons
Crew and stores	50 tons
Fuel oil	2,660 tons
Fresh water	170 tons
Dry cargo deadweight	10,300 tons
Reefer cargo deadweight	300 tons
Gross tonnage	11,500 tons
Net tonnage	7,000 tons
Capacities	
Bale cubic	732,000 cu ft
Reefer cubic	30,000 cu ft
Passengers	12
Number of holds	6
Booms	12, 5 ton
	8, 10 ton
	1, 50 ton
Machinery	
Type	Turbine
Shaft horsepower	12,500
Speed	18 knots
Cruising radius	15,900 miles

The *Clipper* type with engine room aft has the classification of C3-S-RM18a.   This design is comparable to the older C2 prototype. The characteristics follow:

Dimensions	
Length, overall	496 ft
Length, between perpendiculars	460 ft
Beam, molded	73 ft
Depth	41⅓ ft
Loaded draft	28 ft
Light ship draft	11⅓ ft

Displacements and tonnages
Loaded displacement	16,900 tons
Light ship displacement	6,000 tons
Deadweight	10,900 tons
Crew and stores	50 tons
Fuel oil	2,250 tons
Fresh water	190 tons
Cargo deadweight	8,410 tons
Gross tonnage	10,000 tons
Net tonnage	6,000 tons

Capacities
Bale cubic	600,000 cu ft
Reefer cubic	34,000 cu ft
Passengers	12
Number of holds	6
Booms	2, ½ ton
	10, 5 ton
	8, 10 ton
	1, 60 ton

Machinery
Type	Turbine
Shaft horsepower	11,000
Speed	18 knots
Crusing radius	15,000 miles

The *Freedom* type with engine room aft has the classification of C2-S-RM15a. This design is comparable to the C1B type of the older prototypes. The characteristics follow:

Dimensions
Length, overall	440 ft
Length, between perpendiculars	417 ft
Beam, molded	65 ft
Depth	39 ft
Loaded draft	26½ ft
Light ship draft	10¼ ft

Displacements and tonnages
Loaded displacement	13,350 tons
Light ship displacement	4,550 tons
Deadweight	8,800 tons
Crew and stores	40 tons
Fuel oil	1,690 tons
Fresh water	160 tons
Cargo deadweight	6,910 tons
Gross tonnage	7,500 tons
Net tonnage	4,500 tons

Capacities
Bale cubic   497,000 cu ft
Reefer cubic   29,000 cu ft
Passengers   0
Number of holds   5
Booms   2, 1 ton
                                        14, 10 ton
                                         1, 60 ton

Machinery
Type   Turbine
Shaft horsepower   7,000
Speed   16 knots
Cruising radius   13,300 miles

The *Island* type with engine room aft has the classification of
C1-M-RM17a. Like the older prototype C1-M-AV1 she has diesel
engines. The characteristics follow:

Dimensions
Length, overall   383 ft
Length, between perpendiculars   350 ft
Beam, molded   57 ft
Depth   32 ft
Load draft   21 ft
Light ship draft   8½ ft

Displacements and tonnages
Loaded displacement   7,960 tons
Light ship displacement   2,830 tons
Deadweight   5,130 tons
Crew and stores   30 tons
Fuel oil   390 tons
Diesel oil   60 tons
Fresh water   100 tons
Cargo deadweight   4,550 tons
Gross tonnage   4,700 tons
Net tonnage   2,800 tons

Capacities
Bale cubic   274,000 cu ft
Reefer cubic   13,000 cu ft
Passengers   0
Number of holds   4
Booms   2, 1½ ton
                                         6,   5 ton
                                         4, 10 ton
                                         1, 60 ton
Machinery
Type   Diesel
Shaft horsepower   3,200
Speed   14 knots
Cruising radius   9,000 miles

The *Turnpike* type is a trailership or roll on–roll off type ship for coastwise or intercoastal service capable of loading over the stern or through sideports (see pp. 506–510). The classification of this ship is C4-ST-RM21a and the characteristics follow:

Dimensions	
Length, overall	518 ft
Length, between perpendiculars	480 ft
Beam, molded	78 ft
Depth to main deck	42 ft
Loaded draft	19 ft
Light draft	13¼ ft
Displacements and tonnages	
Loaded displacement	11,080 tons
Light ship displacement	6,680 tons
Deadweight	4,400 tons
Crew and stores	50 tons
Fuel oil	650 tons
Fresh water	100 tons
Cargo deadweight	3,600 tons
Gross tonnage	2,850 tons
Net tonnage	10 tons
Capacities	
Trailers averaging 30 ft long and 8 ft wide	
Upper deck	29
Main deck	91
2nd deck	80
Total	200
Passengers	8
Machinery	
Type	Geared turbine
Shaft horsepower	15,000
Speed	20 knots
Fuel consumption per day at sea	87 tons
Fuel consumption per day in port	6½ tons
Crusing radius	3,000 miles

The *Bulk* type was developed to carry heavy ores such as iron ore or light ore such as bauxite, and also coal or grain. This ship's classification by the Maritime Administration is C5-S-RM20a and her characteristics follow:

Dimensions	
Length, overall	609 ft
Length, between perpendiculars	580 ft
Beam, molded	77 ft
Depth	46 ft
Loaded draft	33 ft
Light ship draft	9⅝ ft

Displacements and tonnages
　　Loaded displacement　　　　　　　32,585 tons
　　Light ship displacement　　　　　　8,585 tons
　　Deadweight　　　　　　　　　　24,000 tons
　　Crew and stores　　　　　　　　　50 tons
　　Fuel oil　　　　　　　　　　　2,200 tons
　　Fresh water　　　　　　　　　　150 tons
　　Cargo deadweight　　　　　　　21,600 tons
　　Gross tonnage　　　　　　　　16,800 tons
　　Net tonnage　　　　　　　　　10,200 tons

Capacities
　　Molded volume　　　　　　　816,000 cu ft
　　Passengers　　　　　　　　　　　0
　　Number of holds　　　　　　　　　9

Machinery
　　Type　　　　　　　　　　　Turbine
　　Shaft horsepower　　　　　　　11,900
　　Speed　　　　　　　　　　　16 knots
　　Cruising radius　　　　　　　11,500 miles

The *Pipeline* type was developed as a fast commercial oiler that can be easily converted to a fleet oiler. She is classified as a T5-S-RM2a and her characteristics follow:

Dimensions
　　Length, overall　　　　　　　　615 ft
　　Length, between perpendiculars　　595 ft
　　Breadth, molded　　　　　　　　80 ft
　　Depth, molded　　　　　　　　$44\frac{1}{2}$ ft
　　Loaded draft　　　　　　34 ft $10\frac{1}{8}$ in.

Displacements and tonnages
　　Loaded displacement　　　　　　31,345 tons
　　Light ship displacement　　　　　8,820 tons
　　Deadweight　　　　　　　　　22,525 tons

Capacity in barrels　　　　　　　180,000

Machinery
　　Type　　　　　　　　　　　Turbine
　　Shaft horsepower　　　　　　　20,000
　　Speed　　　　　　　　　　　20 knots
　　Cruising radius　　　　　　　10,450 miles

The U.S. Navy. The work within the naval establishment relative to research and development leading to improved cargo operations is carried on by three groups. All of these are especially interested in solving problems that are common to military operations, but some of the ideas developed by them may become useful in commercial cargo operations. In fact, it is probable that the Landing Ship Tank carrier (LST) idea is the father of the ideas of today that deal with larger and faster roll on–roll off ships in both the commercial and military areas.

The U.S. Naval Supply Research and Development Facility (NSRDF), located in Bayonne, N. J., continually carries on research and development into supply engineering, ashore and afloat, encompassing the fields of packaging, preservation, and materials handling. This group is concerned with problems in logistics and conducts research into any matter that the chief of the Bureau of Supplies and Accounts of the Navy may direct.

The Military Sea Transportation Service (MSTS) maintains a research and development branch under the Division of Planning and Policy in Washington, D. C. This research and development group has the job of keeping the MSTS command abreast of developments in all phases of ship design and operation. This, of course, includes equipment and methods for handling cargo. The MSTS research and development branch concerns itself also with developing plans for making the ships operated by the MSTS more efficient. This latter activity is in addition to evaluating new ideas that appear anywhere in the shipping industry. Their budget does not include funds for actually installing or building new devices. They only make recommendations to the Commander, MSTS, and if approved by that office, the funds for the work come from the Division of Maintenance and Repair, MSTS, or the Bureau of Ships. The MSTS has operational control over two types of ships: (1) Those that are manned by civil service personnel and known as USNS ships, and (2) those manned entirely by naval personnel and known as USS ships. Work on the latter is financed by the Bureau of Ships entirely; work on the former is financed by the Maintenance and Repair Division, MSTS, with some exceptions that remain under the cognizance of the Bureau of Ships.

In addition to the above two groups, the Office of Naval Research (ONR) also may sponsor investigations of cargo operations by providing fiscal support for appropriate studies (see p. 512).

The U.S. Army. The U.S. Army maintains the transportation center at Fort Eustis, Va., which carries on research and development into all phases of military cargo operations and related logistical problems.

The U.S. Coast Guard. The U.S. Coast Guard does not concern itself with the equipment and methods of cargo operations in general. However, under the provisions of R.S. 4472 (46 U.S.C. 170), the Commandant of the Coast Guard has promulgated regulations for handling, stowage, storage, and transportation of explosives and certain other types of dangerous articles. These regulations are contained in the

Coast Guard Publication 187; see pp. 218–228. The Merchant Marine Inspection Division of the Coast Guard also is responsible for examining applicants for licenses as deck officers of Merchant ships to determine their proficiency and knowledge of cargo operations.

The American Bureau of Shipping. The American Bureau of Shipping (ABS) is a classification society and as such they are interested primarily in the ship itself and its equipment; this includes means for protection of the cargo spaces from the sea. They also have developed rules for certification of cargo gear (see pp. 285–286). These particular rules do not affect the ship's classification; they are an entirely separate set of regulations which were developed at the request of the industry by the bureau's special subcommittee on cargo gear. One of the reasons for the development of these cargo gear standards was that many of the principal maritime nations have statutory regulations concerning cargo gear. The United States does not have such regulations, but it is necessary for United States ships to comply with the regulations, or an acceptable equivalent, when they visit ports in those countries having such requirements.

Another connection with the cargo operations of the merchant ship held by the ABS is that of inspections of refrigeration facilities of ships. The ABS's rules provide for the following inspections after the installation of refrigerating facilities for cargo:

1. Loading surveys. A survey made with a view to issuing a certificate stating that the refrigerated holds and the machinery are fit to carry the refrigerated cargo intended.

2. Semiannual surveys. A general survey of the refrigerating machinery and installation.

3. Intermediate surveys. Surveys made every 2 years and providing for increased inspection and requiring the opening up of certain machinery.

4. Special periodical surveys. Survey made every 4 years which is an extension of the intermediate survey. The inspection of all parts is more detailed and careful.

5. Continuous survey. These surveys may be carried out in the case of vessels which are engaged on voyages of 3 months duration or less. They provide for making all of the previous surveys periodically on a step by step basis. This prevents tying up the ship for any length of time.

Because of its functions, it often appears as if the ABS is a government agency. This is not true. The ABS is a self-supporting corporation under the laws of the state of New York; it has no capital stock and pays no dividends. It is financed through fees charged for the services rendered by its surveyors in connection with approval of plans, supervision of vessels under construction, various types of surveys, and for the assignment of load lines. The ABS is recognized officially by the U.S. government for such purposes as classifying vessels owned by the United States and for purposes of making load line surveys in accordance with certain laws of the government.

The National Cargo Bureau, Inc. The National Cargo Bureau (NCB) is governed by a board of directors of 18, including the Commandant of the U.S. Coast Guard and the Maritime Administrator. A group of officers carry out the policies and decisions of the directors and manage the Bureau. The executive, finance, operating, membership, and Pacific Coast advisory committees help to develop policies for consideration by the board of directors. The technical aspects of the NCB are the direct responsibility of the chief surveyor under the guidance and direction of the officers. The chief surveyor is assisted by deputy chief surveyors at New York, Houston, and San Francisco.

The NCB is a nonprofit membership organization incorporated under the laws of the state of New York, and its purposes are:

1. To provide a private agency to formulate recommendations to the government as to regulations concerning the safe stowage of dangerous goods.

2. To work at industry level in the international field to achieve uniformity of safety standards and regulations for the stowage of cargo.

3. To act as an information agency on the problems of transporting the thousands of commodities offered for water transportation and to make this information available to the shipping industry and other groups.

4. To offer the shipping industry a low cost cargo loading inspection service directly at the loading operation.

The cargo loading inspections are made by surveyors who are deemed qualified to advise ship operators and stevedores with regard to the safe stowage of cargo. This service is available, on a cost basis, to shipowners and operators, who wish to avail themselves of it. The presence of an impartial, objective NCB surveyor supports the efficiency of the ship operator's personnel. The surveyor supplements the operating and stevedoring personnel.

When a surveyor completes the inspection of cargo loading and finds the stowage satisfactory, he will issue a certificate of loading as shown in Fig. 9-1.

From the foregoing, it should be clear that the NCB does not concern itself with cargo operation problems except as they are related to the safe stowage of particular commodity types. The NCB is concerned that the stowage does not endanger the cargo itself, adjacent cargo, the ship, or the crew.

No. S-_____

CERTIFICATE OF LOADING COVERING SPECIFIC CARGO
– OF –
NATIONAL CARGO BUREAU, INC

Issued, as to dangerous cargo and grain in bulk, under authority of the United States of America, Commandant, United States Coast Guard, pursuant to (1) the provisions of the International Convention for the Safety of Life at Sea, 1948; (2) the provisions of section 4472, Revised Statutes, as amended (46 U. S. C. 170 (7) (a)); (3) the provisions of section 4417, Revised Statutes, as amended (46 U. S. C. 391); (4) the Magnuson Act of August 9, 1950, amending the Espionage Act (50 U. S. C. 191a); and (5) the provisions of the Act of July 5, 1884, as amended (46 U. S. C. 2) and of section 4403, Revised Statutes, as amended (46 U S. C. 372).

NEW YORK, N. Y._____, 19_____

This is to Certify, That in connection with the loading of the specific cargo hereinafter mentioned the_____whereof_____is Master, of_____Net Tons Measurement, built at_____in 19_____, bound for_____has been under the inspection of a surveyor or surveyors of National Cargo Bureau, Inc., at this port from time to time during the course of the loading of the undermentioned cargo; that so far as it came under the observation of such surveyor or surveyors, the stowage of dangerous cargo and of grain in bulk was in accordance with the regulations of the Commandant, United States Coast Guard, and the stowage of other cargo not subject to Coast Guard Regulations was in accordance with the recommendations of National Cargo Bureau, Inc.

THIS CERTIFICATE IS NOT A CERTIFICATE OF SEAWORTHINESS AND RELATES ONLY TO THE FOLLOWING CARGO

DUPLICATE

Draft of water loaded,   ft.   in. forward,   ft.   in. aft   Freeboard,   ft.   in.
MEAN DRAFT   ft.   in.

THE FOREGOING INSPECTION WAS UNDERTAKEN AND THIS CERTIFICATE IS ISSUED ON THE FOLLOWING TERMS AND CONDITIONS:

While the Officers and Committees of National Cargo Bureau, Inc. use their best endeavors to insure that the functions of the Bureau are properly executed, neither such Officers and Committees, nor the Bureau, nor its surveyors, employees, representatives or agents, are under any circumstances whatever to be held responsible for any inaccuracy in any report or certificate issued by the Bureau or its surveyors, or for any error of judgment, default or negligence of the surveyors or other employees, representatives or agents, of the Bureau. This certificate covers only the cargo herein described as having been loaded at place of issuance of this certificate, and under no conditions is it to be deemed to cover any other cargo whether loaded at place of issuance of this certificate, or any other port. This certificate shall not be valid if upon sailing from any loading port and/or any fueling port and/or during any part of the voyage, the vessel's draft shall exceed that permitted by the law of her flag and/or the draft designated for the vessel in the Classification Society in which she may be classed.

_____Surveyor.

FIG. 9-1.

Accident Prevention Bureau. The Accident Prevention Bureau (APB) of the Pacific Maritime Association was the first and for many years the only organization devoted to the prevention of accidents in cargo handling operations. Started in San Francisco in 1927, its activities soon spread to all of the ports on the west coast.

The APB receives reports on all injuries to longshoremen, analyzes the causes of the accidents which produced them, and makes recommendations for the prevention of those accidents to the members of the Pacific Maritime Association.

Early in the 1930's, the APB coordinated and directed the work of representatives of both labor and management in the development of the Pacific Coast Marine Safety Code. Up until 1948 there was no provision for enforcement other than the evident reasonableness and practicality of its provisions, which were accepted by the majority of the employers. In that year, the code was made a part of the contract between the employers and the union and thus became as enforceable as any other portion of the contract.

The APB has never sought nor been given police power to enforce its recommendations, although it is often called upon to advise on particular conditions which arise. It has relied upon education and persuasion to improve the conditions and practices on the waterfront. Monthly reminders go to all longshoremen in the form of messages on time cards, the supervisors are reached by a monthly bulletin, and posters are placed weekly on all piers. Monthly safety committee meetings of management representatives as well as of joint labor and supervisory representatives are held each month.

The APB sponsors safety contests among the various stevedoring companies in each port and the coast as a whole and makes annual awards to those companies having low compensable injury frequency rates.

It is probable that the very marked reduction in injury frequency rates is due largely to the fact that safety engineers of the APB visit all the ships in the major ports at least once during their stay. The safety engineers promote interest in the APB program by pointing out unsafe practices, calling attention to unsafe gear or other physical conditions, and otherwise stimulating interest in safety on the part of ships' officers, stevedoring supervisors, and the longshoremen themselves.

The APB also serves the steamship company members of the Pacific Maritime Association in the prevention of accidents to crews of the vessels. In addition to monthly bulletins directed to officers and to the unlicensed personnel, there is the Marine Safe Practices Pamphlet Series which contain longer discussions of various phases of safety aboard ship. Some of these are devoted to conditions which affect the safety of longshoremen and the efficiency of cargo handling operations.

Other ports in the United States developed and adopted safety codes 20 years or so ago, but until recent years there has been little attention paid to portwide accident prevention except on the west coast. Many individual companies have developed safety programs and have achieved worthwhile results. Because of the casualness of longshore labor in most ports and the fact that the vast majority of the accidents result from unsafe practices and methods rather than from unsafe gear, a truly effective program of accident prevention in stevedoring must almost necessarily be on a portwide basis so that men are being influenced to follow the same safe practices wherever they may be working.

Early in 1952 the New York Shipping Association developed a Safety Bureau, which is working with the stevedores in the port of New York. Already there has been an appreciable improvement in the injury frequency rates.

Longshoremen working aboard ship are not legally in any state; they are, therefore, covered by the Federal Longshoremen's and Harbor Workers' Compensation Act. This act directs the Department of Labor, through the Bureau of Labor Standards, to: "make studies and investigations with respect to safety provisions and the causes of injuries . . . and to . . . make recommendations as to the best means of preventing such injuries."

The Bureau of Employees' Compensation, which administers the act, collects and publishes data on injuries and their costs, whereas the Bureau of Labor Standards uses the accident reports as a basis for its recommendations.

With the very small staff of four men available to work only part time on waterfront safety, the Bureau of Labor Standards' (BLS) activities are necessarily very limited. They are confined almost exclusively to educational work with supervisors and longshoremen by means of talks illustrated with colored slides taken aboard ship during operations in various ports and through publication of informational material. Because it feels that a uniformity of safe practices from port to port is both practical and desirable, the BLS is currently seeking the cooperation of the industry in developing such a set of minimum standards acceptable throughout the country.

Responsibility for safety. The stevedore comes aboard the ship as a contractor, and he carries the financial and moral responsibility for the safety of his men. Therefore, there is likely to be a tendency for ships' officers to pay little or no attention to the stevedoring operations other than the actual stowage and breaking out of cargo and to make only such replacement or repairs of gear as are brought to their attention.

Although it is true that the stevedore has to pay the cost of compensation insurance from his own pocket, it is, in the last analysis, the ship and the shipper who pay these costs. They are by no means insignificant. In New York, for example, the manual rate is $16.50; this means that for every $100 the stevedore pays in wages, he pays $16.50 to the insurance company. If an individual stevedore's experience is good, he will pay less than that figure but if his losses are above average he may pay more. This tremendous cost is one which is upon the shipping industry as a whole; it therefore behooves every ship's officer to do what he can to avoid injuries to longshoremen regardless of the legal responsibility.

The ship also has a very important direct interest in the safety of longshoremen. The compensation act provides adequate but definitely limited financial aid to an injured longshoreman, and he can get no more than the law allows regardless of how much at fault his employer, the stevedore, may be nor any less no matter how much at fault he himself may be.

However, the injured man can sue the vessel as a third party if any responsibility for the accident can be attributed to the vessel. The judgments which are handed down where the ship is found to be at fault are extremely high, in most cases far exceeding what the man could recover under compensation. For this reason, it is only natural that the injured man seeks to bring suit against the vessel at every opportunity. The narrow hatch board, which the mate may have trouble getting the men to stop long enough to replace, may become an unseaworthy condition after a man has stepped through and broken a leg.

It should be apparent that for the good of the vessel itself and of the industry as a whole, the ship's officers should make every effort not only to keep their own gear and equipment in the best possible condition but also to discourage the use of unsafe gear and practices by the stevedore and the longshoremen.

The International Cargo Handling Coordination Association. Early in the year 1951, a British naval architect and a French economist, A. C. Hardy and F. X. Le Bourgeois by name respectively, were discussing in a private social conversation the need for an organization dedicated to the continuous investigation of methods and equipment for increasing the efficiency of the movement of oceanborne cargoes throughout the world.

As a result of their conversation, they contacted many of their friends to obtain a reaction to the proposal of setting up some type of nonprofit organization or group along the lines of a technical society for the primary purpose of meeting the above mentioned need. The response was immediate and enthusiastic. An inaugural meeting was scheduled to meet in London on October 30, 1951. This was the beginning of the International Cargo Handling Coordination Association (ICHCA). Since that time, the organization has developed until at the present time there are 24 national committees helping to support the objectives of the ICHCA, including the United States national committee which held its first meeting July 28, 1953.

The objectives of the ICHCA are to serve the international public by bringing together all who are interested in improving the efficiency of cargo handling for the common purpose of assisting international seaborne trade. It is hoped, thereby, to coordinate the practical and scientific experience of stevedoring concerns, packers, shippers, shipowners, port authorities, industrialists, and others of kindred professions who acquire knowledge which is of local and possibly limited value when unrelated, but when connected under discussion, examination, and publication by the ICHCA, will tend towards progress and improved efficiency in all aspects of manufacture, packing, transport, handling, and stowage of seaborne goods.

The problems that the ICHCA is dedicated to attack are those problems that have the greatest effect on the future of the merchant marine of any country. Because of the high labor costs in the United States, some of these problems are more acute here.

The fundamental purpose of the merchant ship is to transport cargo. Everyone concerned with the industry should always bear in mind that the efficiency of the merchant marine depends upon the cargo operational efficiency of the companies owning the merchant ships and competing on the world's trade routes. However, one should never lose sight of the fact that the efficiency of any given company is a direct function of the efficiency of each ship. And, finally, no ship is operated well unless the men on her are, in turn, efficient and informed. It is the objective of the ICHCA to foster this total efficiency by general dissemination of information through discussion and publication of the proceedings of symposiums covering the myriad facets of ship operation.

The Maritime Cargo Transportation Conference. The Maritime Cargo Transportation Conference (MCTC) was organized under the National Academy of Sciences–National Research Council at the joint request of the Department of Commerce and the Department of Defense. Its purpose was to provide guidance on means and techniques leading to improvement in systems and systems' elements for the sea transportation of dry cargo. It was also to determine critical factors and remedial measures to reduce current ship turn around times (including total time in ports).

The National Academy of Sciences is a private, nonprofit corporation dedicated to the furtherance of science for the general welfare. It was established by Congressional legislation in 1863 for the purpose of providing advice to the government in the fields of the natural sciences and their applied technologies. The National Research Council was established in 1916 to facilitate the scientific and technical advisory services of the Academy and provided a vigorous program for mustering civilian science in the interest of the war effort. The National Research Council has continued with increasing activity through both World Wars into the present. It deals with scientific problems through committees of outstanding persons who are experts in the various fields of the problems at hand. It organizes and focuses the knowledge and efforts of science in the interests of government and industrial or educational research programs that promise to contribute to national security or general public welfare.

The MCTC consists of a board of advisors constituted of leaders in pertinent phases of maritime cargo handling and transportation who, from their knowledge and experience, provide guidance and review for a small full time professional staff. Emphasis is being given to analysis of current and proposed systems of cargo transportation leading toward improvement in terms of overall performance.

The first study made by the MCTC was an analysis of the time, labor, productivity, and costs involved in transporting a shipload of cargo from the hinterland of the United States to its destination in Europe. This was a preliminary study with the main purpose of defining those areas warranting closer and immediate examination and to help point up logical methods of organizing future studies. This pilot effort is known as the *Warrior Study* and the results will be used to guide the staff of MCTC in future research.

The Society of Naval Architects and Marine Engineers. Through the medium of various technical and research committees, the Society of Naval Architects and Marine Engineers (SNAME) carries on a considerable amount of research. Most of this research is into the engineering aspects of building and powering the vessel, but one committee, known as the Ship Technical Operations Committee, carries research into areas dealing with the efficient operation of the vessel. As an example, Project SO-1, *Cargo Handling and Stowage-Cargo Space Conditioning,* and Project SO-2, *Exchange of Operating Experience,* being studied under the Ship Technical Operations Committee may bring forth data of value in themselves or data that may be very helpful in assisting other research panels.

SHIPS OF THE FUTURE

Precisely what the ship of the distant future may be like is simply an interesting topic for conversation at the present time. Radical changes in pier and ship design may be proposed, but all evidence points to little change in the foreign trade dry cargo common carrier, at least in the foreseeable future. What changes we can expect are limited to those affecting the reliability and safety features of the cargo handling gear.

What holds true for the offshore general cargo ship does not hold true for the industrial bulk carrier or the coastwise or intercoastal general cargo carrier. There are elements in the operation of these last mentioned ships which give hope to the idea that the methods of constructing and operating them will bring about a considerable change for the better.

Ships that sacrifice the use of cubic for dispatch and are operated to take maximum advantage of the unitization concept promise a coastwise shipping trade of renewed vigor. Two such ships are discussed below.

Roll on—roll off ship. One of the most promising developments in the field of merchant and military cargo operations during the last decade is a ship built to be used with a specially designed terminal so that large highway carriers can be quickly and easily driven on or off the ship or maneuvered on or off with specially designed industrial tractors.

The first commercial venture built directly around this idea has already proven that the idea is sound and highly economical. This first venture was carried out by the American Overseas Trading Company on two converted LST's running between New York and Albany on the Hudson River.

About 1946, the late Mr. H. F. Alexander organized the Pacific Coast Steamship Company for the purpose of building two large *trailer-ships* for operation between San Francisco and Long Beach, Calif. These ships were to have been 563 ft overall and have a speed in excess of 20 knots. The trailers would be pulled on board with a specially designed industrial tractor over a ramp connecting the ship's stern with the shore. All trailers would be stowed on the main and second decks in long columns about six abreast. The total trailer capacity was based on the linear footage, and these ships would have handled about 6000 lin ft. All of the trailers could be discharged and another group loaded within about 4 hr.

The plans of Mr. Alexander never materialized due to fiscal problems, but the idea has not been lost. All of the plans and data collected during a number of surveys relative to the venture are still available and simply waiting exploitation by some foresighted group or individual with sufficient capital.

In the meantime the idea is being developed in other areas. In 1953 the McLean Trucking Company launched plans for the development of a similar service between the southeastern and northeastern coasts of the United States. The McLean sea-land trailer-ship service is still in the planning stage, but it is worth while to outline the information on hand regarding the ships and the operation.[1]

---

[1] The material on the McLean Operation is based on a statement of D. G. MacDonald, General Counsel of McLean Trucking Company, before the ICHCA's Third Cargo Handling Symposium, Washington, D. C., October 7, 1954.

Two ships are to be built originally. Each ship will be 638 ft overall and have an extreme breadth of 87 ft. The cruising speed will be 19 knots, displacement 17,000 tons, maximum draft 20 ft, and the ship will carry a crew of 42. These ships will have four cargo decks with a total capacity of 286 trailers with a length of 35 ft, which amounts to 10,010 lin ft of trailers. The two principal trailer decks will have a capacity of 208 trailers. An additional 78 trailers will be accommodated in the hold and on the boat deck. Ramps or elevators will be used to move trailers from the main deck to the hold and from the first deck to the boat deck. Stern ports at the level of both the main deck and the first deck will provide for loading and unloading directly to and from each such deck.

THE CARGO. The trailers will range in length from 16 to 35 ft and in height (for vans) from 12.5 to 14 ft. Their width will be 8 ft. Provision will be made for handling special trailers, including flat body trailers, open top trailers, drop frame (household goods and furniture type) trailers, vehicle carriers, and refrigerator trailers. The average empty weight of a trailer is 5 tons; at full capacity, 1430 tons of trailer weight will be carried. Based on known density factors, the average net weight of cargo expected to be carried has been computed at 15.38 tons per trailer. On this basis, total payload will equal 4399 tons at maximum utilization. In these plans an 80% load factor has been assumed, or 3520 cargo tons per trip.

LOADING AND UNLOADING. When the ship has been placed for loading and unloading, its stern ports, at both the main deck and first deck levels, will be married to the outboard ends of a double deck transfer bridge extending between the head of the ramp and the ship. On both sides of the ramp and extending inland for the required distance, there will be a parking area for trailers numbered according to a fixed port plan. In anticipation of the arrival of the ship, trailers having been received for shipment will have been spotted on numbered positions and a loading manifest will have been prepared. Opposite each row of loaded trailers awaiting shipment will be an empty row in which trailers being unloaded will be dropped near the trailer pickup points. Simultaneous unloading and loading may be employed to the extent possible. For an average port unloading and loading operation of complete loads, there will be an average movement for a trailer between the parking point and the foot of the ramp of 960 ft, between the foot of the ramp and the ship of 490 ft, and within the ship of 300 ft. Double ended, four wheel drive tractors will be used to pull the trailers to the end of the ramp, turn around, and push them up the ramp and to their assigned positions aboard ship. In unloading, trailers will be pulled from the ship to the parking point. The first 25% of the load will be unloaded in one way movements from ship to shore; the next 50% will involve both unloading and loading with each tractor loading a trailer for each trailer unloaded; the last 25% will involve loading only. Time and motion studies made for a simulated operation show that the entire unloading and loading operation can be completed within 4 hr, using the maximum practical number of tractors and crews. The cost of loading a trailer and unloading it at destination port, using an average number of crews, will approximate $2.25 each or $1.12½ for each port operation.

THE PORTS AND SCHEDULES. The proposed operation of the McLean sea-land trailer-ships has been geared to the known requirements of merchandise traffic movements which it is desired to attract. There are definite patterns in the periodicity and volume of such movements between the northeastern and southeastern states. The schedules planned, for the four ship operation proposed, will provide three weekly round trips between Wilmington, N.C., and New York, N.Y., and three weekly round trips between Wilmington and Providence, R.I. Weekly service, coordinated with the Wilmington schedules, will be provided at Charleston and Savannah or Charleston and Jacksonville. Various alternate schedules, serving additional ports, have been worked out for use if traffic does not warrant the frequency of sailings planned for the ports named. The run from Wilmington to New York, pier to pier, will require 34 hr, the run to Providence, 38 hr. A minimum turn around time of 6 hr is provided at each port of call.

USERS OF THE SERVICE. The sea-land trailer-ship operation of McLean will be a common carrier service available to all on a first come first served basis. Rates and charges will be published in tariff form by the sea-land service applicable not only between the ports but between interior points as well. Motor common carriers will be invited to participate through establishment of joint rates and through routes. Pickup and delivery service in the port cities will be given and allowances provided for those tendering or receiving their shipments already loaded in trailers at dockside. It is expected that the level of the rates and charges will be lower than those of competing land transportation agencies as a reflection of the lower cost and somewhat longer time in transit for the McLean sea-land service. The amount of this differential will be greatest for port to port movements and will diminish on traffic moving between interior points as the proportion of the water haul to the land haul becomes less and as the circuity factor increases. The effective area of operation, as measured by the area in which differentially lower rates will be established, will include the five southeastern states of North Carolina, South Carolina, Georgia, Alabama and Florida on the one hand and, on the other, the ten eastern and New England states ranging north from Delaware.

The water line will not leave to its participating connecting line carriers the task of developing traffic for sea-land movement but will encourage its movement through offline solicitation. An economic survey, supplemented by many direct expressions by shippers, shows an abundance of traffic available for sea-land movement at compensatory revenue levels.

Estimated results of the operation. At 80% of capacity, the McLean sea-land operation, as a four ship operation, will transport 2,170,000 tons annually. Return to the water line after payouts to connecting line carriers will amount to $30,708,172 or $26,344,872 after deduction of an expense item of $4,363,300 for consolidation of small shipments into trailer load lots, or distributing them, in port areas. These figures are before a deduction measuring the extent of the differentially lower rates to be charged, somewhere between 4 and 10%. Net profit before reduction for rate differential and before income taxes is computed at $14,714,217.

The factors giving support for this forecast, in addition to the revenue forecast, include a detailed analysis and statement of the expense of the operation and an analysis of the cargo carrying and ship utilization results of the operation. In this connection, a firm of consulting engineers employed by opposing interests in sea-land hearings before the Interstate Commerce Commission were unable to find significant understatement of any individual expense item. Perhaps the best way to secure an insight into fundamental economics of trailer-ship operation is to view the operation in comparison with others. Table 9-1 provides a comparison of condensed income and expense statements, converted to a per ship basis, for the McLean trailer-ship operation, the freight car service of Seatrain Lines, and the Pan-Atlantic Steamship Corporation conventional break bulk coastwise service operating in competition with Seatrain. Figures are for 1953 for the two water carriers.

The comparison in Table 9-1 shows that the McLean operation realizes a much higher gross revenue per vessel. This results both from the makeup of the traffic which the service can attract and from its greater cargo carrying potential. The comparison of the expense items shows that the two container type services, McLean and Seatrain, have realized their economies principally in reduced port calls in relation to tons carried (205 for the McLean ship and 67 for the Seatrain ship) and in reduced cargo expense. Partly offsetting this saving is the increase in other voyage expense which, for McLean and Seatrain, reflect rentals for trailers and cars.

TABLE 9-1

Item	McLean	Seatrain	Pan-Atlantic
Net revenue	$6,586,218	$2,061,192	$1,867,868
Expense			
Vessel expense	887,462	762,528	669,340
Port expense	109,151	49,387	262,056
Cargo expense	146,203	54,987	884,998
Other voyage expense	317,394	75,530	27,078
Total operating expense	1,460,210	942,432	1,843,472
Terminal expense	167,000	91,720	11,725
Overhead	766,133	227,149	82,776
Depreciation	340,000	123,265	30,403
Interest and deductions	174,323	34,124	14,592
Other charges	. . .	19,157	1,226
Total nonoperating expense	1,447,456	491,415	140,772
Total expense	2,907,666	1,437,847	1,984,244
Net profit before taxes and McLean differential	3,678,552	623,345	(116,376)

An additional comparison can be made, principally between McLean and Seatrain, which reveals the advantage of the roll on–roll off operation over the lift in–lift out operation, basically a measure of greater net cargo capacity and greater ship utilization. This comparison of the cargo statistics is shown in Table 9-2.

TABLE 9-2

Item	McLean	Seatrain	Pan-Atlantic
Cargo tons per voyage	4,399	3,200	NR
Voyages per year	154	50	NR
Average miles per voyage	680	1,918	NR
Mileage per year	104,709	95,873	66,434
Cargo tons per year	677,446	160,432	114,015
Cargo ton-miles per year	460,663,000	307,708,600	NR
Per cent of time at sea	74%	69%	53%
Vessel operating expense per ton	$2.69 *	$5.87	$16.17
Vessel operating expense per ton-mile	$0.0032 *	$0.0031	NR
Total expense per ton	5.37 *	8.96	17.41
Total expense per ton-mile	0.008 *	0.0047	NR

* Computed at 80% of capacity or 541,857 cargo tons per year or 3520 tons per voyage.

A loaded Seatrain ship displaces 17,383 tons as compared with the estimated loaded displacement of 16,000 tons for the McLean trailer-ship (and 15,003 for a Pan-Atlantic C-2). The slightly greater speed and capacity of the trailer-ship together with the shorter port time produce a greater ton-mile per year potential. Also, at only 80% of capacity, operating expenses per ton-mile are almost identical with Seatrain's operating expense per ton-mile, approximately one-third of a cent. This fact, together with the generally higher revenue level of the sea-land traffic, demonstrates the economic soundness of the trailer-ship operation.

The container ship. As early as 1944, the late Mr. L. D. Smith applied for patent rights on his ideas of how a ship's hold could be constructed to allow for rapid loading and discharge of large numbers of containers of a uniform size and shape.

Although no ships have been built or converted to handle complete loads of these unit containers as yet, the idea seems to have merit and perhaps may be developed on some special type of trade route in the future. As with many of the ideas relative to improving the efficiency of the deep water carriers, it should be developed as far as possible on paper by research and then given a fair trial by converting at least one hatch on one ship to operate as a container hatch. The data obtained from such a study would answer many questions that cannot be otherwise handled.

The container ship envisions all the cargo being received at the marine loading terminal and then loaded in the unit container, as mentioned on p. 411, or the containers could be loaded by the shipper at his plant in the hinterland. The latter arrangement is the most desirable. After the ship arrives, the containers would be loaded, by some type of ship's crane or extensible boom (see p. 317), into holds containing a system of racks or beams capable of receiving the container quickly and being secured in place without loss of any time or the use of any dunnage or lashings. Discharging and loading would be coordinated on any given pier as it is today.

The container ship concept, operating to the fullest degree, would have the following advantages: (1) The protection to the cargo and reduction in pilferage associated with unit container would be realized. (2) With a ship built especially to handle the containers, the speed of loading and discharging could be increased so that each ship could make a greater number of voyages per year.

The main disadvantage or problem posed by the container ship is that of handling long lengths or bulky items that cannot fit into the containers. The solution of this problem may be to provide deck stowage or one hatch for such items or to avoid booking such items for the container ship. In the latter case, the operator could choose to operate a small fast ship for the bulky items alone or simply devote all of his services to the packaged items that are capable of being placed in the container.

There are undoubtedly some trade routes, probably domestic in nature, where container ships can be utilized with the realization of great economy.

AN ENGINEERING ANALYSIS OF CARGO HANDLING

Under the sponsorship of the Office of Naval Research and the Maritime Administration, the Department of Engineering of the University of California at Los Angeles in 1953 started research into cargo handling problems using certain techniques of mathematics, physics, and industrial engineering. This research is continuing, but the first report, No. 53–21, dated October 1953, has been published under the title of *An Engineering Analysis of Cargo Handling.*

The author gratefully acknowledges permission from the Office of Naval Research and the Department of Engineering, of the University of California at Los Angeles, for permission to present the major part of this report as the last section of this book. It is felt that the presentation of the approach made to cargo handling problems by this research group will assist in illustrating clearly a method of attack that is unique in this area and perhaps give many members of the industry a greater appreciation of the power of the scientific method.

It is quite possible that this analysis, or subsequent studies based on the findings of this one, can be used as the basis for general and specific revisions of the systems extant today. It must be remembered that this is only the first report of what is hoped to be a continuing study. The approach made to some of the problems and the methods used may be changed in the light of future developments.

One should not look for an immediate and crystal clear answer to the problems of the shipping industry relative to cargo operations in this single report of initial research. It would be nothing less than a supernatural miracle if a handful of professors and graduate engineering students, after being briefed concerning the problems of cargo handling, were to arrive at clear cut and positive answers to a question as complex and plagued with untold parameters as the one being considered here.

One should see in this report a clear manifestation of the direction that future events must take to enable port speed to make up its losses to sea speed. There is no question that this is possible; the only question is when will it be done?

The problem. The objectives in undertaking this study were twofold: (1) To determine the time, space, energy, and cost relationships for the loading and unloading of ships; and (2) to propose changes in packaging, mechanisms, and procedures to minimize the costs, time, energy, and space required. The wording of these objectives was intentionally broad since it was suspected that the transportation system would include many complex interrelationships. Such proved to be the case.

On the basis of interviews with military and civilian shipping leaders and observations on military and civilian piers, it was decided to limit the scope of the study, for the time being at least, to the basic system shown in Fig. 9-2.

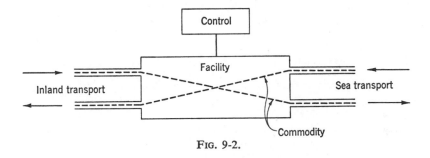

Fɪɢ. 9-2.

The cargo-handling system is defined here as consisting of five major elements: the facility (i.e. the physical equipment, structures, and sources of energy), the transportation routes that are its inland connections, its sea connections, the commodities that flow through it, and the control of the system— a combination of management, labor, and government.

Since this system is based on a single facility and therefore does not take into account the interdependence that exists between facilities, the system shown in Fig. 9-2 may be too specific and, possibly, at the same time, too general for adequate study. Therefore, it is anticipated that, as research progresses, there will be revisions and further analysis of the basic system.

An analysis of the cargo-handling system as defined above is a complex and formidable procedure. For one thing, the interrelations that exist within the system present a major difficulty. An immediate answer to a specific problem would affect the future solution of many others. Determining the present optimum size of the hatch opening, for instance, would affect all future attempts to design larger cargo containers.

Thus, it is apparent that, to avoid such premature solutions of specific problems, it is first necessary to find the relations existing between the system variables. This knowledge will make it possible to predict the effects of any change in one part on the rest of the system and at the same time, it will be possible to decide which specific problems to attack first.

The standards of measurement adopted for measuring the dependency between these variables were *time* and *cost*. In any realistic transportation problem, there is always some combination of both that must be taken into account.

Therefore, the first objective in this study is to *formulate equations that state the relations between significant components of the cargo-handling system in terms of time and cost.*

After these relationships are known and understood, it will be possible to predict the effect of changes on the system and to design optimum systems.

Fortunately, it is not necessary to formulate equations that take into account all variables: a knowledge of only the more significant elements is all that is required to realize reasonable predictability. Of course, the equations can be made more accurate by including more variables since ". . . the behavior of the actual system is the limit of the behavior of the ideal system (I_n) as the idealization is extended,

$$I_n \rightarrow \text{Behavior of actual system}$$

$$\text{as } n \rightarrow \infty$$

where n represents the number of the idealizations, each progressively including the more variables. . . . (or at least more accurately describing their effect)."

The first step in determining the relations between the components is to make a formal description of the system and to develop a working model of it.

A formal analysis of cargo handling. The following formal analysis of the cargo-handling system at first glance may seem elementary and over-simplified, but it is a necessary first step toward the primary objective of this study, to devise equations that state the relations between the significant components of the system.

To begin with, the transfer of cargo between a land carrier and the hold of a ship occurs at what may be called a junction in the transportation network. The cargo handling that takes place at this junction is defined as the transfer of physical objects between a land carrier and a ship by men with machines. The major elements in this system are shown in Fig. 9-2. They are defined as follows:

Facility (F) consists of the structures, materials-handling equipment, and sources of energy at the terminal and the physical features of the port. Structures include the man-made improvements like roads, rails, and outside storage. Materials-handling equipment includes the harbor lighters and barge cranes. The energy sources available for the transportation of cargo are electrical, mechanical, and thermal as well as manpower. Physical features are the contours, tides, and weather. In general, these are natural, but they may be altered, i.e. by dredging or the construction of breakwaters.

Sea transport (S) is the vessel that carries the cargo to another facility. The cargo-handling gear on the ship is included.

Inland transport (L) is the carrier that connects the facility to the inland area. This may be truck, train, airplane, or river barge. All the materials-handling equipment attached to the carrier is included.

Commodity (C) is the item that is shipped, including the package or crate. Dunnage, however, is considered to be a separate commodity.

Control (M) is the communication of information that regulates the movement of the commodity through the facility. The record system is included in control and both labor and management are involved.

The commodity follows a unique path through the facility, determined by all of the elements defined above. If F, S, L, C, and M are considered causes, the path is the effect. The effect may be observed in the field and subsequently used to induce information about the causes. Thus, the dependent element is defined as follows:

Process (P) is the space-time coordinates of the path taken by the commodity or the transporting agent.

Symbolically, the principal elements of the system may be represented as vectors with components as follows:

$$
\begin{array}{ll}
\text{Facility:} & F = (f_1, f_2, \cdots f_n) \\
\text{Sea Transport:} & S = (s_1, s_2, \cdots s_n) \\
\text{Inland Transport:} & L = (l_1, l_2, \cdots l_n) \\
\text{Commodity:} & C = (c_1, c_2, \cdots c_n) \\
\text{Control:} & M = (m_1, m_2, \cdots m_n) \\
\text{Process:} & P = (p_1, p_2, \cdots p_n)
\end{array}
$$

where $f_1, f_2, \ldots f_n$, for example, are numbers that describe the facility; f_1 may be the number of berths, f_2 the net usable area, etc. There will be n different components ordered according to their importance. Thus, the first of the F components may be used to describe the facility within some predetermined level of completeness. This is also true for the components of S, L, C, M, P, although the number of components may be different for each element.

It is postulated that these six elements completely define the cargo-handling system and are necessary and sufficient for the transfer of cargo between a land carrier and the hold of a ship at this junction in the transportation network. Recall that *process* is the dependent element, and as such is a function of the independent elements $F, S, L, C,$ and M. One of the components of *process* is time, a basic measure.

When a transporting agent is used to move the commodity, the operation is cyclic. The transporting agent, which may be a forklift, hook, longshoreman, etc., moves with the commodity from one point to another and then returns to the starting point to repeat the operation. By this definition, pipelines, chutes, and certain types of conveyors, such as roller conveyors, are not considered to be transporting agents. Belt conveyors, however, are cyclic and consequently are considered transporting agents. A schematic diagram of a specific cyclic process is shown in Fig. 9-3.

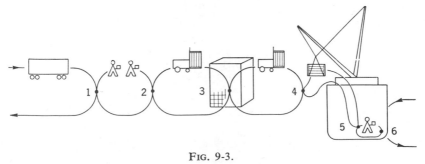

Fig. 9-3.

A commodity, cases of canned peaches, arrives at point 1 by rail. These cases are unloaded by four men, one case at a time, to a pallet at 2. The transporting agent here is a person. There are four transporting agents completing the same cycle. The unit of commodity is one case of canned peaches, described by the dimensions, weight, strength of carton, etc.

A forklift picks up 36 cases stacked on the pallet in a definite pattern and moves the pallet to the transit shed. The unit of commodity is now a pallet of 36 cases. In addition to the dimensions, weight, etc., the maximum allowable acceleration is an important characteristic since the cases should not topple from the forklift en route. Point 3 is the location of the stack in the transit shed. The strength of the carton may become an important component of commodity during storage because it influences the height to which the commodity may be stacked.

After a period of time in storage, the commodity, still a pallet load of peaches, is moved by forklift to the apron, 4. The pallet is hoisted over the side of the ship and into the hold, 5. In the hold the pallet is unloaded by the hold men, one case at a time, and stowed in the wings, 6.

The loading of peaches can be shown schematically in the generalized cycle diagram shown below, in Fig. 9-4.

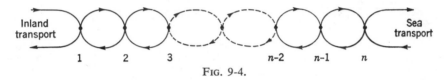

FIG. 9-4.

Each link in the chain represents the space time trajectory of the transporting agent. The trajectory of the commodity is, of course, unidirectional and is represented by either the upper or lower segment of the link. At the nodes (i.e. points) $1, 2, 3 \cdots n$, the commodity is transferred from one transporting agent to another. It is not necessary that the transfer take place at a point in space or time: i.e., the commodity may be moved some distance by a gravity chute or roller conveyor or it may be put in storage for a period of time. See Figs. 9-5 and 9-6.

It is also possible for the unit of commodity to be changed at these nodes; e.g. a case of peaches to a pallet load. Between two consecutive nodes, the

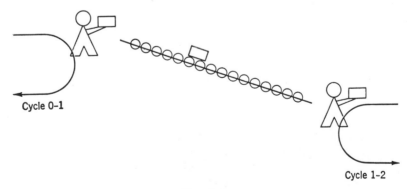

FIG. 9-5.

Fig. 9-6.

commodity is moved by a transporting agent. The unit of the commodity does not change and there are no storage states. If the commodity stops, it is in a delay state. The inland and sea transport are shown as open cycles in Fig. 9-4. However, the inland transport cycle is closed if the inland origin or destination of the commodity is considered, and the sea transport cycle is closed if other facilities are included in the system. In the first case, the box car, barge, or truck is the transporting agent, and, in the second case, the vessel is the transporting agent.

The receiving dock, transit shed, apron, and hold of the ship are nodes, and an analysis of the material flow through the facility may be based on a material balance at each node. The amount of commodity in storage at a node at the end of a specified interval of time is equal to the amount in storage at the start of the interval, plus that delivered by the transporting agent of the preceding cycle, less the amount of commodity taken away by the following cycle. The inputs and outputs can be expressed as Fourier series and their sum is an analytical expression of the quantity in storage. This is developed further in the section discussing the analysis of the quantity of commodity at a storage node (see p. 534).

The amount of the commodity stored at any node can obviously never be less than zero or greater than the maximum capacity of the node. Storage areas are limited by the allowable floor loads, ceiling heights, net usable areas, etc. Instability of the stack, allowable compressive stress, etc., also limit capacity as does the release and pick-up characteristics of the transporting agent. For example, the hook with married fall rigging can only pick up a load from a limited area on the apron. Thus, it is not possible to build a stockpile on the apron that can be hoisted over the side of the ship without additional handling. The vertical travel of the platform of a fork truck is another limitation imposed by the transporting agent.

Consequently, the maximum and minimum allowable storage at the nodes are bounds on the cargo-handling process. No goods can be taken from a node if the quantity in storage is zero, and no goods can be deposited if the maximum amount is already in storage. Thus, there is the feedback situation illustrated in Fig. 9-7. In this example, cargo is picked up at node 1 by a transporting agent and transferred along path 1–2 to node 2, where it is set down. The transporting agent returns along path 2–1 to node 1, where it can proceed to pick up another load. If there is no cargo present at transfer node 1, this information is given to the returning transporting agents.

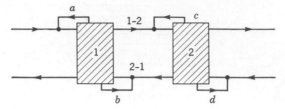

Fig. 9-7.

They are delayed until some minimum quantity of cargo has been deposited at node 1. The path for this information is represented by b. On the other hand, should node 2 be loaded to capacity, that information is given to the approaching transporting agents via path c. This delays them until there is room to deposit the load at node 2. Path a carries the overloading message of node 1 to the preceding cycle. Path d carries the message of the quantity at node 2 to the following cycle. A more detailed analysis is given in the section discussing an electrical analog of the cargo handling operation (see p. 536), which describes an electric analog of the cyclic process.

A material balance at each node may be supplemented by an analysis of material flow between nodes. The commodity is picked up by the transporting agent, carried to the next node, and released. The transporting agent then returns empty to the starting point. At any point in the cycle, there may occur a delay. The delay can originate outside or inside the cycle. If the delay is caused by the storage condition at either node, it is called an induced delay. All others are called internal delays. The total time that it takes to complete one round trip of the transporting agent can be broken down into element times as shown in Fig. 9-8. The operation time, T_o is the sum of the

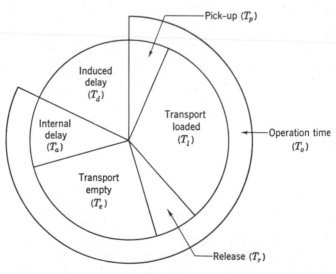

Fig. 9-8.

element times of the particular cycle. Internal delays are included because there are always certain delays associated with the operation. Induced delays, on the other hand, are not charged to the cycle. When the transporting agent makes several round trips in succession, the element times are the average values.

The rate at which the commodity is moved from one node to the next is defined as the weight of the commodity carried by the transporting agents per trip divided by the average time required to make the trip. If during an interval of time the net change in the amount of storage at a node is zero, the average rates of flow in the preceding and succeeding cycles are equal. However, the operating rate of each cycle may be different. It is defined as the weight transported divided by the average operating time T_o. The operating rate is determined by the characteristics of the particular cycle only and is not influenced by the restrictions imposed by the adjacent cycles. The cycle with the lowest operating rate controls the rate at which the commodity is moved from one point of storage to another. For example, in Fig. 9-3 the rates between nodes 1, 2, and 3 are equal, and the rates between 3, 4, 5, and 6 are equal. Furthermore, there is one cycle in each series of cycles that controls the remainder. All other cycles must have induced delay.

The element cycle times can be used as the dependent variable for one set of relations between the major elements. If the element times can be determined as a function of a reasonable number of parameters, the total time required can be calculated for a specific cycle. With additional information about the storage conditions at the nodes, the time required for an entire cargo-handling operation can be predicted.

To sum up: It has been possible to devise equations for the flow of material through a particular ideal cargo-handling system. These equations can be used for the prediction of the time required to load or unload cargo or for the development of optimum methods and designs. They could be extended to the prediction of energy requirements and dollar costs by a transformation of the coordinates.

Methods of problem solution. The scientific method of problem solution can be roughly divided into four major steps: (1) idealization of the system, (2) data gathering, (3) data processing, and (4) comparison of the idealization with the results. This is the approach that has been used here to solve the cargo-handling problem outlined on pp. 512–514. A brief description of the methods used in these four steps is given below as an introduction to the following sections where solutions for sample cargo-handling problems are worked out.

Before starting any investigation, it is necessary to formulate a model system to use as the basis for the inquiry. In this project, the model or idealization is based on the flow of materials. It could be based on the flow of energy or the flow of information. If all three models were formulated, the result would be a set of networks that could be superimposed upon each other. As stated earlier, these idealizations will approach the behavior of the actual system as they progressively include more variables and describe them more accurately.

In data gathering, the primary sources of data are the existing drawings, files, and reports kept by the various management, labor, and government groups that are concerned with cargo handling, but the information derived from these sources consists mainly of cost data and past performances. Other sources are very limited and, in most cases, the data available do not coincide with the data required. It was necessary, therefore, to obtain field data from observation of cargo-handling operations.

There are a number of techniques that could be used to obtain actual time data of cargo-handling operations, but the work-sampling technique discussed on pp. 528–532 has been found in most situations to be less time-consuming, cheaper, and more acceptable to employees than the conventional stopwatch time study. . . .

The data obtained in these ways are then processed in accordance with the hypotheses to be tested, i.e., to check the idealization against the observed results. Processing consists of sorting and classification, computing statistics, multiple correlations, and fitting curves analytically and graphically. An example of the processing of cost data is shown in the section dealing with an analysis of loading costs (see p. 524). . . .

The remainder of this report shows how sample problems can be solved by using the techniques outlined in the above sections. Also included is a description of the procedures developed to obtain field data and a description of an electrical analog that was designed to serve as a conceptual model of the system.

Maximizing revenue tons. The following is an illustration of a programming problem where a known relationship between certain variables is utilized. The specific problem is to maximize the revenue tons carried by a cargo vessel. Before proceeding to the actual solution of the problem, it may be helpful to define and illustrate some of the terms and concepts that are used.

Cargo vessels may be considered to have two measures of capacity. There is the volume capacity, measured by the number of cubic feet of goods that can be stowed, and the weight capacity, measured in tons of stowed goods. The weight capacity is determined by the safe depth to which a vessel may be loaded.

The commodities to be transported by general cargo vessels have a rather wide variation in density or its reciprocal the more commonly used stowage factor. Since some commodities are very dense while others are less so, a problem exists in programming the cargo to be carried so that the vessel will be full and down at the time of sailing: i.e., all the cargo space filled and the ship down to its draft limit marks. If the entire cargo were cotton, the vessel would be full but not down. If, on the other hand, the entire cargo were lead ingots, the ship would be down but not full. There is a combination of cotton and lead, however, that will both fill the ship and bring it down to its draft limit marks.

There are a number of ways of selecting cargos that meet this requirement. For purposes of military logistics, where cost is of less consequence than the scarcity of ships, the maximum quantity must be delivered by each ship in the least amount of time. However, for commercial purposes, the total revenue to be derived is the primary consideration. The unit used is the revenue ton, which is defined as the actual weight of the commodity in long tons or one-fortieth of the volume in cubic feet, whichever is higher. Generally, revenue tons for commodities with a stowage factor greater than forty are computed on the basis of the volume, while for commodities with stowage factors less than forty, the revenue tons are computed from the weight. An additional factor is the shipping charge in dollars per revenue ton prevailing for each class of commodity. Hence, when a steamship company has some leeway in the selection of cargo, certain selections will yield higher values of revenue tons than others and some will yield higher total revenue than others.

Any combination that results in a vessel being full and down is an efficient or usable solution. The programming problem of maximization of revenue tons can be solved readily as follows:

Let f_i = stowage factor of a commodity i that is available for loading and that is greater than 40 ft³/ton. Thus

$$f_i > 40 \quad \text{and} \quad i = 1, 2, 3, \cdots n$$

Let g_j = stowage factor of a commodity j that is available for loading and that is less than 40 ft³/ton. Thus

$$g_j < 40 \quad \text{and} \quad j = 1, 2, 3, \cdots n$$

Then for all f_i's, revenue tons are computed by volume. Let x_i = revenue tons of commodity i. Then

$$x_i = \frac{v_i}{40} \tag{34}$$

where v is the volume occupied in ft³.

For all g_j's, revenue tons are computed by weight. Let y_j = revenue tons of commodities j. Then

$$y_j = d_j \tag{35}$$

where d is the long tons of the commodity stowed.

The total revenue tons for a given ship will be

$$R = \sum_1^n x_i + \sum_1^m y_j \tag{36}$$

where values of $x_i = 0$ and $y_i = 0$ are not excluded. Negative values of x_i and y_j are excluded for physical reasons. A properly loaded cargo vessel will be one for which R is a maximum. The limiting factors are of course the maximum values of any x_i and y_j, the volume of the cargo spaces, and the net displacement of the vessel available for cargo.

These limitations may be expressed as follows:

$$\sum_1^n v_i + \sum_1^m v_j \leq V \tag{37}$$

where V = the net cargo capacity by volume.

$$\sum_1^n d_i + \sum_1^m {}^r d_j \leq D \tag{38}$$

where D = the net cargo capacity by weight.

The optimum system is attained when both equalities hold, i.e.:

$$\sum v_i + \sum v_j = V \tag{39}$$

$$\sum d_i + \sum d_j = D \tag{40}$$

where

$$v_i = 40x_i \tag{34}$$

$$v_j = g_j y_j \tag{41}$$

$$d_i = 40x_i/f_i \tag{42}$$

$$d_j = y_j \tag{35}$$

Therefore the equations

$$V = \sum_1^n 40x_i + \sum_1^m g_j y_j \tag{43}$$

$$D = \sum_1^n 40x_i + \sum_1^m y_j \tag{44}$$

represent a ship loaded full and down; that is, all cargo space is filled and the ship is down to the draft limit marks.

The number of revenue tons loaded will be given by the sum

$$R = \sum_1^n x_i + \sum_1^m y_j \tag{36}$$

with x_i and y_j subject to equations 43 and 44.

For a ship loaded with a single commodity, equations 43 and 44 are independent and R will be determined solely by either the volume capacity of the vessel or its displacement capacity as the stowage factor of the commodity is either greater or less than the stowage factor of the ship.

A vessel may be loaded with two commodities in any combination. If both commodities have a stowage factor greater than 40, or if both are less than 40, then the optimum load would be a homogeneous cargo of one or the other, as for a single commodity. If, however, one has a stowage factor greater than 40 ft³/ton, f_i, and the other less than 40 ft³/ton, g_j, programming is possible to determine the optimum amounts of each commodity to be carried. Equations 43 and 44 now read:

$$40x + gy = V \tag{45}$$

$$40x/f + y = D \tag{46}$$

These equations are not independent and a solution for x and y is possible that will result in the vessel being full and down.

Eliminating x we have

$$y = \frac{fD - V}{f - g} \tag{47}$$

$$x = \frac{f}{40}\left[\frac{V - gD}{f - g}\right] \tag{48}$$

As an example of equations 47 and 48, consider the problem of loading a vessel which, after allowance for stores, fuel, etc., has a gross tonnage of 7000 and a deadweight capacity of 10,000 tons. The vessel is to be loaded with cotton and steel with stowage factors of 100 and 10 respectively.

Substitution in equations 47 and 48 yields:

$$x = 16,666 \text{ revenue tons of cotton}$$

$$y = 3,333 \text{ revenue tons of steel}$$

so that the total revenue tons carried,

$$R = 20,000 \text{ tons}$$

This quantity is considerably greater than either the nominal displacement or nominal volumetric capacity of the vessel by a substantial amount. It is apparent that there is an important economic reason for a ship owner to attempt to maximize revenue tons in this way.

The next question that may be raised is: what should the values of f and g be to make R a maximum?

Substituting equation 47 and 48 into 36

$$R = \frac{f}{40}\left(\frac{V - gD}{f - g}\right) + \left(\frac{fD - V}{f - g}\right) \tag{49}$$

(Note that in equation 49 $f \neq g$ except for a one-commodity system in which R is determined by either weight or volume, whichever is larger.)

Differentiating 49 with respect to f and g with V and D as parameters gives

$$\frac{\partial R}{\partial f} = \frac{1}{f - g}\left[\frac{V - gD}{40} - \frac{f}{40}\left(\frac{V - gD}{f - g}\right) + D - \frac{fD - V}{f - g}\right] = 0 \tag{50}$$

$$\frac{\partial R}{\partial g} = \frac{1}{f - g}\left[\frac{-fg}{40} + \frac{f}{40}\left(\frac{V - gD}{f - g}\right) + \frac{fD - V}{f - g}\right] = 0 \tag{51}$$

One solution to equations 50 and 51 is

$$f = \infty, \quad g = 0 \tag{52}$$

This solution determines the absolute maximum revenue tons since it represents a ship loaded with two hypothetical materials, one which has volume but no weight and the other which has weight but no volume. . . .

Now consider the general system consisting of commodities available for loading of $f_1, f_2, f_3 \cdots f_n$, and $g_1, g_2, g_3 \cdots g_n$. Since $f_i > 40 > g_j$, we may arrange the f_i's in descending order of magnitude while the g_j's may be ordered in increasing values.

$$f_1 > f_2 > f_3 \cdots > f_n$$

$$g_1 < g_2 < g_3 \cdots < g_m$$

Since a combination of f_1 and g_1 will give a greater value of revenue tons than any other combination, it follows that, with a limited commodity store, the maximum revenue tons subject to equations 43, 44, and 36, will be obtained when the highest and lowest density materials available are loaded until one or the other ceases to be available. In this case, the remaining displacement and volumetric capacity, together with the remaining commodity selection, form a new programming problem whose solution is obtained in exactly the same manner.

The implications of this solution are that very high or very low density commodities might have a lower cost per revenue ton, since they yield a higher total revenue tonnage when they are shipped together. This problem, however, is further complicated by the fact that the cost per revenue ton for various commodities is dependent on many other factors that have not been considered here. Future study along this line will probably be fruitful and, of necessity, more complicated.

Analysis of loading costs. There are many costs associated with the loading of a ship. The manner in which they are broken down varies with the different shipping companies. For the following analysis, the costs are divided into the same categories used at one of the installations under study. These costs are of two types: the fixed costs, which are not dependent on the tonnage being loaded, and the variable costs, which are dependent on the tonnage being loaded. They include:

> Fixed costs
> > Tug service
> > Pilotage
> > Dockage
> > Ship operating expense
> > Office expense
> Variable costs
> > Handling and clerking
> > Dunnage and shoring material
> > Lashing labor

The following is a discussion of the actual values of these costs and is representative for one port and for the loading of a Liberty type vessel.

TUG SERVICE. The total charge for tug service for a ship inbound and outbound is $100, providing there is no shifting from berth to berth.

PILOTAGE. The pilotage charge is $0.005 per gross registered ton inbound and the same charge outbound. For Liberty type vessels, which have an average gross registered tonnage of around 7200, this charge is $72 total, inbound and outbound.

DOCKAGE. This cost is computed as $12 for 1000–1500 net registered tons per 24 hours or fraction thereof and $3 per 24 hours for each additional 500 net registered tons or fraction thereof. For simplicity, the turn around time of a ship will be reported in this analysis to the full day above any fraction of a day. Therefore, the dockage cost can be approximated as:

$$\text{Dockage} = T\left[12 + 3\,\frac{N - 1500}{500}\right] \tag{53}$$

where T = turn around time (in 24 hours).
$\quad\quad N$ = net registered tonnage.

Since the net registered tonnage of a Liberty is 4414, equation 53 reduces to

$$\text{Dockage} = 30T \tag{54}$$

SHIP OPERATING EXPENSE. This is the expense that the ship incurs while in port, i.e., wages, food, fuel, etc. This cost is estimated to be $2200 per day for a Liberty type vessel. Thus, in equation form, the ship operating expense is:

$$\text{Ship operating expense} = 2200T \tag{55}$$

OFFICE EXPENSE. This cost can be charged as a fixed cost per long ton loaded because office costs are fairly constant within the range of operations. This assumes that office expense is independent of the turn around time. Therefore, the office expense can be expressed as:

$$\text{Office expense} = L\left(\frac{E}{R}\right) \tag{56}$$

where L = long tons.
E = office expense per year.
R = tonnage per year.

Since the amount of tonnage per year (R) is confidential for the facility in question, this cost has not been included in the analysis. The only effect of this cost would be to shift the resulting family of curves upward on the ordinate scale.

HANDLING AND CLERKING. Certain assumptions must be made in order to evaluate the handling costs. First of all, a uniform loading rate of 25 long tons per gang hour is used for all commodities and all working time. An 18 man gang with the required clerking aid is assumed with a maximum of 5 gangs during the day and a maximum overtime shift of 5 additional gangs. Analytically, the handling and clerking cost is expressed as:

$$\text{Handling} = A_D C_D + A_O C_O \tag{57}$$

where A_D = number of "day time" gang shifts.
A_O = number of overtime gang shifts.
C_D = cost per "day time" gang shift (i.e., 6 hours straight time and 2 hours overtime).
C_O = cost per overtime gang shift (i.e., 8 hours overtime).

and

$$C_D < C_O \tag{58}$$

From the assumptions made above it is also seen that:

$$A_D \leq 5T \tag{59}$$

and

$$A_D + A_O = \frac{L}{25(8)} = \frac{L}{200} \tag{60}$$

Thus to obtain minimum cost in handling:

$$A_D = 5T \qquad \text{when } \frac{L}{200} > 5T$$

$$\tag{61}$$

$$A_D = \frac{L}{200} \qquad \text{when } \frac{L}{200} \leq 5T$$

Substituting equations 60 and 61 into 57 and the resulting handling cost is also expressed as:

$$\text{Handling} = 5TC_D + \left(\frac{L}{200} - 5T\right) C_O \qquad \text{when } \frac{L}{200} > 5T \qquad (62)$$

$$\text{Handling} = \frac{L}{200} C_D \qquad \text{when } \frac{L}{200} \leq 5T$$

The following numerical example illustrates these equations.

Assume that a Liberty type vessel is to be loaded with 2000 long tons of average commodities. The total gang shifts required for this operation, as determined from equation 60, are:

$$A_D + A_O = \tfrac{2000}{200} = 10 \text{ total gang shifts} \qquad (63)$$

If the turn around time is one day, then the maximum number of "day time" shifts is determined from equation 61.

$$A_D = 5(1) = 5 \text{ "day time" gang shifts} \qquad (64)$$

and

$$A_O = 10 - 5 = 5 \text{ overtime gang shifts} \qquad (65)$$

Assuming that the C_D = \$475 and C_O = \$600, substituting these values in equation 57 **gives:**

$$\text{Handling} = \$5375 \qquad (66)$$

If, however, the vessel can remain in port for 2 days, then equation 63 still holds but the value of A_D changes.

$$A_D = 5(2) = 10 \text{ "day time" gang shifts} \qquad (67)$$

and

$$A_O = 10 - 10 = 0 \text{ overtime gang shifts} \qquad (68)$$

The cost of handling now becomes:

$$\text{Handling} = \$4750 \qquad (69)$$

Thus, the extra day in port has reduced the handling costs but the other costs, such as ship operating expense, would have nullified this saving.

DUNNAGE AND STORING MATERIAL. This cost is determined from data obtained at the facility. If a linear relation is assumed between these costs and the long tons, then, in the facility under study, the relationship has been found to be approximated by the following equation:

$$\text{Dunnage} = 300 + 1.11(L) \qquad (70)$$

LASHING LABOR. This cost is primarily a function of the commodity and cargo plan as well as the tonnage loaded, but since it is quite variable and less significant than many of the other costs, it is omitted in this analysis.

The resulting total cost for loading a Liberty type vessel can then be expressed as:

Total cost = Tug service + Pilotage + Dockage + Ship operating expense

+ Handling and clerking + Dunnage and storing material

(71)

Substituting the values discussed above, equation 71 now becomes:

Total cost $= 100 + 72 + 30T + 2200T$

$$+ (3L - 625T) + (300 + 1.11L) \qquad \text{when } \frac{L}{200} > 5T \quad (72)$$

Total cost $= 100 + 72 + 30T + 2200T + 2.38L$

$$+ (300 + 1.11L) \qquad \text{when } \frac{L}{200} \leq 5T$$

By dividing both sides of equation 72 by the long tons (L) being loaded, the equation for cost per long ton is found to be:

$$\frac{\text{Cost}}{\text{Long ton}} = \frac{100}{L} + \frac{72}{L} + \frac{30T}{L} + \frac{2200T}{L} + \left[3 + \frac{625T}{L} \right]$$

$$+ \left[\frac{300}{L} + 1.11 \right] \qquad \text{when } \frac{L}{200} > 5T \qquad (73)$$

$$\frac{\text{Cost}}{\text{Long ton}} = \frac{100}{L} + \frac{72}{L} + \frac{30T}{L} + \frac{2200T}{L} + 2.38$$

$$+ \left(\frac{300}{L} + 1.11 \right) \qquad \text{when } \frac{L}{200} \leq 5T$$

Gathering terms reduces equation 73 to:

$$\frac{\text{Cost}}{\text{Long ton}} = \frac{472}{L} (1 + 3.4T) + 4.11 \qquad \text{when } \frac{L}{200} > 5T \qquad (74)$$

$$\frac{\text{Cost}}{\text{Long ton}} = \frac{472}{L} (1 + 4.72T) + 3.49 \qquad \text{when } \frac{L}{200} \leq 5T$$

Equation 74 is plotted in Fig. 9-9 with cost per long ton vs. the tonnage loaded, and turn around time (T) as the parameter of the family of curves. For the example being studied, these curves show that with a given tonnage the most economical time to load in is the shortest time. It also shows that, for a given turn around time, the optimum tonnage to load is the largest possible tonnage. This conclusion can be derived directly from equation 72, which shows that the only costs varying with turn around time are dockage, ship operating, and handling costs. Both dockage and ship operating costs are increasing straight line functions of time. Handling cost, on the other hand, is a decreasing step function of time as illustrated above in the discussion of handling costs because, for two-thirds of a day, the handling costs are charged with overtime penalty. However, the decrease in the handling cost with time is always smaller than the increase in ship operating and dockage costs. This situation exists for the assumptions and limitations made in this analysis, i.e., a specific longshore pay structure, a particular ship type, etc. It is obvious that the smaller the ship operating cost (and dockage cost), the smaller the saving becomes from using a minimum turn around time. Thus, a break-even point may exist for certain low-operating cost vessels.

In addition to the factors mentioned above, there are others that are important. They include the cost of the increased period of the commodity in transit and the loss of potential business while a ship is tied up in port. These may be appreciable and further stress the importance of shortening the turn around time by working overtime.

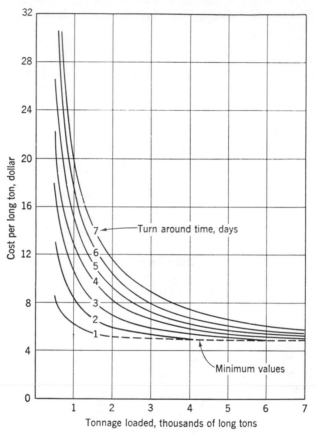

FIG. 9-9.

Work-sampling technique for determining cycle element times. The work-sampling technique, originated by L. H. C. Tippet in 1935, suggests itself as a possible tool for obtaining actual time data of cargo loading and unloading operations. The use of work-sampling in this situation is a good deal more complicated than in the usual industrial situation. For one thing, the technique has usually been used for observations on individual workers; in the present study it is being used on gang or group activities. The resulting complications are, however, of a practical rather than a theoretical nature, and result mainly from the physical layout of the work place.

The work-sampling method itself is based on the random sampling theory employed in statistical quality control. The procedure is to select samples at random from the population, and, when a sufficient number of observations have been taken, a prediction is made for the population. The prediction is based upon the theory that the percentage of readings recording the activity in a certain state of operation is an estimate of the percentage of time spent in that operation.

Before proceeding to the actual design of the work sampling method, it is necessary to review and expand the model of the cargo-handling operation developed in the section giving a formal analysis of cargo handling. In that section, the cargo operations are recognized and defined as a series of adjoining cycles. Each of the cycles is broken down into six time elements:

T_p = picking up load.
T_l = transport loaded.
T_r = transport release.
T_e = transport empty.
T_a = internal delay.
T_d = induced delay.

From Fig. 9-8, it is seen that the sum of these elements equals the total cycle time (T):

$$T = T_p + T_l + T_r + T_e + T_a + T_d \qquad (75)$$

Also, from Fig. 9-8, the cycle operating time (T_o) is defined as:

$$T_o = T_p + T_l + T_r + T_e + T_a \qquad (76)$$

The element times can be used in determining the effect that changes in the components have on the system. These element times can also be used in determining the rate at which the commodity is moved between nodes. For example, the rate of movement of a commodity between nodes 1 and 2 (r_{1-2}) is defined as:

$$r_{1-2} = \left(\frac{nw}{T}\right)_{1-2} \qquad (77)$$

where n = number of transporting agents.
w = weight of commodity carried by a transporting agent during each cycle.

If a series of cycles have no storage nodes, then the rates of commodity movement are interdependent and

$$r_{1-2} = r_{2-3} = r_{3-4} = \cdots = r \qquad (78)$$

However, the operating rates (r_o) are different and

$$(r_o)_{1-2} = \left(\frac{nw}{T_o}\right)_{1-2} \qquad (79)$$

The cycle with the slowest operating rate (min r_o) and, therefore, the one with longest operating time, is the controlling cycle in the series of cycles. This relationship can be expressed as:

$$r \leq \min r_o \qquad (80)$$

Turning now to the work-sampling method of obtaining the element times the following definitions are required:

N_p = number of random observations of picking up load.
N_l = number of random observations of transport loaded.
N_r = number of observations of transport release.
N_e = number of observations of transport empty.
N_a = number of observations of internal delay.
N_d = number of observations of induced delay.

Similarly to equation 75, the total number of random observations (N) is

$$N = N_p + N_l + N_r + N_e + N_a + N_d \tag{81}$$

Also, the number of random observations of cycle operating time is defined as

$$N_o = N_p + N_l + N_r + N_e + N_a \tag{82}$$

By hypothesis from the statistical theory underlying work sampling,

$$\frac{N_\alpha}{N} = \frac{T_\alpha}{T} = \frac{p_\alpha}{100} \tag{83}$$

where N_α = number of random observations of element (i.e., pickup, transport loaded, release, etc.).
T_α = time required for element.
p_α = the α time element's percentage of total cycle time.

Before any actual observations can start, it is necessary to obtain descriptive data on the type of ships, facilities, commodities, schedules, etc. that affect the systems being studied. It is then possible to make random observations of the activities with the more important activities receiving proportionately more observations. Therefore, the first step in designing the sampling plan consists of an analysis of the operation to be studied.

The next step is to determine the number of samples to be taken. This number is a function of the risk, the maximum size of confidence, the length of the time interval, and the variance. For a binomially distributed population the number of samples can be determined from the formula for the standard error of a binomial.

$$\sigma_p = \sqrt{\frac{p(1-p)}{N}} \tag{84}$$

where p = a time element's percentage of the total cycle time.

If a per cent of accuracy (β) is required in the determination of p, and if a per cent of confidence (γ) is also required, then the usual statistic follows:

$$\frac{\beta}{100} p = Z_\gamma \sigma_p \tag{85}$$

Equations 84 and 85 can be combined to give

$$N = \left(\frac{Z_\gamma}{\frac{\beta}{100}}\right)^2 \left(\frac{1-p}{p}\right) \tag{86}$$

Equation 86 is plotted in Fig. 9-10 with β and γ as parameters. The resulting relationship between p and N is hyperbolic and N decreases greatly with increases in p (i.e., increases in the length of the element time interval).

The important effect of this can be illustrated by an example. Assume a maximum allowable variance of $\pm 5\%$ in the calculated p, and a confidence

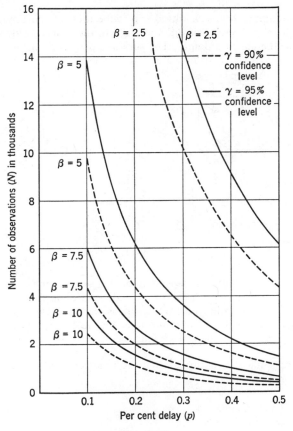

Fᴵɢ. 9-10.

interval of 95%. If the value of $p = 0.1$, then 13,800 observations are required. However, if $p = 0.5$ then only 1500 readings are required. Thus, in a sampling plan with several p's, it is necessary to balance the reliability requirements and the practical number of observations that can be made. Since N is theoretically based on the smallest estimated p, it is sometimes necessary to combine some of the smaller elements or compromise on the reliability of prediction of the less important elements.

After the number of samples has been determined, the next step is the actual observation. Training procedure has been developed so that all observers will define the time elements in the same manner. The work sampling observation sheets have also been developed as an aid in standardizing the procedure.

Optimum weight transport problem. The following is also an illustration of the way in which a relationship between variables can be utilized to find an optimum solution of a problem.

Suppose that a forklift is used to move cargo from one point on the pier to another as shown in Fig. 9-11.

The time required for each round trip is the total of the time required to pick up the load, transport it from one place to the other, set down the load, and return to the starting point. The time required for certain of the steps,

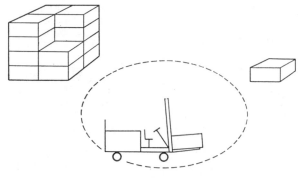

Fig. 9-11.

e.g., the return trip, will not depend upon the size of the load. The time required for the other steps, however, may depend upon the size of the load. If it takes longer to make the round trip as the load carried per trip gets heavier, there may be some optimum load that allows a higher rate in tons moved per hour than lighter loads carried faster or heavier loads carried slower.

It seems reasonable to postulate that the time required for a round trip is some function of the load

$$t = f(w) \tag{87}$$

where t = round trip time.

w = weight carried per trip.

In many cases, the function could be expanded into a power series,

$$t = a_0 + a_1 w + a_2 w^2 + a_3 w^3 \cdots + a_i w^i \cdots + a_n w^n \tag{88}$$

where a_i = constant for $i = 0, 1, 2 \cdots n$.

Consider the situation that can be described by the first three terms. (Often the higher power terms can be omitted without seriously reducing the value of the solution.)

$$t = a_0 + a_1 w + a_2 w^2 \tag{89}$$

Equation 89 can be made dimensionless by letting

$$t' = \frac{t}{a_1 w} \qquad \text{time number and} \tag{90}$$

$$w' = \frac{a_1 w}{a_0} \qquad \text{weight number} \tag{91}$$

Note that t' and w' are dimensionless numbers. Equation 89 becomes

$$t' = \frac{1}{w'} + 1 + \frac{a_0 a_2}{a_1{}^2} w' \tag{92}$$

Equation 89 is represented in Fig. 9-12 as a family of curves with $a_0 a_2/a_1{}^2$ as the parameter. Note that there is a minimum number t' for each value of $a_0 a_2/a_1{}^2$.

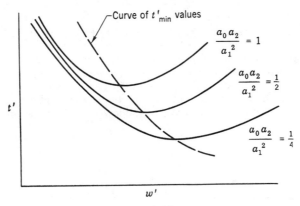

Fig. 9-12.

To find the expression for the curve drawn through these minimum points, the standard method of calculus is used.

$$\frac{dt'}{dw'} = -\frac{1}{(w')^2} + \frac{a_0 a_2}{a_1{}^2} = 0 \tag{93}$$

$$(w')_{\text{opt}} = \frac{a_1}{\sqrt{a_0 a_2}} \tag{94}$$

Substitute equation 94 into equation 92 and eliminate the parameter $a_0 a_2/a_1{}^2$.

$$(t')_{\min} = 1 + \frac{2}{(w')_{\text{opt}}} \tag{95}$$

Equation 95 is represented by Fig. 9-13. This shows the relation between minimum time number and optimum weight number for the condition postulated in equation 89.

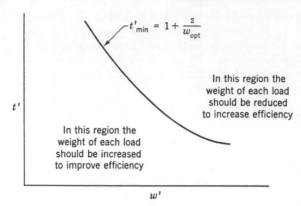

$$-t'_{min} = 1 + \frac{2}{w_{opt}}$$

In this region the weight of each load should be reduced to increase efficiency

t'

In this region the weight of each load should be increased to improve efficiency

w'

Fig. 9-13.

An analysis of the quantity of commodity at a storage node. In the section presenting a formal analysis of cargo handling it was pointed out that the quantity of commodity that is in storage at any node depends on the amount delivered and the amount taken away. The following is a more detailed treatment of the conditions that exist at the node.

Assume that the upper curve in Fig. 9-14 is a graphical representation of an input and output to a node, and that the lower curve represents the resulting storage.

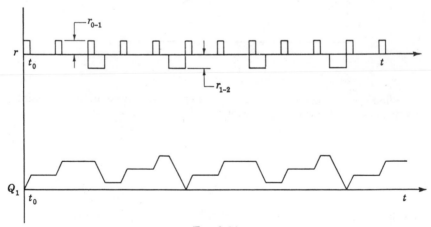

Fig. 9-14.

Both curves have time (t) as the abscissa. However, the ordinate of the upper curve is the rate of commodity movement in quantity per unit time (r), and the ordinate of the lower curve is the quantity of storage at node 1 (Q_1). In Fig. 9-14 the positive portion of the upper curve is the input to node 1. This can be thought of as representing delivery trucks that arrive periodically at the node and are then unloaded at the rate r_{0-1}. The output rate from the node, or the negative portion of the upper curve, can represent ships that arrive periodically and are loaded at the rate $r_{1\text{-}2}$. The lower curve now represents the quantity that is in storage at node 1 at any time. This curve is obtained by integrating the upper curve from t_0 to t, plus the storage existing at t_0. In the example chosen, the storage existing at t_0 is assumed to be zero.

The foregoing graphical representation can be developed analytically by simply expressing the periodic input and output as Fourier series. For example, assume the input to a storage node 1 to be that shown in Fig. 9-15.

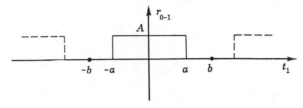

FIG. 9-15.

Similarly, assume the output from storage node 1 to be that shown in Fig. 9-16.

From Fig. 9-15 it is seen that

$$r_{0\text{-}1} = f(t_1) = \begin{cases} 0 & (-b \le t_1 < -a) \\ A & (-a \le t_1 < a) \\ 0 & (a \le t_1 < b) \end{cases} \tag{96}$$

Since an even function is assumed, a cosine series can be used.

$$r_{0\text{-}1} = \frac{\alpha_0}{2} + \sum_{n=1}^{\infty} \alpha_K \cos \frac{K\pi}{b} t_1 \tag{97}$$

where α_0 and α_K are the Fourier coefficients. When these are determined in the usual way, the expression becomes

$$r_{0\text{-}1} = A \left[\frac{a}{b} + \frac{2}{\pi} \sum_{K=1}^{\infty} \frac{1}{K} \sin \frac{K\pi a}{b} \cos \frac{K\pi}{b} t_1 \right] \tag{98}$$

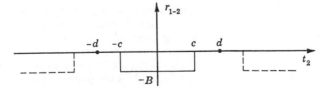

FIG. 9-16.

Similarly, from Fig. 9-16 it is seen that

$$r_{1\text{-}2} = g(t_2) = \begin{cases} 0 & (-d \le t_2 < -c) \\ -B & (-c \le t_2 < c) \\ 0 & (c \le t_2 < d) \end{cases} \tag{99}$$

Again, an even function is assumed and a cosine series is used.

$$r_{1-2} = \frac{\alpha_0}{2} + \sum_{K=1}^{\infty} \alpha_K \cos \frac{K\pi}{d} t_2 \tag{100}$$

and

$$r_{1-2} = -B \left[\frac{c}{d} + \frac{2}{\pi} \sum_{K=1}^{\infty} \frac{1}{K} \sin \frac{K\pi c}{d} \cos \frac{K\pi}{d} t_2 \right] \tag{101}$$

In the foregoing, it was assumed that the input and output are timed separately with times t_1 and t_2. If they are timed simultaneously, then $t_1 = t_2 = t$ and the total rate of storage at node 1 is

$$\frac{dQ_1}{dt} = r_{0-1} + r_{1-2} \tag{102}$$

Substitute equations 98 and 101 into 102 and the resulting rate of storage is

$$\frac{dQ_1}{dt} = \left(\frac{aA}{b} - \frac{cB}{d} \right) + \frac{2}{\pi} \left[\sum_{K=1}^{\infty} \frac{1}{K} \left(A \sin \frac{K\pi a}{b} \cos \frac{K\pi}{b} - B \sin \frac{K\pi c}{d} \cos \frac{K\pi}{d} t \right) \right] \tag{103}$$

The storage is the integral of the equation 103:

$$Q_1 = \left(\frac{aA}{b} - \frac{cB}{d} \right) t + \frac{2}{\pi} \left[\sum_{n=1}^{\infty} \frac{1}{K^2} \left(\frac{bA}{\pi} \sin \frac{K\pi a}{b} \sin \frac{K\pi}{b} t - \frac{dB}{\pi} \sin \frac{K\pi c}{d} \cos \frac{K\pi}{d} t \right) \right] \tag{104}$$

Since there is a maximum and a minimum storage, there can be no continuous increase of storage with time. Thus,

$$\frac{aA}{b} - \frac{cB}{d} = 0 \tag{105}$$

and the first term of equation 104 drops out. This relationship can then be utilized in solving for the constants in the remainder of the equation.

The foregoing analysis is also useful in solving for maximum storage areas required for specific cargo-handling situations. The use of the Fourier series makes it possible to express any of the complex input and output rates in analytic form if they are periodic.

An electrical analog of the cargo-handling operation. The electrical analog shown in Fig. 9-17 is useful as a conceptual aid in depicting the cyclic operation described in the section presenting a formal analysis of cargo handling. The portion of operations illustrated includes parts of two connecting cycles, A and B, and the transfer node between them. The node is represented by the boxed-in area. To explain the operation of the circuit, a few of the many possible cases encountered in the transfer of cargo are discussed below.

The first case is a situation where the commodity is loaded by longshoremen directly on a tractor-trailer combination. The setting down of the commodity by the men occurs simultaneously with the pick-up by the tractor-trailer. To simulate this situation, switch 1 is in position m and switch 2 is in position p. Pulse generator 1 in cycle A and its counterpart in cycle B,

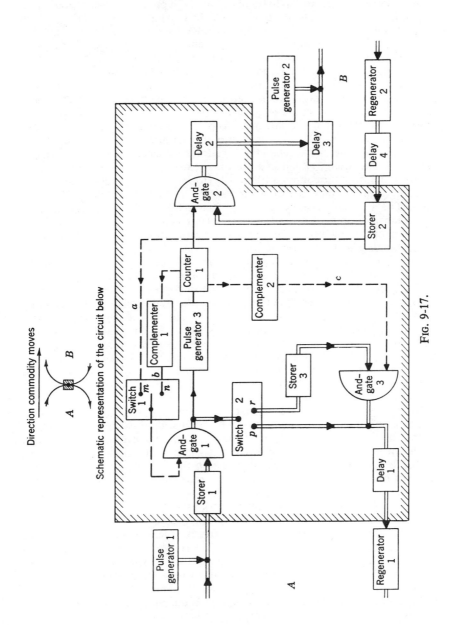

Fig. 9-17.

pulse generator 2, deliver a number of pulses corresponding to the number of transporting agents in the particular cycle. Suppose a pulse, representing a longshoreman and his load, arrives from the previous node at storer 1. The longshoreman may be held up until a tractor-trailer combination arrives. Thus, the initial pulse remains in storer 1 and also energizes the lower path into and-gate 1. This condition remains until there is at least one pulse, representing the tractor-trailer, in storer 2. If there is a pulse in storer 2, a signal is sent over path *a* which energizes the upper line into and-gate 1. The operation of the and-gate is such that it allows a pulse to go through it only if both input lines are energized. Therefore, when there is a pulse in both storer 1 and storer 2, it allows a pulse to pass through and-gate 1 and to continue on through switch 2, delay 1, and regenerator 1. Delay 1 represents the unloading time and regenerator 1 restores the energy that has been dissipated in the circuit. Each impulse that passes through and-gate 1 acts to subtract one from the count on storer 1. However, for the sake of simplicity, this part of the circuit is not shown in Fig. 9-17. In addition, the pulses from and-gate 1 also energize pulse generator 3, which in turn delivers to counter 1 the number of units of cargo for each pulse received. In this case, there is one unit of commodity carried by each transporting agent or pulse going through and-gate 1. Therefore, pulse generator 3 serve no purpose in this particular example. When the pulses stored in counter 1 reach a specified number, representing a fully loaded tractor-trailer combination, it energizes and-gate 2, allowing the pulse in storer 2 to be released. This pulse passes on through delay 2, representing pick-up time, and delay 3, representing transit time. The pulse from and-gate 2 also acts on counter 1 and storer 2 in order to subtract one unit from each of them. Again, this subtracting circuit is not shown in Fig. 9-17. Delays 2 and 3 can, of course, be combined, but they are separated here to clarify their function. The return path of the pulse in cycle *B* is through regenerator 2 and delay 4. Regenerator 2 restores the energy that is dissipated in the circuit, and delay 4 is set to correspond to the time of the return trip.

From this example, it is seen that the heavy lines can be thought of as representing the paths of the transporting agents, the light lines the transfer of the commodity from óne cycle to the next, and the broken lines the paths of the various energizing or information signals.

The second case is the situation in which the arriving transporting agent deposits its load and returns immediately, thus leaving the commodity until it is picked up by the subsequent carrier. In this case, a forklift brings its cargo to a point on the pier where the cargo is set down. The forklift then returns to the place where it can pick up another load to be delivered to the pier. Meanwhile, the commodity that is ón the pier remains until the ship's hook can carry it away. The analogous electrical operation exists when switch 1 is in position *n* and switch 2 is in position *p*. Counter 1 now records the units of commodity that are on the pier where the hook may pick them up. In most operations, the hook can pick up from only one point on the pier, thus the maximum storage at counter 1 is one unit. If there are no units at counter 1, then a signal is sent from complementer 1 over path *b* that energizes the upper line into and-gate 1. This occurs because a complementer reverses whatever signal it receives. With the upper path into and-gate 1 energized a pulse in cycle *A*, which arrives at storer 1, will continue on through and-gate 1 and will return to the previous node as in the first case. However, if counter 1 shows that there is a unit of commodity on the pier, then complementer 1 sends no signal over path b and in turn does not energize the upper line into and-gate 1. Therefore, the arriving pulses will be held in storer 1 until counter 1 indicates zero. Counter 1 also controls and-gate 2. Thus, one unit on counter 1 energizes the upper line into and-gate 2, and zero units on counter 1 fail to energize it. A pulse in cycle B, representing the hook, arrives at storer 2 and remains there or passes on depending on whether the upper line into and-gate 2 is energized or not. The delays and regenerators in this example have the same functions as those described in the first case.

The third case is the situation that occurs when longshoremen are unloading a tractor and trailer combination. In the electrical analogy, switch 1 is in position n and switch 2 is in position r. The pulses in cycle A represent the tractor and trailer combinations and the pulses in cycle B represent the longshoremen. An impulse arriving at storer 1 will be held there unless counter 1 indicates zero units. This is a similar condition to the one described in the second case. If counter 1 has zero units, the impulse in storer 1 can proceed into the path to storer 3 and into the path to pulse generator 3. Pulse generator 3 will then deliver to counter 1 the number of units of commodity corresponding to one arriving impulse. For example, a tractor and trailer combination are represented by one pulse in cycle A, but this same tractor-trailer may carry a dozen drums, which are then moved individually by the longshoremen. Therefore, for every pulse that enters pulse generator 3, twelve pulses will be delivered to counter 1. And-gate 2 is controlled by counter 1 and the pulses that enter storer 2 can only proceed if there are one or more units of commodity indicated on counter 1. When counter 1 indicates zero a signal is sent via path c from complementer 2, which energizes and-gate 3. This allows the pulse, which has been held at storer 3, to continue on its return trip. As noted in the other examples, there must also be a subtracting circuit to storer 3 in order to reduce the count on it after the pulses pass through and-gate 3. The delays and regenerators in this case again have the same functions as those described in the first example.

Aside from the three cargo-transfer operations described above, there are many other transfer operations that can be simulated by the same electrical analog. A series of these analogs could be set up to reproduce an entire loading operation from the storage in the transit shed to the storage in the ship, the storage points being counters that can stop the flow when a predetermined maximum is reached. Although the usefulness of this type of model is mainly conceptual, it is also possible to utilize it in determining loading times for commodities that have not been handled before.

Index

ATE